Techniques of Calculus

Techniques
of
Calculus

Robert E. Dressler
Karl Stromberg

Kansas State University

AMSCO COLLEGE PUBLICATIONS
315 Hudson Street / New York, N.Y. 10013

Dedicated to the memory of our fathers

Isidore Dressler *and* Johan Emil Stromberg

who taught us by example the fundamental lessons of
decency, responsibility, and basic humanity.

Specify **CR 263 P** or TECHNIQUES OF CALCULUS, PAPERBACK

ISBN 0-87720-978-2

Printed in the United States of America

PREFACE

THIS BOOK IS INTENDED to serve as the text for a one-year course on the differential and integral calculus of functions of one real variable. In addition to its suitability for college and university students, all topics recommended by the College Entrance Examination Board for advanced placement have been covered.

We have included many applications of the calculus to the physical sciences and, unlike many traditional texts, we also give numerous applications of the calculus to business. The only prerequisite for this course is two years of high school algebra, although prior exposure to some plane geometry and trigonometry would be very helpful to most students. No previous experience with analytic geometry or calculus is assumed.

Our emphasis is on the techniques of solving problems. Clear statements and explanations of all the theorems and principles that are used in problem solving are given. We concentrate on giving the student an intuitive understanding of these principles without belaboring rigorous theory. Our purpose is to teach the student how to produce correct solutions to particular types of problems, not how to give logically pristine *proofs* of the theorems upon which such solutions are based. That is, we teach the student how to drive the car competently, not how to design and manufacture it. In an effort to aid the student to a better understanding of the tools that he or she is learning to use, we do include some of the easier proofs in the main text. As a convenience to those readers who are interested, Appendix A at the back of the book provides proofs of the harder theorems. We include numerous examples and exercises, since we believe that the student can best learn the calculus by doing the calculus. A short table of integrals and useful numerical tables and answers to odd-numbered exercises can also be found at the back of the book.

We wish to express our appreciation to those who have read manuscript and proof and offered helpful suggestions for improving the work: Harold Baron, August Martin High School, Jamaica, N.Y.; Herbert Grossman, Roosevelt High School, Yonkers, N.Y.; James B. Jones, Jr., Central Piedmont Community College, Charlotte, N.C.; Melvin P. Klein, Brooklyn Technical High School, Brooklyn, N.Y.; Nathan Newman, Manhattan Community College, New York, N.Y.; Lee Spallone, Island Trees High School, Levittown, N.Y.; John Pawlak, Bell Laboratories, Holmdel, N.J.; Robert Reinstein, Department of Energy, Washington, D.C.; and Thomas J. Smith, Manhattan College, Riverdale, N.Y. We are also grateful to Marlyn Logan, who typed much of our manuscript, and to the production and editorial staff of Amsco College Publications. The patience, encouragement, and cooperation of these people, and of others unnamed, have made this book possible.

Robert E. Dressler
Karl R. Stromberg

CONTENTS

Chapter 3 / Differentiation

Chapter 4 / Applications of the Derivative

Chapter 5 / Trigonometric, Exponential, and Logarithmic Functions and Indeterminate Forms

Chapter 6 / Integration

Chapter 7 / Techniques of Integration

Chapter 8 / Applications of the Definite Integral

Chapter 9 / Approximations

Chapter 10 / Infinite Series

Chapter 11 / Differential Equations

Chapter 12 / Vectors in the Plane

Appendix A / Some Difficult Theorems

Appendix B / The Exponential Function

Appendix C / Integrals and Tables

Answers / Odd-numbered Exercises

Index

Introduction

Review

1 Polynomials and Polynomial Arithmetic

In algebra you no doubt studied polynomials in some detail. Examples of polynomials are $4x^2 + 2x - 1$ and $3.5z^7 + 2z^5 - \pi z$. In the first example x is called the **variable** and in the second example z is the variable. In the first example the coefficient of x^2 is 4, the coefficient of x is 2, and -1 is called the **constant term** or **constant coefficient**. When we write a specific polynomial, it is conventional not to use 0 as a coefficient — any term with a zero coefficient is simply not written.

It is also conventional to collect together all terms of a polynomial in which the variable has the same exponent. Thus, instead of writing $3x^3 + 2x^2 + 4x^3 - x^2 + 4$, we would write $7x^3 + x^2 + 4$. The **degree** of a polynomial is the largest exponent of the variable. Thus, the degree of $2y^3 - 3y^2 + 1$ is 3 and the degree of $\frac{1}{2}z^{94} + 100z$ is 94. The degree of a constant polynomial (there is only the constant term) is 0, except for the zero polynomial (constant polynomial equal to zero), which has no degree.

The general form of a polynomial of degree n is $a_n x^n + a_{n-1} x^{n-1} + a_{n-2} x^{n-2} + \cdots + a_2 x^2 + a_1 x + a_0$, where $a_n \neq 0$ and n is a nonnegative integer. Notice that since all powers of x up to x^n have been written,

1

we have to allow for the possibility that some coefficients, or some a_k's, may be 0. However, since the degree is n, a_n cannot be zero — otherwise there would be no term with x^n.

We add and subtract polynomials by combining like terms, that is, terms in which the variable has the same exponent.

EXAMPLE   Add $(2x^4 - x^3 + 3x^2 - x) + (6x^3 - 2x^2 + x + 4)$.

Solution
$$
\begin{array}{l}
2x^4 - x^3 + 3x^2 - x \\
\underline{+ 6x^3 - 2x^2 + x + 4} \\
2x^4 + 5x^3 + x^2 + 4 \quad \textit{Answer}
\end{array}
$$

EXAMPLE   Subtract $(5x^5 + 2x^4 - x^2 + 1) - (6x^5 - 4x^3 + 3x + 5)$.

Solution   First change all the signs of the subtrahend (the polynomial we are subtracting), then add.

$$
\begin{array}{l}
5x^5 + 2x^4 - x^2 + 1 \\
\underline{+-6x^5 + 4x^3 - 3x - 5} \\
-x^5 + 2x^4 + 4x^3 - x^2 - 3x - 4 \quad \textit{Answer}
\end{array}
$$

E X E R C I S E S

In 1–6 (a) add the polynomials and (b) subtract the second polynomial from the first.

1. $x^2 + 5x - 2$; $3x^2 + x + 4$
2. $2y^3 - y + 7$; $y^2 - y - 1$
3. $\dfrac{1}{2}x^2 + x + \dfrac{1}{2}$; $\dfrac{1}{2}x^2 - x + \dfrac{3}{2}$
4. $x^{14} + 20x^7 + 5x$; $x^{13} - \dfrac{1}{2}x^2 + 15x$
5. $z^3 + \pi z^2 + 1$; $z^2 + z - 1$
6. $ax^2 + bx + c$; $rx^2 + sx + t$

IN ORDER TO MULTIPLY two polynomials, we use the distributive law and combine like terms. That is, we multiply each term of the first polynomial by each term of the second polynomial and then combine the terms in which the variable has the same exponent. Remember that in order to multiply two terms we make use of the law of exponents: $x^m \cdot x^n = x^{m+n}$. Thus, $x^5 \cdot x^2 = x^{5+2} = x^7$ and $(2x^4) \cdot (3x^3) = (2 \cdot 3)(x^{4+3}) = 6x^7$.

EXAMPLE   Multiply $(2x^4 + 3x^2 - x + 1) \cdot (2x^2 - 5x + 3)$.

Solution   It is often convenient to arrange the polynomials one above the other and then multiply the top polynomial by each term of the bottom polynomial, going from right to left.

$$2x^4 \qquad\qquad + \ 3x^2 - \ x + 1$$
$$2x^2 - 5x + 3$$

multiplication of
$2x^4 + 3x^2 - x + 1$ $\longrightarrow$ $\qquad 6x^4 \qquad\qquad + \ 9x^2 - 3x + 3$
by 3

multiplication of
$2x^4 + 3x^2 - x + 1$ $\longrightarrow$ $-10x^5 \qquad\qquad - 15x^3 + \ 5x^2 - 5x$
by $-5x$

multiplication of
$2x^4 + 3x^2 - x + 1$ $\longrightarrow$ $4x^6 \qquad\quad + \ 6x^4 - \ 2x^3 + \ 2x^2$
by $2x^2$

$$4x^6 - 10x^5 + 12x^4 - 17x^3 + 16x^2 - 8x + 3$$
Answer

E X E R C I S E S

In 1–10, perform the indicated operations.

1. $(x^2 - x + 2) \cdot (2x^2 + x + 3)$

2. $(2y^3 + y^2 - y) \cdot (3y^2 - 4)$

3. $\left(\frac{1}{2}x^3 + x^2 + \frac{1}{2}\right) \cdot (x^2 - 2x + 4)$

4. $(.5z^3 + 2z - .6) \cdot (z^4 + 2)$

5. $(ax^3 + b) \cdot (3x + 4)$

6. $(ax^2 + bx + c) \cdot (rx^2 + sx + t)$

7. $(x + 1)^3$

8. $(y^2 + y + 1)^4$

9. $(2x + 1)^2 + (3x - 1)^2$

10. $(y^2 - y)^3 - (y + 1)^2$

11. If two polynomials are multiplied, how is the degree of the product related to the degrees of the factors?

IN OUR LATER WORK it will be useful for us to know how to factor $x^n - y^n$, where n is a positive integer. This can be done as follows:

$$x^n - y^n = (x - y)(x^{n-1} + x^{n-2}y + x^{n-3}y^2 + \cdots + x^2y^{n-3} + xy^{n-2} + y^{n-1})$$

For example, $x^4 - y^4 = (x - y)(x^3 + x^2y + xy^2 + y^3)$.

To verify that this formula is correct, simply multiply the right-hand side out. All but two terms will cancel and $x^n - y^n$ will remain.

Notice that if $y = 1$, the formula becomes

$$x^n - 1 = (x - 1)(x^{n-1} + x^{n-2} + \cdots + x^2 + x + 1)$$

or,

$$1 + x + x^2 + \cdots + x^{n-2} + x^{n-1} = \frac{x^n - 1}{x - 1} \qquad (x \neq 1)$$

EXAMPLE   Find the sum $1 + 2 + 2^2 + \cdots + 2^6$.

Solution   Since $1 + x + x^2 + \cdots + x^{n-1} = \dfrac{x^n - 1}{x - 1}$, let $x = 2$ and $n = 7$.

Then $1 + 2 + 2^2 + \cdots + 2^6 = \dfrac{2^7 - 1}{2 - 1} = \dfrac{128 - 1}{1} = 127$.

E X E R C I S E S

In 1–4, factor.

1. $x^2 - y^2$
2. $a^3 - 8$
3. $c^5 - d^5$
4. $x^8 - y^8$

In 5–8, find the sum by using the formula.

5. $1 + 2 + 2^2 + \cdots + 2^5$
6. $1 + 3 + 3^2 + \cdots + 3^6$
7. $1 + \dfrac{1}{2} + \dfrac{1}{4} + \cdots + \dfrac{1}{32}$
8. $1 + (-2) + 4 + (-8) + \cdots + (-32)$

2 The Quadratic Formula

A polynomial of degree 2 is called a **quadratic** polynomial. Thus, $2x^2 - x + 4$ and $\dfrac{1}{2}z^2 + 1$ are both quadratic polynomials, whereas $x^3 + x^2$ and $x^4 + x + 1$ are not. The general form of a quadratic polynomial is $ax^2 + bx + c$, where $a \neq 0$.

The quadratic formula tells us which values of the variable, x, satisfy the quadratic equation $ax^2 + bx + c = 0$. That is, it tells us which values of x make the equation $ax^2 + bx + c = 0$ true. These values of x are called the **zeros** of $ax^2 + bx + c$ and they are also called the **roots** of the equation $ax^2 + bx + c = 0$. Here is the formula:

$$x = \frac{-b \pm \sqrt{b^2 - 4ac}}{2a}$$

The number $b^2 - 4ac$ is called the **discriminant** because it discriminates among three possibilities:

(1) There are two equal real roots of $ax^2 + bx + c = 0$ if $b^2 - 4ac = 0$.

(2) There are two unequal real roots of $ax^2 + bx + c = 0$ if $b^2 - 4ac$ is positive.

(3) There are no real roots of $ax^2 + bx + c = 0$ if $b^2 - 4ac$ is negative.

EXAMPLE (a) Without finding the roots of $2x^2 - 9x + 1 = 0$, discuss their nature.

(b) Find the zeros of $2x^2 - 9x + 1$.

Solution (a) For the quadratic polynomial $2x^2 - 9x + 1$, we have $a = 2$, $b = -9$, and $c = 1$. The discriminant is $b^2 - 4ac = (-9)^2 - 4(2)(1) = 73$. Since $b^2 - 4ac$ is positive, we see that there are two unequal real roots.

(b) We have $a = 2$, $b = -9$, and $c = 1$. Substitution in the formula

$$x = \frac{-b \pm \sqrt{b^2 - 4ac}}{2a}$$

gives

$$x = \frac{-(-9) \pm \sqrt{(-9)^2 - 4(2)(1)}}{2 \cdot 2} = \frac{9 \pm \sqrt{73}}{4} \quad Answer$$

That is, the two zeros are $\dfrac{9 + \sqrt{73}}{4}$ and $\dfrac{9 - \sqrt{73}}{4}$.

EXAMPLE Find all real zeros of $5x^2 + x + 1$.

Solution We are asked to find all real roots of the equation $5x^2 + x + 1 = 0$. Since $a = 5$, $b = 1$, and $c = 1$, we see that the discriminant $b^2 - 4ac = 1^2 - 4 \cdot (5)(1) = -19$. Since $b^2 - 4ac$ is negative, there are no real roots of the equation $5x^2 + x + 1 = 0$.

EXAMPLE Find all real solutions of the equation $-3x^2 + 1 = -2x$.

Solution The equation is equivalent to (has the same roots as) $-3x^2 + 2x + 1 = 0$. Here, $a = -3$, $b = 2$, and $c = 1$. Thus, we have

$$x = \frac{-2 \pm \sqrt{4 - 4(-3)(1)}}{2 \cdot (-3)}$$

$$= \frac{-2 \pm \sqrt{16}}{-6} = \frac{-2 \pm 4}{-6} = \frac{-1 \pm 2}{-3}$$

Thus, the solutions are

$$x = \frac{-1 + 2}{-3} = \frac{-1}{3} \quad Answer$$

and

$$x = \frac{-1-2}{-3} = 1 \quad Answer$$

Note. It is important to remember that in order to apply the quadratic formula, we must have an equation in the form $ax^2 + bx + c = 0$, $a \neq 0$.

E X E R C I S E S

In 1-6, (a) investigate the nature of the roots without actually finding the roots and (b) find the real roots (if there are any).

1. $x^2 - 3x + 2 = 0$
2. $x^2 + 2x + 4 = 0$
3. $-2y^2 + 2y + 1 = 0$
4. $-y^2 + 4y + 1 = 0$

5. $\frac{x^2}{2} + 2x + 1 = 0$

6. $3y^2 + \sqrt{2}y - 2 = 0$

In 7-10, find all real solutions of the equation (if there are any).

7. $x^2 = x + 1$
8. $2 = y + 4y^2$

9. $(x + 1) \cdot (x + 2) = 2x$
10. $(y - 1) \cdot (y + 2) = -2y^2$

3 The Binomial Theorem

The **Binomial Theorem** gives us a systematic method for expanding (writing out) powers of the form $(x + y)^n$, where x and y represent real numbers and n represents a positive integer. When n is small, say no more than 3, it appears that there is no great need for any help in expanding powers like $(x + y)^2 = (x + y) \cdot (x + y) = x^2 + 2xy + y^2$ or $(2x + y)^3 = (2x + y) \cdot (2x + y) \cdot (2x + y) = 8x^3 + 12x^2y + 6xy^2 + y^3$. However, no one would want to expand $(x + y)^{10}$ by using $x + y$ as a factor 10 times. Here is where the Binomial Theorem really comes in handy.

Before we can state the Binomial Theorem, we state what is meant by a **binomial coefficient.** If n and k are positive integers and k is less than or equal to n (in symbols, $0 < k \leq n$), then the binomial coefficient $\binom{n}{k}$ is defined to be

$$\binom{n}{k} = \frac{n(n-1)(n-2) \cdot \ldots \cdot (n-k+1)}{1 \cdot 2 \cdot 3 \cdot \ldots \cdot k}$$

Also, for any positive integer n, the binomial coefficient $\binom{n}{0}$ is defined to be 1. If we use the **factorial** symbol, we can also write

$$\binom{n}{k} = \frac{n!}{k!(n-k)!}$$

where for any positive integer n, $n! = 1 \cdot 2 \cdot \ldots \cdot n$. Also, 0! is, by definition, 1.

EXAMPLE Calculate the binomial coefficients (a) $\binom{5}{2}$, (b) $\binom{10}{6}$, and (c) $\binom{7}{0}$.

Solution (a) $\binom{5}{2}$ is, by definition (using $n = 5$ and $k = 2$), $\dfrac{5 \cdot 4}{1 \cdot 2} = 10$

(b) Here $n = 10$ and $k = 6$ so that

$$\binom{10}{6} = \frac{10 \cdot 9 \cdot 8 \cdot 7 \cdot 6 \cdot 5}{1 \cdot 2 \cdot 3 \cdot 4 \cdot 5 \cdot 6} = \frac{10 \cdot \overset{3}{\cancel{9}} \cdot \cancel{8} \cdot 7}{1 \cdot \cancel{2} \cdot \cancel{3} \cdot \cancel{4}} = 210$$

(c) Here $n = 7$ and $k = 0$, so that $\binom{7}{0} = 1$.

Note. An important property of binomial coefficients which often comes in handy is $\binom{n}{k} = \binom{n}{n-k}$, for any binomial coefficient $\binom{n}{k}$. Thus $\binom{10}{6} = \binom{10}{4}$, $\binom{8}{8} = \binom{8}{0}$, and $\binom{248}{247} = \binom{248}{1}$.

Also, observe that $\binom{n}{1} = n$ for all positive integers n, so that $\binom{4}{1} = 4$ and $\binom{248}{1} = 248$.

We are now prepared to state the **Binomial Theorem.** For any real numbers x and y and any positive integer n,

$$\begin{aligned}
(x+y)^n = {} & \binom{n}{0}x^n y^0 + \binom{n}{1}x^{n-1}y^1 + \binom{n}{2}x^{n-2}y^2 + \binom{n}{3}x^{n-3}y^3 + \cdots \\
& + \binom{n}{k}x^{n-k}y^k + \cdots + \binom{n}{n-3}x^3 y^{n-3} \\
& + \binom{n}{n-2}x^2 y^{n-2} + \binom{n}{n-1}x^1 y^{n-1} + \binom{n}{n}x^0 y^n
\end{aligned}$$

In terms of the $\sum$ notation for summation, which is explained in Chapter 6, we may restate the **Binomial Theorem** as follows:

Binomial Theorem

$$(x + y)^n = \sum_{k=0}^{n} \binom{n}{k} x^{n-k} y^k$$

Note. In the expansion of $(x + y)^n$ there are always $n + 1$ terms. In each term, the sum of the exponent of x and the exponent of y is n, and, as we go from left to right, the exponents of x start at n and decrease to 0, while the exponents of y start at 0 and increase to n.

EXAMPLE Use the Binomial Theorem to expand (a) $(x + y)^6$, (b) $(2x + 3y)^4$, and (c) $(a - 3b)^5$.

Solution   (a) By the Binomial Theorem (with $n = 6$),

$$(x + y)^6 = \binom{6}{0}x^6y^0 + \binom{6}{1}x^5y^1 + \binom{6}{2}x^4y^2 + \binom{6}{3}x^3y^3 + \binom{6}{4}x^2y^4$$
$$+ \binom{6}{5}x^1y^5 + \binom{6}{6}x^0y^6$$
$$= x^6 + 6x^5y + 15x^4y^2 + 20x^3y^3 + 15x^2y^4 + 6xy^5 + y^6$$

(b) We use the Binomial Theorem (with $n = 4$) and replace x by $2x$ and y by $3y$. Thus,

$$(2x + 3y)^4 = \binom{4}{0}(2x)^4(3y)^0 + \binom{4}{1}(2x)^3(3y)^1 + \binom{4}{2}(2x)^2(3y)^2$$
$$+ \binom{4}{3}(2x)^1(3y)^3 + \binom{4}{4}(2x)^0(3y)^4$$
$$= 16x^4 + 4 \cdot 8x^3 \cdot 3y + 6 \cdot 4x^2 \cdot 9y^2 + 4 \cdot 2x \cdot 27y^3 + 81y^4$$
$$= 16x^4 + 96x^3y + 216x^2y^2 + 216xy^3 + 81y^4$$

(c) We use the Binomial Theorem (with $n = 5$) and replace x by a and y by $-3b$. Thus,

$$(a - 3b)^5 = \binom{5}{0}a^5(-3b)^0 + \binom{5}{1}a^4(-3b)^1 + \binom{5}{2}a^3(-3b)^2 + \binom{5}{3}a^2(-3b)^3$$
$$+ \binom{5}{4}a^1(-3b)^4 + \binom{5}{5}a^0(-3b)^5$$
$$= a^5 - 15a^4b + 90a^3b^2 - 270a^2b^3 + 405ab^4 - 243b^5$$

E X E R C I S E S

In 1–8, calculate the binomial coefficient.

1. $\binom{5}{4}$ 3. $\binom{9}{8}$ 5. $\binom{8}{5}$ 7. $\binom{987}{987}$

2. $\binom{7}{3}$ 4. $\binom{17}{0}$ 6. $\binom{14{,}400}{1}$ 8. $\binom{19}{17}$

In 9–16, use the Binomial Theorem to write the indicated expansion.

9. $(x + y)^5$ 11. $(x - y)^4$ 13. $(-x + 2y)^3$ 15. $\left(\dfrac{x}{2} + y\right)^4$

10. $(a + b)^6$ 12. $(2x + 1)^5$ 14. $(\sqrt{2}x + 2y)^4$ 16. $\left(\dfrac{3x}{2} + \dfrac{y}{3}\right)^5$

4   Rational Exponents

In algebra, we learned that

$$x^0 = 1$$
$$x^1 = x$$
$$x^2 = x \cdot x$$
$$x^3 = x \cdot x \cdot x$$

and, in general, for a positive integer n

$$x^n = x \cdot x \cdot \ldots \cdot x \qquad (n \text{ factors})$$

Also, if $x \neq 0$,

$$x^{-1} = \frac{1}{x}$$

$$x^{-2} = \frac{1}{x^2}$$

$$x^{-3} = \frac{1}{x^3}$$

and, in general, for a positive integer n

$$x^{-n} = \frac{1}{x^n}$$

We may use rational exponents to replace radicals as follows.

$$x^{1/2} = \sqrt{x} \qquad x \text{ greater than or equal to } 0$$
$$x^{1/3} = \sqrt[3]{x}$$
$$x^{1/4} = \sqrt[4]{x} \qquad x \text{ greater than or equal to } 0$$
$$x^{1/5} = \sqrt[5]{x}$$

and, in general, for an integer n greater than or equal to 2,

$$x^{1/n} = \sqrt[n]{x}$$

where if n is even, we require that x is greater than or equal to 0.

EXAMPLE   Find (a) $4^{1/2}$, (b) $27^{1/3}$, and (c) $(-243)^{1/5}$.

Solution   (a) $4^{1/2} = \sqrt{4} = 2$
   (b) $27^{1/3} = \sqrt[3]{27} = 3$
   (c) $(-243)^{1/5} = \sqrt[5]{-243} = -3$

Note 1. For x greater than or equal to 0, the symbol $\sqrt{x}$ refers to the **principal square root** of x. That is, $\sqrt{x}$ is the nonnegative number whose square is x. Thus, for x greater than or equal to 0, $x^{1/2} = \sqrt{x}$ is greater than or equal to 0. In general, if x is greater than or equal to 0 and n is a positive even integer, then $x^{1/n}$ is the principal n^{th} root of x. That is, $x^{1/n}$ is the nonnegative number whose n^{th} power is x — in particular, $x^{1/n}$ is nonnegative.

Finally, if m is an integer, n is a positive integer, and m and n have no factor in common, then

$$x^{m/n} = (x^{1/n})^m$$

Note 2. If m is negative, we require that $x \neq 0$. Also, if n is even, we require that x is greater than or equal to 0. Whenever, in this text, we write $x^{m/n}$ for a specific choice of m and n, it will be assumed that the variable x represents a real number for which $x^{m/n}$ is defined.

EXAMPLE   Find the indicated number.

(a) $8^{2/3}$ (c) $\left(\dfrac{1}{4}\right)^{-1/2}$ (e) $(.01)^{3/2}$

(b) $(-27)^{4/3}$ (d) $16^{-5/4}$ (f) $(4/25)^{.5}$

Solution   (a) $8^{2/3} = (8^{1/3})^2 = (2)^2 = 4$
   (b) $(-27)^{4/3} = ((-27)^{1/3})^4 = (-3)^4 = 81$
   (c) $\left(\dfrac{1}{4}\right)^{-1/2} = \left(\left(\dfrac{1}{4}\right)^{1/2}\right)^{-1} = \left(\dfrac{1}{2}\right)^{-1} = 2$
   (d) $16^{-5/4} = (16^{1/4})^{-5} = (2)^{-5} = 1/32$
   (e) $(.01)^{3/2} = ((.01)^{1/2})^3 = (.1)^3 = .001$
   (f) $(4/25)^{.5} = (4/25)^{1/2} = 2/5$

The beauty of the extension from integer exponents to rational exponents is that all the laws of exponents are preserved. Specifically, this means that for any rational numbers m/n and r/s in lowest terms, where n and s are positive, we have

$$Law\ 1. \quad x^{m/n} \cdot x^{r/s} = x^{m/n+r/s}$$
$$Law\ 2. \quad x^{m/n}/x^{r/s} = x^{m/n-r/s}$$
$$Law\ 3. \quad (x^{m/n})^{r/s} = x^{m/n \cdot r/s}$$
$$Law\ 4. \quad (x \cdot y)^{m/n} = x^{m/n} \cdot y^{m/n}$$

EXAMPLE Simplify (a) $(1/2)^{1/7} \cdot (1/2)^{6/7}$
(b) $x^{3/2}/x^{1/3}$
(c) $(8^{5/9})^{-6/5}$
(d) $(x^{2/3} \cdot y^{-1/2})^6$

Solution (a) By Law 1 above,

$$(1/2)^{1/7} \cdot (1/2)^{6/7} = (1/2)^{1/7+6/7} = (1/2)^1 = 1/2$$

(b) By Law 2 above,

$$x^{3/2}/x^{1/3} = x^{3/2-1/3} = x^{7/6}$$

(c) By Law 3 above,

$$(8^{5/9})^{-6/5} = 8^{5/9 \cdot -6/5} = 8^{-2/3} = (8^{1/3})^{-2} = (2)^{-2} = \frac{1}{4}$$

(d) By Law 4 above,

$$(x^{2/3} \cdot y^{-1/2})^6 = (x^{2/3})^6 \cdot (y^{-1/2})^6 = x^4 \cdot y^{-3}$$

(You may prefer to write this as x^4/y^3, but this is not required.)

E X E R C I S E S

In 1–15, find the indicated number.

1. $9^{1/2}$
2. $(-27)^{1/3}$
3. $16^{1/4}$
4. $27^{2/3}$
5. $32^{2/5}$

6. $32^{-3/5}$
7. $\left(\dfrac{1}{4}\right)^{3/2}$
8. $(4/9)^{-3/2}$
9. $(-243)^{-3/5}$
10. $(.01)^{5/2}$

11. $(-.008)^{2/3}$
12. $\left(\dfrac{1}{4}\right)^{.5}$
13. $(.04)^{1.5}$
14. $(-32/243)^{.4}$
15. $(8)^{.666\cdots}$

In 16–32, use the laws of exponents to simplify the given expression.

16. $2^{1/2} \cdot 2^{1/2}$
17. $3^{1/3} \cdot 3^{-4/3}$
18. $x^{3/5} \cdot x^{4/5}$
19. $y^{-2/3} \cdot y^{5/2}$
20. $x^{.4} \cdot x^{.6}$
21. $(2^{1/4})^2$

22. $(x^{2/3})^{-3/5}$
23. $(x^{.5})^4$
24. $(z^{.4})^{1/2}$
25. $5^{1/2}/5^{1/4}$
26. $\left(\dfrac{1}{2}\right)^{2/3} / \left(\dfrac{1}{2}\right)^{-1/2}$
27. $x^{-4/3}/x^{3/2}$

28. $x^{1/2}/x^{2/3}$
29. $(4x)^{1/2}$
30. $(x^{1/2} \cdot y^{1/5})^{20}$
31. $(z^{-1/2} \cdot x^{4/3})^{-2}$
32. $(9x^6y^{1/2})^{.5}$

5 Inequalities and Intervals

If a and b are different real numbers, then one of them is less than the other. If a is less than b, we write $a < b$. To say that a is less than b is the same thing as saying b is greater than a. The statement that b is greater than a is symbolized $b > a$. Thus, $a < b$ and $b > a$ mean the same thing. A statement that one number is less than (or greater than) another is called an **inequality**. An inequality may be true or false. For example, $5 < 7$ is true but $5 < 3$ is false. Similarly, $9 > -15$ is true but $-7 > -1$ is false.

Sometimes, for economy of notation, two inequalities may be strung together. Instead of writing $4 < 7$ and $7 < 12$, we write $4 < 7 < 12$. The inequality $a < x < b$ means $a < x$ *and* $x < b$. Of course, we could not string together the inequalities $-1 < 4$ and $5 < 10$ because the same number isn't in the middle. The meaning of the symbol $c > x > d$ should now be clear. It means $c > x$ and $x > d$.

EXAMPLE Relate the given numbers with a true inequality or string of inequalities: (a) $-1, 5$; (b) $1/2, 2, -1$; (c) $0, 8, -3/2, \pi$.

Solution   (a) $-1 < 5$ or $5 > -1$
   (b) $-1 < 1/2 < 2$ or $2 > 1/2 > -1$
   (c) Since $\pi = 3.14 \ldots$, we see that $3 < \pi < 8$, and so the answer is $-3/2 < 0 < \pi < 8$ or $8 > \pi > 0 > -3/2$.

It is often the case in mathematics that we know one number, a, does not exceed another number, b. That is, a is either less than or equal to b. We symbolize this by $a \le b$. Thus, it is true that $5 \le 5, 4 \le 5$, $-1 \le -1$, and $-1 \le 0$, but it is false that $2 \le 1$ and $0 \le -2$. The symbol $b \ge a$ means that $a \le b$. Hence $15 \ge 15, 2 \ge -1/2$, and $0 \ge 0$ are all true. By the way, the statement that a is a nonnegative real number is usually written by the symbol $a \ge 0$.

It is possible to string together inequalities involving the symbol $\le$ and also to string together inequalities involving the symbol $\ge$. Here are some examples.

$$2 \le 2 \le 4 \text{ means } 2 \le 2 \text{ and } 2 \le 4$$
$$1 \le 2 < 3 \text{ means } 1 \le 2 \text{ and } 2 < 3$$
$$-1 \ge -2 \ge -3 \text{ means } -1 \ge -2 \text{ and } -2 \ge -3$$
$$5 > 0 \ge 0 \text{ means } 5 > 0 \text{ and } 0 \ge 0$$

Note. It is important to remember that in order for a string of inequalities to be true, each inequality in the string must be true. Thus, $2 < 2 \le 3$ is false because $2 < 2$ is false.

EXERCISES

In 1–12, state whether the string of inequalities is true or false.

1. $2 \leq 2 < 5$ **5.** $4 > 2 > 2$ **9.** $0 \leq 0 \leq 0$

2. $4 < 6 < 3$ **6.** $-2 > -2\,1/2 \geq -6$ **10.** $5.1 \leq 5.7 \leq 5.9$

3. $-2 \leq -2 < -3$ **7.** $3 < \pi < 4$ **11.** $2 > -1.9 \geq -5/2$

4. $0 < 1/2 \leq 5$ **8.** $-3 > -\pi > -4$ **12.** $10 \geq 10 > 10$

In 13–24, arrange the numbers in a correct string of inequalities. If both symbols $<$ and $\leq$ are correct, use $<$. If both symbols $>$ and $\geq$ are correct, use $>$.

13. 1, 3, 2   **17.** $0, \pi, -1$ **21.** 2, 1, 4, 3

14. $-1, -2, -3$ **18.** 1/2, 1/3, 1/4   **22.** $-1, 2, -3, 4$

15. 0, 0, 4   **19.** 2, 2, 2   **23.** 2, 3, 2, 1/2

16. $-2, 1/2, -3$ **20.** $-1/2, -1/4, -1/3$ **24.** $\pi, 1/2, -1/4$

Now suppose a and b are real numbers and that $a < b$. There are four **intervals** whose **endpoints** are a and b. They are defined as follows:

The symbol $]a,b[$ (see Fig. 1) denotes the set of all real numbers x such that $a < x < b$. The set $]a,b[$ is called an **open interval**. Thus, $]2,4[$ is the set of all real numbers x such that $2 < x < 4$. It follows that $3 \in\,]2,4[$ because $2 < 3 < 4$. (Recall that the symbol $\in$ means "is an element of the set.") However, $2 \notin\,]2,4[$ because $2 < 2 < 4$ is false. (Recall that the symbol $\notin$ means "is not an element of the set.") Notice that neither endpoint of an open interval belongs to (is an element of) the interval. That is, $a \notin\,]a,b[$ and $b \notin\,]a,b[$. The set $]a,b[$ may be pictured as the portion of the number line between a and b, excluding the endpoints a and b.

   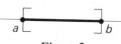

Figure 1   Figure 2

The open interval $]a,b[$. The open   The closed interval $[a,b]$. The dots
circles at a and b indicate that a and   at a and b indicate that a and b both
b both do not belong to the interval   belong to the interval $[a,b]$.
$]a,b[$.

The symbol $[a,b]$ (see Fig. 2) denotes the set of all real numbers x such that $a \leq x \leq b$. The set $[a,b]$ is called a **closed interval**. Thus,

[−1,6] is the set of all real numbers x such that $−1 \le x \le 6$. It follows that $0 \in [−1,6]$ because $−1 \le 0 \le 6$. Also $−1 \in [−1,6]$ because $−1 \le −1 \le 6$. Notice that both endpoints of a closed interval belong to the interval. That is, $a \in [a,b]$ and $b \in [a,b]$. The set $[a,b]$ may be pictured as the portion of the number line between a and b, including both a and b.

Figure 3	Figure 4
The half-open interval $[a,b[$, open at the right. Notice that a belongs to the interval $[a,b[$, whereas b does not.	The half-open interval $]a,b]$, open at the left. Notice that b belongs to the interval $]a,b]$, whereas a does not.

The symbol $[a,b[$ (see Fig. 3) denotes the set of all real numbers x such that $a \le x < b$. The set $[a,b[$ is called a **half-open interval, open at the right.** Thus, $[1/2,4[$ is the set of all real numbers x such that $1/2 \le x < 4$. It follows that $2/3 \in [1/2,4[$ because $1/2 \le 2/3 < 4$. Also, $1/2 \in [1/2,4[$ since $1/2 \le 1/2 < 4$. However, $4 \notin [1/2,4[$ because $1/2 \le 4 < 4$ is false. Notice that $a \in [a,b[$ and $b \notin [a,b[$. The interval $[a,b[$ may be pictured as the portion of the number line between a and b, including a, but excluding b.

The symbol $]a,b]$ (see Fig. 4) denotes the set of all real numbers x such that $a < x \le b$. The set $]a,b]$ is called a **half-open interval, open at the left.** Thus, $]−4,−1]$ is the set of all real numbers x such that $−4 < x \le −1$. It follows that $−2 \in]−4,−1]$ because $−4 < −2 \le −1$. Also, $−1 \in]−4,−1]$ because $−4 < −1 \le −1$. However, $−4 \notin]−4,−1]$ because $−4 < −4 \le −1$ is false. Notice that $b \in]a,b]$, but $a \notin]a,b]$. The interval $]a,b]$ may be pictured as the portion of the number line between a and b, including b, but excluding a.

We remark that in many books our reversed square brackets used for indicating open ends of intervals are replaced by ordinary round parentheses. The reader should always become familiar with the notational conventions of the book that is being read. In many books our $]a,b[$ is replaced by (a,b) while $[a,b[$ and $]a,b]$ are replaced by $[a,b)$ and $(a,b]$, respectively. In this book we shall always adhere to the square bracket notation that we have just defined. Thus, the open interval $]1,3[$ cannot be confused with the point $(1,3)$ in the plane whose coordinates are 1 and 3.

E X E R C I S E S

In 1-12, tell whether the given number is in the given interval.

1. 4; [5,6]

2. 1;]0,2]

3. −1; [−1,0[

4. 1/2;]1/2,2[

5. 5; [5,8]

6. −1/2; [−1,2]

7. π;]0,4[

8. 1.2; [1,3]

9. 4;]−2,6]

10. −2.6; [−3.1,4.2[

11. 2/3;]1/2,7/8]

12. −4/3; [−3/2,−2/3[

In 13-16, express the indicated set as an interval.

13. The set of all real numbers which are greater than 2 and less than 6.

14. The set of all real numbers which are greater than or equal to −1 and less than or equal to 1.

15. The set of all real numbers which are greater than or equal to 1/2 and less than 3/2.

16. The set of all real numbers which are greater than 14.6 and less than or equal to 83.7.

WHEN YOU STUDIED algebra, you learned how to transform certain inequalities whose solutions were not obvious into inequalities whose solutions were obvious. For example, it is not immediately obvious which real numbers x satisfy the inequality $2x + 3 < 4x − 5$. However, this inequality is **equivalent** to (has the same solutions as) the inequality $x > 4$, and it is obvious which real numbers satisfy the inequality $x > 4$. Remember that we say that two inequalities are equivalent if they have exactly the same solutions.

Here are the rules which we use to transform inequalities into equivalent inequalities.

▷ **Rule 1** If the same real number is added to both sides of an inequality or subtracted from both sides of an inequality, then the resulting inequality is equivalent to the original inequality.

For example, if we start with the inequality $x − 5 < 7$, then adding 5 to both sides results in the equivalent inequality $x < 12$.

Also, the inequality $x + 4 > 2$ is (upon subtracting 4 from both sides) equivalent to the inequality $x > −2$.

▷ **Rule 2** If both sides of an inequality are multiplied by the same *positive* real number, or if both sides of an inequality are divided by the same *positive* real number, then the resulting inequality is equivalent to the original inequality.

For example, if both sides of the inequality $\frac{1}{2}x \geq 5$ are multiplied by the *positive* number 2, then the equivalent inequality $x \geq 10$ results.

Also, the inequality $3x < 21$ is equivalent (upon division by the *positive* number 3) to the inequality $x < 7$.

▷ **Rule 3** If both sides of an inequality are multiplied by the same *negative* real number, or if both sides of an inequality are divided by the same *negative* real number, then the resulting inequality *with the inequality sign reversed* is equivalent to the original inequality.

For example, if both sides of the inequality $-\frac{1}{3}x < 6$ are multiplied by the *negative* number -3 *and the inequality is reversed,* then the equivalent inequality $x > -18$ results.

Also, the inequality $-4x \geq -24$ is equivalent (upon division by the *negative* number -4 *and reversing the inequality*) to the inequality $x \leq 6$.

Note. In order to solve an inequality—that is, find all values of the variable which make the inequality true—we use the rules to transform the inequality into an equivalent inequality whose solution is obvious.

EXAMPLE   Solve the following inequalities:
   (a) $2x + 5 < 7$
   (b) $-x + 2 \geq 4x + 6$
   (c) $2y/3 + 1 \geq -y/2 + 5$
   (d) $-2x < 4 - x$

Solution   (a) $2x + 5 < 7$

Subtract 5 from both sides (Rule 1) to get $2x < 2$. Divide both sides by 2 (Rule 2) to get $x < 1$. *Answer*

   (b) $-x + 2 \geq 4x + 6$

Add x to both sides (Rule 1) to get $2 \geq 5x + 6$. Subtract 6 from both sides (Rule 1) to get $-4 \geq 5x$. Divide both sides by 5 (Rule 2) to get $-4/5 \geq x$ or $x \leq -4/5$. *Answer*

   (c) $2y/3 + 1 \geq -y/2 + 5$

Subtract 1 from both sides and add $y/2$ to both sides (Rule 1) to get

$2y/3 + y/2 \geq 4$ or $7y/6 \geq 4$. Divide both sides by 7/6 (Rule 2) to get $y \geq 24/7$. *Answer*

(d) $-2x < 4 - x$

Add x to both sides (Rule 1) to get $-x < 4$. Divide both sides by -1 and reverse the inequality (Rule 3) to get $x > -4$. *Answer*

E X E R C I S E S

In 1–12, solve the inequality.

1. $x + 2 < 5$
2. $2x \geq x + 4$
3. $-2x > -8$
4. $-12x \leq 4x + 32$
5. $x/3 \geq 2$
6. $x/2 < -4$
7. $-2x/5 \leq 10$

8. $2x - 3 \geq 11x + 6$
9. $2x/3 + 5 < 3x/2 - 1$
10. $(x + 1)^2 \leq (x + 2)^2$
    [*Hint:* First square both sides.]
11. $.6x + 1 < .9x + 4$
12. $-3.2x \geq 64$

BEFORE WE FINISH this section, we should recall an important property of inequalities: if $a < b$ and $b < c$, then $a < c$. This is called the **transitive** property of inequalities. Other variants of this property are:

$$\text{If } a > b \text{ and } b > c, \text{ then } a > c.$$
$$\text{If } a \geq b \text{ and } b \geq c, \text{ then } a \geq c.$$
$$\text{If } a \leq b \text{ and } b \leq c, \text{ then } a \leq c.$$

Now notice that if $a < b$ and $c < d$, then we may conclude that $a + c < b + c$ and also $b + c < b + d$. The transitive property now allows us to say that $a + c < b + d$. We have just seen that inequalities may be added to each other. It follows that if $2 < x$ and $5 < y$, then $7 < x + y$. Also, if $-1 \geq x \geq -2$ and $4 \geq y + 1 \geq 1$, then $3 \geq x + y + 1 \geq -1$ or $2 \geq x + y \geq -2$.

6 Absolute Values and the Triangle Inequality

If a is a real number, then the **absolute value** of a is denoted by $|a|$; $|a|$ is defined as follows:

$$|a| = \begin{cases} a \text{ if } a \geq 0 \\ -a \text{ if } a < 0 \end{cases}$$

Thus, $|5| = 5$ because $5 \geq 0$. Also, $|-4| = 4$ because, since $-4 < 0$,

$|-4| = -(-4) \doteq 4$. Other examples are $|\pi| = \pi, |-1/2| = 1/2$, and $|0| = 0$.

Here are some important facts about absolute value:

(1) $|a| = \sqrt{a^2}$ for all real numbers a. (Remember that $\sqrt{a^2}$ signifies the *nonnegative* square root of a^2.)

(2) $|a| \geq 0$ for all real numbers a.

(3) $|a| = |-a|$ for all real numbers a.

(4) $|a \cdot b| = |a| \cdot |b|$ for all real numbers a and b. Thus, $|4 \cdot (-7)| = |4| \cdot |-7|$ and $|1/2 \cdot 5| = |1/2| \cdot |5|$.

(5) $-|a| \leq a \leq |a|$ for all real numbers a. Thus, $-|3| \leq 3 \leq |3|$ and $-|-2/3| \leq -2/3 \leq |-2/3|$.

Now, if a and b are any real numbers, then $-|a| \leq a \leq |a|$ and $-|b| \leq b \leq |b|$. Adding these inequalities gives $-|a| - |b| \leq a + b \leq |a| + |b|$, which is the same as $-(|a| + |b|) \leq a + b \leq |a| + |b|$. If $a + b \geq 0$, then $|a + b| = a + b \leq |a| + |b|$ and so $|a + b| \leq |a| + |b|$. Also, if $a + b < 0$, then $|a + b| = -(a + b) \leq |a| + |b|$ and so $|a + b| \leq |a| + |b|$. Therefore, in any case, we have

(6) $|a + b| \leq |a| + |b|$ for all real numbers a and b.

This very important inequality is called the **triangle inequality** and we will use it time and again.

It is immediate from the triangle inequality that

(6′) $|a - b| \leq |a| + |b|$ for all real numbers a and b.

If a and b are any real numbers then, if we let $x = a + b$ and $y = -b$, from the triangle inequality it follows that $|x + y| \leq |x| + |y|$. Thus, $|a| \leq |a + b| + |b|$, or

(7) $|a + b| \geq |a| - |b|$ for all real numbers a and b.

Clearly, we also have

(7′) $|a - b| \geq |a| - |b|$ for all real numbers a and b.

We may capsulize (6), (6′), (7), and (7′) with

(8) $||a| - |b|| \leq |a \pm b| \leq |a| + |b|$ for all real numbers a and b.

Chapter 1
The Cartesian Plane and Functions

1 The Cartesian Plane, the Midpoint Formula, and the Distance Formula

The **Cartesian plane** (or **coordinate plane**) is a plane with two perpendicular lines called **axes.** The axes are number lines and they have the same unit of distance. The point at which the axes intersect, called the **origin,** is the zero point on both axes. Figure 1-1 shows the Cartesian plane. For the sake of conformity, the axes are called the ***x*-axis** and the ***y*-axis** and they are oriented as shown in Fig. 1-1.

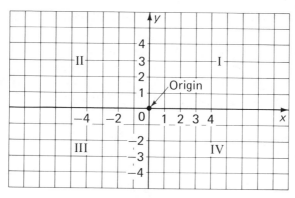

Figure 1–1

You have seen how the points of the Cartesian plane correspond, in a natural fashion, to **ordered pairs** of real numbers. In the ordered pair (2,5), 2 is called the **x-coordinate** (or **abscissa** or **first coordinate**) and 5 is called the **y-coordinate** (or **ordinate** or **second coordinate**). In general, the x-coordinate of (a,b) is a and the y-coordinate of (a,b) is b.

To locate the point representing the ordered pair (2,5), we count (starting at the origin) two units along the positive side of the x-axis (to the right) and then count 5 units up (that is, parallel to and in positive direction of the y-axis). In Fig. 1-2, the point P represents the ordered pair (2,5). To locate the point representing the ordered pair (−3,−2), we count (starting at the origin) 3 units along the negative side of the x-axis (to the left) and then count 2 units down. In Fig. 1-2, the point Q represents the ordered pair (−3,−2). You should check for yourself that the point R represents (−2,4) and that the point S represents (2,−3).

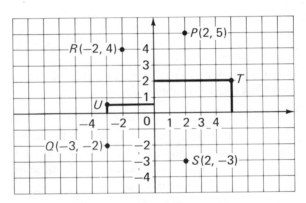

Figure 1–2

If we are given a point in the Cartesian plane and asked to find the ordered pair it represents, that is, to find its coordinates, we drop perpendiculars from the point to the x and y axes and read off the coordinates where these perpendiculars intersect the axes. For example, in Fig. 1-2, the coordinates of the point T are (5,2) and the coordinates of the point U are (−3,1/2). The coordinates of the origin are (0,0).

The Cartesian plane, with the exception of the axes themselves, is divided into four regions called **quadrants I, II, III, and IV** (see Fig. 1-1). Quadrant I consists of all points whose coordinates are both positive. Thus, (3,4) is in quadrant I. Quadrant II consists of all points whose x-coordinate is negative and whose y-coordinate is positive.

Thus, (−2,7) is in quadrant II. Quadrant III consists of all points whose coordinates are both negative. Thus, (−1,−6) is in quadrant III. Quadrant IV consists of all points whose x-coordinate is positive and whose y-coordinate is negative. Thus, (5,−2) is in quadrant IV.

EXERCISES

1. Draw a Cartesian plane and on it locate the points whose coordinates are given. If the point is in a quadrant, state which quadrant it is in. (You may wish to use a large scale on the axes so that the points are easily distinguished from one another.)

   (a) (4,2)
   (b) (−5,−4)
   (c) (2,1/2)
   (d) (−3,4)
   (e) (3,−1/2)
   (f) (3/2,−2)
   (g) (0,0)
   (h) (−1/2,−1/2)
   (i) (0,3)

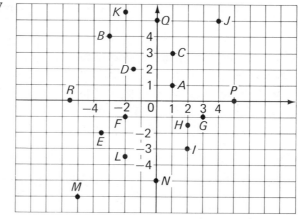

Figure 1–3

2. In the accompanying Cartesian plane (Fig. 1-3), give the coordinates for each point.
3. Characterize all points of the x-axis according to their y-coordinate.
4. Characterize all points of the y-axis according to their x-coordinate.

IF WE ARE GIVEN the points $P(1,1)$ and $Q(5,5)$ and are asked to find the coordinates of the midpoint of the line segment joining P and Q, we could graph P and Q, as in Fig. 1-4, and then draw the line segment from P to Q. We could see by inspection that the midpoint is $M(3,3)$. Similarly, we can see that the midpoint of $R(−6,2)$ and $S(−4,−2)$ is $N(−5,0)$. In each case, observe that the x-coordinate of the midpoint is halfway between the given x-coordinates. That is, 3 is halfway between 1 and 5 and −5 is halfway between −6 and −4. Another way to say this is that 3 is the average of 1 and 5 and −5 is the average of −6 and −4. Similarly, the y-coordinates behave the same way, with 3 being halfway between 5 and 1 and 0 being halfway between 2 and −2.

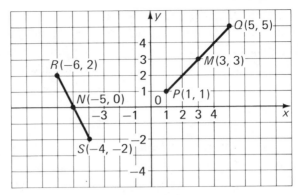

Figure 1-4

Now, if we are given the coordinates of any two points in the plane, we can easily find the coordinates of the midpoint of the line segment joining the two given points. Suppose we call the two given points (x_1,y_1) and (x_2,y_2). Certainly the x-coordinate of the midpoint must be halfway between x_1 and x_2. Thus, the x-coordinate of the midpoint must be $\dfrac{x_1 + x_2}{2}$. Similarly, the y-coordinate of the midpoint must be halfway between y_1 and y_2. Thus, the y-coordinate of the midpoint must be $\dfrac{y_1 + y_2}{2}$.

We have just established the **Midpoint Formula.** If (x_1,y_1) and (x_2,y_2) are any points in the plane, then their midpoint is $\left(\dfrac{x_1 + x_2}{2},\right.$ $\left.\dfrac{y_1 + y_2}{2}\right)$.

In other words, to find the coordinates of the midpoint of two given points, average their x-coordinates (abscissas) and average their y-coordinates (ordinates).

EXAMPLE Without using a plane, find the midpoint of the two given points: (a) (4,5) and (6,3); (b) (−2,1) and (0,4); (c) (1/2,4) and (2,−1/2).

Solution (a) Here $x_1 = 4$ and $x_2 = 6$, so that $\dfrac{x_1 + x_2}{2} = \dfrac{4 + 6}{2} = 5$. Also, $y_1 = 5$ and $y_2 = 3$, so that $\dfrac{y_1 + y_2}{2} = \dfrac{5 + 3}{2} = 4$.

The midpoint is (5,4). *Answer*

(b) $\dfrac{-2+0}{2} = -1$ and $\dfrac{1+4}{2} = 5/2$

The midpoint is (−1,5/2). *Answer*

(c) $\dfrac{1/2+2}{2} = 5/4$ and $\dfrac{4+(-1/2)}{2} = 7/4$

The midpoint is (5/4,7/4). *Answer*

EXAMPLE   The point (5,2) is the midpoint of (7,−1) and (x,y). Find x and y.

Solution   We know that $\dfrac{7+x}{2} = 5$, so that $7+x = 10$ and $x = 3$. Also,

$\dfrac{-1+y}{2} = 2$, so that $-1 + y = 4$ and $y = 5$.

$x = 3$ and $y = 5$. *Answer*

EXERCISES

In 1−10, find the midpoint of the two given points without using a plane.

1. (4,2) and (6,8)
2. (−1,6) and (3,2)
3. (1/2,3/2) and (1,2)
4. (0,2) and (2,0)
5. (−1,−2) and (−3,−4)
6. (−3,7) and (2,−4)
7. (2/3,1) and (1/2,−1/2)
8. (1.2,2.4) and (2.6,1.8)
9. (−2.1,3.6) and (−2.6,−2.8)
10. (x,y) and (−x,−y)

11. Point (2,−3) is the midpoint of (−3,4) and (x,y). Find x and y.
12. Point (x,4) is the midpoint of (2,y) and (3,6). Find x and y.
13. If the origin is the midpoint of (x_1,y_1) and (x_2,y_2), what is the relationship between x_1 and x_2 and between y_1 and y_2?

IN ADDITION TO CONSIDERING the midpoint of two points in the plane, we may wish to determine the distance between them. If the two points are conveniently situated, this may be a very simple problem. For example, in Fig. 1-5, the distance from P(1,2) to Q(3,2) is easily seen to be 2 and the distance from R(−3,3) to S(−3,−4) is clearly 7.

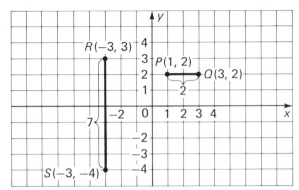

Figure 1-5

However, it is not at all obvious from inspection of Fig. 1-6 what the distance from $A(2,3)$ to $B(7,6)$ is. To calculate this distance, let us draw the indicated dotted lines parallel to the two axes. The two lines intersect in the point $C(7,3)$ (since the x-coordinate must be 7 and the y-coordinate must be 3). The distance from $A(2,3)$ to $C(7,3)$ is 5 and the distance from $B(7,6)$ to $C(7,3)$ is 3.

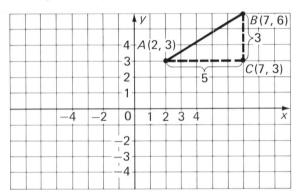

Figure 1-6

Before we continue, it will be helpful to recall the following:

▷ **Pythagorean Theorem** If $a \leq b < c$ are the three sides of a triangle, then that triangle is a right triangle if and only if $a^2 + b^2 = c^2$.

Thus, any triangle whose sides are 3, 4, and 5 must be a right triangle since $3^2 + 4^2 = 5^2$. Also, any triangle whose sides are 2, 3, and 4 cannot be a right triangle since $2^2 + 3^2 \neq 4^2$.

Since the triangle we have formed is a right triangle, with a right angle at C, the Pythagorean Theorem tells us that $AB^2 = 5^2 + 3^2$, where AB is the distance from A to B. It now follows that $AB^2 = 25 + 9 = 34$ and so $AB = \sqrt{34}$.

Now, let us investigate the more general problem of finding the distance between two points $A(x_1, y_1)$ and $B(x_2, y_2)$ which do not lie on the same horizontal or vertical line, i.e., $x_1 \neq x_2$ and $y_1 \neq y_2$. In Fig. 1-7, we draw the dotted lines, one parallel to the x-axis, and one parallel to the y-axis. They meet in a point C whose coordinates are (x_1, y_2), forming a right triangle with a right angle at C. The Pythagorean Theorem now tells us that $AB^2 = (x_1 - x_2)^2 + (y_1 - y_2)^2$. Thus,

$$AB = \sqrt{(x_1 - x_2)^2 + (y_1 - y_2)^2}$$

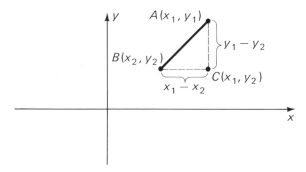

Figure 1–7

Two comments are in order here. First, if either $x_1 = x_2$ or $y_1 = y_2$ (the points are on the same vertical or horizontal line), then the above formula works anyway, even though there is no right triangle to be formed. Thus, the distance between $(1,2)$ and $(3,2)$ (see Fig. 1-5), which we already know to be 2, could be calculated as $\sqrt{(1 - 3)^2 + (2 - 2)^2} = \sqrt{4 + 0} = 2$. Also, if it turns out that the points (x_1, y_1) and (x_2, y_2) are in some other configuration than that of Fig. 1-7, the above formula still gives us the correct distance. It would be instructive for you to take some other configuration, say with (x_1, y_1) below and to the left of (x_2, y_2), draw the appropriate lines, and determine that the distance from (x_1, y_1) to (x_2, y_2) is still $\sqrt{(x_1 - x_2)^2 + (y_1 - y_2)^2}$.

We are now able to state the following:

Distance Formula If (x_1, y_1) and (x_2, y_2) are any points in the plane, then the distance between (x_1, y_1) and (x_2, y_2) is given by

$$\sqrt{(x_1 - x_2)^2 + (y_1 - y_2)^2}$$

EXAMPLE   Find the distance between $(2,-3)$ and $(5,6)$.

Solution   Say $(2,-3) = (x_1,y_1)$ and $(5,6) = (x_2,y_2)$. Then the distance formula tells us that the distance is

$$\sqrt{(x_1 - x_2)^2 + (y_1 - y_2)^2} = \sqrt{(2 - 5)^2 + (-3 - 6)^2}$$
$$= \sqrt{9 + 81} = \sqrt{90} = 3\sqrt{10} \quad Answer$$

Note. If we had designated $(2,-3) = (x_2,y_2)$ and $(5,6) = (x_1,y_1)$, we clearly would have arrived at the same distance. It makes absolutely no difference which point is called (x_1,y_1) and which point is called (x_2,y_2).

EXAMPLE   Show that the points $A(-9,11)$, $B(-2,-2)$, and $C(1,8)$ are the vertices of an isosceles right triangle with right angle at C.

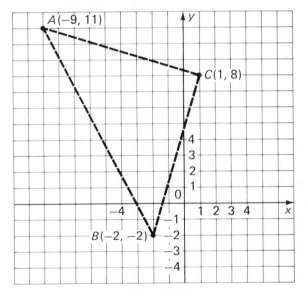

Figure 1-8

Solution   From the distance formula, we learn that

$$AC = \sqrt{(-9 - 1)^2 + (11 - 8)^2} = \sqrt{100 + 9} = \sqrt{109}$$

and

$$CB = \sqrt{[1 - (-2)]^2 + [8 - (-2)]^2} = \sqrt{9 + 100} = \sqrt{109}$$

and

$$AB = \sqrt{[-9 - (-2)]^2 + [11 - (-2)]^2} = \sqrt{49 + 169} = \sqrt{218}$$

Clearly $(\sqrt{109})^2 + (\sqrt{109})^2 = (\sqrt{218})^2$. That is, $AC^2 + CB^2 = AB^2$. It follows from the Pythagorean Theorem that triangle ABC is a right triangle with right angle at C. Finally, since $AC = CB$, our triangle is isosceles. See Fig. 1-8.

EXAMPLE A circle has center (4,2). The points (7,3) and $(x,5)$ are points on the circle. (a) Find the radius of the circle. (b) What values may x have?

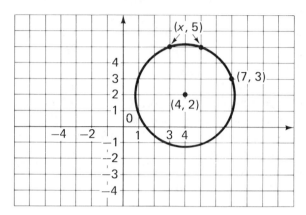

Figure 1-9

Solution (a) Since the radius of a circle is the distance from the center to any point of the circle, the radius must be

$$\sqrt{(7 - 4)^2 + (3 - 2)^2} = \sqrt{9 + 1} = \sqrt{10} \quad Answer$$

(b) Since the point $(x,5)$ is to be on the circle, its distance from the center, (4,2), must be $\sqrt{10}$. We thus have

$$\sqrt{(x - 4)^2 + (5 - 2)^2} = \sqrt{10}$$

That is,

$$\sqrt{(x - 4)^2 + 9} = \sqrt{10}$$

It follows that $(x - 4)^2 = 1$, so that (see Fig. 1-9)

$$x = 5 \text{ or } x = 3 \quad Answer$$

EXERCISES

In 1-6, find the distance between the two given points.

1. (4,2) and (7,6)
2. (−1,4) and (5,−3)

3. (1,1/2) and (3,1)
4. (−3/2,1/3) and (1/2,2/3)

5. $(2.1,-3)$ and $(1.9,2)$ 6. $(3 + \sqrt{2}, 7 - \sqrt{3})$ and $(3,7)$

7. Show that the points $A(2,0)$, $B(-2,5)$, and $C(3,9)$ are the vertices of an isosceles right triangle.

8. Show that the points $A(3,2)$, $B(4,-1)$, $C(0,-7)$, and $D(-1,-4)$ are the vertices of a parallelogram.

9. Show that the points $A(3,-1)$, $B(5,1)$, $C3,3)$, and $D(1,1)$ are the vertices of a square.

10. Three points A, B, and C are collinear (lie on the same straight line) with B being between A and C if $AB + BC = AC$. In (a) and (b), determine if the three points are collinear with the second point being between the other two.

    (a) $(2,7)$, $(1,5)$, $(-1,3)$

    (b) $(-1,5)$, $(2,9)$, $(5,13)$

11. (a) Write an equation involving x and y which expresses the fact that (x,y) is a distance 5 from the origin $(0,0)$.

    (b) Write an equation involving x, y, h, and k which expresses the fact that (x,y) is a distance 5 from the point (h,k).

    (c) Write an equation involving x, y, h, k, and r which expresses the fact that the point (x,y) is a distance r $(r > 0)$ from the point (h,k).

    (d) If $r > 0$ and (h,k) is any point in the plane, write an equation describing all points (x,y) which lie on the circle whose center is (h,k) and whose radius is r.

2 Straight Lines

Throughout the study of the calculus, one is confronted with equations involving two variables. Such an equation expresses some relationship between the variables. Consider, for example, the equation $y = 2x + 1$. Some ordered pairs, such as $(2,5)$, **satisfy** this equation. That is, if we substitute 2 for x and 5 for y, we find that $5 = 2 \cdot 2 + 1$ is a true equation. Other ordered pairs, such as $(-3,4)$, do not satisfy the equation. That is, if we substitute -3 for x and 4 for y, then we obtain the false equation $4 = 2 \cdot (-3) + 1$. In general, if we have an equation involving the variables x and y, then the ordered pair (x_0, y_0) **satisfies** the equation if when we substitute the value x_0 for x and the value y_0 for y, we obtain a true equation. The **graph** of an equation with variables x and y is the set of all ordered pairs (x,y) in the plane which satisfy the equation. If (x_0, y_0) satisfies an equation, we say (x_0, y_0) is on the graph of the equation.

Two equations are called **equivalent** if the set of all ordered pairs which satisfy one of the equations is exactly the same as the set of ordered pairs which satisfy the second equation. In other words, two equations are equivalent if their graphs are identical. Of course, we may have some very complicated equations such as $487x^5 - x^4y^3 + 47 = \sqrt{x^{96} + y^{81}}$ whose graphs are virtually impossible to exhibit. In the next four sections, we will concern ourselves with graphing certain simple equations whose graphs are called **conic sections**. Later on, with the aid of derivatives, we will be able to graph some more complicated equations. However, you may rest assured that we will never have the ability or the inclination to graph the horror mentioned above — that is a job for the computer.

We begin here with some equations whose graphs are straight lines.

We have seen that the ordered pair (2,5) satisfies the equation $y = 2x + 1$. That is, (2,5) is on the graph of the equation $y = 2x + 1$. Let us make a short table of some ordered pairs which satisfy the equation $y = 2x + 1$.

If $x = 0$, then $y = 2 \cdot 0 + 1 = 1$. If $x = 1$, then $y = 3$. If $x = -1$, then $y = -1$, etc. Thus we have:

x	0	1	-1	2	-2	3	-3	4	-4
$y = 2x + 1$	1	3	-1	5	-3	7	-5	9	-7

If we plot (graph) the points listed in our table, we find that we are able to join them with a straight line. This should come as no surprise, since you learned in algebra that the graph of the equation $y = 2x + 1$ is a straight line. In fact, if m and b are any real numbers, then the graph of the equation $y = mx + b$ is a straight line. We will henceforth refer to "the line $y = mx + b$" instead of "the line which is the graph of the equation $y = mx + b$."

Observe, in Fig. 1-10, that for every unit that x increases, y increases 2 units. We say that the **slope** of the line $y = 2x + 1$ is 2. In general, we have the following:

▷ **Definition** The **slope** of the line $y = mx + b$ is m.

Notice that if $y = mx + b$ and x increases by 1, then y increases by m. Since the slope of the line $y = -3x + 2$ (see Fig. 1-11) is -3, we see that for every unit x increases, y increases by -3 (that is, y decreases by 3).

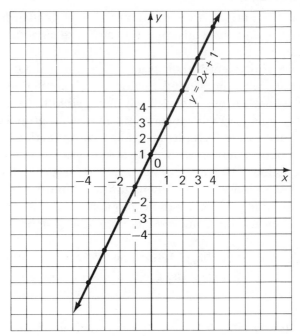

Figure 1-10

Also notice (refer to the table) that it appears that if (x_1, y_1) and (x_2, y_2) are any two distinct points on the line $y = 2x + 1$, then $\dfrac{y_2 - y_1}{x_2 - x_1} = 2$.

For example, if $(x_1, y_1) = (1,3)$ and $(x_2, y_2) = (-2,-3)$, then $\dfrac{y_2 - y_1}{x_2 - x_1} = \dfrac{-3 - 3}{-2 - 1} = \dfrac{-6}{-3} = 2$, which is the slope. Also, if $(x_1, y_1) = (4,9)$ and $(x_2, y_2) = (2,5)$, then $\dfrac{y_2 - y_1}{x_2 - x_1} = \dfrac{5 - 9}{2 - 4} = \dfrac{-4}{-2} = 2$.

In general, we can show algebraically that if (x_1, y_1) and (x_2, y_2) are any two points on the line $y = mx + b$, with $x_1 \neq x_2$, then $\dfrac{y_2 - y_1}{x_2 - x_1} = m$, the slope. We proceed as follows: Since (x_1, y_1) and (x_2, y_2) are on the graph of $y = mx + b$, we have

$$y_2 = mx_2 + b \tag{1}$$

and

$$y_1 = mx_1 + b \tag{2}$$

Subtract equation (2) from equation (1) to get $y_2 - y_1 = mx_2 - mx_1$.

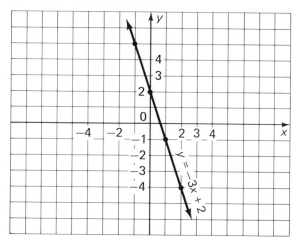

Figure 1-11

Thus, $\dfrac{y_2 - y_1}{x_2 - x_1} = m$. (Notice that $x_2 - x_1 \neq 0$, since $x_1 \neq x_2$.)

We thus see that in order to find the slope of a line, it is sufficient to select any two points (x_1,y_1) and (x_2,y_2), with $x_1 \neq x_2$, and compute the ratio $\dfrac{y_2 - y_1}{x_2 - x_1}$.

EXAMPLE (a) Find the slope of the straight line which contains the points $(2,7)$ and $(4,-8)$.

(b) Write an equation, in the form $y = mx + b$, of this line.

Solution (a) Let $(x_1,y_1) = (2,7)$ and $(x_2,y_2) = (4,-8)$. Then $m = \dfrac{y_2 - y_1}{x_2 - x_1} = \dfrac{-8 - 7}{4 - 2} = \dfrac{-15}{2}$. Notice that if we chose $(x_1,y_1) = (4,-8)$ and $(x_2,y_2) = (2,7)$, then we still would have obtained

$$m = \frac{7 - (-8)}{2 - 4} = \frac{15}{-2} = \frac{-15}{2} \quad Answer$$

(b) Since we have $y = mx + b$ and we know that $m = -15/2$, we see that our equation must be $y = -\dfrac{15}{2}x + b$. Now, we need only find the value of b. This may be done by substituting either pair $(2,7)$ or $(4,-8)$ in the last equation. Using $(2,7)$ gives us $7 = -\dfrac{15}{2} \cdot 2 + b$, so that $b = 7 + 15 = 22$, thus, our equation is

$$y = -\frac{15}{2}x + 22 \quad Answer$$

EXAMPLE   Write an equation in the form $y = mx + b$, of the line whose slope is 2 and which passes through the point $(-1,4)$.

Solution   Since $m = 2$, we have $y = 2x + b$. Substitute the values $x = -1$ and $y = 4$ to obtain $4 = -2 + b$. Thus, $b = 6$ and our equation is

$$y = 2x + 6 \quad \textit{Answer}$$

In order to see geometrically that if (x_1, y_1) and (x_2, y_2), with $x_1 \neq x_2$, are any two points on the line $y = mx + b$, then $m = \dfrac{y_2 - y_1}{x_2 - x_1}$, let us look at Fig. 1-12.

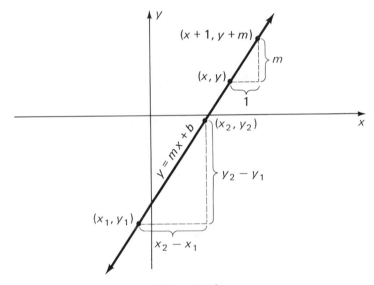

Figure 1–12

We know that as x increases by 1, y increases by m. Hence, the sides of the upper right triangle are m and 1. The lower right triangle has sides $y_2 - y_1$ and $x_2 - x_1$. Since the two triangles are similar, we see that

$$\frac{m}{1} = \frac{y_2 - y_1}{x_2 - x_1} \quad \text{or} \quad \frac{y_2 - y_1}{x_2 - x_1} = m$$

We may tell much about a line from its slope. A line with positive slope rises as x increases. A line with negative slope falls as x increases. A line with zero slope is a horizontal line, one that is parallel to the x-axis. Also, the greater the absolute value of the slope of a line, the steeper (more vertical) the line. Thus, the line $y = 5x - 4$

is steeper than the line $y = \frac{9}{2}x + 10$.

Now, notice that if, in the equation $y = mx + b$, we let $x = 0$, then $y = b$. But when $x = 0$, the line clearly crosses the y-axis. Thus, the line $y = mx + b$ intersects the y-axis in the point $(0,b)$. This is why b is called the **y-intercept** of the line $y = mx + b$. We can thus tell by inspection that the y-intercept of $y = -2x + 3$ is 3 and that the y-intercept of $y = 5x - 6$ is −6. Also, the y-intercept of $y = 4x$ is 0.

It is important to realize that an equation of a line may take several forms. For example, the equation $4x + 2y = 3$ is equivalent to $2y = -4x + 3$ which, in turn, is equivalent to $y = -2x + 3/2$. This last equation is in the form $y = mx + b$. In fact, with the exception of vertical lines, any equation whose graph is a straight line is equivalent to an equation of the form $y = mx + b$. The form $y = mx + b$ is called the **slope-intercept** form of the line, since m is the slope and b is the y-intercept. In order to determine the slope of a line, you should express the equation of the line in the slope-intercept form and then read off the slope.

EXAMPLE Find the slope and y-intercept of the line whose equation is $3x - 2y = -7$.

Solution $3x - 2y = -7$ is equivalent to $2y = 3x + 7$, which is equivalent to $y = \frac{3}{2}x + \frac{7}{2}$. Hence, the slope is 3/2 and the y-intercept is 7/2.

EXAMPLE If A, B, and C are real numbers ($B \neq 0$), find the slope and y-intercept of the line whose equation is $Ax + By + C = 0$.

Solution $Ax + By + C = 0$ is equivalent to $By = -Ax - C$, which is the same as $y = -\frac{A}{B}x - \frac{C}{B}$ (remember that $B \neq 0$). Thus, the slope is $-\frac{A}{B}$ and the y-intercept is $-\frac{C}{B}$.

There is still one type of line we need to discuss — the vertical line. You can see in Fig. 1-13 that the vertical line we have graphed represents the set of points whose x-coordinate is 3. That is, the vertical line is the graph of the equation $x = 3$. In general, the graph of $x = a$ is the vertical line passing through the point $(a,0)$. It is the vertical line intersecting the x-axis at a. A vertical line has no slope. Slope is simply not defined for vertical lines.

We are now able to present the **general form** of the equation of a

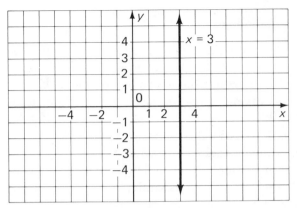

Figure 1-13

straight line. An equation is the equation of a straight line (in the plane) if and only if it is equivalent to an equation of the form $Ax + By + C = 0$, where at least one of A and B is not 0. For this reason, an equation of the form $Ax + By + C = 0$, where A or B is not 0, is called a **linear equation.** If $A = 0$, the line is horizontal and has zero slope. If $B = 0$, the line is vertical and has no slope. If $B \neq 0$, the equation may be put in the slope-intercept form $y = \dfrac{-A}{B}x - \dfrac{C}{B}$.

Note. The equation $x^2 + 2xy + y^2 = 4(x + y - 1)$ is not a linear equation (due to the presence of x^2 and y^2). Nevertheless, the equation is equivalent to a linear equation. That is, its graph is a straight line. We can see this as follows:

$$0 = x^2 + 2xy + y^2 - 4(x + y - 1)$$
$$= (x + y)^2 - 4(x + y) + 4 = (x + y - 2)^2$$

Since $(x + y - 2)^2 = 0$ if and only if $x + y - 2 = 0$, we see that the equation $x^2 + 2xy + y^2 = 4(x + y - 1)$ is equivalent to the equation $x + y - 2 = 0$, which is linear.

Two very important applications of the slopes of two lines are that they can be used to tell us about the possible parallelism or perpendicularity of the lines. Let us begin by looking at Fig. 1-14, which shows the graphs of several lines whose slopes are all 1, and at Fig. 1-15, which shows the graphs of several lines whose slopes are all −2. It appears that in each figure the lines are parallel. Let us prove that if two lines have the same slope, then they are parallel.

Suppose $y = mx + b_1$ and $y = mx + b_2$ are two lines with the same slope, m. (By the way, in this book we will adopt the convention that

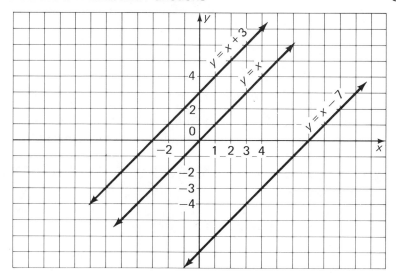

Figure 1-14

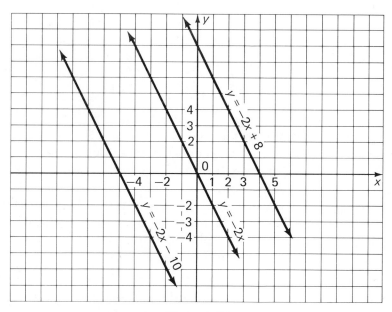

Figure 1-15

a line is parallel to itself, so that it may be that $b_1 = b_2$.) If $b_1 = b_2$, then clearly the lines are the same since the equations are the same. Thus, the lines are parallel. If, on the other hand, $b_1 \neq b_2$, then there can be no point which is on both lines. For, if (x_0, y_0) were on both lines, then we would have

$$y_0 = mx_0 + b_1$$

and

$$y_0 = mx_0 + b_2$$

Subtraction gives $b_1 - b_2 = 0$ and so $b_1 = b_2$. This is a contradiction. So, if $b_1 \neq b_2$, then the two lines do not intersect and hence they are parallel.

We can also show that if two (nonvertical) lines are parallel, then they have the same slope.

Suppose $y = m_1x + b_1$ and $y = m_2x + b_2$ are parallel. Subtraction of the second equation from the first gives us

$$0 = m_1x + b_1 - m_2x - b_2$$

or

$$(m_2 - m_1)x = b_1 - b_2$$

If $m_2 \neq m_1$, then we can solve for x and get $x = \dfrac{b_1 - b_2}{m_2 - m_1}$. This means that the point

$$\left(\frac{b_1 - b_2}{m_2 - m_1}, \frac{m_1(b_1 - b_2)}{m_2 - m_1} + b_1 \right)$$

is on both the lines $y = m_1x + b_1$ and $y = m_2x + b_2$. This is a contradiction of the assumption that the lines are parallel. We therefore know that $m_1 = m_2$ and the lines have the same slope.

In summary, we may say that two lines, each having a slope, are parallel if and only if the slopes are equal.

Since vertical lines have no slope, we must treat them separately. If each of two lines has no slope, then they are both vertical and hence parallel. Also, if a line is parallel to a vertical line, it also is vertical and, therefore, neither line has a slope.

EXAMPLE   Write an equation of the line parallel to the line $2y - 3x = 4$ and passing through the point (1,2).

Solution   First we put the equation $2y - 3x = 4$ in the form $y = mx + b$. We have $2y = 3x + 4$, so that $y = \dfrac{3}{2}x + 2$. The slope of this line is $\dfrac{3}{2}$, and so since the line we want is parallel to this line, its slope must also be $\dfrac{3}{2}$. Therefore its equation is $y = \dfrac{3}{2}x + b$. To find b, we use the fact that the line passes through (1,2) and substitute the values $x = 1$ and $y = 2$ to obtain $2 = \dfrac{3}{2} \cdot 1 + b$. Thus, $b = \dfrac{1}{2}$ and our equation is

$$y = \frac{3}{2}x + \frac{1}{2} \quad Answer$$

EXAMPLE Determine whether or not the two given lines are parallel.

(a) $x = 2y + 4$ and $y - \dfrac{1}{2}x = 2$

(b) $x = 3$ and $y + x = 2$

Solution (a) The two lines, in slope-intercept form, are $y = \dfrac{1}{2}x - 2$ and $y = \dfrac{1}{2}x + 2$. Since each line has slope $\dfrac{1}{2}$, the lines are parallel.

(b) The line $x = 3$ has no slope. The line $y + x = 2$ has slope -1. Thus, the two lines are not parallel.

EXAMPLE Show that the points $A(7,0)$, $B(5,4)$, $C(-1,-2)$, and $D(1,-6)$ are the vertices of a parallelogram.

Solution The slope of side $\overline{AB}$ is $\dfrac{4-0}{5-7} = -2$. The slope of side $\overline{CD}$ is $\dfrac{-6-(-2)}{1-(-1)} = \dfrac{-4}{2} = -2$. Thus, side $\overline{AB}$ is parallel to side $\overline{CD}$.

The slope of side $\overline{BC}$ is $\dfrac{-2-4}{-1-5} = 1$. The slope of side $\overline{AD}$ is $\dfrac{-6-0}{1-7} = 1$. Thus, side $\overline{BC}$ is parallel to side $\overline{AD}$.

Since both pairs of opposite sides are parallel, we have a parallelogram.

Note. This problem could also have been done by applying the distance formula to show that both pairs of opposite sides have equal length. Or, we could have used both techniques to show that one pair of opposite sides is both parallel and of equal length.

We will now see how the perpendicularity of two lines is related to their slopes. In Fig. 1-16, we see two lines whose slopes are 2 and $-1/2$. The lines appear to be perpendicular. Also, in Fig. 1-17, we see two lines whose slopes are 2/3 and $-3/2$. These lines also appear to be perpendicular. In each case, the product of the slopes is -1. We

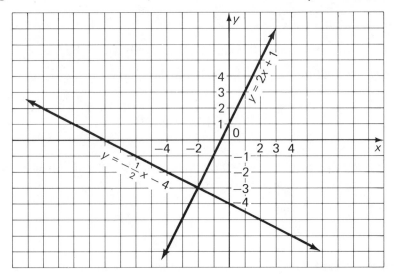

Figure 1-16

will now show that if $y = mx + b$ and $y = m_1x + b_1$ are two lines and $m_1 = -1/m$, then the lines are perpendicular.

Since $m_1 = -1/m$, we can see that $mm_1 = -1$, so that $m \neq m_1$ (if $m = m_1$, then m^2 would be negative). Thus, the two lines $y = mx + b$ and $y = m_1x + b_1$ are not parallel and, therefore, they intersect in a unique point. Call this point (x_0, y_0), as shown in Fig. 1-18.

Now, the point $(x_0 + 1, y_0 + m)$ is on the line $y = mx + b$ since, on this line, if x_0 is increased by 1, y_0 is increased by m. Also, the point $(x_0 + 1, y_0 + m_1)$ is on the line $y = m_1x + b_1$ since, on this line, if x_0 is increased by 1, y_0 is increased by m_1.

The distance from (x_0, y_0) to $(x_0 + 1, y_0 + m)$ is $\sqrt{1^2 + m^2}$.

The distance from (x_0, y_0) to $(x_0 + 1, y_0 + m_1)$ is $\sqrt{1^2 + m_1^2} = \sqrt{1 + \dfrac{1}{m^2}}$.

The distance from $(x_0 + 1, y_0 + m)$ to $(x_0 + 1, y_0 + m_1)$ is

$$\sqrt{0^2 + (m - m_1)^2} = \sqrt{\left(m + \dfrac{1}{m}\right)^2} = \sqrt{m^2 + 2 + \dfrac{1}{m^2}}.$$

Thus, (x_0, y_0), $(x_0 + 1, y_0 + m)$, and $(x_0 + 1, y_0 + m_1)$ are the vertices of a triangle whose sides are $\sqrt{1 + m^2}$, $\sqrt{1 + \dfrac{1}{m^2}}$, and $\sqrt{m^2 + 2 + \dfrac{1}{m^2}}$.

Since $(\sqrt{1 + m^2})^2 + \left(\sqrt{1 + \dfrac{1}{m^2}}\right)^2 = \left(\sqrt{m^2 + 2 + \dfrac{1}{m^2}}\right)^2$, we see, from the Pythagorean Theorem, that the triangle is a right triangle. It follows

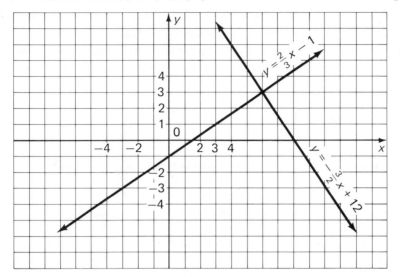

Figure 1-17

that the lines $y = mx + b$ and $y = -\dfrac{1}{m}x + b_1$ are perpendicular.

On the other hand, if two lines $y = mx + b$ and $y = m_1x + b_1$ are perpendicular, then the exact reverse of the reasoning we just used shows that $m_1 = -1/m$.

In summary, we may say that two lines, each having a slope, are perpendicular if and only if the product of the slopes is -1.

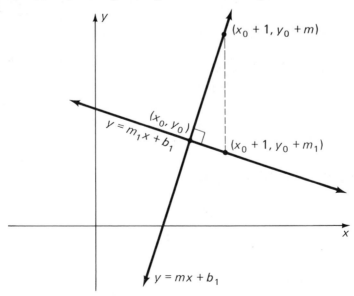

Figure 1-18

Since vertical lines have no slope, we must treat them separately. However, this case is really very simple. A line is perpendicular to a vertical line if and only if it is horizontal. In other words, a line is perpendicular to a line with no slope if and only if the line has zero slope.

EXAMPLE Write an equation of a line perpendicular to the line $-3x + 4y = 8$ and passing through the point $(-3,5)$.

Solution When we put the equation $-3x + 4y = 8$ in slope-intercept form, it becomes $y = \frac{3}{4}x + 2$. Therefore, its slope is 3/4.

The slope of a line perpendicular to this line must be $-4/3$. Therefore, the equation of the line we are seeking is $y = -\frac{4}{3}x + b$. It remains for us to find b. Substituting the values $x = -3$ and $y = 5$ gives us $5 = -4/3 \cdot (-3) + b$, so that $b = 1$. The desired equation is $y = -\frac{4}{3}x + 1$.

EXAMPLE Determine whether the two given lines are perpendicular.
  (a) $x = 5$ and $y = 7$
  (b) $3x - y = 1$ and $3y = x + 2$

Solution (a) Since $x = 5$ is vertical and $y = 7$ is horizontal, the lines are perpendicular.
  (b) Since the two lines in slope-intercept form are $y = 3x - 1$ and $y = \frac{1}{3}x + \frac{2}{3}$, we see that their slopes are 3 and 1/3. Since $3 \cdot 1/3 \neq -1$, the lines are not perpendicular.

EXAMPLE Show that the points $A(6,1)$, $B(10,5)$, $C(7,8)$, and $D(3,4)$ are the vertices of a rectangle.

Solution Side $\overline{AB}$ has slope $\dfrac{5-1}{10-6} = 1$.

  Side $\overline{BC}$ has slope $\dfrac{8-5}{7-10} = -1$.

  Side $\overline{CD}$ has slope $\dfrac{4-8}{3-7} = 1$.

  Side $\overline{AD}$ has slope $\dfrac{4-1}{3-6} = -1$.

Thus, side $\overline{AB}$ is perpendicular to both side $\overline{BC}$ and side $\overline{AD}$. Also, side $\overline{CD}$ is perpendicular to both side $\overline{BC}$ and side $\overline{AD}$.

We see that the four points are the vertices of a quadrilateral with four right angles, i.e., a rectangle.

EXERCISES

In 1–8, find the slope of the line joining the two points. If the line has no slope, write "none."

1. (2,3); (3,5)
2. (−3,4); (−1,8)
3. (4,2); (5,2)
4. (2,4); (2,5)

5. (3/2,1); (2,−4)
6. (1/3,1/2); (−2/3,−3/2)
7. (4.2,3.8); (2.4,6.6)
8. (2,$\sqrt{2}$); ($\sqrt{3}$,1)

In 9–20, (a) find the slope of the given line, (b) the y-intercept, and (c) the x-intercept (the x-value where the line crosses the x-axis). If any of these three numbers does not exist, write "none."

9. $y = 3x + 1$
10. $2y = -4x + 5$
11. $x - y = 1$
12. $2x + 3y = 4$
13. $3x + 2y + 1 = 0$

14. $x + 1 = 0$
15. $-2 = y$
16. $\frac{1}{2}x + y = 4$

17. $\frac{2}{3}x - \frac{1}{2}y = 1$
18. $x = 0$
19. $.4x = .2y - 2$
20. $x + y = \sqrt{2}$

21. Find an equation of the line whose slope is 2 and which passes through the point (−1,3).
22. Find an equation of the line which is parallel to $y + 2x = 3$ and passes through the point (2,5).
23. Find an equation of the line through the points (2,3) and (4,7).
24. Find the point of intersection of the two lines $y = 3x - 1$ and $y = 2x + 4$. [*Hint:* Solve the simultaneous system $y = 3x - 1$ and $y = 2x + 4$.]
25. Find the point of intersection of the two lines $2x + 3y + 5 = 0$ and $-x + 2y - 4 = 0$.
26. Find an equation of the line perpendicular to the line $3x + 2y = 4$ and passing through (−1,−2).
27. Find the values of x and y so that the points (−1,−3), (2,5), (4,7), and (x,y) are the vertices of a parallelogram and (x,y) is in quadrant IV.

In 28–34, decide whether the two lines are parallel, perpendicular, or neither.

28. $y = 3x + 4;\ y = 3x - 2$

29. $y = -2x;\ y = \dfrac{1}{2}x + 2$

30. $y + x = 1;\ y - x = 1$

31. $2x + 3y = 2;\ 5x - y = 4$

32. $4x - 2y + 2 = 0;\ 5 = 2x - y$

33. $x - 2y = 0;\ 3x = y + 7$

34. $x + 2 = 0;\ y + 4 = 0$

35. Show that $A(-6,-2)$, $B(-2,3)$, $C(-5,4)$, and $D(-9,-1)$ are the vertices of a parallelogram.

36. Show that $A(2,4)$, $B(4,8)$, $C(8,6)$, and $D(6,2)$ are the vertices of a square.

37. If $a \neq 0$ and $b \neq 0$, show that $\dfrac{x}{a} + \dfrac{y}{b} = 1$ is the equation of a line whose x-intercept is a and whose y-intercept is b. What is the slope of this line?

38. (a) Find an equation of the line which passes through the point $(3,1)$ and is perpendicular to the line $3x + 2y + 28 = 0$.

(b) By solving two equations in x and y, find the coordinates of the point where the line whose equation you found in (a) intersects the line $3x + 2y + 28 = 0$.

(c) Find the distance from the point whose coordinates you found in (b) to the point $(3,1)$. You have just found the (perpendicular) distance from the point $(3,1)$ to the line $3x + 2y + 28 = 0$.

(d) If A and B are not both zero, $Ax + By + C = 0$ is the equation of a straight line. Show that the (perpendicular) distance from the point (x_0, y_0) to the line $Ax + By + C = 0$ is $\dfrac{|Ax_0 + By_0 + C|}{\sqrt{A^2 + B^2}}$. You should consider the two cases $B = 0$ and $B \neq 0$ separately, since in the first case the line $Ax + By + C = 0$ has no slope and in the second case it does.

3   The Parabola

Starting with this section, we will investigate certain graphs called **conic sections**. They are called the parabola, the ellipse, the circle (a special type of ellipse), and the hyperbola. These figures are called conic sections because they can be formed by intersecting a plane with a double cone (see Fig. 1-19).

In this section, we will consider graphs of equations which have the form $y = ax^2 + by + c$, $a \neq 0$ or $x = ay^2 + by + c$, $a \neq 0$. The graph

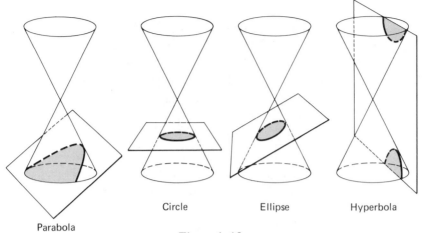

Circle   Ellipse   Hyperbola

Parabola

Figure 1-19

of an equation which is equivalent to an equation of either of these forms is called a **parabola**.

If we graph the equation $y = x^2 + 2x + 1$ by using the table of values

x	0	1	-1	2	-2	3	-3	-4	-5
$y = x^2 + 2x + 1$	1	4	0	9	1	16	4	9	16

and then connecting the indicated points with the "natural" curve, we wind up with the graph in Fig. 1-20.

In a similar fashion, we derive the graph of the equation $x = y^2 + 2y + 1$ in Fig. 1-21.

You can see why the graph of the equation $y = x^2 + 2x + 1$ is called a **vertical parabola** and the graph of the equation $x = y^2 + 2y + 1$ is called a **horizontal parabola**. The general form of a vertical parabola is $y = ax^2 + bx + c$, $a \neq 0$, and the general form of a horizontal parabola is $x = ay^2 + by + c$, $a \neq 0$. In this section, when we refer to an equation of either of these forms as a parabola, it will generally be assumed that $a \neq 0$.

In Fig. 1-22, we see the graph of $y = -x^2 + 2x + 1$. This vertical parabola opens downward. Compare this to the graph, in Fig. 1-20, of the vertical parabola $y = x^2 + 2x + 1$, which opens upward. In general, if $a > 0$, the vertical parabola $y = ax^2 + bx + c$ opens upward, and if $a < 0$, the vertical parabola $y = ax^2 + bx + c$ opens downward.

In Fig. 1-23, we see the graph of $x = -y^2 + 2y + 1$. This horizontal parabola opens to the left. Compare this to the graph, in Fig. 1-21, of the horizontal parabola $x = y^2 + 2y + 1$, which opens to the right. In

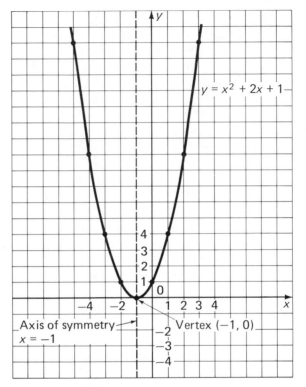

Figure 1-20

general, if $a > 0$, the horizontal parabola $x = ay^2 + by + c$ opens to the right, and if $a < 0$, the horizontal parabola $x = ay^2 + by + c$ opens to the left.

It is important to know that with each vertical parabola there is

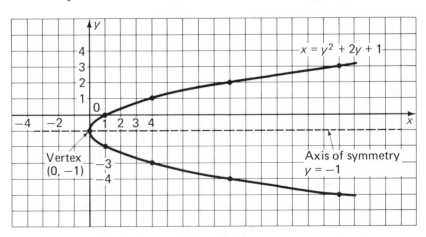

Figure 1-21

associated a vertical line, called the **axis of symmetry**. If the plane were "folded" along the axis of symmetry, then the two halves of the parabola would coincide. For example, in Fig. 1-20, the axis of symmetry of the vertical parabola $y = x^2 + 2x + 1$ is the vertical line $x = -1$. In Fig. 1-22, we can see that the axis of symmetry of the vertical parabola $y = -x^2 + 2x + 1$ is the vertical line $x = 1$.

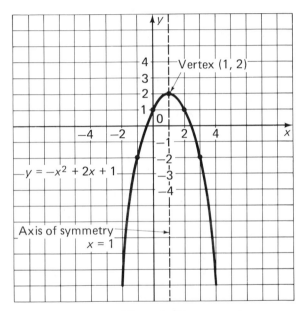

Figure 1-22

With each horizontal parabola is associated a horizontal axis of symmetry. In Fig. 1-21, we can see that the axis of symmetry of the horizontal parabola $x = y^2 + 2y + 1$ is the horizontal line $y = -1$. Also, the axis of symmetry of the horizontal parabola $x = -y^2 + 2y + 1$ is the horizontal line $y = 1$ (see Fig. 1-23).

It can be shown that the equation of the axis of symmetry of the vertical parabola $y = ax^2 + bx + c$ is $x = \dfrac{-b}{2a}$. Here is a sketch of how this can be done: The parabola $y = ax^2 + bx + c$ is symmetric about the line $x = -b/2a$ if and only if, for any x_0, when we substitute the values $\dfrac{-b}{2a} + x_0$ and $\dfrac{-b}{2a} - x_0$ for the variable x, we obtain the same y value. Indeed, when these substitutions are made, the same y value is obtained. You should check the algebra for yourself.

It can also be shown, in a similar way, that the equation of the axis

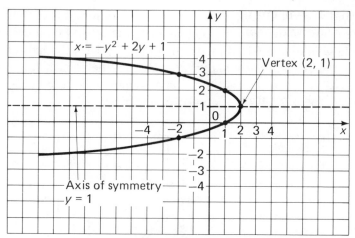

Figure 1-23

of symmetry of the horizontal parabola $x = ay^2 + by + c$ is $y = \dfrac{-b}{2a}$.

The point at which a parabola intersects its axis of symmetry is called the **vertex**, or **turning point**, of the parabola. The x-coordinate of the vertex of the vertical parabola $y = ax^2 + bx + c$, is $-b/2a$. The y-coordinate is, therefore, $a(-b/2a)^2 + b(-b/2a) + c$, which reduces to $\dfrac{-b^2 + 4ac}{4a}$. Thus, the vertex of the vertical parabola $y = ax^2 + bx + c$ is the point $\left(\dfrac{-b}{2a}, \dfrac{-b^2 + 4ac}{4a}\right)$.

In a similar fashion, we see that the vertex of the horizontal parabola $x = ay^2 + by + c$ is the point $\left(\dfrac{-b^2 + 4ac}{4a}, \dfrac{-b}{2a}\right)$.

EXAMPLE Find the axis of symmetry and the vertex of the parabolas (a) $y = 2x^2 - x + 3$ and (b) $2x - 6y = 4 - 2y^2$. Describe the direction in which each parabola opens.

Solution   (a) The parabola is vertical. Here $a = 2$, $b = -1$, and $c = 3$. The axis of symmetry is $x = \dfrac{-b}{2a} = \dfrac{1}{4}$. The vertex is $\left(\dfrac{-b}{2a}, \dfrac{-b^2 + 4ac}{4a}\right) = \left(\dfrac{1}{4}, \dfrac{23}{8}\right)$. Since $a > 0$, the parabola opens upward.

Axis of symmetry: $x = \dfrac{1}{4}$

Vertex: $\left(\dfrac{1}{4}, \dfrac{23}{8}\right)$ *Answer*

The parabola opens upward.

(b) The given equation is equivalent to $x = -y^2 + 3y + 2$. The parabola is horizontal. Here $a = -1$, $b = 3$, and $c = 2$. The axis of symmetry is $y = \dfrac{-b}{2a} = \dfrac{3}{2}$. The vertex is $\left(\dfrac{-b^2 + 4ac}{4a}, \dfrac{-b}{2a}\right) = \left(\dfrac{17}{4}, \dfrac{3}{2}\right)$.

Since $a < 0$, the parabola opens to the left.

$$\text{Axis of symmetry: } y = \frac{3}{2}$$

$$\text{Vertex: } \qquad \left(\frac{17}{4}, \frac{3}{2}\right) \quad Answer$$

The parabola opens to the left.

In order to graph a parabola from an equation, it will be helpful to follow these steps.

(1) Write the equation in the form $y = ax^2 + bx + c$ ($a \neq 0$) or $x = ay^2 + by + c$ ($a \neq 0$).

(2) By inspection of the equation resulting from step (1), determine if the parabola is horizontal or vertical: $y = ax^2 + bx + c$ is vertical; $x = ay^2 + by + c$ is horizontal.

(3) Determine the vertex. The vertex for $y = ax^2 + bx + c$ is $\left(\dfrac{-b}{2a}, \dfrac{-b^2 + 4ac}{4a}\right)$. The vertex for $x = ay^2 + by + c$ is $\left(\dfrac{-b^2 + 4ac}{4a}, \dfrac{-b}{2a}\right)$.

(4) Plot the vertex and several points on either side of the vertex.

(5) Draw the parabolic graph connecting the points you plotted in step (4).

Parabolas have a very important geometric property. In order to investigate this property, let us first look, in Fig. 1-24, at the parabola

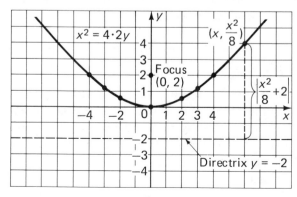

Figure 1-24

whose equation is $y = \frac{1}{8}x^2$. For reasons which will become clear later, we rewrite the equation as $x^2 = 4 \cdot 2y$.

The point (0,2) and the line $y = -2$ stand in a special relation to the parabola $x^2 = 4 \cdot 2y$. An arbitrary point of the parabola is represented by $\left(x, \frac{x^2}{8}\right)$. The distance from the point $\left(x, \frac{x^2}{8}\right)$ to the point (0,2) is $\sqrt{x^2 + \left(\frac{x^2}{8} - 2\right)^2}$. Also, the distance from the point $\left(x, \frac{x^2}{8}\right)$ to the line $y = -2$ (see exercise 38, pg. 42) is $\left|\frac{x^2}{8} + 2\right| = \frac{x^2}{8} + 2$. Now observe that

$$\sqrt{x^2 + \left(\frac{x^2}{8} - 2\right)^2} = \sqrt{x^2 + \frac{x^4}{64} - \frac{x^2}{2} + 4} = \sqrt{\frac{x^4}{64} + \frac{x^2}{2} + 4} = \sqrt{\left(\frac{x^2}{8} + 2\right)^2} = $$

$\frac{x^2}{8} + 2$. Thus the distance from any point $\left(x, \frac{x^2}{8}\right)$ of the parabola to the point (0,2) is the same as the distance from the point $\left(x, \frac{x^2}{8}\right)$ to the line $y = -2$.

Exactly the same type of computations show us that any point on the parabola $x^2 = 4py$ is equidistant from the point (0,p) and the line $y = -p$. The point (0,p) is called the **focus** of the parabola $x^2 = 4py$ and the line $y = -p$ is called its **directrix**. Also, any point on the parabola $y^2 = 4px$ is equidistant from the point (p,0), its **focus**, and the line $x = -p$, its **directrix**.

More generally, if we have any vertical or horizontal parabola (not just one of the form $x^2 = 4py$ or $y^2 = 4px$), there is a unique point, called the **focus**, and a unique line, called the **directrix**, such that the parabola is the locus (set) of all points which are equidistant from both the point and the line. Also, the focus is on the axis of symmetry and the directrix is perpendicular to the axis of symmetry.

Let us look at a specific example.

EXAMPLE Find the focus and the directrix of the parabola given by $y = x^2 + 2x + 4$.

Solution Examine the graph of $y = x^2 + 2x + 4$ in Fig. 1-25. Let us move that graph to obtain the dotted congruent graph also shown in Fig. 1-25. We can do this by taking 3 from each y-coordinate and adding 1 to each x-coordinate. Thus, for example, the vertex (−1,3) gets moved to (−1 + 1,3 − 3) = (0,0), the origin.

The dotted graph represents the set of all points (x,y) such that $y + 3 = (x - 1)^2 + 2(x - 1) + 4$, i.e., such that $y = x^2$. Thus, the dotted graph is a parabola with equation $x^2 = 4 \cdot \frac{1}{4}y$. The dotted parabola has focus $\left(0,\frac{1}{4}\right)$ and directrix $y = -\frac{1}{4}$. It should now be clear that the original parabola $y = x^2 + 2x + 4$ has focus $\left(-1,3\frac{1}{4}\right)$ and directrix $y = 2\frac{3}{4}$. Notice that the focus is on the axis of symmetry, $x = -1$, and that the directrix is perpendicular to the axis of symmetry.

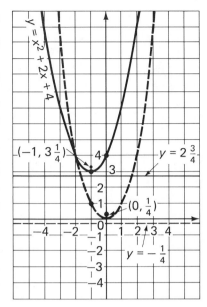

Figure 1-25

In the previous example we used an important technique called **translation of axes**. Suppose h and k are any numbers. If we have any equation in the variables x and y and we substitute $x - h$ for x and $y - k$ for y, then the graph of the resulting equation is obtained from the graph of the original equation by moving each point (x_0,y_0) of the original graph to the point $(x_0 + h,y_0 + k)$. In other words, $(x_0 + h,y_0 + k)$ is a solution of the second equation if and only if (x_0,y_0) is a solution of the original equation. For example, the graph of the equation $y - 6 = 2(x + 2)^2 + 3(x + 2) + 4$ is obtained from the graph of the equation $y = 2x^2 + 3x + 4$ by moving each point of the latter graph 6 units up and 2 units left. That is, $(x_0 - 2,y_0 + 6)$ is a solution of $y - 6 = 2(x + 2)^2 + 3(x + 2) + 4$ if and only if (x_0,y_0) is a solution of $y = 2x^2 + 3x + 4$. Translation of axes is often used in order to shift a graph into a desirable position so that information may be obtained. The information is then "translated" back to the original graph, just as we did in the previous example.

We could also have worked the previous example by "completing the square," a technique you learned in algebra, as follows: We begin with $y = x^2 + 2x + 4$. This is equivalent to $y = (x^2 + 2x + 1) + 3$, that is, $y = (x + 1)^2 + 3$, or $y - 3 = (x + 1)^2$. Thus, our parabola can be obtained by moving the parabola $y = x^2$ one unit to the left and three units up. Since the parabola $y = x^2$ has focus $\left(0,\frac{1}{4}\right)$ and directrix $y = -\frac{1}{4}$, our parabola has focus $\left(-1,3\frac{1}{4}\right)$ and directrix $y = 2\frac{3}{4}$.

You can see that whether we translate the axes or we complete the square, it really amounts to the same thing—namely, that the parabolas $y = x^2 + 2x + 4$ and $y = x^2$ are translates of each other and therefore we are able to determine the focus and directrix of the former from the focus and directrix of the latter.

A parabola need not be horizontal or vertical, as we see from the following:

▷ **Definition**   A parabola is the locus of all points which are equidistant from some fixed point F and some fixed line l not containing F. F is called the **focus** and l is called the **directrix.**

EXAMPLE   Find an equation (without radicals) of the parabola whose focus is (1,2) and whose directrix is $x - y + 2 = 0$.

Solution   Let (x_0,y_0) be any point. Then (x_0,y_0) is on the parabola if and only if the distance from (x_0,y_0) to the point (1,2) is equal to the distance from (x_0,y_0) to the line $x - y + 2 = 0$. The distance (see exercise 38, page 42) from (x_0,y_0) to the line $x - y + 2 = 0$ is

$$\frac{|x_0 - y_0 + 2|}{\sqrt{1^2 + 1^2}} = \frac{|x_0 - y_0 + 2|}{\sqrt{2}}$$

The distance from (x_0,y_0) to (1,2) is $\sqrt{(x_0 - 1)^2 + (y_0 - 2)^2}$. Thus, we have

$$\frac{|x_0 - y_0 + 2|}{\sqrt{2}} = \sqrt{(x_0 - 1)^2 + (y_0 - 2)^2}$$

Therefore,

$$|x_0 - y_0 + 2|^2 = 2[(x_0 - 1)^2 + (y_0 - 2)^2]$$

So,

$$x_0^2 - 2x_0y_0 + y_0^2 + 4x_0 - 4y_0 + 4 = 2x_0^2 - 4x_0 + 2 + 2y_0^2 - 8y_0 + 8$$

Thus, $x_0^2 + y_0^2 + 2x_0y_0 - 8x_0 - 4y_0 + 6 = 0$. The equation of the parabola is

$$x^2 + y^2 + 2xy - 8x - 4y + 6 = 0$$

E X E R C I S E S

In 1-8, for the given parabola, find (a) the axis of symmetry, (b) the vertex, (c) the focus, and (d) the directrix. Graph each parabola.

1. $4y = x^2$
2. $4x = y^2$
3. $x^2 - \dfrac{1}{4}y = 0$

4. $2x^2 + y = 0$
5. $x = y^2 + 4y + 4$
6. $x^2 - y + x + 3 = 0$

7. $y = -2x^2 - 2x + 1$
8. $x = -y^2 + y - \dfrac{1}{4}$

9. (a) Suppose l is a horizontal line and F is a point not on l. Show that the set of all points (x,y) which are equidistant from F and l is a vertical parabola. [*Hint:* Suppose l has equation $y = r$ and suppose F has coordinates (s,t), where $t \neq r$. If (x_0,y_0) is any point, write down the distance from (x_0,y_0) to l and the distance from (x_0,y_0) to (s,t). Set these distances equal to each other and conclude that (x_0,y_0) satisfies an equation of the form $y = ax^2 + bx + c$, $a \neq 0$.]

(b) Suppose l is a vertical line and F is a point not on l. Show that the set of all points (x,y) which are equidistant from F and l is a horizontal parabola.

10. Write an equation of the parabola whose focus is $(-1,3)$ and whose directrix is $2x + y + 1 = 0$.

11. Find an equation of the parabola whose focus is $(0,3)$ and whose vertex is the origin.

12. Find an equation of the parabola whose focus is $(4,0)$ and whose vertex is the origin.

13. Find an equation of the parabola whose vertex is $(-1,0)$ and whose directrix is $y = -2$.

14. Find an equation (without radicals) of the parabola whose focus is $(-2,3)$ and whose directrix is $x + y = 2$.

4 The Circle

A **circle** is the locus (set) of all points which are equidistant from a fixed point, called the **center**. The distance from any point of a circle to the center is called the **radius** of the circle.

Let us use the distance formula to write an equation which describes the set of all points (x,y) which are on the circle of radius $r > 0$ and center (h,k) (see Fig. 1-26). The point (x,y) is on the circle if and only if the distance from (x,y) to (h,k) is equal to r. Thus,

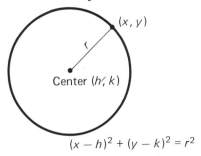

the distance formula tells us that (x,y) is on the circle if and only if $\sqrt{(x-h)^2+(y-k)^2}=r$.

Since $r>0$, this is equivalent to $(x-h)^2+(y-k)^2=r^2$.

This is the general form of the equation of the circle centered at (h,k) and with radius r.

Figure 1-26

EXAMPLE Write an equation of the circle of radius 6 centered at $(-2,3)$.

Solution Here $(h,k)=(-2,3)$ and $r=6$. The equation is $[x-(-2)]^2+(y-3)^2=6^2$ or

$$(x+2)^2+(y-3)^2=36 \quad Answer$$

EXAMPLE Find the center and radius of the circle whose equation is $(x-4)^2+(y+1)^2=5$.

Solution Since the general form of the equation of a circle is $(x-h)^2+(y-k)^2=r^2$, where (h,k) is the center and r is the radius, we see that $-h=-4$ and $-k=1$ and $r^2=5$. Thus, $h=4$, $k=-1$, and $r=\sqrt{5}$. The center is $(4,-1)$ and the radius is $\sqrt{5}$. *Answer*

EXAMPLE Show that $x^2+2x-6y+y^2=15$ is the equation of a circle. Find the center and radius of this circle.

Solution We complete the square twice as follows: Since $x^2+2x+y^2-6y=15$, we may add 1 to both sides to obtain $(x^2+2x+1)+y^2-6y=15+1=16$. Since $\left(\dfrac{-6}{2}\right)^2=9$, we next add 9 to both sides to obtain $(x^2+2x+1)+(y^2-6y+9)=16+9=25$. Thus, $(x+1)^2+(y-3)^2=5^2$. This is an equation of the circle of radius 5 centered at $(-1,3)$. *Answer*

EXAMPLE Graph the circle whose equation is $x^2-2x+y^2+10y-10=0$.

Solution We complete the square in both x and y to obtain the equivalent equation $(x^2-2x+1)+(y^2+10y+25)-10=26$, or $(x-1)^2+(y+5)^2=6^2$.

The center of our circle is (1,−5) and the radius is 6. The graph is shown in Fig. 1-27.

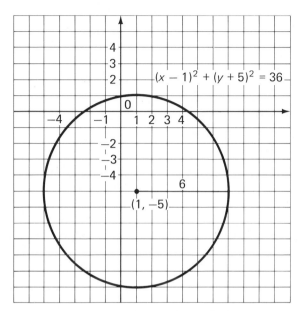

$$(x - 1)^2 + (y + 5)^2 = 36$$

Figure 1-27

E X E R C I S E S

In 1–8, (a) write an equation of the circle with the given center C and given radius r, and (b) graph the circle.

1. $C = (1,2)$; $r = 3$
2. $C = (−3,0)$; $r = 2$
3. $C = (4,−4)$; $r = \dfrac{1}{2}$
4. $C = (−2,5)$; $r = \sqrt{2}$
5. $C = (0,1)$; $r = 1$

6. $C = (0,0)$; $r = \pi$
7. $C = \left(2,\dfrac{1}{2}\right)$; $r = \sqrt{3}$
8. $C = \left(\dfrac{2}{3},-\dfrac{3}{5}\right)$; $r = \dfrac{1}{2}$

In 9–17, (a) find the center and the radius of the circle whose equation is given, and (b) graph the circle.

9. $x^2 + y^2 = 25$
10. $(x − 2)^2 + y^2 = 16$
11. $(x + 2)^2 + (y + 3)^2 = 16$
12. $\left(x - \dfrac{1}{2}\right)^2 + \left(y + \dfrac{2}{3}\right)^2 = 3$
13. $(x − 1)^2 + \left(y + \dfrac{1}{2}\right)^2 = 1$

14. $x^2 + 4x + y^2 + 6y = 36$
15. $x^2 − 2x − 2y + y^2 = 1$
16. $x^2 + 3x + y^2 + 8y = 0$
17. $y^2 − \dfrac{y}{2} + \dfrac{x}{3} + x^2 = 2$

18. If $a^2 + b^2 > c$, then show that the graph of the equation $x^2 + 2ax + y^2 + 2by + c = 0$ is the graph of a circle with center $(-a,-b)$ and radius $\sqrt{a^2 + b^2 - c}$.

19. Find an equation of the circle which passes through the points $(3,1)$, $(0,-1)$, and $(1,0)$. [*Hint:* Solve for a, b, and c in the equation of exercise 18.]

20. If the point $(x,2)$ is on the circle whose center is $(1,0)$ and whose radius is $\sqrt{29}$, then find the value or values of x.

21. Find the point which lies on the circle whose equation is $(x + 2)^2 + (y - 4)^2 = 16$ and which has (a) the greatest y-coordinate and (b) the smallest x-coordinate.

5   The Ellipse

The graph of an equation which is equivalent to an equation of the form $\dfrac{x^2}{a^2} + \dfrac{y^2}{b^2} = 1$, $a > 0$ and $b > 0$, is called an **ellipse**. We will see in a little while that there is an even more general form of an ellipse, but for the moment we will direct our attention to the equation $\dfrac{x^2}{a^2} + \dfrac{y^2}{b^2} = 1$.

First of all, it is easy to check, by substitution, that the points $(a,0)$, $(-a,0)$, $(0,b)$, and $(0,-b)$ are all on the ellipse.

Also, if the point (x,y) is on the ellipse, then we see immediately that the points $(x,-y)$ and $(-x,y)$ are also on the ellipse. This tells us that the ellipse $\dfrac{x^2}{a^2} + \dfrac{y^2}{b^2} = 1$ is symmetric about both the x-axis and the y-axis. That is, if the plane were folded along either axis, the portion of the ellipse on one side of the axis would coincide with the portion of the ellipse on the other side of the axis. Let us now look at some specific examples.

EXAMPLE   Graph the ellipse whose equation is $\dfrac{x^2}{9} + \dfrac{y^2}{4} = 1$.

Solution   Here, $a = 2$ and $b = 3$. Therefore, the points $(3,0)$, $(-3,0)$, $(0,2)$, and $(0,-2)$ are all on the ellipse. We may plot a few more points, like $\left(\sqrt{9\left(1 - \dfrac{1}{4}\right)},1\right) = \left(\dfrac{3\sqrt{3}}{2},1\right)$, and use the symmetry of the ellipse to obtain the graph in Fig. 1-28.

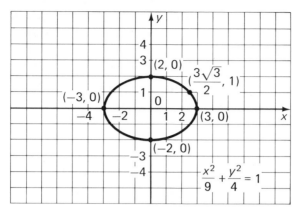

Figure 1-28

EXAMPLE   Graph the ellipse whose equation is $\dfrac{x^2}{4} + \dfrac{y^2}{9} = 1$.

Solution   Here $a = 2$ and $b = 3$ so that the points $(2,0)$, $(-2,0)$, $(0,3)$, and $(0,-3)$ are all on the ellipse. By plotting a few more points, like $\left(1, \dfrac{3\sqrt{3}}{2}\right)$, and using the symmetry of the ellipse, we obtain the graph in Fig. 1-29.

There is an obvious relation between the ellipses in Figs. 1-28 and 1-29 – namely, they are congruent. They have the same size and shape. In general, the ellipses which have equations $\dfrac{x^2}{a^2} + \dfrac{y^2}{b^2} = 1$ and $\dfrac{x^2}{b^2} + \dfrac{y^2}{a^2} = 1$ are congruent. Also, if $a > b$, as in Fig. 1-28, then the horizontal dimension, $2a$, which is called the length of the **major axis**

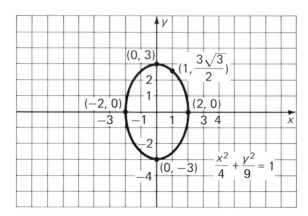

Figure 1-29

of the ellipse, is greater than the vertical dimension, $2b$, which is called the length of the **minor axis** of the ellipse. Thus, the length of the major axis of the ellipse $\dfrac{x^2}{9} + \dfrac{y^2}{4} = 1$ is 6 and the length of the minor axis is 4. If $a < b$, as in Fig. 1-29, then the length of the major axis is $2b$ and the length of the minor axis is $2a$. In case $a = b$, the equation $\dfrac{x^2}{a^2} + \dfrac{y^2}{b^2} = 1$ reduces to $x^2 + y^2 = a^2$ and we see that our ellipse is a circle which is centered at the origin and has radius a.

If $a \geq b$, it is possible to show (see exercise 12 on page 59) that there are two points $(c,0)$ and $(-c,0)$ called the **foci** of the ellipse such that the ellipse $\dfrac{x^2}{a^2} + \dfrac{y^2}{b^2} = 1$ is the locus of all points the sum of whose distances from each of the foci is $2a$. In fact, we can show that $c = \sqrt{a^2 - b^2}$.

In an entirely similar fashion, if $a \leq b$ it can be shown (see exercise 13) that the ellipse $\dfrac{x^2}{a^2} + \dfrac{y^2}{b^2} = 1$ is the locus of all points the sum of whose distances from each of the foci $(0,-\sqrt{b^2 - a^2})$ and $(0,\sqrt{b^2 - a^2})$ is $2b$.

EXAMPLE Find the foci of the ellipse whose equation is $4x^2 + 25y^2 = 100$.

Solution First, we rewrite the equation in the standard form as $\dfrac{x^2}{25} + \dfrac{y^2}{4} = 1$. This was done by dividing through by 100. Here $a = 5$, $b = 2$, and so $a > b$. Thus, the foci are $(-c,0)$ and $(c,0)$ where $c = \sqrt{a^2 - b^2} = \sqrt{25 - 4} = \sqrt{21}$. (See Fig. 1-30.)
The foci are $(-\sqrt{21}, 0)$ and $(\sqrt{21}, 0)$. *Answer*

Now let us look at the equation $\dfrac{(x - 1)^2}{9} + \dfrac{(y + 3)^2}{4} = 1$. If we think in terms of translation of axes, we see that the graph of the equation $\dfrac{(x - 1)^2}{9} + \dfrac{(y + 3)^2}{4} = 1$ may be obtained by moving the graph of the equation $\dfrac{x^2}{9} + \dfrac{y^2}{4} = 1$ one unit to the right and three units down (see Fig. 1-31). In other words, the point $(x + 1, y - 3)$ is on the graph of $\dfrac{(x - 1)^2}{9} + \dfrac{(y + 3)^2}{4} = 1$ if and only if the point (x,y) is on the graph of

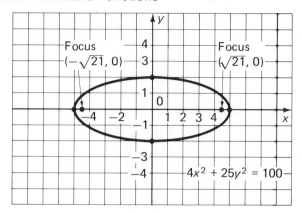

Figure 1-30

$\dfrac{x^2}{9} + \dfrac{y^2}{4} = 1$. The graph of $\dfrac{(x-1)^2}{9} + \dfrac{(y+3)^2}{4} = 1$, since it is a translate of an ellipse, is also called an ellipse. Notice that since the foci of the ellipse $\dfrac{x^2}{9} + \dfrac{y^2}{4} = 1$ are $(-\sqrt{5}, 0)$ and $(\sqrt{5}, 0)$, it follows that the foci of the ellipse $\dfrac{(x-1)^2}{9} + \dfrac{(y+3)^2}{4} = 1$ are $(1 - \sqrt{5}, -3)$ and $(1 + \sqrt{5}, -3)$.

In general, the graph of the equation $\dfrac{(x-h)^2}{a^2} + \dfrac{(y-k)^2}{b^2} = 1$ $(a, b > 0)$ is an ellipse. The graph is congruent to the graph of $\dfrac{x^2}{a^2} + \dfrac{y^2}{b^2} = 1$ and is obtained from it by translating it h units to the right and k units up.

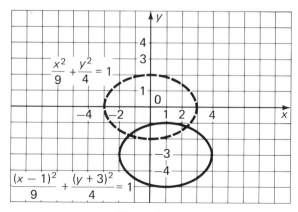

Figure 1-31

EXAMPLE   Show algebraically that $4x^2 - 8x + y^2 + 2y + 2 = 0$ is the equation of an ellipse. Find the lengths of the major and minor axes and also find the foci.

Solution   Let us begin by writing $4x^2 - 8x + y^2 + 2y + 2 = 4(x^2 - 2x) + y^2 + 2y + 2 = 0$. Now, we add 4 to both sides of the last equation to complete the square in x and obtain $4(x^2 - 2x + 1) + y^2 + 2y + 2 = 4$, or, subtracting 1 from both sides, $4(x - 1)^2 + (y + 1)^2 = 3$. Thus, we have $\dfrac{(x - 1)^2}{3/4} + \dfrac{(y + 1)^2}{3} = 1$.

This is an equation of an ellipse with $a = \sqrt{3/4} = \sqrt{3}/2$ and $b = \sqrt{3}$. The length of the major axis is $2b = 2\sqrt{3}$ (since $b > a$) and the length of the minor axis is $2a = \sqrt{3}$. Since the foci of the ellipse $\dfrac{x^2}{3/4} + \dfrac{y^2}{3} = 1$ are $(0, -3/2)$ and $(0, 3/2)$, the foci of the elipse $\dfrac{(x - 1)^2}{3/4} + \dfrac{(y + 1)^2}{3} = 1$ are $(1, -5/2)$ and $(1, 1/2)$.

In this section, all the ellipses we have investigated have their foci on either a vertical or a horizontal line. There is a more general form of an ellipse whose locus definition we will merely state.

▷ **Definition**   An ellipse is the locus of points the sum of whose distances from two fixed points (the foci) is a constant, C, where C is greater than the distance between the foci. (If the foci coincide, then the ellipse is a circle.)

E X E R C I S E S

In 1–10, (a) graph the ellipse, (b) find the lengths of the major and minor axes, and (c) find the foci.

1. $\dfrac{x^2}{25} + \dfrac{y^2}{4} = 1$

2. $\dfrac{x^2}{4} + \dfrac{y^2}{25} = 1$

3. $\dfrac{x^2}{1} + \dfrac{y^2}{4} = 1$

4. $\dfrac{x^2}{4} + \dfrac{y^2}{1} = 1$

5. $9x^2 + 25y^2 = 225$

6. $25x^2 + 9y^2 = 225$

7. $\dfrac{x^2}{2} + \dfrac{y^2}{3} = 1$

8. $x^2 + 3y^2 = 3$

9. $\dfrac{(x + 2)^2}{4} + \dfrac{(y + 1)^2}{9} = 1$

10. $\dfrac{(x - 3)^2}{4} + \dfrac{(y + 2)^2}{25} = 1$

11. Show that $4x^2 - 8x + 9y^2 + 36y = -4$ is the equation of an ellipse. Find the lengths of the major and minor axes and find the foci.

12. If $a \geq b > 0$ and $c = \sqrt{a^2 - b^2}$, use the distance formula to show that the point (x,y) is on the ellipse $\dfrac{x^2}{a^2} + \dfrac{y^2}{b^2} = 1$ if and only if the distance from (x,y) to $(-c,0)$ plus the distance from (x,y) to $(c,0)$ is equal to $2a$.

13. If $b \geq a > 0$ and $c = \sqrt{b^2 - a^2}$, use the distance formula to show that the point (x,y) is on the ellipse $\dfrac{x^2}{a^2} + \dfrac{y^2}{b^2} = 1$ if and only if the distance from (x,y) to $(0,-c)$ plus the distance from (x,y) to $(0,c)$ is equal to $2b$.

14. Put two nails in a flat piece of wood and put a loop of string on the flat surface so that the two nails are inside the string. Take a pencil and put its point inside the loop and pull it tight around the nails. Keeping the string tight, draw a curve by moving the pencil along the string as far as it will go in each direction. Now, repeat the procedure on the other side of the loop of string. What is the figure you have drawn? Give a reason. What do the nails represent?

15. Write an equation (without radicals) of the ellipse which is the locus of points the sum of whose distances from $(2,1)$ and $(-1,0)$ is 5. [*Hint:* Use the distance formula to get an equation involving two radicals. Isolate one radical and square. The resulting equation will have one radical. Isolate it and square again.]

6   The Hyperbola

The graph of an equation which is equivalent to an equation of the form $\dfrac{x^2}{a^2} - \dfrac{y^2}{b^2} = 1$ $(a,b > 0)$ or the form $\dfrac{y^2}{a^2} - \dfrac{x^2}{b^2} = 1$ $(a,b > 0)$ or the form $xy = c$ $(c \neq 0)$ is called a **hyperbola.** Let us look at a few examples.

In Fig. 1-32, we see the graph of the equation $\dfrac{x^2}{4} - \dfrac{y^2}{9} = 1$. We obtained this graph by plotting some points, such as $(2,0)$, $(-2,0)$, $\left(3, \dfrac{3\sqrt{5}}{2}\right)$, $\left(3, \dfrac{-3\sqrt{5}}{2}\right)$, $\left(-3, \dfrac{3\sqrt{5}}{2}\right)$, $\left(-3, -\dfrac{3\sqrt{5}}{2}\right)$, and connecting them with

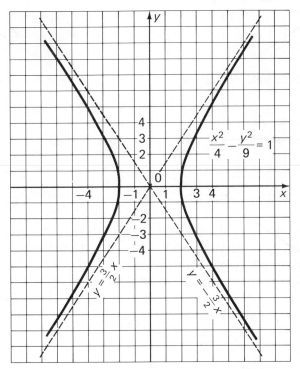

Figure 1-32

a graph whose shape we already had in mind from previous experience. It appears that, as x becomes larger and larger in absolute value, the graph of $\dfrac{x^2}{4} - \dfrac{y^2}{9} = 1$ becomes closer and closer to the dotted lines $y = \dfrac{3}{2}x$ and $y = \dfrac{-3}{2}x$. Indeed, this is the case, although we will not prove it here. For this reason, the lines $y = \dfrac{3}{2}x$ and $y = \dfrac{-3}{2}x$ are called the **asymptotes** of the hyperbola $\dfrac{x^2}{4} - \dfrac{y^2}{9} = 1$. More generally, the asymptotes of the hyperbola $\dfrac{x^2}{a^2} - \dfrac{y^2}{b^2} = 1$ $(a,b > 0)$ are the lines $y = \dfrac{b}{a}x$ and $y = \dfrac{-b}{a}x$.

In Fig. 1-33, we see the graph of the equation $\dfrac{y^2}{4} - \dfrac{x^2}{9} = 1$. We obtained this graph in much the same way as we obtained the graph in Fig. 1-32. It can be shown that the lines $y = \dfrac{2}{3}x$ and $y = \dfrac{-2}{3}x$ are the

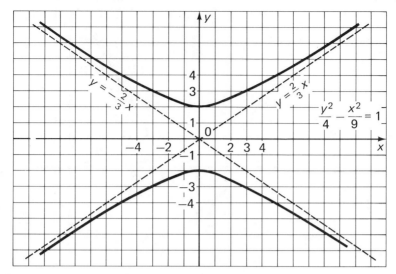

Figure 1–33

asymptotes of the hyperbola $\dfrac{y^2}{4} - \dfrac{x^2}{9} = 1$. More generally, the asymptotes of the hyperbola $\dfrac{y^2}{a^2} - \dfrac{x^2}{b^2} = 1$ $(a,b > 0)$ are the lines $y = \dfrac{a}{b}x$ and $y = \dfrac{-a}{b}x$. In Fig. 1-34, we see the graph of the equation $xy = 2$. Here, it can be shown that the axes are the asymptotes of the hyperbola. Notice that the graph lies in quadrants I and III.

In Fig. 1-35, we see the graph of the equation $xy = -2$. The axes are also asymptotes here. Notice that the graph lies in quadrants II and IV. More generally, the graph of the hyperbola $xy = c$ $(c \neq 0)$ has the axes as asymptotes. If $c > 0$, the graph lies in quadrants I and III. If $c < 0$, the graph lies in quadrants II and IV.

An important observation is in order here. Once we are given an equation of a hyperbola, we can readily determine its asymptotes. Once we know the asymptotes, it becomes easier to sketch the graph of the hyperbola. We simply draw the asymptotes, plot a few points of the hyperbola, and then draw the hyperbola through the plotted points, making the graph asymptotic (closer and closer) to the asymptotes.

EXAMPLE   Show that $x^2 - 4y^2 = 4$ is an equation of a hyperbola. Find the asymptotes and graph the hyperbola.

Solution   If we divide through by 4, we obtain $\dfrac{x^2}{4} - \dfrac{y^2}{1} = 1$. The

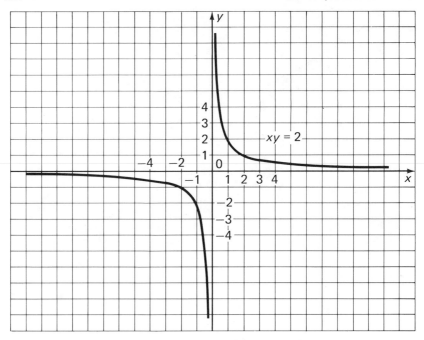

Figure 1-34

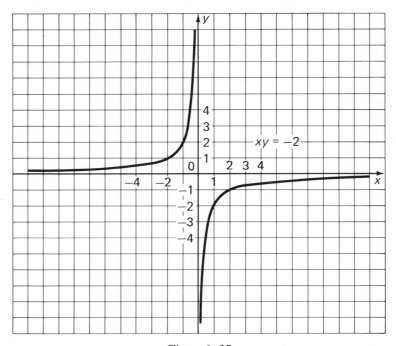

Figure 1-35

equation is of the form $\dfrac{x^2}{a^2} - \dfrac{y^2}{b^2} = 1$, where $a = 2$ and $b = 1$. Therefore,

the asymptotes are $y = \dfrac{b}{a}x$ and $y = \dfrac{-b}{a}x$, that is, $y = \dfrac{1}{2}x$ and $y = \dfrac{-1}{2}x$. In

order to graph the hyperbola, we first draw the asymptotes (see Fig. 1-36) and then plot several points, such as $(2,0)$, $(-2,0)$, $(4,\sqrt{3})$, $(-4,\sqrt{3})$, $(4,-\sqrt{3})$, and $(-4,-\sqrt{3})$. Then we sketch the graph, making it appear asymptotic to the asymptotes.

Suppose we now consider the graph of the equation $\dfrac{(x+3)^2}{25} - \dfrac{(y-4)^2}{4} = 1$. By thinking in terms of translation of axes, we see that this

graph may be obtained by moving the graph of the hyperbola $\dfrac{x^2}{25} - \dfrac{y^2}{4} = 1$ three units to the left and four units up. We may see the rela-

tionship between these two graphs in Fig. 1-37. Since the graph of $\dfrac{(x+3)^2}{25} - \dfrac{(y-4)^2}{4} = 1$ is a translate of a hyperbola, we say that it is

itself a hyperbola. This graph has asymptotes which are parallel to the asymptotes of the hyperbola $\dfrac{x^2}{25} - \dfrac{y^2}{4} = 1$. Thus, one asymptote has

slope 2/5 and the other has slope $-2/5$. The asymptotes of the hyperbola $\dfrac{(x+3)^2}{25} - \dfrac{(y-4)^2}{4} = 1$ also pass through the point $(-3,4)$. We there-

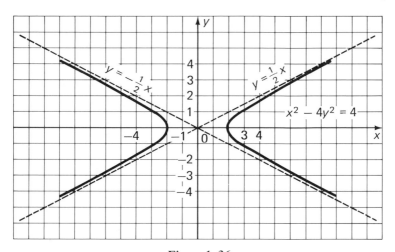

Figure 1-36

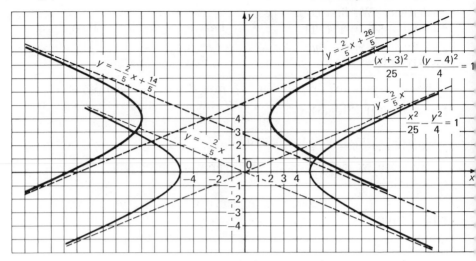

Figure 1–37

fore see that the asymptotes of $\dfrac{(x+3)^2}{25} - \dfrac{(y-4)^2}{4} = 1$ are the lines $y = -\dfrac{2}{5}x + \dfrac{14}{5}$ and $y = \dfrac{2}{5}x + \dfrac{26}{5}$.

In general, the graph of the hyperbola $\dfrac{(x-h)^2}{a^2} - \dfrac{(y-k)^2}{b^2} = 1$ can be obtained by translating the graph of the hyperbola $\dfrac{x^2}{a^2} - \dfrac{y^2}{b^2} = 1$ h units to the right and k units up. Its asymptotes pass through the point (h,k) and they are parallel to (have the same slope as) the asymptotes of the hyperbola $\dfrac{x^2}{a^2} - \dfrac{y^2}{b^2} = 1$. In a similar way, the graph of the hyperbola

$$\frac{(y-k)^2}{a^2} - \frac{(x-h)^2}{b^2} = 1$$

is a translate of the graph of the hyperbola $\dfrac{y^2}{a^2} - \dfrac{x^2}{b^2} = 1$ and the graph of the hyperbola $(x-h)(y-k) = c$ is a translate of the graph of the hyperbola $xy = c$.

EXAMPLE   Show that $x^2 + 2x - 9y^2 + 54y - 116 = 0$ is the equation of a hyperbola and find equations for its asymptotes.

Solution We first complete the square in x and obtain $x^2 + 2x + 1 - 9y^2 + 54y = 117$. Then we complete the square in y and obtain $x^2 + 2x + 1 - 9(y^2 - 6y + 9) = 36$. Thus, $(x + 1)^2 - 9(y - 3)^2 = 36$ and so $\dfrac{(x + 1)^2}{36} - \dfrac{(y - 3)^2}{4} = 1$. This is the equation of a hyperbola which is a translate of the hyperbola $\dfrac{x^2}{36} - \dfrac{y^2}{4} = 1$. The asymptotes of the latter hyperbola are $y = \dfrac{1}{3}x$ and $y = \dfrac{-1}{3}x$. Therefore, the asymptotes of the hyperbola $\dfrac{(x + 1)^2}{36} - \dfrac{(y - 3)^2}{4} = 1$ have slopes $\dfrac{1}{3}$ and $\dfrac{-1}{3}$ and they each pass through $(-1,3)$. Therefore, the asymptotes are $y = \dfrac{1}{3}x + \dfrac{10}{3}$ and $y = -\dfrac{1}{3}x + \dfrac{8}{3}$.

In closing we mention that there is a more general form of a hyperbola than those we have discussed in this section. We will only state the general locus definition.

▷ **Definition** A hyperbola is the locus of points the difference of whose distances from two fixed points (the foci) has a constant positive absolute value, C, where C is less than the distance between the foci.

E X E R C I S E S

In 1–12, (a) find equations for the asymptotes of the hyperbola and (b) graph the hyperbola.

1. $\dfrac{x^2}{1} - \dfrac{y^2}{4} = 1$

2. $\dfrac{y^2}{1} - \dfrac{x^2}{4} = 1$

3. $9x^2 - 25y^2 = 225$

4. $xy = 4$

5. $xy = -3$

6. $\dfrac{(x - 2)^2}{4} - \dfrac{(y - 1)^2}{9} = 1$

7. $\dfrac{(y + 1)^2}{1} - \dfrac{(x - 4)^2}{4} = 1$

8. $(x + 1)(y - 1) = 2$

9. $xy + 2y - 3x = 7$

10. $4y^2 + 8y - 25x^2 - 100x = 196$

11. $\dfrac{x^2}{1} - \dfrac{y^2}{2} = 1$

12. $3y^2 - 2x^2 = 6$

13. Write an equation (without radicals) of the hyperbola which is the locus of points the difference of whose distances from (0,0) and (0,2) has absolute value 1. [*Hint:* If (x,y) represents a point on the locus, write the indicated absolute value equation. Square both sides of this equation (removing the absolute value sign) and isolate the radical. Square again and simplify.]

7 Functions

The concept of a function is central throughout much of mathematics. Certainly this is the case in calculus, where functions play a crucial role.

▷ ***Definition*** A **function** is a pairing which pairs each member of one set (the **domain** of the function) with a unique member of a second set (the **range** of the function).

Note. Throughout this book, both the domain and range of our functions will be sets of real numbers. Also, throughout this book, ℝ will stand for the set of all real numbers. Thus, the symbol $x \in \mathbb{R}$ means x is a real number.

We often use lower case letters like f, g, or h to represent a function. If f is a function which, starting with the number 2, pairs the number 4 with it, then we write $f(2) = 4$. This is read "f of 2 equals 4." Here 2 is a member of the domain of f and 4 is a member of the range of f. The symbol $f(x) = y$ (read "f of x equals y") means that the function f pairs with the element x of the domain the element y of the range.

Another way to think about the domain and range of a function f is this: The domain of f is the set of all elements x for which $f(x)$ is defined, that is, for which $f(x)$ makes sense. The range of f is the set of all $f(x)$'s. If the set X is the domain of f, written $X = \text{dom } f$, and the set Y contains the range of f, written $Y \supset \text{rg} f$, then we sometimes use the symbol $f: X \to Y$ to convey this information. If, in addition, we have $Y = \text{rg } f$, then we say that f is *onto* Y, and we sometimes write $f: X \xrightarrow[\text{onto}]{} Y$.

Two functions f and g are said to be equal if $\text{dom } f = \text{dom } g$ and $f(x) = g(x)$ for all x in their common domain. Thus, the functions f and g defined by $f(x) = \sqrt{x^2}$ for all $x \in \mathbb{R}$ and $g(x = |x|$ for all $x \in \mathbb{R}$ are equal because they have the same domain, ℝ , and for any $x \in \mathbb{R}$, $\sqrt{x^2} = |x|$.

The next example will give us some practice in manipulating functional notation.

EXAMPLE If $f(x) = 2x^2 + 3$ for all $x \in \mathbb{R}$, then find

(a) $f(1)$ (d) $f(y)$ (f) $f(x + y)$

(b) $f(-2)$ (e) $f(3y^2)$

(c) $f(2x)$ (g) $f\left(\dfrac{1}{x}\right)$ $(x \neq 0)$

Solution To do each of these parts, we merely substitute the indicated member of the domain for x in the formula $f(x) = 2x^2 + 3$. Thus,

(a) $f(1) = 2 \cdot 1^2 + 3 = 5$

(b) $f(-2) = 2(-2)^2 + 3 = 11$

(c) $f(2x) = 2 \cdot (2x)^2 + 3 = 8x^2 + 3$

(d) $f(y) = 2y^2 + 3$

(e) $f(3y^2) = 2(3y^2)^2 + 3 = 18y^4 + 3$

(f) $f(x + y) = 2(x + y)^2 + 3 = 2x^2 + 4xy + 2y^2 + 3$

(g) $f\left(\dfrac{1}{x}\right) = 2 \cdot \left(\dfrac{1}{x}\right)^2 + 3 = \dfrac{2}{x^2} + 3$

Now suppose g is the function which, starting with any real number x, pairs with it the real number $2x$. Then we write $g(x) = 2x$ for all $x \in \mathbb{R}$, or more simply $g(x) = 2x$.

EXAMPLE What is the largest set of real numbers which can serve as the domain of the function $f(x) = 1 + \sqrt{x}$. For this domain, what is the range?

Solution What we are really being asked is: "For which real numbers x is $1 + \sqrt{x}$ defined?" The answer, of course, is any $x \geq 0$. Thus, $\mathrm{dom}\, f = \{x \mid x \geq 0\}$. The range of f then becomes the set of all numbers $1 + \sqrt{x}$, where $x \geq 0$. Thus, $\mathrm{rg}\, f = \{y \mid y \geq 1\}$.

Note. If the domain of a function is not specified, then it is to be assumed that the domain is the largest set of real numbers for which the function is defined, i.e., for which the function makes sense.

There are two important types of functions which deserve special mention here. If X is any nonempty set of real numbers, then we can define a function whose domain and range are both X by the formula $f(x) = x$ for all $x \in X$. This function is called the **identity function on the set X** because it pairs each element of the set X with itself. Next, suppose c is any fixed (constant) element whatever (it need not be in X). Then we can define another function whose domain is X by the formula $f(x) = c$ for all $x \in X$. This function is called a **constant function on the set X**, because no matter which element x of X we choose, $f(x)$ is always the same — namely c. Clearly, the range of this function is $\{c\}$.

Thus, $f(x) = x$ for all $x \in \mathbb{R}$ defines the identity function on the set of real numbers and $f(x) = 2$ for all $x \in \mathbb{R}$ defines a constant function on the set of real numbers.

E X E R C I S E S

In 1–16, state the largest set of real numbers which can serve as the domain of the function. For this domain, what is the range?

1. $f(x) = x$

2. $f(x) = -1$

3. $f(x) = \dfrac{1}{x}$

4. $f(x) = x + 2$

5. $g(x) = \dfrac{1}{x + 2}$

6. $h(x) = x^2$

7. $f(x) = \sqrt{x - 1}$

8. $g(x) = \sqrt[3]{x}$

9. $h(x) = \dfrac{1}{2x + 1}$

10. $f(x) = x^2 + 2x + 1$

11. $g(x) = x^2 + 2x + 2$

12. $g(x) = \dfrac{1}{x + 1}$

13. $f(x) = x^3$

14. $g(x) = \dfrac{1}{x^3 + 1}$

15. $f(x) = \sqrt{1 - x^2}$

16. $g(x) = \dfrac{1}{\sqrt{4 - x^2}}$

17. If $f(x) = 2x - 1$ for all $x \in \mathbb{R}$ then find:

   (a) $f(0)$ (c) $f(-3)$ (e) $f(2x)$ (g) $f(x^2)$

   (b) $f(1)$ (d) $f\!\left(\dfrac{1}{2}\right)$ (f) $f\!\left(\dfrac{3}{2y}\right)$ (h) $f(x^2 + 1)$

18. If $g(x) = 2x^2 - \sqrt{x}$ for all $x > 0$, find:

   (a) $g(0)$ (c) $g(5)$ (e) $g(x^2)$ (g) $g(x + 1)$

   (b) $g(4)$ (d) $g(2x)$ (f) $g(4x^2)$ (h) $g\!\left(\dfrac{9}{x^2}\right)$

19. If $h(x) = x^2 + x + 2$ for all $x \in \mathbb{R}$, for which numbers x is $h(2x) = 2 \cdot h(x)$?

20. Let $f(x) = 2x$ and $g(x) = 3x - x$. Is $f = g$? Give a reason.

21. Let $f(x) = x + 1$ and $g(x) = \dfrac{x^2 - 1}{x - 1}$. Is $f = g$? Give a reason.

22. Let $f(x) = 2x + 1$. Suppose h is a nonzero real number. Find:

   (a) $f(x + h)$ (b) $f(x + h) - f(x)$ (c) $\dfrac{f(x + h) - f(x)}{h}$

23. Let $g(x) = x^2$. Suppose h is a nonzero real number. Find:

   (a) $g(x + h)$ (b) $g(x + h) - g(x)$ (c) $\dfrac{g(x + h) - g(x)}{h}$

OFTEN IN CALCULUS, we will combine functions to produce another function. The following example illustrates one way in which we do this.

Suppose $g : \{2, 8, 50\} \to \{4, 16, 100\}$ and g is defined by $g(x) = 2x$. Suppose $f : \{4, 16, 100\} \to \{2, 4, 10\}$ and f is defined by $f(x) = \sqrt{x}$. Let us start with each element of $\{2,8,50\}$ and first apply g to it and then apply f to the number we just obtained. We have $g(2) = 4$ and $f(4) = 2$. Thus, $f(g(2)) = f(4) = 2$. Also, $g(8) = 16$ and $f(16) = 4$. Thus, $f(g(8)) = f(16) = 4$. Finally, $g(50) = 100$ and $f(100) = 10$. Thus, $f(g(50)) = f(100) = 10$. By first applying g and then applying f, we obtained a new function, written $f \circ g$, whose domain is $\{2,8,50\}$ and whose range is $\{2,4,10\}$. In symbols, $f \circ g : \{2,8,50\} \to \{2,4,10\}$; $f \circ g$ (read "f circle g") is called the **composition of f and g.**

Notice that it was crucial that every element in the range of g was in the domain of f (rg $g \subset$ dom f) so that we could apply f after applying g. Once we have this condition, it should be clear that dom $(f \circ g) =$ dom g, since $f \circ g$ is defined exactly where g is defined. Also, every element of rg $(f \circ g)$ is an element of rg f, since every value which the function $f \circ g$ takes must be a value which f takes.

Notice that if $f(x) = 2x$ for all $x \in \mathbb{R}$ and $g(x) = x^2$ for all $x \in \mathbb{R}$, then, for any $x \in \mathbb{R}$, $f \circ g(x) = f(g(x)) = f(x^2) = 2x^2$. The domain of $f \circ g(x)$ is $\mathbb{R}$, which is the domain of g. The range of $f \circ g(x) = 2x^2$ is the set of all nonnegative real numbers and the range of f is $\mathbb{R}$. Thus, although every element of rg $(f \circ g)$ is an element of rg f, we do not have, in general, that the two ranges are equal.

The formal definition of the composition of functions is as follows:

▷ **Definition** If f and g are functions with rg $g \subset$ dom f, then the function $f \circ g$, the **composition of f and g,** is defined by the equation $f \circ g(x) = f(g(x))$ for all $x \in$ dom g.

It is important to realize that the composition of functions is not, in general, commutative. That is, even if both $f \circ g$ and $g \circ f$ are defined, they may not be equal.

EXAMPLE Let $f(x) = 2x$ for all $x \in \mathbb{R}$ and let $g(x) = x + 1$ for all $x \in \mathbb{R}$.
  (a) Write a formula for $f \circ g(x)$.
  (b) Write a formula for $g \circ f(x)$.
  (c) Show $f \circ g \neq g \circ f$.

Solution
  (a) Since every element of rg g is an element of dom f, $f \circ g$ is defined and $f \circ g(x) = f(g(x)) = f(x + 1) = 2(x + 1) = 2x + 2$. Thus, $f \circ g(x) = 2x + 2$ for all $x \in \mathbb{R}$.
  (b) Since every element of rg f is an element of dom g, $g \circ f$ is defined and $g \circ f(x) = g(f(x)) = g(2x) = 2x + 1$. Thus, $g \circ f(x) = 2x + 1$ for all $x \in \mathbb{R}$.
  (c) Since $f \circ g(x) = 2x + 2$ and $g \circ f(x) = 2x + 1$, clearly $f \circ g(0) = 2$

and $g \circ f(0) = 1$. So, $f \circ g \neq g \circ f$. Indeed, for this particular f and g, $f \circ g(x) \neq g \circ f(x)$ for *any* $x \in \mathbb{R}$.

We will now look at two functions between which there is a crucial difference. The relevance of this difference will become clear shortly.

Suppose $f:\{1,2,3\} \to \{4,5,6\}$ and $f(1) = 4$, $f(2) = 5$, and $f(3) = 6$. Also suppose $h:\{1,2,3\} \to \{4,5\}$ and $h(1) = 4$, $h(2) = 5$, and $h(3) = 5$.

Notice that h has paired the number 5 of its range with two different elements, 2 and 3, of its domain. However, f pairs each element of its range with precisely one element of its domain. We say that f is a **1–1** (read "one-to-one") **function**. In general, we have:

▷ **Definition** The function f is a **1–1 function** if for every element $y \in \operatorname{rg} f$, there is precisely one $x \in \operatorname{dom} f$ such that $f(x) = y$.

Note. An equivalent formulation of the concept of $1-1$ is this: if $f:X \to Y$, then f is $1-1$ if whenever $x_1 \neq x_2$ in X, then $f(x_1) \neq f(x_2)$.

EXAMPLE Show that the function $f(x) = 3x - 1$ is $1-1$.

Solution If $x_1 \neq x_2$, then $3x_1 \neq 3x_2$ and so $3x_1 - 1 \neq 3x_2 - 1$. Thus, $f(x_1) \neq f(x_2)$ for any $x_1 \neq x_2$. Thus, $f(x) = 3x - 1$ is $1-1$.

EXAMPLE Show that the function $f(x) = x^2$ is not $1-1$.

Solution Since $1 \neq -1$ and $f(1) = 1 = f(-1)$, we see that the number 1 of the range of f is corresponded to two different members, 1 and -1, of the domain. Thus, $f(x) = x^2$ is not $1-1$.

Let us go a step further. Suppose $f:\{1,2,3\} \to \{4,5,6\}$ and $f(1) = 4$, $f(2) = 5$, and $f(3) = 6$, and suppose we wish to find a function $g:\{4,5,6\} \to \{1,2,3\}$ such that $g \circ f$ is the identity function on $\{1,2,3\}$. We can easily do this. Let $g(4) = 1$, $g(5) = 2$, and $g(6) = 3$. Then $g \circ f(1) = g(f(1)) = g(4) = 1$; $g \circ f(2) = g(f(2)) = g(5) = 2$; and $g \circ f(3) = g(f(3)) = g(6) = 3$. So, $g \circ f$ is the identity function on $\{1,2,3\}$. We say that g is the **inverse** of f and we write $g = f^{-1}$. We call g the inverse of f because if we take any element $x \in \operatorname{dom} f$ and then apply f and then apply g, we arrive back at x; g "undoes" whatever f "does."

▷ **Definition** If $f:X \xrightarrow{\text{onto}} Y$ and $g:Y \to X$ and $g \circ f$ is the identity function on X, then g is called the **inverse** of f.

Note. We stated earlier that if g is the inverse of f we write $g = f^{-1}$. This notation does *not* mean that g is the reciprocal of f. We do not mean that $g(x) = \dfrac{1}{f(x)}$ or that $g(x) = f\!\left(\dfrac{1}{x}\right)$. We mean only that $g \circ f$ is the identity function on $\operatorname{dom} f$. The "onto" means $\operatorname{rg} f = Y = \operatorname{dom} g$.

Notice that the function $h:\{1,2,3\} \to \{4,5\}$ (above), which is not $1-1$, clearly has no inverse. In general, a function has an inverse if and only if it is $1-1$. We can see this as follows:

First, suppose that $f:X \xrightarrow[\text{onto}]{} Y$ and that f is $1-1$ (we write $f:X \xrightarrow[\text{onto}]{1-1} Y$). For every element $y \in Y$, there is a unique element $x \in X$ such that $f(x) = y$. Let $g(y) = x$. We then have that $g:Y \to X$ and for any $x \in X$, $g \circ f(x) = g(f(x)) = g(y) = x$ and so $g = f^{-1}$.

On the other hand, suppose that $f:X \to Y$ and that f has an inverse, say $g = f^{-1}$. If $f(x_1) = f(x_2)$ for any elements x_1 and x_2 of X, then $x_1 = g \circ f(x_1) = g(f(x_1)) = g(f(x_2)) = g \circ f(x_2) = x_2$. Thus, $x_1 = x_2$. This shows that f is $1-1$.

EXAMPLE Find the inverse of the function $f(x) = 3x - 1$.

Solution On page 70 we saw that $f(x) = 3x - 1$ is $1-1$. Thus, f has an inverse. If we write $3x - 1 = y$, then we want to solve for x in terms of y, or, $3x = y + 1$ and $x = \dfrac{y+1}{3}$. Let $g(y) = \dfrac{y+1}{3}$. This is the same thing as $g(x) = \dfrac{x+1}{3}$. Let us see that $g = f^{-1}$. For any $x \in \mathbb{R}$, $g \circ f(x) = g(f(x)) = g(3x - 1) = \dfrac{(3x-1)+1}{3} = x$. Thus, indeed, $g = f^{-1}$. So, $f^{-1}(x) = \dfrac{x+1}{3}$.

Note. In general, if $f:X \xrightarrow[\text{onto}]{1-1} Y$, then in order to find f^{-1}, we set $f(x) = y$ and solve for x in terms of y.

EXAMPLE For $f(x) = x^2$, where $x \geq 0$, find f^{-1}.

Solution Set $f(x) = y$. Thus, $x^2 = y$. Solve for x (remembering $x \geq 0$) and get $x = \sqrt{y}$. Thus, we let $g(y) = \sqrt{y}$, or what is the same thing, $g(x) = \sqrt{x}$. Thus, $f^{-1}(x) = \sqrt{x}$.

Note. Since the function $f(x) = x^2$, $x \in \mathbb{R}$, is not $1-1$ (see page 70), it has no inverse. However, since $f(x) = x^2$, $x \geq 0$, is $1-1$, this function does have an inverse. Here $X = Y = [0,\infty[$.

EXAMPLE For $h(x) = x^2$, where $x \leq 0$, find h^{-1}.

Solution If $h(x) = y$, then $x^2 = y$, and since $x \leq 0$, $x = -\sqrt{y}$. Thus, set $g(y) = -\sqrt{y}$, or $g(x) = -\sqrt{x}$. Hence, $h^{-1}(x) = -\sqrt{x}$. Here dom $h =]-\infty,0]$ and rg $h =$ dom $h^{-1} = [0,\infty[$.

EXERCISES

In 1–8, (a) find $f \circ g$ and (b) find $g \circ f$.

1. $f(x) = x^2$; $g(x) = x - 1$
2. $f(x) = 2x + 1$; $g(x) = 3x$
3. $f(x) = x^3$; $g(x) = x^2$
4. $f(x) = \sqrt{x}$, $x \geq 0$; $g(x) = x^2$
5. $f(x) = |x|$; $g(x) = 2x$
6. $f(x) = x^2 + 1$; $g(x) = x - 1$
7. $f(x) = 2x^2 - x + 3$; $g(x) = x^2 + x$
8. $f(x) = x^2 + |x|$; $g(x) = x^2$

9. If $f(x) = 2x$, $g(x) = x^2$, and $h(x) = 3x - 1$, what is $f \circ (g \circ h)(x)$?

In 10–16, find the inverse of the function.

10. $f(x) = 2x + 1$
11. $g(x) = x^3$
12. $h(x) = |x|$, $x \geq 0$
13. $f(x) = |x|$, $x \leq 0$
14. $f(x) = x^2 + 1$, $x \geq 0$
15. $g(x) = 2x^2 - 3$, $x \leq 0$
16. $f(x) = x^2 + 2x + 1$, $x \geq -1$

17. If $f(x) = x$ for all $x \in \mathbb{R}$ and g is any function whose domain is $\mathbb{R}$, show that $f \circ g = g$ and $g \circ f = g$.
18. If $f: X \xrightarrow[\text{onto}]{1-1} Y$ and $g = f^{-1}$, then show that $f \circ g$ is the identity function on Y.

8 Graphing Functions

We saw earlier in this chapter how to graph certain equations involving the variables x and y. It is also possible to graph functions.

Suppose $f(x) = 2x$. If we think of $f(x)$ as y, then we have the equation $y = 2x$. The graph of the equation $y = 2x$ (see Fig. 1-38) is called the graph of the function $f(x) = 2x$, or simply the graph of the function $2x$. In general, we have the following:

▷ **Definition** If f is a function, then the **graph** of f is the graph of the equation $y = f(x)$, where $x \in \text{dom } f$. That is, the **graph** of f is the set of all ordered pairs $(x, f(x))$, where $x \in \text{dom } f$.

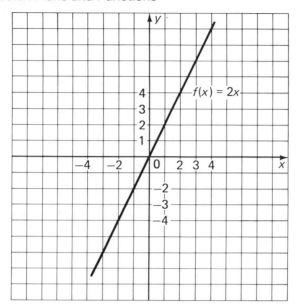

Figure 1-38

EXAMPLE   Graph the function $f(x) = |x|$, $x \in \mathbb{R}$.

Solution   For $x \geq 0$, we see that $|x| = x$ and the graph of $|x|$ coincides with the graph of $y = x$, while for $x < 0$, we see that $|x| = -x$ and the graph of $|x|$ coincides with the graph of $y = -x$.

The graph of $|x|$ can be seen in Fig. 1-39.

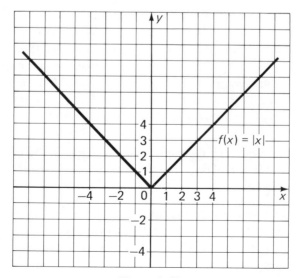

Figure 1-39

E X E R C I S E S

In 1–14, graph the function.

1. $f(x) = 2x + 1$

2. $g(x) = 3$

3. $h(x) = x^2$

4. $f(x) = 2x^2 + 3x + 3$

5. $f(x) = |x + 1|$

6. $g(x) = |2x - 1|$

7. $g(x) = |-x|$

8. $f(x) = |-2x + 2|$

9. $f(x) = \sqrt{x}$, $x \geq 0$ [*Hint:* Plot the points for $x = 0, 1, 4, 9, 25$ and draw a smooth curve connecting them.]

10. $f(x) = x^3$

11. $f(x) = \dfrac{1}{x} \cdot x \neq 0$

12. $f(x) = \begin{cases} 2 \text{ if } x \geq 0 \\ 1 \text{ if } x < 0 \end{cases}$

13. $g(x) = \begin{cases} x \text{ if } x \geq 1 \\ -2x + 3 \text{ if } x < 1 \end{cases}$

14. $h(x) = \begin{cases} 2x - 1 \text{ if } x \geq 1 \\ x^2 \text{ if } -1 < x < 1 \\ -3x - 2 \text{ if } x \leq -1 \end{cases}$

WHENEVER YOU DRAW the graph of a function, you will see that every vertical line intersects the graph in at most one point. That is, to each real number x, there is corresponded by f at most one real number y, or $f(x)$. If $x \notin \text{dom} f$, then, clearly, there is no corresponding y-value, since $f(x)$ is not defined. If $x \in \text{dom} f$, then there must be precisely one y-value, i.e., one value for $f(x)$.

On the other hand, whenever some vertical line intersects a graph (any set of points in the plane) in two or more points, then the graph cannot be the graph of a function. This is so because if the graph contains two different points with the same x-value, then it must mean that two different y-values are corresponded to the same x-value.

We may summarize these ideas as follows:

▷ **The Vertical Line Test**   A graph (a set of points in the plane) is the graph of a function if and only if each vertical line intersects the graph in at most one point.

Note. If just one vertical line intersects a graph in more than one point, then the graph is not the graph of a function.

See Fig. 1-40 for an illustration of the Vertical Line Test.

We close this section with a discussion of two notions that will be useful when we graph functions in detail in Chapter 4.

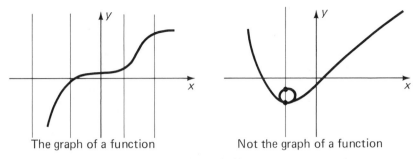

The graph of a function   Not the graph of a function

Figure 1–40

⇒ **Definition**   A function f is called *even* if $f(-x)=f(x)$ for all $x \in$ dom f. A function f is called *odd* if $f(-x)=-f(x)$ for all $x \in$ dom f.

Geometrically, an even function is one whose graph is symmetric about the y-axis; the graph is not altered if it is reflected through the y-axis. An odd function is one whose graph is symmetric about the origin; the graph is not altered if it is reflected through the origin.

EXAMPLE   (a) Show that the function $f(x) = |x|$ is even.
(b) Show that the function $f(x) = 2x$ is odd.

Solution   (a) Since $f(-x) = |-x| = |x| = f(x)$, f is an even function. The graph of f, which may be seen in Fig. 1-39, is symmetric about the y-axis.
(b) Since $f(-x) = 2(-x) = -2x = -f(x)$, f is an odd function. The graph of f, which may be seen in Fig. 1-38, is symmetric about the origin.

The next example justifies our terminology.

EXAMPLE   Show that $f(x) = x^n$ is even if n is an even integer and odd if n is an odd integer.

Solution   If n is even, then $f(-x) = (-x)^n = (-1)^n x^n = x^n = f(x)$. Thus, f is even.
If n is odd, then $f(-x) = (-x)^n = (-1)^n x^n = -x^n = -f(x)$. Thus, f is odd.

E X E R C I S E S

In 1–12 (Fig. 1-41, pages 76–77), tell whether or not the graph is the graph of a function.

13. Devise a geometrical test to determine whether or not the graph of a function is the graph of a 1–1 function.

1.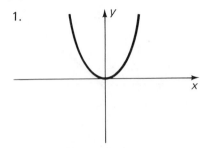

2.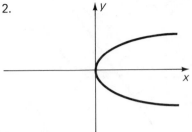

3.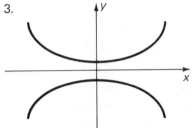

4.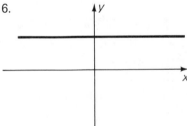

5.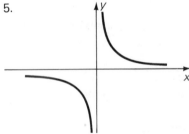

6.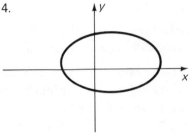

Figure 1–41

In 14–24, tell whether the function is odd or even (or neither).

14. $f(x) = x$

15. $f(x) = x^2$

16. $f(x) = x^4 - x^2 + x$

17. $f(x) = x^5 + x^3 + x$

18. $f(x) = 4x^{1/3}$

19. $f(x) = 2x^{4/5}$

20. $f(x) = 3|x| - 2x^{1/4}$

21. $f(x) = \dfrac{x^2 + 1}{x^4 - 2}$

22. $f(x) = \dfrac{x^3 + x^2}{x^5 - x}$

23. $f(x) = x^{1/3} + x^{2/3}$

24. $f(x) = x^{1/3} + x^{1/5}$

7.
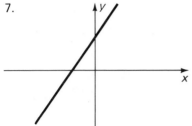

8.
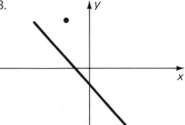

9.

10.

11.
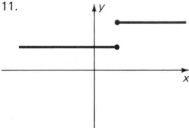

12.
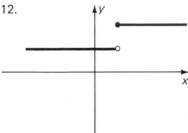

Figure 1–41

9 The Arithmetic of Functions

Just as we can add, subtract, multiply, and divide real numbers, so we can perform these operations for certain functions, as we see in the next definition.

▷ **Definition** Let f and g be functions with the same domain X. Then we define the four functions $f + g, f - g, f \cdot g$, and $\dfrac{f}{g}$ as follows:

(1) $(f + g)(x) = f(x) + g(x)$ for all $x \in X$
(2) $(f - g)(x) = f(x) - g(x)$ for all $x \in X$

(3) $(f \cdot g)(x) = f(x) \cdot g(x)$ for all $x \in X$

(4) $\left(\dfrac{f}{g}\right)(x) = \dfrac{f(x)}{g(x)}$ for all $x \in X$ such that $g(x) \neq 0$

Note. Do not confuse $f \cdot g$ with $f \circ g$. They have nothing to do with each other. For example, if $f(x) = x$ and $g(x) = x^2$, then $(f \cdot g)(x) = x^3$, whereas $(f \circ g)(x) = x^2$.

Suppose $f(x) = x^2$ and $g(x) = 2x + 1$. Then, according to the definition,

$(f + g)(x) = f(x) + g(x) = x^2 + 2x + 1$

$(f - g)(x) = f(x) - g(x) = x^2 - (2x + 1) = x^2 - 2x - 1$

$(f \cdot g)(x) = f(x) \cdot g(x) = x^2 \cdot (2x + 1) = 2x^3 + x^2$

$\left(\dfrac{f}{g}\right)(x) = \dfrac{f(x)}{g(x)} = \dfrac{x^2}{2x + 1}$, if $2x + 1 \neq 0$, i.e., $\dfrac{f}{g}$ is not defined for $x = -\dfrac{1}{2}$

Thus, $(f + g)(2) = 9$, $(f - g)(0) = -1$, $(f \cdot g)(-2) = -12$, and $\left(\dfrac{f}{g}\right)(5) = \dfrac{25}{11}$.

In general, if f and g both have domain X, then so do $f + g, f - g$, and $f \cdot g$. The domain of $\dfrac{f}{g}$ is the set of all elements $x \in X$ such that $g(x) \neq 0$.

E X E R C I S E S

In 1-6, find $f + g, f - g, f \cdot g$, and $\dfrac{f}{g}$. Be sure to tell where, if anywhere, $\dfrac{f}{g}$ is not defined, or, equivalently, tell the domain of $\dfrac{f}{g}$.

1. $f(x) = x$; $g(x) = 3x - 1$

2. $f(x) = 2x + 3$; $g(x) = 2x - 3$

3. $f(x) = x^2$; $g(x) = x$ (Be careful.)

4. $f(x) = 2x^2$; $g(x) = x^3$ (Be careful.)

5. $f(x) = 2x - 1$; $g(x) = x^2 - 3x + 2$

6. $f(x) = x^2 - 1$; $g(x) = x - 1$ (Be careful.)

7. If $f(x) = |x|$ and $g(x) = -x$, find (a) $(f + g)(-3)$; (b) $(f - g)(2)$; (c) $(f \cdot g)(1)$; and (d) $\left(\dfrac{f}{g}\right)(-4)$.

8. If $f(x) = 7$ and $(f + g)(x) = 11$, find (a) $g(x)$; (b) $(f - g)(x)$; (c) $(f \cdot g)(x)$; and (d) $\left(\dfrac{f}{g}\right)(x)$.

9. If $f(x) = 2$ and $(f - g)(x) = 2$, then what can you say about $\left(\dfrac{f}{g}\right)(x)$?

Chapter 2
Limits and Continuity

A COMPREHENSION OF the notion of limit is essential to an understanding of the calculus. For example, the central concepts of continuity, derivative, and definite integral are each defined in terms of limits.

1 Neighborhoods and Deleted Neighborhoods

In the Introduction we had the following:

▷ **Definition** If $a < b$, then the set of all numbers y such that $a < y < b$ is called the **open interval** $]a,b[$. Point a is called the **left endpoint** of $]a,b[$ and b is called the **right endpoint** of $]a,b[$.

Thus, $]5,8[$ is the set of all numbers y such that $5 < y < 8$. That is, $]5,8[= \{y \mid 5 < y < 8\}$. The numbers 6, 7, and $\sqrt{53}$ are in $]5,8[$, but the numbers 5, 8, and $\dfrac{34}{7}$ are not.

▷ **Definition** If x_0 is any real number and $]a,b[$ is any open interval containing x_0, then we say that $]a,b[$ is a **neighborhood** of x_0 (Fig. 2-1).

Thus, $]5,8[$ is a neighborhood of 6 because $5 < 6 < 8$. Also, $]-3,2[$ is a neighborhood of $-3/2$ because $-3 < -3/2 < 2$.

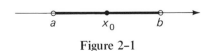

$$a \qquad x_0 \qquad b$$

Figure 2–1

79

We will sometimes use the symbol $N(x_0)$ to denote a neighborhood of x_0. Thus, $N(3)$ represents a neighborhood of 3, that is, some open interval containing 3.

The darkened portion of the real line in Fig. 2-1 represents the neighborhood $]a,b[$ of x_0.

EXAMPLE If $b > 0$ and a is any real number, then show that $]a - b, a + b[$ is a neighborhood of a.

Solution Since $b > 0$, we see that $a - b < a$ and also $a < a + b$. Thus, a is between $a - b$ and $a + b$, and so a is in the open interval $]a - b, a + b[$.

▷ **Definition** Suppose $]a,b[$ is a neighborhood of x_0. If we remove the point x_0 from the set $]a,b[$, then the remaining set is called a **deleted neighborhood** of x_0.

We will sometimes use the symbol $N'(x_0)$ to denote a deleted neighborhood of x_0. The darkened portion of the real line represents a deleted neighborhood of x_0, obtained by deleting x_0 from $]a,b[$ (see Fig. 2-2).

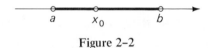

Figure 2-2

EXAMPLE Show that a deleted neighborhood $N'(x_0)$ is the union of two open intervals.

Solution Suppose $N'(x_0)$ is $]a,b[$ with the point x_0 removed. The numbers y in the set $N'(x_0)$ are those numbers which satisfy the relationships $a < y < b$ and $y \neq x_0$. Since $a < x_0 < b$, we see that for such numbers y, either $a < y < x_0$ or $x_0 < y < b$ (see Fig. 2-2). Thus, $y \in]a,x_0[$ or $y \in]x_0,b[$ and so $N'(x_0) =]a,x_0[\cup]x_0,b[$.

E X E R C I S E S

In 1–4, express the indicated set as an interval.

1. $]0,2[\cup]1,4[$ 3. $]4,10[\cap]5,11[$
2. $]-8,-5[\cup]-6,3[$ 4. $]-3,2[\cap]-5,0[$

5. Which open interval is a neighborhood of 3: (a) $]1,2[$, (b) $]2,4[$, (c) $]2,3[$, or (d) $]3,4[$?

6. If $b < c$, then is the intersection of the open intervals $]a,b[$ and $]c,d[$
   (a) an open interval, (b) the empty set, $\varnothing$, or (c) neither of these?
7. If $b < c$, then is the union of the open intervals $]a,b[$ and $]c,d[$ (a) an
   open interval, (b) the empty set, $\varnothing$, or (c) neither of these?

2 The Limit of a Function

   It often happens in calculus, and, indeed, in much of mathematics, that it is necessary to answer the following type of question: Suppose f is a function and a is a real number. What happens to the value $f(x)$ as x gets closer and closer to a?

   Let's take a specific example. Figure 2-3 shows the graph of the function $f(x) = x^2 + 1$. Suppose we wish to investigate the behavior of $x^2 + 1$ as x gets closer and closer to 0.

   The following table of values of $f(x) = x^2 + 1$ may prove helpful.

x	1	-1	1/2	$-1/2$	1/3	$-1/3$	1/4	$-1/4$	1/5
$x^2 + 1$	2	2	1 1/4	1 1/4	1 1/9	1 1/9	1 1/16	1 1/16	1 1/25

$-1/5$	1/10	$-1/100$	1/1000
1 1/25	1 1/100	1 1/10,000	1 1/1,000,000

   It appears from the table that as x gets closer and closer to 0, $x^2 + 1$ gets closer and closer to 1.

   Now let us consider a slightly different example. Figure 2-4 shows the graph of the function

$$f(x) = \begin{cases} x^2 + 1 & \text{if } x \neq 0 \\ 2 & \text{if } x = 0 \end{cases}$$

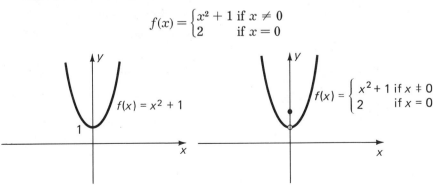

Figure 2–3   Figure 2–4

This function agrees with the function $f(x) = x^2 + 1$ at all points except at 0, where its value is 2 instead of 1.

As x gets closer and closer to 0, the values from the table in Fig. 2-2 indicate that $f(x)$ gets closer and closer to 1, even though the value of f at 0 is 2. Since we are concerned only with the behavior of $f(x)$ as x gets near 0 and not at 0, we see that the actual value of f at the point 0 is immaterial in determining the behavior of $f(x)$ as x gets closer and closer to 0. In fact, for some functions f, it may be that f is not even defined at the point in question (see exercises 11 and 12 below).

E X E R C I S E S

In 1–12, discuss the behavior of the function as x gets closer and closer to the indicated value a. It may be helpful to graph the function.

1. $f(x) = 2x$, $a = 1$

2. $f(x) = \begin{cases} 2x \text{ if } x \neq 1 \\ 0 \ \ \text{ if } x = 1 \end{cases}$, $a = 1$

3. $f(x) = x^2 + 2x$, $a = 2$

4. $f(x) = \begin{cases} x^2 + 2x \text{ if } x \neq 2 \\ 3 \ \ \ \ \ \ \ \ \ \text{ if } x = 2 \end{cases}$, $a = 2$

5. $g(x) = 3x - 1$, $a = -1$

6. $g(x) = \begin{cases} 3x - 1 \text{ if } x \neq -1 \\ 0 \ \ \ \ \ \ \ \text{ if } x = -1 \end{cases}$, $a = -1$

7. $h(x) = 3x^2 - 2x + 1$, $a = 1$

8. $h(x) = \begin{cases} 3x^2 - 2x + 1 \text{ if } x \neq 1 \\ -4 \ \ \ \ \ \ \ \ \ \ \ \ \ \text{ if } x = 1 \end{cases}$, $a = 1$

9. $f(x) = 6$, $a = 3$

10. $f(x) = \begin{cases} 6 \text{ if } x \neq 3 \\ 4 \text{ if } x = 3 \end{cases}$, $a = 3$

11. $f(x) = \dfrac{x^2 - 2x + 1}{x - 1}$, $a = 1$

(This function is not defined when $x = 1$, but this does not matter.)

12. $g(x) = \dfrac{2x^2 + 5x + 2}{x + 2}$, $a = -2$

(This function is not defined when $x = -2$, but this does not matter.)

BEFORE WE PROCEED to state precisely what we mean by the intuitive statement "as x gets closer and closer to the value a, $f(x)$ gets closer and closer to the value l," let us try to see how we can describe the notion "closer and closer" in terms of neighborhoods.

If l is a real number, we can guarantee that a number y is close to l (that is, within a prescribed distance from l) by requiring that it be in some appropriately small neighborhood $N(l)$ of l.

Here is a specific example. How "close" must x ($x \neq 2$) be to 2 in order to assure that $x^2 + 1$ is in the neighborhood $N(5) =]4.99,5.009[$ of 5? More precisely, the problem is to find some deleted neighborhood, $N'(2)$, of 2 such that $x^2 + 1$ is in $N(5)$ whenever x is in $N'(2)$. The requirement that $x^2 + 1$ is in $N(5)$ is equivalent to requiring that $4.99 < x^2 + 1 < 5.009$, which is fulfilled if $\sqrt{3.99} < x < \sqrt{4.009}$.

Thus, it suffices to choose $N(2) =]1.999,2.001[$, so that $N'(2) =]1.999,2[\cup]2,2.001[$, because $1.999 \geq \sqrt{3.99}$ and $2.001 \leq \sqrt{4.009}$. Therefore, we see that if the number x ($x \neq 2$) is within .001 of 2, then $x^2 + 1$ is in $N(5)$. This leads to the following.

> **Definition** If f is a function which is defined in some neighborhood of a, except possibly at a itself, then we say that **the limit of $f(x)$ as x approaches a is l,** if for every neighborhood $N(l)$, there is a deleted neighborhood $N'(a)$ such that if $x \in N'(a)$, then $f(x) \in N(l)$. In this case we write $\lim_{x \to a} f(x) = l$.

Thus, $\lim_{x \to a} f(x) = l$ means that we can make $f(x)$ as close to l as we wish provided we take x suitably close to a, without actually taking the value a itself. Notice that we do not allow x to take the value a because we are concerned with the values of $f(x)$ when x is near a, not at a.

Here is the situation. In order to defend the statement that $\lim_{x \to a} f(x) = l$, we must, when challenged with any particular neighborhood $N(l)$ of l, be able to come up with some deleted neighborhood $N'(a)$ of a having the property that $f(x)$ is in $N(l)$ for all values of x that are in $N'(a)$: if someone gives us the $N(l)$, we must be able to supply the $N'(a)$. In order to show that the statement $\lim_{x \to a} f(x) = l$ is false, all we need to do is find one neighborhood $N(l)$ of l having the property that, no matter what $N'(a)$ we try, it is always possible to find at least one c in $N'(a)$ for which $f(c)$ is not in $N(l)$.

It is important to realize that for some functions f and some numbers a, $\lim_{x \to a} f(x)$ does not exist. Here is a specific example. Let

$$f(x) = \begin{cases} 1 \text{ if } x \geq 0 \\ -1 \text{ if } x < 0 \end{cases}$$

The graph of f is shown in Fig. 2-5. Notice that in any deleted neighborhood of 0, f takes both the value 1 and the value -1. Thus, as x approaches 0, $f(x)$ does not get closer and closer to any one value.

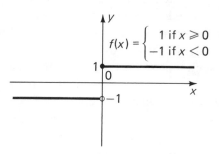

Figure 2–5

To be precise, if we consider some fixed number $l \neq 1$, we see that $\lim_{x \to a} f(x) \neq l$ as follows. Choose a neighborhood $N(l)$ of l that does not contain 1. Any deleted neighborhood $N'(0)$ of 0 that we try contains some $c > 0$ and $f(c) = 1 \notin N(l)$. This chosen $N(l)$ shows that the limit is not l. Thus, we conclude that if $f(x)$ has a limit l as x approaches 0, then $l = 1$. But $]0,2[$ is a neighborhood of 1 that fails to contain $f(c)$ when $c < 0$, so $\lim_{x \to 0} f(x)$ cannot be 1 either. Having eliminated all real numbers l as candidates (first all $l \neq 1$, then $l = 1$), we see that $\lim_{x \to 0} f(x)$ does not exist.

EXAMPLE   Evaluate the following limits:

(a) $\lim_{x \to 2} (x + 1)$

(b) $\lim_{x \to -1} (2x + 3)$

(c) $\lim_{x \to 0} \dfrac{2}{x + 1}$

(d) $\lim_{x \to 1} \dfrac{x^2 - 1}{x - 1}$

(e) $\lim_{x \to 3} (2x^2 + 4x + 1)$

(f) $\lim_{x \to 3} \sqrt{x + 1}$

Solution   (a) Since, as x approaches 2, the value of $x + 1$ gets closer and closer to 3, we have $\lim_{x \to 2} (x + 1) = 3$.

(b) Since as x approaches -1, $2x$ approaches -2, and thus $2x + 3$ approaches 1, we have

$$\lim_{x \to -1} (2x + 3) = 1$$

(c) Since as x approaches 0, $x + 1$ approaches 1, and thus $\dfrac{2}{x + 1}$ approaches 2, we have

$$\lim_{x \to 0} \frac{2}{x + 1} = 2$$

(d) Notice that $\dfrac{x^2 - 1}{x - 1}$ is not defined at $x = 1$. However, for all other values of x we have

$$\frac{x^2 - 1}{x - 1} = \frac{(x + 1)(x - 1)}{x - 1} = x + 1$$

Since we are not concerned with what happens at $x = 1$, we may write

$$\lim_{x \to 1} \frac{x^2 - 1}{x - 1} = \lim_{x \to 1} x + 1 = 2$$

because as x approaches 1, $x + 1$ approaches 2.

(e) As x approaches 3, x^2 approaches 9 and $2x^2$ approaches 18. Also, as x approaches 3, $4x$ approaches 12. Thus, as x approaches 3, $2x^2 + 4x + 1$ approaches $18 + 12 + 1 = 31$. Thus, $\lim_{x \to 3} (2x^2 + 4x + 1) = 31$.

(f) Since as x approaches 3, $x + 1$ approaches 4, we see that as x approaches 3, $\sqrt{x + 1}$ approaches 2. Thus, $\lim_{x \to 3} \sqrt{x + 1} = 2$.

There is an alternate definition of the limit with which we close this section.

Definition   We say that $\lim\limits_{x \to a} f(x) = l$ if for every number $\epsilon > 0$ there exists a number $\delta > 0$ such that if $0 < |x - a| < \delta$, then $|f(x) - l| < \epsilon$.

In other words, if we choose any number $\epsilon > 0$, we can force $f(x)$ to be within a distance ϵ of l provided we make $x \neq a$ within a distance δ of a. Thus the definition we have just given jibes with our earlier neighborhood definition of limit. The only difference (which is unimportant) is that the $\epsilon - \delta$ definition uses only symmetric neighborhoods — the ϵ-neighborhood of l is centered at l and the deleted δ-neighborhood of a is centered at a.

EXAMPLE   Use the $\epsilon - \delta$ definition of a limit to show that $\lim\limits_{x \to 2} (3x - 1) = 5$.

Solution   Suppose $\epsilon > 0$ is given. We wish to find $\delta > 0$ (depending on ϵ) such that if $0 < |x - 2| < \delta$, then $|(3x - 1) - 5| < \epsilon$, i.e., $|3x - 6| < \epsilon$. Now, if $3x$ is to be within ϵ of 6, it seems natural to require

x to be within $\frac{\epsilon}{3}$ of 2. Thus, choose $\delta = \frac{\epsilon}{3}$. Then, if $0 < |x-2| < \frac{\epsilon}{3}$, then, multiplying through by 3, we have $0 < |3x - 6| < \epsilon$, and we are done.

EXAMPLE Use the $\epsilon - \delta$ definition of a limit to show that $\lim_{x \to -1} (x^2 + 1) = 2$.

Solution Suppose $\epsilon > 0$ is given. We wish to find $\delta > 0$ (depending on ϵ) such that if $0 < |x - (-1)| < \delta$, then $|(x^2 + 1) - 2| < \epsilon$, i.e., $|x^2 - 1| < \epsilon$ if $0 < |x + 1| < \delta$. Now, let's backtrack and assume $|x + 1| < \delta < 1$ so that $-1 - \delta < x < -1 + \delta < 0$. Then $1 + 2\delta + \delta^2 > x^2 > 1 - 2\delta + \delta^2$ and so $2\delta + \delta^2 > x^2 - 1 > -2\delta + \delta^2$. If $2\delta + \delta^2 < \epsilon$ and $-2\delta + \delta^2 > -\epsilon$, then $\epsilon > x^2 - 1 > -\epsilon$. Thus, $|x^2 - 1| < \epsilon$. Therefore, we need only choose $\delta > 0$ such that $2\delta + \delta^2 < \epsilon$ and $-2\delta + \delta^2 > -\epsilon$. Now, if we choose $\delta < 1$ and $\delta < \frac{\epsilon}{3}$, then $2\delta + \delta^2 < 3\delta < \epsilon$ and $-2\delta + \delta^2 > -3\delta > -\epsilon$. Thus if $\delta > 0$ is any number with $\delta < 1$ and $\delta < \frac{\epsilon}{3}$, then $|x^2 - 1| < \epsilon$ whenever $0 < |x + 1| < \delta$, and so we are done.

As you can see, a rigorous $\epsilon - \delta$ proof of a particular limit statement may be quite involved even if the function is relatively simple.

E X E R C I S E S

In 1–24, evaluate the limit.

1. $\lim_{x \to 3} x$

2. $\lim_{x \to -2} (x + 1)$

3. $\lim_{t \to 0} (2t + 1)$

4. $\lim_{x \to 1/2} (3x - 2)$

5. $\lim_{x \to -1} x^2$

6. $\lim_{x \to 2} (2x^2 + 3)$

7. $\lim_{x \to 1} (2x^2 + 3x + 1)$

8. $\lim_{s \to 2} s^3$

9. $\lim_{x \to 2} \dfrac{x^2 - 5x + 6}{x - 2}$

10. $\lim_{h \to 0} \dfrac{h^2}{h}$

11. $\lim_{x \to 1} \dfrac{x^3 - 1}{x - 1}$

12. $\lim_{x \to 5} \sqrt{x + 4}$

13. $\lim_{t \to 6} \sqrt{t - 2}$

14. $\lim_{x \to 5} 2\sqrt{x + 11}$

15. $\lim_{x \to -1} \sqrt[3]{x}$

16. $\lim_{x \to 7} \sqrt[3]{x + 1}$

17. $\lim_{x \to 2} |x|$

18. $\lim\limits_{x \to -2} |x|$

19. $\lim\limits_{r \to 3} |r + 1|$

20. $\lim\limits_{x \to 4} |-x - 2|$

21. $\lim\limits_{x \to 1/4} \left| \dfrac{1}{x} \right|$

22. $\lim\limits_{x \to 2} |x^2|$

23. $\lim\limits_{x \to 9} \dfrac{\sqrt{x} - 3}{x - 9}$

24. $\lim\limits_{x \to 1} \dfrac{x^3 - 3x^2 + 3x - 1}{x^2 - 2x + 1}$

25. (a) Evaluate $\lim\limits_{x \to 1} x$.

    (b) Evaluate $\lim\limits_{x \to -2} x$.

    (c) Evaluate $\lim\limits_{x \to a} x$ in terms of a.

26. (a) Evaluate $\lim\limits_{x \to 2} x^2$.

    (b) Evaluate $\lim\limits_{x \to -3} x^2$.

    (c) Evaluate $\lim\limits_{x \to b} x^2$ in terms of b.

27. If n is a positive integer, evaluate $\lim\limits_{x \to a} x^n$ in terms of a.

28. (a) Evaluate $\lim\limits_{x \to 4} \sqrt{x}$.

    (b) Evaluate $\lim\limits_{x \to 25} \sqrt{x}$.

    (c) If a is positive, evaluate $\lim\limits_{x \to a} \sqrt{x}$.

29. (a) Evaluate $\lim\limits_{x \to 8} \sqrt[3]{x}$.

    (b) Evaluate $\lim\limits_{x \to -27} \sqrt[3]{x}$.

    (c) If b is any real number, evaluate $\lim\limits_{x \to b} \sqrt[3]{x}$.

30. Give an example of a function f and a number a such that $\lim\limits_{x \to a} f(x)$ does not exist. (Refer to the example in this section but construct your own example.)

31. (a) Evaluate $\lim\limits_{h \to 0} \dfrac{(1 + h)^2 - 1^2}{h}$.

    (b) Evaluate $\lim\limits_{h \to 0} \dfrac{(2 + h)^2 - 2^2}{h}$.

    (c) Evaluate $\lim\limits_{h \to 0} \dfrac{(3 + h)^2 - 3^2}{h}$.

    (d) Let x_0 be a fixed real number. Evaluate

$$\lim\limits_{h \to 0} \dfrac{(x_0 + h)^2 - x_0^2}{h}.$$

32. (a) Evaluate $\lim\limits_{h\to 0} \dfrac{(1+h)^3 - 1^3}{h}$.

   (b) Evaluate $\lim\limits_{h\to 0} \dfrac{(2+h)^3 - 2^3}{h}$.

   (c) Evaluate $\lim\limits_{h\to 0} \dfrac{(3+h)^3 - 3^3}{h}$.

   (d) Let x_0 be a fixed real number. Evaluate
$$\lim\limits_{h\to 0} \dfrac{(x_0 + h)^3 - x_0{}^3}{h}.$$

33. (a) Evaluate $\lim\limits_{h\to 0} \dfrac{\sqrt{1+h} - \sqrt{1}}{h}$.

$\left[\textit{Hint: For } h \neq 0, \; \dfrac{\sqrt{1+h} - \sqrt{1}}{h} = \dfrac{(\sqrt{1+h} - \sqrt{1})(\sqrt{1+h} + \sqrt{1})}{h(\sqrt{1+h} + \sqrt{1})} \right.$
$$\left. = \dfrac{1+h-1}{h(\sqrt{1+h} + \sqrt{1})} = \dfrac{1}{\sqrt{1+h} + 1}. \right]$$

   (b) Evaluate $\lim\limits_{h\to 0} \dfrac{\sqrt{2+h} - \sqrt{2}}{h}$.

   (c) Evaluate $\lim\limits_{h\to 0} \dfrac{\sqrt{3+h} - \sqrt{3}}{h}$.

   (d) Let x_0 be a fixed positive real number.
   Evaluate $\lim\limits_{h\to 0} \dfrac{\sqrt{x_0 + h} - \sqrt{x_0}}{h}$.

34. (a) Evaluate $\lim\limits_{h\to 0} \dfrac{\sqrt[3]{1+h} - \sqrt[3]{1}}{h}$.

   [*Hint:* Observe that $a - b = (\sqrt[3]{a} - \sqrt[3]{b})(\sqrt[3]{a^2} + \sqrt[3]{ab} + \sqrt[3]{b^2})$.]

   (b) Evaluate $\lim\limits_{h\to 0} \dfrac{\sqrt[3]{2+h} - \sqrt[3]{2}}{h}$.

   (c) Evaluate $\lim\limits_{h\to 0} \dfrac{\sqrt[3]{3+h} - \sqrt[3]{3}}{h}$.

   (d) Let x_0 be a fixed real number.
   Evaluate $\lim\limits_{h\to 0} \dfrac{\sqrt[3]{x_0 + h} - \sqrt[3]{x_0}}{h}$.

In 35–40, evaluate $\lim\limits_{h\to 0} \dfrac{f(x+h) - f(x)}{h}$.

35. $f(x) = x^2 + 1$

36. $f(x) = x^3 + x$

37. $f(x) = \dfrac{1}{x}$

38. $f(x) = \dfrac{2}{x^2} - 1$

39. $f(x) = \sqrt{x - 1}$

40. $f(x) = \sqrt{x^2 + 1}$

In 41–48, use the $\epsilon - \delta$ definition of a limit to establish the equality.

41. $\lim\limits_{x \to 1} (x + 2) = 3$

42. $\lim\limits_{x \to 3} (2x + 5) = 11$

43. $\lim\limits_{x \to -2} (3x - 2) = -8$

44. $\lim\limits_{x \to \frac{1}{2}} (4x + 1) = 3$

45. $\lim\limits_{x \to 1} (x^2 + 1) = 2$

46. $\lim\limits_{x \to 2} |x - 1| = 1$

47. $\lim\limits_{x \to -2} (x^2 + 2) = 6$

48. $\lim\limits_{x \to 0} (x^2 + 2x + 1) = 1$

3 Limits at Infinity

Suppose we are interested in investigating the behavior of the function $f(x) = 1/x$ as the variable x takes on larger and larger positive values.

If we look at the graph in Fig. 2-6, it appears that as x moves to the right along the positive x-axis, the value of $1/x$ gets closer and closer to 0. We may also do some numerical computations to convince ourselves of this fact. For example, $f(1) = 1$, $f(2) = 1/2$, $f(5) = 1/5$, $f(10) = 1/10$, $f(100) = 1/100$, $f(1000) = 1/1000$, etc.

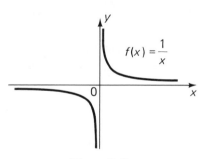

Figure 2–6

There will be many times when we will be interested in investigating the behavior of a function f as the variable x takes on arbitrarily large positive or negative values. For this purpose we introduce the two **extended real numbers** $+\infty$ (plus infinity) and $-\infty$ (minus infinity). These two new symbols are not equal, i.e., $-\infty \neq +\infty$, and they are *not* real numbers. We *do not* now define any arithmetic operations involving these symbols, but we do find it convenient to *define* $-\infty < +\infty$, $-\infty < x$, and $x < +\infty$ for every real number x. In this book we will usually use the abbreviated notation ∞ instead of $+\infty$ although we may use the symbol $+\infty$ for emphasis. If a is any real number, then $]a,\infty]$ represents the set of all real numbers greater than a together with the extended real number ∞. Also, $[-\infty,a[$ represents the set of all real numbers less than a together with the extended real number $-\infty$. Any interval $]a,\infty]$ is called a **neighborhood of** ∞ and any interval $[-\infty,a[$ is called a **neighborhood of** $-\infty$.

For any real number a, $]a,\infty[$ represents the set of all real numbers greater than a and $]-\infty,a[$ represents the set of all real numbers less than a. The **interval** $]a,\infty[$ is called a **deleted neighborhood of** ∞ and the **interval** $]-\infty,a[$ is called a **deleted neighborhood of** $-\infty$.

We also may use the notations $N(\infty)$, $N(-\infty)$, $N'(\infty)$, $N'(-\infty)$ to represent, respectively, a neighborhood of ∞, a neighborhood of $-\infty$, a deleted neighborhood of ∞, a deleted neighborhood of $-\infty$.

The definition for a limit at infinity now parallels our earlier definition of limit.

▷ **Definition** If f is a function which is defined in some deleted neighborhood of ∞, then we say that **the limit of $f(x)$ as x approaches ∞ is l** if for every neighborhood $N(l)$ there is a deleted neighborhood $N'(\infty)$ such that if $x \in N'(\infty)$, then $f(x) \in N(l)$. In this case we write $\lim_{x \to \infty} f(x) = l$.

The definition for a limit at $-\infty$ is entirely similar. We can see that $\lim_{x \to \infty} f(x) = l$ means that we can make $f(x)$ as close to l as we wish provided we take x bigger than some suitably chosen number. That is, as x gets larger and larger without bound, then $f(x)$ gets closer and closer to l. Also, $\lim_{x \to -\infty} f(x) = l$ means that as x gets smaller and smaller without bound, then $f(x)$ gets closer and closer to l.

EXAMPLE Evaluate the following limits:

(a) $\lim\limits_{x \to \infty} \dfrac{2}{x-1}$

(b) $\lim\limits_{x \to -\infty} \dfrac{x+3}{5x+1}$

(c) $\lim\limits_{x \to \infty} \dfrac{x^2 + x^3}{x^3}$

(d) $\lim\limits_{x \to \infty} (\sqrt{x+1} - \sqrt{x})$

Solution (a) As x approaches ∞, so does $x - 1$. Hence, as x approaches ∞, $\dfrac{2}{x-1}$ gets closer and closer to 0, because we are dividing 2 by numbers which get larger and larger without bound. Thus,

$$\lim_{x \to \infty} \frac{2}{x-1} = 0.$$

(b) Notice that, for $x \neq 0$, or $-\dfrac{1}{5}$,

$$\frac{x+3}{5x+1} = \frac{\left(\dfrac{x+3}{x}\right)}{\left(\dfrac{5x+1}{x}\right)} = \frac{1 + \dfrac{3}{x}}{5 + \dfrac{1}{x}}$$

Since $\lim\limits_{x \to -\infty} \dfrac{3}{x} = 0$ and $\lim\limits_{x \to -\infty} \dfrac{1}{x} = 0$, we see that

$$\lim_{x \to -\infty} \frac{x+3}{5x+1} = \lim_{x \to -\infty} \frac{1 + \dfrac{3}{x}}{5 + \dfrac{1}{x}} = \frac{1}{5}$$

(c) $\lim\limits_{x \to \infty} \dfrac{x^2 + x^3}{x^3} = \lim\limits_{x \to \infty} \left(\dfrac{1}{x} + 1\right) = 1$

(d) In order to evaluate $\lim\limits_{x \to \infty} (\sqrt{x+1} - \sqrt{x})$ we resort to a trick. We observe that

$$\sqrt{x+1} - \sqrt{x} = \frac{(\sqrt{x+1} - \sqrt{x})(\sqrt{x+1} + \sqrt{x})}{(\sqrt{x+1} + \sqrt{x})}$$

$$= \frac{(x+1) - x}{\sqrt{x+1} + \sqrt{x}} = \frac{1}{\sqrt{x+1} + \sqrt{x}}$$

Now notice that as x approaches ∞, both $\sqrt{x+1}$ and $\sqrt{x}$ also approach ∞. Thus, $\sqrt{x+1} + \sqrt{x}$ approaches ∞. Thus, $\dfrac{1}{\sqrt{x+1} + \sqrt{x}}$ approaches 0. We therefore see that $\lim\limits_{x \to \infty} (\sqrt{x+1} - \sqrt{x}) = 0$.

EXERCISES

In 1–12, evaluate the limits.

1. $\lim\limits_{x \to \infty} \dfrac{2}{x+2}$

2. $\lim\limits_{t \to -\infty} \dfrac{2}{t+2}$

3. $\lim\limits_{x \to \infty} \dfrac{2x-1}{3x+1}$

4. $\lim\limits_{x \to -\infty} \dfrac{x+1}{x^2-1}$

5. $\lim\limits_{s \to \infty} \dfrac{s^2+1}{-2s^2+2}$

6. $\lim\limits_{x \to -\infty} \dfrac{x^2+2x}{x^2+1}$

7. $\lim\limits_{x \to \infty} \dfrac{1}{\sqrt{x}}$

8. $\lim\limits_{h \to -\infty} \dfrac{1}{2\sqrt{-h}+2}$

9. $\lim\limits_{x \to \infty} (\sqrt{x+2} - \sqrt{x})$

10. $\lim\limits_{x \to \infty} (\sqrt{x+1} - \sqrt{x-1})$

11. $\lim\limits_{x \to -\infty} \dfrac{x^2+1}{x^3+1}$

12. $\lim\limits_{x \to \infty} \dfrac{x^2+3x+4}{2x^2+x+1}$

13. Evaluate $\lim\limits_{x \to \infty} (\sqrt{x^2+2x+1} - x)$.

14. Evaluate $\lim\limits_{x \to \infty} (\sqrt{x^2 + x} - x)$. [*Hint:* Observe that, for $x > 0$,

$$\sqrt{x^2 + x} - x = \frac{(\sqrt{x^2 + x} - x)(\sqrt{x^2 + x} + x)}{\sqrt{x^2 + x} + x}$$

$$= \frac{x^2 + x - x^2}{\sqrt{x^2 + x} + x} = \frac{x}{\sqrt{x^2 + x} + x} = \frac{1}{\sqrt{1 + 1/x} + 1}.\bigg]$$

15. Evaluate $\lim\limits_{x \to -\infty} (\sqrt[3]{x + 1} - \sqrt[3]{x})$.

[*Hint:* Observe that $a - b = (\sqrt[3]{a} - \sqrt[3]{b})(\sqrt[3]{a^2} + \sqrt[3]{ab} + \sqrt[3]{b^2})$.]

16. Let n represent an integer greater than or equal to 2. Evaluate $\lim\limits_{x \to \infty} (\sqrt[n]{x + 1} - \sqrt[n]{x})$.

4   The Limit Theorems

In the preceding two sections we have given exact definitions of what we mean by saying $\lim\limits_{x \to a} f(x) = l$, but we have been proceeding pretty much on intuitive grounds in the actual evaluation of limits in particular examples. We have not rigorously justified our answers on the basis of our definitions or on any other firm foundation. Such justifications based directly on the definitions are usually either very difficult or very tedious and consequently are seldom given. The most commonly followed practice is to base our claims that certain limit statements are true on certain theorems which are themselves proved on the basis of the definitions. In this section we present several so-called limit theorems and we show by several examples how they can be used to evaluate limits with complete justification that our answers are correct. First, however, partly to convince the reader of the utility of the limit theorems and partly to show how the definitions can actually be used directly to justify limit statements, we give two examples. These examples involve simple functions, yet the proofs are quite elaborate. We present them in all their gory detail in order to convince you of the need for a simpler way to evaluate and justify limits.

EXAMPLE   Prove the following two equalities on the basis of the definitions.

(a) $\lim\limits_{x \to 0} \dfrac{2}{x + 1} = 2$ [see example (c), page 84]

(b) $\lim\limits_{x \to \infty} \dfrac{x + 3}{5x + 1} = \dfrac{1}{5}$ [see example (b), pages 90–91]

Solution (a) Let $N(2) =]c,d[$ be any given neighborhood of 2, the asserted limit. Then $c < 2 < d$. It is our job to find some deleted neighborhood $N'(0)$ such that $2/(x + 1)$ is in $N(2)$ whenever x is in $N'(0)$. That is, we want to have $c < 2/(x + 1) < d$. Observe that we might as well assume $c > 0$ (for if not, we could work with the even smaller neighborhood $]1,d[$). Also, we may assume that $x > -1$ so that $x + 1 > 0$. Now, solving $c < 2/(x + 1)$ gives $c(x + 1) < 2$. This yields $x + 1 < 2/c$ and we have $x < \dfrac{2}{c} - 1$. In a similar way, $2/(x + 1) < d$ is equivalent to $x > \dfrac{2}{d} - 1$. Thus, if we choose $N(0) = \left] \dfrac{2}{d} - 1, \dfrac{2}{c} - 1 \right[$, then for x in $N'(0)$ we have that $2/(x + 1)$ is in $]c,d[$. This establishes (a).

(b) Let $N(1/5) =]c,d[$ be any given neighborhood of 1/5, the asserted limit. We want to find some deleted neighborhood $N'(\infty)$ of ∞ such that if x is in $N'(\infty)$ then $\dfrac{x + 3}{5x + 1}$ is in $]c,d[$. That is, we want to find some real number a such that if $x > a$, then $c < \dfrac{x + 3}{5x + 1} < d$. We will actually solve the more restrictive inequality $\dfrac{1}{5} < \dfrac{x + 3}{5x + 1} < d$. First of all, it will be easier for us if we assume $x > 0$, which we may do by requiring $a > 0$. Now, for $x > 0, \dfrac{1}{5} < \dfrac{x + 3}{5x + 1}$ is always true. Also, $\dfrac{x + 3}{5x + 1} < d$ is equivalent to $x > \dfrac{3 - d}{5d - 1}$. Thus, for $a > 0$ and $a \geq \dfrac{3 - d}{5d - 1}$, it follows that if $x > a$, then $c < \dfrac{1}{5} < \dfrac{x + 3}{5x + 1} < d$ and (b) is established.

Note. It will be of interest for the student to try to construct $\epsilon - \delta$ proofs of these two equalities.

Amusing and instructive as these examples may be, it seems clear that no person in his right mind would want to struggle with such inequalities every time that he wanted to find a limit or prove his answer to be correct. Fortunately, our limit theorems come to the rescue and render trivial problems like those in examples 1 and 2 above. We state them and explain how they are used here and, for those readers who want to know why Theorem 1 is true, we put its proof in the Appendix in the back of the book.

Limit Theorem 1 Let a be an extended real number (this means that a is a real number or $a = +\infty$ or $a = -\infty$) and let f and g be real-valued functions (that is, functions whose ranges are sets of real numbers) that are defined on some deleted neighborhood of a such that $\lim_{x \to a} f(x) = l_1$ and $\lim_{x \to a} g(x) = l_2$, where l_1 and l_2 are real numbers. Also, let n be a positive integer. Then we have:

(i) $\lim_{x \to a} [f(x) + g(x)] = l_1 + l_2$

(ii) $\lim_{x \to a} [f(x) - g(x)] = l_1 - l_2$

(iii) $\lim_{x \to a} [f(x) \cdot g(x)] = l_1 \cdot l_2$

(iv) $\lim_{x \to a} \dfrac{f(x)}{g(x)} = \dfrac{l_1}{l_2}$ provided that $l_2 \neq 0$

(v) $\lim_{x \to a} [f(x)]^n = l_1{}^n$

(vi) $\lim_{x \to a} [f(x)]^{1/n} = l_1{}^{1/n}$ provided, in the case that n is even, that $f(x) \geqq 0$ for all x in some deleted neighborhood of a.

Note. We could also have expressed (vi) using radical notation: $\lim_{x \to a} \sqrt[n]{f(x)} = \sqrt[n]{l_1}$.

This theorem allows us to evaluate limits of functions that can be built up by use of the basic operations of algebra from functions whose limits we already know. The following very simple theorem gives us four basic limits upon which we can base this building process.

▷ **Limit Theorem 2**   Let c and a be real numbers. Then

(i) $\lim_{x \to a} c = c$ (iii) $\lim_{x \to \infty} \dfrac{1}{x} = 0$

(ii) $\lim_{x \to a} x = a$ (iv) $\lim_{x \to -\infty} \dfrac{1}{x} = 0$

[In (i), the first c stands for the constant function whose value at every x is c and we can, in (i), allow $a = \infty$ or $a = -\infty$ as well.]

Proof   Equality (i) is trivial because $c \in N(c)$ for any $N(c)$ no matter what the value of x. Equality (ii) is also obvious because $x \in N(a)$ whenever $x \in N'(a)$ regardless of which $N(a)$ is given. To prove (iii) and (iv), let $N(0) = \,]r,s[$ be any given neighborhood of 0. Then $r < 0 < s$. Let p be the smaller of the two positive numbers $-r$ and s. Then $r \leqq -p < p \leqq s$ and so we have $r < 0 < \dfrac{1}{x} < s$ whenever $\dfrac{1}{p} < x < \infty$ and $r < \dfrac{1}{x} < 0 < s$ whenever $-\infty < x < -\dfrac{1}{p}$. That is, $\dfrac{1}{x}$ is in $N(0)$

whenever x is in the deleted neighborhood $N'(\infty) =]1/p,\infty[$ or in the deleted neighborhood $N'(-\infty) =]-\infty,-1/p[$ and this proves both (iii) and (iv). ■

EXAMPLE Use Limit Theorems 1 and 2 (not the definitions) to find $\lim\limits_{x\to\infty} h(x)$ where

$$h(x) = \frac{7x^2 - 13x + \sqrt{9x+4}}{3x^2 - \sqrt[3]{x^6-1}}$$

Solution Although this problem may appear difficult, we will break it down into a long series of much simpler problems and then combine our answers to get the desired solution. We first divide top and bottom by x^2 to see that for $x \neq 0$ we have

$$h(x) = \frac{7 - \dfrac{13}{x} + \sqrt{\dfrac{9}{x^3} + \dfrac{4}{x^4}}}{3 - \sqrt[3]{1 - \dfrac{1}{x^6}}}$$

It may now be apparent that the required limit is 7/2. However, we justify this guess in several steps:

(a) By Limit Theorem 1(v) and Limit Theorem 2(iii),

$$\lim_{x\to\infty} \frac{1}{x^4} = \left(\lim_{x\to\infty} \frac{1}{x}\right)^4 = 0^4 = 0$$

and so, by Limit Theorem 1(iii) and Limit Theorem 2(i),

$$\lim_{x\to\infty} \frac{4}{x^4} = (\lim_{x\to\infty} 4)\left(\lim_{x\to\infty} \frac{1}{x^4}\right) = 4 \cdot 0 = 0$$

(b) Similarly, $\lim\limits_{x\to\infty} \dfrac{9}{x^3} = 0$, $\lim\limits_{x\to\infty} \dfrac{13}{x} = 0$, and $\lim\limits_{x\to\infty} \dfrac{1}{x^6} = 0$.

(c) By Limit Theorem 1(i),

$$\lim_{x\to\infty} \left[\frac{9}{x^3} + \frac{4}{x^4}\right] = \lim_{x\to\infty} \frac{9}{x^3} + \lim_{x\to\infty} \frac{4}{x^4} = 0 + 0 = 0$$

(d) By Limit Theorem 1(ii) and Limit Theorem 2(i),

$$\lim_{x\to\infty} \left[1 - \frac{1}{x^6}\right] = \lim_{x\to\infty} 1 - \lim_{x\to\infty} \frac{1}{x^6} = 1 - 0 = 1$$

(e) By Limit Theorem 1(vi), $\lim\limits_{x\to\infty} \sqrt{\dfrac{9}{x^3} + \dfrac{4}{x^4}} = \sqrt{0} = 0$ and

$$\lim_{x\to\infty} \sqrt[3]{1 - \frac{1}{x^6}} = \sqrt[3]{1} = 1.$$

(f) By Limit Theorem 1(ii) and Limit Theorem 2(i),

$$\lim_{x \to \infty} \left[3 - \sqrt[3]{1 - \frac{1}{x^6}} \right] = 3 - 1 = 2 \text{ and } \lim_{x \to \infty} \left(7 - \frac{13}{x} \right) = 7 - 0 = 7.$$

(g) By Limit Theorem 1(i), $\lim_{x \to \infty} \left[7 - \frac{13}{x} + \sqrt{\frac{9}{x^3} + \frac{4}{x^4}} \right] = 7 + 0 = 7.$

(h) Finally, Limit Theorem 1(iv) yields $\lim_{x \to \infty} h(x) = \frac{7}{2}.$

EXAMPLE　If $\lim_{x \to 2} f(x) = 3$, then evaluate

(a) $\lim_{x \to 2} (f(x) + 1/x)$

(b) $\lim_{x \to 2} (f(x) - \sqrt{x^2 + 5})$

(c) $\lim_{x \to 2} (f(x)(x^2 + 1))$

(d) $\lim_{x \to 2} \dfrac{f(x)}{3x - 4}$

(e) $\lim_{x \to 2} (f(x))^3$

(f) $\lim_{x \to 2} \sqrt[5]{f(x)}$

Solution　(a) Since $\lim_{x \to 2} 1/x = 1/2$, we may apply Limit Theorem 1(i) to obtain $\lim_{x \to 2} (f(x) + 1/x) = 3 + 1/2 = 3\ 1/2$.

(b) Since $\lim_{x \to 2} (x^2 + 5) = 9$, we see by Limit Theorem 1(vi) that $\lim_{x \to 2} \sqrt{x^2 + 5} = 3$. So, we may apply Limit Theorem 2(ii) to obtain $\lim_{x \to 2} (f(x) - \sqrt{x^2 + 5}) = 3 - 3 = 0$.

(c) Since $\lim_{x \to 2} (x^2 + 1) = 5$, we may apply Limit Theorem 1(iii) to obtain $\lim_{x \to 2} (f(x))(x^2 + 1) = 3 \cdot 5 = 15$.

(d) Since $\lim_{x \to 2} (3x - 4) = 2$, we may apply Limit Theorem 1(iv) to obtain $\lim_{x \to 2} \dfrac{f(x)}{3x - 4} = \dfrac{3}{2}.$

(e) Since $\lim_{x \to 2} f(x) = 3$, we may apply Limit Theorem 1(v) to obtain $\lim_{x \to 2} (f(x))^3 = 3^3 = 27$.

(f) Since $\lim_{x \to 2} f(x) = 3$, we may apply Limit Theorem 1(vi) to obtain $\lim_{x \to 2} \sqrt[5]{f(x)} = \sqrt[5]{3}.$

EXAMPLE　Use Limit Theorem 1(iii) to prove the following: If a is an extended real number, c and l are real numbers, and f is a function such that $\lim_{x \to a} f(x) = l$, then $\lim_{x \to a} cf(x) = cl$.

Solution　We define the function g by $g(x) = c$ for all real numbers x. We then have $\lim_{x \to a} g(x) = c$ by Limit Theorem 2(i). By Limit Theorem 1(iii), we see that $\lim_{x \to a} cf(x) = \lim_{x \to a} (g(x) \cdot f(x)) = cl$.

E X E R C I S E S

1. If $\lim_{x \to -1} f(x) = 2$, then evaluate:

(a) $\lim_{x \to -1} (f(x) + x^2)$

(b) $\lim_{x \to -1} (f(x) - x^3)$

(c) $\lim_{x \to -1} (f(x))(x^2 + 2x)$

(d) $\lim_{x \to -1} \dfrac{f(x)}{x^3 + x}$

(e) $\lim_{x \to -1} (f(x))^5$

(f) $\lim_{x \to -1} \sqrt[4]{f(x)}$

2. If $\lim_{x \to \infty} f(x) = 4$ and $\lim_{x \to \infty} g(x) = 2$, then evaluate:

(a) $\lim_{x \to \infty} (f(x) + g(x))$

(b) $\lim_{x \to \infty} (f(x) - g(x))$

(c) $\lim_{x \to \infty} (f(x) \cdot g(x))$

(d) $\lim_{x \to \infty} \dfrac{f(x)}{g(x)}$

(e) $\lim_{x \to \infty} (g(x))^3$

(f) $\lim_{x \to \infty} \sqrt{f(x)}$

3. Prove that if $\lim_{x \to a} f(x) = l$, then $\lim_{x \to a} (f(x) - l) = 0$.

4. If $\lim_{x \to a} f(x) = l$ and $\lim_{x \to a} g(x)$ doesn't exist, then prove that

$lim_{x \to a} (f(x) + g(x))$ doesn't exist.

5. If $\lim_{x \to 2} f(x) = l_1$ and $\lim_{x \to 3} f(x) = l_2$, must it be true that $\lim_{x \to 5} f(x) = l_1 + l_2$? If so, give a proof. If not, give an example to show that it is false.

6. If $\lim_{x \to a} f(x) = 4$, then what is $\lim_{x \to a} (\sqrt{f(x)})^3$? [*Hint*: Apply Limit Theorem 1(v) and (vi).]

In 7–12, use Limit Theorems 1 and 2 to prove that the equality is correct.

7. $\lim_{x \to 2} ((x^2 + 2x + 3)(x^3 + 3x - 13)) = 11$

8. $\lim_{x \to 1} \dfrac{\sqrt[3]{7 + x}}{\sqrt{8 + x}} = \dfrac{2}{3}$

9. $\lim_{x \to -\infty} \left(\dfrac{1}{x} + \dfrac{1}{x + 1} \right) = 0$

10. $\lim_{x \to \infty} \left(\dfrac{1}{\sqrt{x}} \left(\dfrac{2}{x} + 3 \right) \right) = 0$

11. $\lim_{x \to -2} \dfrac{\sqrt[3]{x^2 + 4} - \sqrt{-x + 7}}{x^2 + 3x + 1} = 1$

12. $\lim_{x \to 0} \dfrac{\left(\dfrac{1}{x}(2x^2 + x^3) - x + 1 \right)^3}{(x^2 + 3x - 1)^4} = 1$

5 One-sided Limits

We saw earlier that the function

$$f(x) = \begin{cases} 1 \text{ if } x \geq 0 \\ -1 \text{ if } x < 0 \end{cases}$$

has no limit as x approaches 0. The graph of f is shown in Fig. 2-7.

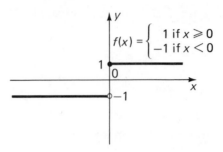

Figure 2-7

In spite of the fact that $\lim_{x \to 0} f(x)$ does not exist, we can still describe the behavior of $f(x)$ as x approaches 0 in terms of **one-sided limits.**

Notice that as x approaches 0 through values which are greater than 0, the value of $f(x)$ approaches 1. Also notice that as x approaches 0 through values which are less than 0, the value of $f(x)$ approaches -1. We say that the limit of $f(x)$ as x approaches 0 from the right is 1. This is symbolized by $\lim_{x \to 0^+} f(x) = 1$.

Also, we may say that the limit of $f(x)$ as x approaches 0 from the left is -1. This is symbolized by $\lim_{x \to 0^-} f(x) = -1$.

In general, we have the following definitions:

▷ **Definition**   Let a and l be real numbers and let f be a function defined on some open interval $]a,b[$. If for every neighborhood $N(l)$ there is a real number $c \in]a,b[$ such that if $x \in]a,c[$, then $f(x) \in N(l)$, then we say that **the limit of $f(x)$ as x approaches a from the right is l.** In this case we write $\lim_{x \to a^-} f(x) = l$.

▷ **Definition**   Let a and l be real numbers and let f be a function defined in some open interval $]b,a[$. If for every neighborhood $N(l)$ there is a real number $c \in]b,a[$ such that if $x \in]c,a[$, then $f(x) \in N(l)$, then we say that the limit of $f(x)$ as x approaches a from the left is l. In this case we write $\lim_{x \to a^-} f(x) = l$.

Notice that if $\lim_{x \to a} f(x) = l$, then $\lim_{x \to a^+} f(x) = l$ and $\lim_{x \to a^-} f(x) = l$. That is, "if the limit exists, then both one-sided limits exist and are equal to the limit." On the other hand, we have seen that even if both one-sided limits exist at a point, the limit may not exist. However, it can be shown (see exercise 13) that if both one-sided limits exist at a point and they are equal, then the limit exists at that point and it is equal to the one-sided limits.

It is also important to mention that Limit Theorems 1 and 2 of the previous section all hold for one-sided limits.

EXAMPLE Evaluate $\lim_{x \to 2^+} \sqrt{x - 2}$.

Solution As x approaches 2 from the right, $x - 2$ approaches 0. Thus, $\sqrt{x - 2}$ approaches 0 and we see that

$$\lim_{x \to 2^+} \sqrt{x - 2} = 0$$

Notice that we cannot talk about $\lim_{x \to 2} \sqrt{x - 2}$ or $\lim_{x \to 2^-} \sqrt{x - 2}$ because the function $f(x) = \sqrt{x - 2}$ is not defined for $x < 2$.

EXAMPLE Evaluate (a) $\lim_{x \to 0^+} \dfrac{|x|}{x}$ and (b) $\lim_{x \to 0^-} \dfrac{|x|}{x}$.

Solution Recall that

$$|x| = \begin{cases} x & \text{if } x \geq 0 \\ -x & \text{if } x < 0 \end{cases}$$

Thus, $\dfrac{|x|}{x} = 1$ if $x > 0$ and $\dfrac{|x|}{x} = -1$ if $x < 0$.

We have $\lim_{x \to 0^+} \dfrac{|x|}{x} = \lim_{x \to 0^+} 1 = 1$ and $\lim_{x \to 0^-} \dfrac{|x|}{x} = \lim_{x \to 0^-} (-1) = -1$.

EXAMPLE For any real number x, we define $[x]$ to be the greatest integer which does not exceed x. For example, $[2] = 2$, $[3\ 1/2] = 3$, $[-4\ 1/3] = -5$, $[\pi] = 3$, and $[\sqrt{2}] = 1$. Fig. 2-8 shows the graph of $f(x) = [x]$.

(a) Evaluate $\lim_{x \to 2^+} [x]$.

(b) Evaluate $\lim_{x \to -1^-} [x]$.

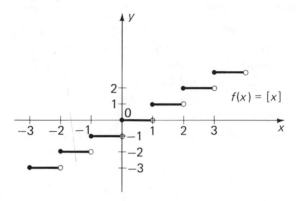

Figure 2-8

Solution   (a) From the graph it is clear that for $2 < x < 3$, $[x] = 2$. Thus, $\lim_{x \to 2^+} [x] = 2$.

(b) From the graph, it is clear that for $-2 < x < -1$, $[x] = -2$. Thus, $\lim_{x \to -1^-} [x] = -2$.

EXAMPLE   Suppose g is the function defined by

$$g(s) = \begin{cases} s^2 + 2 & \text{if } s \geq 2 \\ 3s & \text{if } s < 2 \end{cases}$$

(a) Draw the graph of g.   (c) Evaluate $\lim_{s \to 2^-} g(s)$.

(b) Evaluate $\lim_{s \to 2^+} g(s)$.

(d) Evaluate $\lim_{s \to 2} g(s)$.

Solution   (a) The graph of g is shown in Fig. 2-9 and consists of the portion of the parabola $g(s) = s^2 + 2$ ($s \geq 2$) together with the portion of the straight line $g(s) = 3s$ ($s < 2$).

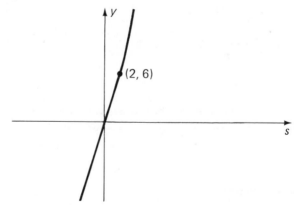

Figure 2-9

(b) Since for $s > 2$, $g(s) = s^2 + 2$, we have $\lim\limits_{s \to 2^+} g(s) = \lim\limits_{s \to 2^+} (s^2 + 2) = 6$.

(c) Since for $s < 2$, $g(s) = 3s$, we have $\lim\limits_{s \to 2^-} g(s) = \lim\limits_{s \to 2^-} 3s = 6$.

(d) Since $\lim\limits_{s \to 2^+} g(s) = 6 = \lim\limits_{s \to 2^-} g(s)$, then $\lim\limits_{s \to 2} g(s) = 6$.

E X E R C I S E S

In 1–4, evaluate the one-sided limit.

1. $\lim\limits_{x \to 3^+} \sqrt{x - 3}$

2. $\lim\limits_{x \to 0^-} \sqrt{-x}$

3. $\lim\limits_{x \to 2^+} |x - 2|$

4. $\lim\limits_{x \to -1^-} (3x + |x + 1|)$

5. (a) Give an example of a function f such that $\lim\limits_{x \to 0^+} f(x) = 3$ and $\lim\limits_{x \to 0^-} f(x) = 1$.

(b) Give an example of a function g such that $\lim\limits_{t \to 2^+} g(t) = 4$ and $\lim\limits_{t \to 2^-} g(t) = -3$.

6. Let $f(x) = \begin{cases} x^2 + 1 & \text{if } x \geq 1 \\ x & \text{if } x < 1 \end{cases}$ and $g(x) = \begin{cases} 2x - 1 & \text{if } x \geq 1 \\ 2x^2 & \text{if } x < 1 \end{cases}$

(a) Evaluate $\lim\limits_{x \to 1^+} f(x)$ and $\lim\limits_{x \to 1^-} f(x)$. Does $\lim\limits_{x \to 1} f(x)$ exist?

(b) Evaluate $\lim\limits_{x \to 1^+} g(x)$ and $\lim\limits_{x \to 1^-} g(x)$. Does $\lim\limits_{x \to 1} g(x)$ exist?

(c) Write formulas for $f(x) + g(x)$ and $f(x) \cdot g(x)$.

(d) Evaluate $\lim\limits_{x \to 1} (f(x) + g(x))$.

(e) Evaluate $\lim\limits_{x \to 1} (f(x) \cdot g(x))(f(x) + g(x))$.

In 7–12, draw a graph of the function and evaluate the indicated limits. If a particular limit does not exist, tell why.

7. $f(x) = \begin{cases} x^2 & \text{if } x \geq 1 \\ x & \text{if } x < 1 \end{cases}$

$\lim\limits_{x \to 1^+} f(x); \ \lim\limits_{x \to 1^-} f(x); \ \lim\limits_{x \to 1} f(x)$

8. $g(x) = \begin{cases} 2x^2 - 1 & \text{if } x \geq 0 \\ x + 2 & \text{if } x < 0 \end{cases}$

$\lim\limits_{x \to 0^+} g(x); \ \lim\limits_{x \to 0^-} g(x); \ \lim\limits_{x \to 0} g(x)$

9. $h(t) = \begin{cases} t^2 + 1 & \text{if } t \geq 2 \\ 2t^2 - 3 & \text{if } t < 2 \end{cases}$

$\lim\limits_{t \to 2^+} h(t); \ \lim\limits_{t \to 2^-} h(t); \ \lim\limits_{t \to 2} h(t)$

10. $f(s) = \begin{cases} s^2 + s + 1 & \text{if } s \geq -1 \\ 2s^2 + s & \text{if } s < -1 \end{cases}$

$\lim_{s \to -1^+} f(s); \ \lim_{s \to -1^-} f(s); \ \lim_{s \to -1} f(s)$

11. $f(x) = \begin{cases} 2x^2 - 3 & \text{if } x > 0 \\ 1 & \text{if } x = 0 \\ x^2 + x - 3 & \text{if } x < 0 \end{cases}$

$\lim_{x \to 0^+} f(x); \ \lim_{x \to 0^-} f(x); \ \lim_{x \to 0} f(x)$

12. $g(x) = \begin{cases} x^2 + x & \text{if } x \geq 2 \\ 6 & \text{if } 1 \leq x < 2 \\ -x^2 + 3x + 5 & \text{if } x < 1 \end{cases}$

$\lim_{x \to 2^+} g(x); \ \lim_{x \to 2^-} g(x); \ \lim_{x \to 2} g(x); \ \lim_{x \to 1^+} g(x); \ \lim_{x \to 1^-} g(x); \ \lim_{x \to 1} g(x)$

13. Prove that if $\lim_{x \to a^+} f(x)$ and $\lim_{x \to a^-} f(x)$ both exist and equal l, then

$\lim_{x \to a} f(x)$ exists and equals l.

14. Let $f(x) = \dfrac{1/x}{\sqrt{1 + 1/x^2}}$, where $x \neq 0$.

(a) Evaluate $\lim_{x \to 0^+} f(x)$.

$$\left[Hint: \text{For } x > 0, \ \sqrt{1 + 1/x^2} = \sqrt{\frac{x^2 + 1}{x^2}} = \frac{1}{x}\sqrt{x^2 + 1}. \right]$$

(b) Evaluate $\lim_{x \to 0^-} f(x)$.

$$\left[Hint: \text{For } x < 0, \ \sqrt{1 + 1/x^2} = \sqrt{\frac{x^2 + 1}{x^2}} = -\frac{1}{x}\sqrt{x^2 + 1}. \right]$$

(c) Does $\lim_{x \to 0} f(x)$ exist? Give a reason.

15. Let $g(x) = x - [x]$. For example, $g(1) = 1 - 1 = 0$, $g\left(2\frac{1}{2}\right) = 2\frac{1}{2} - 2 = \frac{1}{2}$, $g(3.809) = 3.809 - 3 = .809$, $g(-2.7) = -2.7 - (-3) = .3$, etc. The

expression $x - [x]$ is called the fractional part of x.

(a) Draw the graph of g.

(b) Evaluate $\lim_{x \to 1^+} g(x)$ and $\lim_{x \to 1^-} g(x)$.

(c) Evaluate $\lim_{x \to 1\frac{1}{2}^+} g(x)$ and $\lim_{x \to 1\frac{1}{2}^-} g(x)$.

(d) For which real numbers a does $\lim_{x \to a} g(x)$ not exist?

For which real numbers a does $\lim_{x \to a} g(x)$ exist?

16. Prove that $\lim_{x \to 0^+} (-1)^{[1/x]}$ does not exist.

$$\left[Hint: \text{If } n \text{ is a positive integer and } \frac{1}{n+1} < x \leq \frac{1}{n}, \text{then } [1/x] = n. \right]$$

6 Infinite Limits

Up to now, the only possible values for a limit or a one-sided limit have been real numbers. We shall now see that limits and one-sided limits may be infinite. That is, limits and one-sided limits may have the value ∞ or $-\infty$.

Let us consider the function $f(x) = 1/x^2$ whose graph is shown in Fig. 2-10. Suppose we wish to determine the behavior of $f(x)$ as x approaches 0. We might begin by calculating some values of $f(x)$ for x near 0: $f(1/2) = 4$, $f(-1/3) = 9$, $f(1/4) = 16$, $f(-1/5) = 25$, $f(1/10) = 100$, $f(-1/100) = 10,000$, $f(1/1000) = 1,000,000$. It certainly appears that as x approaches 0, the value $f(x)$ gets larger and larger without bound. We say that the limit of $1/x^2$ as x approaches 0 is ∞ and we write $\lim_{x \to 0} 1/x^2 = \infty$.

In general, if a is an extended real number, then $\lim_{x \to a} f(x) = \infty$ means that as x approaches a, the value of $f(x)$ gets larger and larger without bound.

If we next consider the function $f(x) = -1/x^2$, whose graph is shown in Fig. 2-11, we see that as x approaches 0, the values of $f(x)$ get smaller and smaller without bound. For example, $f(1/2) = -4$, $f(-1/3) = -9$, $f(1/4) = -16$, $f(-1/5) = -25$, $f(1/10) = -100$, $f(-1/100) = -10,000$, and $f(1/1000) = -1,000,000$.

We say that the limit of $-1/x^2$ as x approaches 0 is $-\infty$, and we write $\lim_{x \to 0} -1/x^2 = -\infty$.

In general, if a is an extended real number, then $\lim_{x \to a} f(x) = -\infty$ means that as x approaches a, the value of $f(x)$ gets smaller and smaller without bound.

The following precise definition includes the definitions given in sections 2 and 3 as special cases.

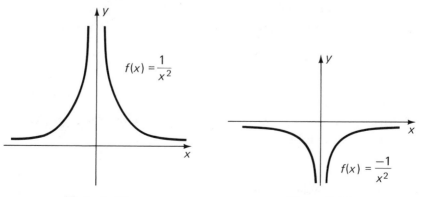

Figure 2-10   Figure 2-11

▷ **Definition** If f is a real-valued function defined on some deleted neighborhood of an extended real number a and if l is an extended real number, then

$$\lim_{x \to a} f(x) = l$$

means that for each neighborhood $N(l)$ of l there exists some deleted neighborhood $N'(a)$ of a such that for every $x \in N'(a)$, we have $f(x) \in N(l)$.

It is also possible to have infinite one-sided limits. Let us look at the graph of the function $f(x) = 1/x$ which is shown in Fig. 2-12.

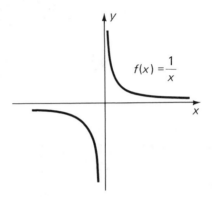

Figure 2–12

We see that as x approaches 0 from the right, the value of $1/x$ gets larger and larger without bound. We say that the limit of $1/x$ as x approaches 0 from the right is ∞ and we write $\lim_{x \to 0^+} 1/x = \infty$.

Also, as x approaches 0 from the left, the value of $1/x$ gets smaller and smaller without bound. We say that the limit of $1/x$ as x approaches 0 from the left is $-\infty$, and we write $\lim_{x \to 0^-} 1/x = -\infty$.

Since $\lim_{x \to 0^+} 1/x = +\infty$ and $\lim_{x \to 0^-} 1/x = -\infty$, we see that $\lim_{x \to 0} 1/x$ does not exist.

EXAMPLE Evaluate $\lim_{x \to \infty} (2x + 3)$.

Solution Since as x approaches ∞, the value of $2x + 3$ gets larger and larger without bound, we have $\lim_{x \to \infty} (2x + 3) = \infty$.

EXAMPLE Evaluate $\lim_{x \to 1^+} \dfrac{1}{\sqrt{x - 1}}$.

Solution As x approaches 1 from the right, $x - 1$ approaches 0 from the right and so $\sqrt{x-1}$ approaches 0 from the right. Thus, $\dfrac{1}{\sqrt{x-1}}$ approaches ∞. Therefore, $\lim\limits_{x \to 1^+} \dfrac{1}{\sqrt{x-1}} = \infty$. Notice that $\lim\limits_{x \to 1^-} \dfrac{1}{\sqrt{x-1}}$ does not exist because $\sqrt{x-1}$ is not defined for $x < 1$.

EXAMPLE Evaluate $\lim\limits_{x \to \infty} (\sqrt{x} - x)$.

Solution For $x > 0$, $\sqrt{x} - x = \dfrac{(\sqrt{x} - x)(\sqrt{x} + x)}{\sqrt{x} + x} = \dfrac{x - x^2}{\sqrt{x} + x} = \dfrac{1 - x}{\dfrac{1}{\sqrt{x}} + 1}$. As x approaches ∞, $\dfrac{1}{\sqrt{x}}$ approaches 0 and so $\dfrac{1}{\sqrt{x}} + 1$ approaches 1. Also, as x approaches ∞, $1 - x$ approaches $-\infty$. Since, as x approaches ∞, $1 - x$ gets smaller and smaller without bound and $\dfrac{1}{\sqrt{x}} + 1$ gets closer and closer to 1, we see that $\lim\limits_{x \to \infty} (\sqrt{x} - x) = \lim\limits_{x \to \infty} \dfrac{1 - x}{\dfrac{1}{\sqrt{x}} + 1} = -\infty$.

Note. Observe that $\lim\limits_{x \to \infty} \sqrt{x} = \infty$ and $\lim\limits_{x \to \infty} x = \infty$. However, we cannot say $\lim\limits_{x \to \infty} (\sqrt{x} - x) = \infty - \infty$. In fact, we have just seen that $\lim\limits_{x \to \infty} (\sqrt{x} - x) = -\infty$. This shows that Limit Theorem 1(ii) does not hold for infinite limits. In general, although there are certain exceptions, none of the limit theorems applies if any of the limits is infinite.

EXERCISES

In 1–16, evaluate the limit. The limits may be finite or infinite.

1. $\lim\limits_{x \to \infty} (x + 2)$

2. $\lim\limits_{x \to 0} (1 + 1/x)$

3. $\lim\limits_{x \to 2^+} \sqrt{x - 2}$

4. $\lim\limits_{x \to 2^-} \sqrt{2 - x}$

5. $\lim\limits_{x \to -\infty} \dfrac{1}{x + 1}$

6. $\lim\limits_{x \to -\infty} (x + 1)$

7. $\lim\limits_{x \to \infty} (x - \sqrt{x})$

8. $\lim\limits_{x \to 0} \dfrac{1}{\sqrt{x} + x}$

9. $\lim\limits_{x \to \infty} (x^2 + 2x + 3)$

10. $\lim\limits_{x \to -\infty} (x^2 + 2x + 3)$

11. $\lim\limits_{x \to \infty} x^3$

12. $\lim\limits_{x \to -\infty} x^3$

13. $\lim\limits_{x \to 1^+} \dfrac{x^2}{1 - x^3}$

14. $\lim\limits_{x \to 3^+} \dfrac{\sqrt{x^2 - 9}}{x - 3}$

15. $\lim\limits_{x \to 4} \dfrac{3x^2 + x + 1}{x^2 - x + 2}$

16. $\lim\limits_{x \to 0} \dfrac{1}{|x| + 1}$

17. (a) Evaluate $\lim\limits_{x \to 0^+} \dfrac{1}{|x|}$.   (b) Evaluate $\lim\limits_{x \to 0^-} \dfrac{1}{|x|}$.

(c) Does $\lim\limits_{x \to 0} \dfrac{1}{|x|}$ exist? Give a reason for your answer.

18. Prove that if $\lim\limits_{x \to a} f(x) = \infty$ and $\lim\limits_{x \to a} g(x) = l$, where l is a real number, then $\lim\limits_{x \to a} (f(x) + g(x)) = \infty$.

19. Evaluate $\lim\limits_{x \to \infty} (\sqrt{x^2 + 2ax} - x)$ by rationalizing the numerator as in example (d) on page 90.

20. Evaluate $\lim\limits_{x \to -\infty} (\sqrt[3]{x^3 + ax^2} - \sqrt[3]{x^3 + bx})$ by first doing some algebra.

7 Continuous Functions

We are now ready to study an important concept – that of continuity. Continuity plays a central role in the calculus, as we shall see in subsequent chapters.

We have seen that for certain functions, evaluating the limit at a number amounts to "plugging the number into the function." For example, to evaluate $\lim\limits_{x \to 2} (x^2 + 2x - 1)$, we simply "plug in" the value 2, i.e., substitute 2 for x, and obtain the value 7. We say that $x^2 + 2x - 1$ is **continuous** at 2. Also, to evaluate $\lim\limits_{x \to -3} \sqrt{1-x}$, we substitute -3 for x and obtain the value 2. We say that the function $\sqrt{1-x}$ is continuous at -3.

In general, we have the following definition.

▷ **Definition** Let a be a real number and let f be a function defined at a.

(1) If $\lim\limits_{x \to a} f(x)$ exists and equals $f(a)$, then we say **f is continuous at a.**

(2) If $\lim\limits_{x \to a^+} f(x)$ exists and equals $f(a)$, then we say **f is right continuous at a.**

(3) If $\lim\limits_{x \to a^-} f(x)$ exists and equals $f(a)$, then we say **f is left continuous at a.**

According to this definition, the function

$$f(x) = \begin{cases} 1 & \text{if } x \geq 0 \\ -1 & \text{if } x < 0 \end{cases}$$

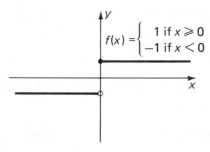

$$f(x) = \begin{cases} 1 \text{ if } x \geqslant 0 \\ -1 \text{ if } x < 0 \end{cases}$$

Figure 2-13

whose graph is shown in Fig. 2-13, is not continuous at the point 0. This is so because $\lim_{x \to 0} f(x)$ does not exist (and, therefore, certainly cannot equal $f(0)$).

Notice that f is right continuous at 0 because $\lim_{x \to 0^+} f(x) = 1 = f(0)$. Also, f is not left continuous at 0 because $\lim_{x \to 0^-} f(x) = -1 \neq f(0)$.

It may happen that a function f is continuous at every point of an open interval $]a,b[$. In this case we say that f is **continuous on** $]a,b[$. For example, the function $f(x) = \sqrt{x - 1}$ is continuous on $]1,2[$ because $\sqrt{x - 1}$ is continuous at every point a of $]1,2[$. That is, for every point a of $]1,2[$, $\lim_{x \to a} \sqrt{x - 1} = \sqrt{a - 1}$.

In the Introduction we said that if a and b are real numbers and $a < b$, then the **closed interval** $[a,b]$ is defined to be the set of all numbers x such that $a \leq x \leq b$. That is, $[a,b]$ consists of all points of $]a,b[$ together with the points a and b themselves.

We say that a function f is **continuous on the closed interval** $[a,b]$ if f is continuous on $]a,b[$, right continuous at a, and left continuous at b.

Finally, we have the following:

> **Definition** A function f defined for all real numbers is called **continuous** if f is continuous at every real number.

Thus, f is continuous if $\lim_{x \to a} f(x) = f(a)$ for every real number a.

It follows immediately from Limit Theorem 2 of section 4 that any constant function is continuous and that the function $f(x) = x$ is continuous. The following six theorems, each of which is easily proved by using the corresponding part of Limit Theorem 1 of section 4, show how we can use this simple observation and the basic algebraic operations to build up continuous functions.

▷ **Continuity Theorem 1** If f and g are both continuous at a, then $f + g$ is continuous at a. It follows that if f and g are continuous, then $f + g$ is continuous.

Thus, since x^2 and $|x|$ are both continuous, then $x^2 + |x|$ is continuous.

▷ **Continuity Theorem 2** If f and g are both continuous at a, then $f - g$ is continuous at a. It follows that if f and g are continuous, then $f - g$ is continuous.

Thus, since x^2 and $|x|$ are both continuous, then $x^2 - |x|$ is continuous.

▷ **Continuity Theorem 3** If f and g are both continuous at a, then $f \cdot g$ is continuous at a. It follows that if f and g are continuous, then $f \cdot g$ is continuous.

Thus, since x^2 and $|x|$ are both continuous, then $x^2 \cdot |x|$ is continuous.

▷ **Continuity Theorem 4** If f and g are both continuous at a and if $g(a) \neq 0$, then $\dfrac{f}{g}$ is continuous at a. It follows that if f and g are continuous, then $\dfrac{f}{g}$ is continuous at all points a where $g(a) \neq 0$.

Thus, since x^2 and $|x|$ are both continuous, then $\dfrac{x^2}{|x|}$ is continuous at all points a such that $a \neq 0$.

▷ **Continuity Theorem 5** Every polynomial function $f(x) = a_n x^n + a_{n-1} x^{n-1} + \cdots + a_1 x + a_0$ is continuous.

Thus, since $5x^2 + 2x$, $13x^3 - 19x^2 + 1$, $-47x^7 + 19x^4 - 3x^2 + 2x + 1$, and $\pi x^4 + \dfrac{3}{8} x^2 + \sqrt{2}$ are each polynomial functions, they are each continuous.

Note. A rational function is one which is the quotient of two polynomial functions. It follows from Continuity Theorems 4 and 5 that every rational function is continuous at all points where the denominator is not 0.

For example, the function $f(x) = \dfrac{2x^2 + 3x - 1}{3x^2 - x - 7}$ is continuous at all points a such that $3a^2 - a - 7 \neq 0$. Also, the function $f(x) = \dfrac{3x^3 - x/2 + 10}{4x^4 - 11}$ is continuous at all points a such that $4a^4 - 11 \neq 0$.

> **Continuity Theorem 6** If n is an odd positive integer, then the function $f(x) = x^{1/n}$ (or $\sqrt[n]{x}$) is continuous. If n is an even positive integer, then the function $f(x) = x^{1/n}$ is continuous at all nonnegative numbers.

Note. The function $x^{1/n}$, for n even, is continuous at all positive values and right continuous at 0. We therefore say that $x^{1/n}, n$ even, is continuous on $[0,\infty[$ and we can restate Continuity Theorem 6 as follows:

If n is a positive integer, the function $f(x) = x^{1/n}$ is continuous on its domain.

Before we state the next continuity theorem, which will be proved in the Appendix, let us recall what is meant by the composition of functions. If f and g are functions and f is defined on the range of g, then the composition $f \circ g$ is defined by $f \circ g(x) = f(g(x))$.

For example, if $f(x) = 2x + 3$ and $g(x) = x^2 + 1$, then $f \circ g(x) = f(g(x)) = f(x^2 + 1) = 2(x^2 + 1) + 3 = 2x^2 + 5$.

> **Continuity Theorem 7** If f and g are functions, f is defined on the range of g, g is continuous at a, and f is continuous at $g(a)$, then $f \circ g$ is continuous at a. It follows that if f and g are continuous, then $f \circ g$ is continuous.

Thus, since $f(x) = 2x^2 + 3x - 1$ and $g(x) = 3x - 1$ are both continuous, then $f \circ g(x) = f(g(x)) = f(3x - 1) = 2(3x - 1)^2 + 3(3x - 1) - 1 = 18x^2 - 3x - 2$ is continuous.

Also, since $f(x) = \sqrt[3]{x}$ and $g(x) = |x| + 2x^2$ are both continuous, it follows that $f \circ g(x) = f(g(x)) = f(|x| + 2x^2) = \sqrt[3]{|x| + 2x^2}$ is continuous.

EXAMPLE (a) Determine all points where the function $f(x) = \dfrac{x^2 - 1}{x - 1}$ is continuous.

(b) What value should we give to $f(1)$ in order to make f continuous at 1?

Solution   (a) Since $x^2 - 1$ and $x - 1$ are both polynomial functions, they are both continuous by Continuity Theorem 5. By Continuity Theorem 4, $\dfrac{x^2 - 1}{x - 1}$ is continuous at all points except 1.

(b) Since, for $x \neq 1$, $\dfrac{x^2 - 1}{x - 1} = x + 1$ and since $\lim\limits_{x \to 1} (x + 1) = 2$, we see that $\lim\limits_{x \to 1} \dfrac{x^2 - 1}{x - 1} = 2$. Thus, if we take $f(1) = 2$, then f will be continuous at 1. To see this graphically, look at the graph of f in Fig. 2-14.

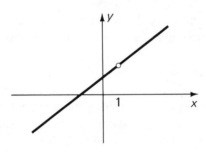

Figure 2–14

EXAMPLE   Determine all points where the function

$$g(t) = \frac{\sqrt[4]{t - 4}}{\sqrt{t - 1}}$$

is continuous.

Solution   By Continuity Theorem 6, $\sqrt[4]{t - 4}$ is continuous wherever it is defined, that is, for $t \geq 4$. Also, $\sqrt{t - 1}$ is continuous for $t \geq 1$. In addition, $\sqrt{t - 1}$ is not zero for $t > 1$. Thus, by Continuity Theorem 4, $\dfrac{\sqrt[4]{t - 4}}{\sqrt{t - 1}}$ is continuous for $t \geq 4$.

EXAMPLE   If f is continuous, prove that $g(x) = f(x^2)$ is continuous.

Solution   Since x^2 is a polynomial function, it is continuous. It then follows from Continuity Theorem 7 that $f(x^2)$ is continuous. In other words, if $h(x) = x^2$, then h is continuous. Thus, $g = f \circ h$ is continuous by Continuity Theorem 7.

We close this section with an important continuity theorem that will be proved in the Appendix. We will have many occasions to apply this theorem in Chapter 4 and we will there see its crucial importance.

◇ **Intermediate Value Theorem (IVT)** If f is continuous on the interval $[a,b]$ and if c is some number between (or possibly equal to) $f(a)$
and $f(b)$, then there exists some number $x \in [a,b]$ such that $f(x) = c$.

The reader should look at Fig. 2-15 to help visualize IVT.

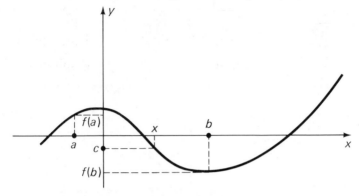

Figure 2–15

EXAMPLE Let $f(x) = x^2 - 2$ and
let $[a,b] = [2,5]$. Then $f(2) = 2$ and
$f(5) = 23$. Let $c = 10$. Then IVT
guarantees an $x \in [2,5]$ such that
$f(x) = 10$. Indeed, if we set $f(x) = 10$,
we get $x^2 - 2 = 10$, or $x = \pm\sqrt{12}$.
Since $x \in [2,5]$, $x = \sqrt{12}$ is the desired value. See Fig. 2-16.

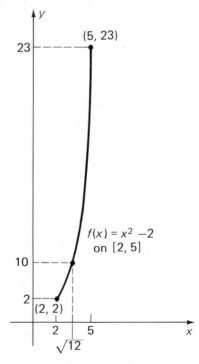

Figure 2–16

E X E R C I S E S

In 1–16, determine all points where the function is continuous.

1. $f(x) = \dfrac{x^2 + 2}{x - 2}$

2. $g(x) = \dfrac{2x}{x}$

3. $f(x) = \dfrac{1}{x}$

4. $h(t) = \dfrac{1}{t^2}$

5. $f(x) = (x + 2)(x^2 + 3x + 1)$

6. $f(s) = |s + 1|$

7. $g(x) = \dfrac{1}{x^2 - 1}$

8. $g(x) = \dfrac{1}{x^2 + 1}$

9. $f(x) = \dfrac{x^2 + 2}{x^2 - 3x + 2}$

10. $f(x) = \dfrac{|x|}{|x + 1|}$

11. $g(t) = \dfrac{\sqrt{t}}{\sqrt{t + 1}}$

12. $f(x) = \dfrac{\sqrt[3]{x} - 1}{\sqrt[3]{x} + 1}$

13. $h(x) = \dfrac{\sqrt{x^2 + 1}}{\sqrt[3]{x}}$

14. $f(x) = \dfrac{x - 1}{\sqrt[3]{x^2 + 1}}$

15. $f(x) = \dfrac{1}{x^2 + x + 1}$

16. $f(x) = \dfrac{\sqrt{x + 1}}{x}$

17. What value should we give to $f(2)$ in order to make the function $f(x) = \dfrac{x^2 - 4}{x - 2}$ continuous at 2?

18. What value should we give to $f(1)$ in order to make the function $f(t) = \dfrac{t^3 - 1}{t^2 - 1}$ continuous at 1?

19. Is there any value we can give to $f(0)$ in order to make the function $f(x) = 1/x$ continuous at 0? Give a reason.

20. Is there any value we can give to $f(0)$ in order to make the function $f(x) = \dfrac{|x|}{x}$ continuous at 0? Give a reason.

21. Prove that if f is continuous at a and if g is not continuous at a, then $f + g$ is not continuous at a.

22. Find two functions f and g such that f is continuous at 0, g is not continuous at 0, and $f \cdot g$ is continuous at 0.

23. Show that the function
$$f(x) = \begin{cases} 2 & \text{if } x \geq 3 \\ 1 & \text{if } x < 3 \end{cases}$$
is (a) right continuous at 3, and (b) not left continuous at 3.

24. Show that the function
$$f(x) = \begin{cases} 2 & \text{if } x > 3 \\ 1 & \text{if } x \leq 3 \end{cases}$$
is (a) not right continuous at 3, and (b) left continuous at 3.

25. Determine at which points the function $f(x) = [x]$ is (a) continuous, (b) right continuous, and (c) left continuous.

26. In this exercise, we will examine a function f with the surprising property that f is not continuous at any point. Recall from algebra that a rational number is a number which can be expressed as the ratio of an integer and a nonzero integer. For example, 1/2, 3, and $-1/5$ are all rational numbers. An irrational number is a real number which is not a rational number. Define
$$f(x) = \begin{cases} 1 & \text{if } x \text{ is rational} \\ 0 & \text{if } x \text{ is irrational} \end{cases}$$
(a) Use the fact that for every real number a, every deleted neighborhood $N'(a)$ contains both rational and irrational numbers to prove that for every real number a, $\lim_{x \to a} f(x)$ does not exist.

(b) Use the results of part (a) to prove that f is not continuous at any real number a.

In 27–30, find the number x with $f(x) = c$ guaranteed by IVT.

27. $f(x) = x^3$ on [4,8]; $c = 200$

28. $f(x) = \sqrt{x}$ on [1,10]; $c = 2$

29. $f(x) = x^2 - 2x$ on [0,4]; $c = 3$

30. $f(x) = 3x$ on [−5,4]; $c = -1$?

Chapter 3

Differentiation

1 The Definition of the Derivative

You know that when a car gets on a freeway, it accelerates until it reaches its cruising speed and then it travels along at a more or less constant rate. If you are sitting in the car while it is accelerating, you can feel that the velocity of the car is continually changing. It would be interesting if we could somehow find a method to determine the velocity at any given time. Let us look at a specific example. Suppose a car starts from a dead stop and then accelerates in a straight line for 10 seconds. Let $s(t)$ be the directed distance, in feet, the car has traveled from the starting point in the first t seconds $(0 \leq t \leq 10)$. Suppose $s(t)$ is given by the formula $s(t) = 3t^2 + 20t$. Thus, after one second the car has gone 23 feet. After two seconds the car has traveled 52 feet. After 10 seconds the car has traveled 500 feet. Let us try to find the velocity of the car when it has been going for 3 seconds, i.e., when $t = 3$.

Before we can answer this question, it is most important that we decide precisely what is meant by "the velocity when $t = 3$."

We know that when a car travels 1000 feet in 20 seconds, it has an average velocity of $\dfrac{1000}{20}$, or 50 feet per second. (Since a velocity of 1 foot per second is approximately the same as .68 miles per hour, we see that the car has an average velocity of 34 miles per hour.)

114

Let us return to our original problem and first determine the average velocity between the times $t = 3$ and $t = 5$. During this two second period of time, the car has traveled $s(5) - s(3)$, or 88 feet. Its average velocity is therefore 44 ft/sec. Suppose we consider the smaller interval of time from $t = 3$ to $t = 4$. This should give us an even better idea about "the velocity of the car when $t = 3$." We find that on this interval of time, the average velocity is $\dfrac{s(4) - s(3)}{4 - 3} = \dfrac{128 - 87}{1} = 41$ ft/sec.

In addition, the average velocity on the interval $t = 3$ to $t = 3.5$ is 39.5 ft/sec; the average velocity on the interval from $t = 3$ to $t = 3.01$ is 38.03 ft/sec; and the average velocity on the very small interval of time $t = 3$ to $t = 3.001$ is 38.003 ft/sec. From this data (see Table 3-1), it seems plausible to conjecture that as the positive number h approaches 0, the average velocity on the time interval $t = 3$ to $t = 3 + h$

Table 3-1. $s(t) = 3t^2 + 20t$

Time interval (sec)	Distance traveled (ft)	Average velocity (ft/sec)
$t = 3$ to $t = 5$	$s(5) - s(3) = 88$	$\dfrac{88}{5 - 3} = 44$
$t = 3$ to $t = 4$	$s(4) - s(3) = 41$	$\dfrac{41}{4 - 3} = 41$
$t = 3$ to $t = 3.5$	$s(3.5) - s(3) = 19.75$	$\dfrac{19.75}{3.5 - 3} = 39.5$
$t = 3$ to $t = 3.01$	$s(3.01) - s(3) = .3803$	$\dfrac{.3803}{.01} = 38.03$
$t = 3$ to $t = 3.001$	$s(3.001) - s(3) = .038003$	$\dfrac{.038003}{.001} = 38.003$
$t = 2$ to $t = 3$	$s(3) - s(2) = 35$	$\dfrac{35}{3 - 2} = 35$
$t = 2.5$ to $t = 3$	$s(3) - s(2.5) = 18.25$	$\dfrac{18.25}{3 - 2.5} = 36.5$
$t = 2.99$ to $t = 3$	$s(3) - s(2.99) = .3797$	$\dfrac{.3797}{.01} = 37.97$
$t = 2.999$ to $t = 3$	$s(3) - s(2.999) = .037997$	$\dfrac{.037997}{.001} = 37.997$

approaches the limit 38 ft/sec. Indeed, we can verify this as follows:

$$\lim_{h \to 0^+} \frac{s(3 + h) - s(3)}{h} = \lim_{h \to 0^+} \frac{3(3 + h)^2 + 20(3 + h) - 87}{h}$$

$$= \lim_{h \to 0^+} \frac{18h + 3h^2 + 20h}{h} = \lim_{h \to 0^+} (38 + 3h) = 38$$

We may also do some calculations of average velocity for intervals of time which start before $t = 3$ and end at $t = 3$. The average velocity on the interval $t = 2$ to $t = 3$ is 35 ft/sec; the average velocity on the interval $t = 2.5$ to $t = 3$ is 36.5 ft/sec; the average velocity on the interval $t = 2.99$ to $t = 3$ is 37.97 ft/sec; and the average velocity on the interval $t = 2.999$ to $t = 3$ is 37.997 ft/sec. From this data (see Table 3-1), it also seems plausible to conjecture that as the negative number h approaches 0, the average velocity on the time interval $t = 3 + h$ to $t = 3$ approaches the limit 38 ft/sec. Indeed, as above, we can show that this is the case because

$$\lim_{h \to 0^-} \frac{s(3 + h) - s(3)}{h} = 38$$

We may now conclude that $\lim_{h \to 0} \dfrac{s(3 + h) - s(3)}{h} = 38$ and this is what we will *mean* by "the velocity at the time $t = 3$." In fact, for any time t in the interval $0 < t < 10$, we will say that the velocity of the car at time t is $\lim_{h \to 0} \dfrac{s(t + h) - s(t)}{h}$. It is important to note here that this limit does exist because

$$\lim_{h \to 0} \frac{s(t + h) - s(t)}{h} = \lim_{h \to 0} \frac{3(t + h)^2 + 20(t + h) - (3t^2 + 20t)}{h}$$

$$= \lim_{h \to 0} \frac{3t^2 + 6th + 3h^2 + 20t + 20h - 3t^2 - 20t}{h}$$

$$= \lim_{h \to 0} \frac{6th + 3h^2 + 20h}{h} = \lim_{h \to 0} (6t + 3h + 20) = 6t + 20$$

We can now easily compute the velocity at time t for any t in the interval $0 < t < 10$. For example when $t = 5$ seconds, the velocity is $6 \cdot 5 + 20$, or 50 ft/sec and when t = 1.7 seconds, the velocity is 30.2 ft/sec.

Let us now look at what appears to be an entirely different situation. We will presently see that these situations are intimately related.

Consider the parabola whose equation is $f(x) = x^2 + x + 2$. Let us try to find the slope of the tangent to the curve when $x = 1$, i.e., at the point (1,4) (see Fig. 3-1). First, we must decide what we mean by "the

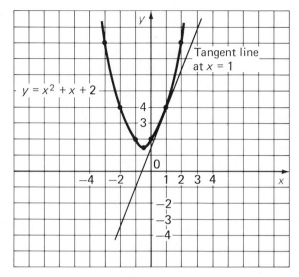

Figure 3-1

slope of the tangent to the curve." Suppose we first draw the **secant** line segment joining the points (1,4) and (2,8) on the parabola (see Fig. 3-2). The slope of this line segment is $\dfrac{8-4}{2-1} = 4$. Next, instead of 2, we'll take a value of x closer to 1, say 1.5. The slope of the secant

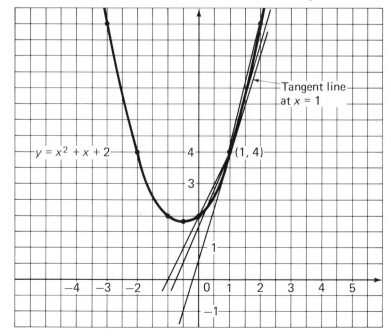

Figure 3-2

line joining the points (1,4) and (1.5,5.75) of the parabola is $\dfrac{1.75}{.5} = 3.5$.

In addition, the slope of the secant running from $x = 1$ to $x = 1.1$ is 3.1, and the slope of the secant running from $x = 1$ to $x = 1.01$ is 3.01. As you might suspect from the above data, as h decreases to 0, the slope of the secant line running from 1 to $1 + h$ approaches 3. We can verify this as follows:

$$\lim_{h \to 0^+} \frac{f(1 + h) - f(1)}{h} = \lim_{h \to 0^+} \frac{(1 + h)^2 + (1 + h) + 2 - 4}{h}$$

$$= \lim_{h \to 0^+} \frac{h^2 + 3h}{h} = \lim_{h \to 0^+} (h + 3) = 3$$

Also, if we consider secant lines running from values of x smaller than 1 up to $x = 1$, we observe that from $x = 0$ to $x = 1$, the slope is $\dfrac{f(0) - f(1)}{0 - 1} = 2$; from $x = .5$ to $x = 1$, the slope is 2.5; from $x = .9$ to $x = 1$, the slope is 2.9; and from $x = .99$ to $x = 1$, the slope is 2.99. Again, we

Table 3-2. $f(x) = x^2 + x + 2$

Points on secant line	Slope of secant line
(1,4) and (2,8)	$\dfrac{8 - 4}{2 - 1} = 4$
(1,4) and (1.5,5.75)	$\dfrac{5.75 - 4}{1.5 - 1} = 3.5$
(1,4) and (1.1,4.31)	$\dfrac{4.31 - 4}{1.1 - 1} = 3.1$
(1,4) and (1.01,4.0301)	$\dfrac{4.0301 - 4}{1.01 - 1} = 3.01$
(1,4) and (0,2)	$\dfrac{2 - 4}{0 - 1} = 2$
(1,4) and (.5,2.75)	$\dfrac{2.75 - 4}{.5 - 1} = 2.5$
(1,4) and (.9,3.71)	$\dfrac{3.71 - 4}{.9 - 1} = 2.9$
(1,4) and (.99,3.9701)	$\dfrac{3.9701 - 4}{.99 - 1} = 2.99$

may conjecture that as h increases to 0, the slope of the secant running from $x = 1 + h$ to $x = 1$ approaches 3. We may verify this as in the earlier case because

$$\lim_{h \to 0^-} \frac{f(1 + h) - f(1)}{h} = \lim_{h \to 0^-} (h + 3) = 3$$

It should be clear now that $\lim_{h \to 0} \dfrac{f(1+h) - f(1)}{h} = 3$ and this is how we *define* the slope of the tangent to the curve $f(x) = x^2 + x + 2$ at $x = 1$. The slope of the tangent is defined to be the limit of the slopes of the secant lines, where we take the limit as above.

Notice also that if we wish to find the slope of the tangent to the curve $f(x) = x^2 + x + 2$ at any value of x, we need merely evaluate

$$\lim_{h \to 0} \frac{f(x + h) - f(x)}{h} = \lim_{h \to 0} \frac{(x + h)^2 + (x + h) + 2 - (x^2 + x + 2)}{h}$$

$$= \lim_{h \to 0} \frac{x^2 + 2xh + h^2 + x + h + 2 - x^2 - x - 2}{h}$$

$$= \lim_{h \to 0} \frac{h^2 + 2xh + h}{h} = \lim_{h \to 0} (h + 2x + 1) = 2x + 1$$

Thus, the slope of the tangent when $x = 2$ is 5; the slope of the tangent when $x = -4$ is -7; and the slope of the tangent when $x = \sqrt{3}$ is $2\sqrt{3} + 1$.

Now, observe that in both our first example (when we calculated the velocity of a car) and in our second example (when we calculated the slope of a tangent to a parabolic curve) we were ultimately concerned with the evaluation of a limit of the form $\lim_{h \to 0} \dfrac{f(x + h) - f(x)}{h}$ (in the first example, the function was called s and the variable was called t, but the form of the limit was the same).

The evaluation of such a limit is central to the calculus and, in what follows, we will give it a great deal of attention.

We are now prepared to give a formal definition of such limits called **derivatives**.

> **Definition** Let f be a function defined on an open interval containing the point x. If $\lim_{h \to 0} \dfrac{f(x + h) - f(x)}{h}$ exists, then we say that f has a **derivative at x**. The **derivative of f at x** is the number

$$\lim_{h \to 0} \frac{f(x + h) - f(x)}{h}$$

Note. If is important to point out from the outset that there are certain functions that do not have a derivative at certain points. That is, there are functions for which the above limit at a given value of x does not exist. For example, suppose we attempt to calculate "the slope of the tangent to the curve $f(x) = |x|$ at $x = 0$." If we proceed as we did in the case of the parabola $x^2 + x + 2$, we are led to the evaluation of $\lim\limits_{h \to 0} \dfrac{|0 + h| - |0|}{h}$. Now notice that $\lim\limits_{h \to 0^+} \dfrac{|0 + h| - |0|}{h} = \lim\limits_{h \to 0^+} \dfrac{h}{h} = 1$. However, $\lim\limits_{h \to 0^-} \dfrac{|0 + h| - |0|}{h} = \lim\limits_{h \to 0^-} \dfrac{-h}{h} = -1$. Thus, $\lim\limits_{h \to 0} \dfrac{|0 + h| - |0|}{h}$ does not exist and so we may not talk about "the slope of the tangent to the curve $f(x) = |x|$ at $x = 0$." However, you should be able to verify for yourself that for any $x \neq 0$, the limit $\lim\limits_{h \to 0} \dfrac{|x + h| - |x|}{h}$ does exist and if $x > 0$, the limit is 1, whereas if $x < 0$, the limit is -1.

If f has a derivative at x, then:

(1) We write $f'(x)$ for the value of that derivative. The symbol $f'(x)$ is read "f prime at x."

(2) We say "f is **differentiable** at x" if $f'(x)$ exists *and is finite*.

(3) If we have $y = f(x)$, then the symbol y' (read "y prime") means $f'(x)$.

It is important to realize that differentiability (the existence of a finite derivative) is a phenomenon which occurs at a point, just as was the case with continuity. Thus, a function may be differentiable at one point and not at another ($f'(x_1)$ may exist, while $f'(x_2)$ may not). Recall, for example, our discussion above of the function $f(x) = |x|$. We saw that $f'(x) = 1$ if $x > 0$, $f'(x) = -1$ if $x < 0$, but $f'(0)$ fails to exist.

It is possible that a derivative (which is a certain limit as defined above) may exist and be infinite. For example, let us compute $f'(0)$ where $f(x) = x^{1/3}$:

$$f'(0) = \lim\limits_{h \to 0} \frac{f(0 + h) - f(0)}{h} = \lim\limits_{h \to 0} \frac{h^{1/3}}{h} = \lim\limits_{h \to 0} h^{-2/3} = +\infty$$

This f is *not* differentiable at $x = 0$ because the derivative, although it exists, is infinite.

At the outset we note that there is an important relationship between differentiability and continuity.

⇨ **Theorem**   If f is differentiable at x, then f is continuous at x.

Proof We want to show that f is continuous at x. This means that $\lim_{t \to x} f(t) = f(x)$ or, what is the same thing,

$$\lim_{h \to 0} f(x + h) = f(x) \text{ (think of } h \text{ as } t - x)$$

Thus, it will be sufficient to show that

$$\lim_{h \to 0} [f(x + h) - f(x)] = 0$$

Now

$$\lim_{h \to 0} (f(x + h) - f(x)) = \lim_{h \to 0} \left[\frac{f(x + h) - f(x)}{h} \cdot h \right]$$

$$= \lim_{h \to 0} \frac{f(x + h) - f(x)}{h} \cdot \lim_{h \to 0} h = f'(x) \cdot 0 = 0$$

because $f'(x)$ is finite. Thus, f is continuous at x. ∎

The converse of this theorem is false. The function $f(x) = |x|$ is continuous at 0, but it is *not* differentiable there. The function g defined by

$$g(x) = \begin{cases} -1 & \text{if } x < 0 \\ 0 & \text{if } x = 0 \\ 1 & \text{if } x > 0 \end{cases}$$

satisfies $g'(0) = +\infty$, but g is *not* continuous at $x = 0$. This does not contradict the above theorem because g is *not* differentiable at 0 even though $g'(0)$ exists.

It may happen that a function f is differentiable at every point of an open (possibly infinite) interval I. In this case, we say that f is **differentiable on I**. If f is differentiable at every real number x, then we say f is **differentiable everywhere**.

Just as we have previously discussed one-sided continuity, we have the analogous notion of one-sided derivatives. If f is defined on $[a,b[$ and $\lim_{h \to 0^+} \dfrac{f(a + h) - f(a)}{h} = \alpha$, then we say that f has a **right-hand derivative** α at a and we write $f_+'(a) = \alpha$.

Similarly, if f is defined on $]a,b]$ and $\lim_{h \to 0^-} \dfrac{f(b + h) - f(b)}{h} = \beta$, then we say f has a **left-hand derivative** β at b and we write $f_-'(b) = \beta$. We now say that if f is differentiable at every point of an interval I (where we mean one-sided derivatives at any endpoints I may have in I), then f is **differentiable on I**. Equivalently, we say f' exists and is finite on I.

EXAMPLE Show that the function $\dot{f}(x) = [x]$ is differentiable on $[0,1[$.

Solution To see this, we will show that f has a right-hand derivative equal to 0 at 0 and for any x such that $0 < x < 1, f'(x) = 0$, and so the derivative exists and is finite. First of all, recall that $[x]$ means the greatest integer which does not exceed x (see page 99). Thus, $[x] = 0$ whenever $0 \le x < 1$. It should be clear that $\lim\limits_{h \to 0^+} \dfrac{f(0 + h) - f(0)}{h} = 0$

and $\lim\limits_{h \to 0} \dfrac{f(x + h) - f(x)}{h} = 0$ for $0 < x < 1$. Notice that $f(x) = [x]$ is not differentiable on $[0,1]$ because f does not have a finite left-hand derivative at 1. This is so because $\lim\limits_{h \to 0^-} \dfrac{[1 + h] - [1]}{h} = \lim\limits_{h \to 0^-} \dfrac{-1}{h} = +\infty$.

E X E R C I S E S

In 1–5, for the given distance function s, (a) find the velocity at time $t = 2$ and (b) find the velocity at an arbitrary time t.

1. $s(t) = 4t + 3$ **4.** $s(t) = t^3$

2. $s(t) = t^2 + 5t$ **5.** $s(t) = t^3 + 3$

3. $s(t) = 2t^2 + t + 1$

In 6–10, for the given function f, (a) find the slope of the tangent to the graph of $y = f(x)$ at $x = -2$ and (b) find the slope of the tangent to the graph of $y = f(x)$ at an arbitrary value x.

6. $f(x) = -3x + 2$ **9.** $f(x) = x^3 + x$

7. $f(x) = x^2 - x$ **10.** $f(x) = 2x^3$

8. $f(x) = 2x^2 + 3x$

2   Differentiation of Positive Integral Powers

If the only way to find the derivative of a function at a certain point were to actually compute the limit in the definition, then much of the calculus would be, to say the least, extremely tedious. Fortunately, there are certain rules which allow us to **differentiate** (find the derivative of) certain classes of functions in a fairly simple manner.

Let us begin here with functions which are positive integral powers, that is, functions of the form $f(x) = x^n$, $n = 1,2,3, \ldots$.

▷ **Theorem (The Power Rule)** For any positive integer n, the function $f(x) = x^n$ is differentiable everywhere (at every point) and for any x, $f'(x) = nx^{n-1}$

Proof By definition, $f'(x)$ (if it exists) is given by

$$f'(x) = \lim_{h \to 0} \frac{f(x+h) - f(x)}{h} = \lim_{h \to 0} \frac{(x+h)^n - x^n}{h} = \lim_{t \to x} \frac{t^n - x^n}{t - x}$$

(by letting $t = x + h$ so $h \to 0$ if and only if $t \to x$). By the use of a factorization formula (see page 3), this last limit is equal to

$$\lim_{t \to x} \frac{(t-x)(t^{n-1} + t^{n-2}x + t^{n-3}x^2 + \ldots + tx^{n-2} + x^{n-1})}{t - x}$$

$$= \lim_{t \to x} (t^{n-1} + t^{n-2}x + t^{n-3}x^2 + \ldots + tx^{n-2} + x^{n-1})$$

$$= x^{n-1} + x^{n-1} + x^{n-1} + \ldots + x^{n-1} + x^{n-1} = nx^{n-1}$$

because of Limit Theorem 1 (see page 93) and the fact that there are n terms in the second factor. ■

The simple rule which we have just proved tells us immediately that:

(1) If $f(x) = x^2$, then $f'(5) = 2 \cdot 5^1 = 10$.

(2) If $g(x) = x^7$, then $g'\left(\dfrac{1}{2}\right) = 7 \cdot \left(\dfrac{1}{2}\right)^6 = \dfrac{7}{64}$.

(3) If $f(x) = x$, then $f'(-3) = 1 \cdot (-3)^0 = 1$.

Note. Although 0^0 is sometimes taken to be undefined, we take it here that if $f(x) = x$, then $f'(0) = 1 \cdot 0^0 = 1$. From now on we shall *define* the symbol 0^0 to denote the number 1; that is, $0^0 = 1$ by definition.

EXERCISES

1. If $f(x) = x^3$ find
   (a) $f'(0)$ (c) $f'(-2)$ (e) $f'(\sqrt{2})$

   (b) $f'(2)$ (d) $f'\left(\dfrac{2}{3}\right)$ (f) $f'(a)$

2. If $g(x) = x^6$, find $g'(4)$.
3. If $h(x) = x$, find $h'(-\pi)$.
4. Use the Binomial Theorem to give an alternate proof of the theorem on differentiation of positive integral powers.

3 The Linearity of the Derivative and the Differentiation of Polynomials

▷ **Theorem (The Linearity of the Derivative)**   If a and b are any real numbers and if f and g are two functions which are differentiable at a point x, then the function $h = af + bg$ is differentiable at x and $h'(x) = (af + bg)'(x) = af'(x) + bg'(x)$.

Proof   The theorem follows from the definition of derivative and the properties of limits, as follows: $h'(x) = (af + bg)'(x)$ is defined to be

$$\lim_{h \to 0} \frac{(af + bg)(x + h) - (af + bg)(x)}{h}$$

$$= \lim_{h \to 0} \frac{af(x + h) + bg(x + h) - (af(x) + bg(x))}{h}$$

$$= \lim_{h \to 0} \frac{a(f(x + h) - f(x)) + b(g(x + h) - g(x))}{h}$$

$$= \lim_{h \to 0} \frac{a(f(x + h) - f(x))}{h} + \lim_{h \to 0} \frac{b(g(x + h) - g(x))}{h}$$

$$= a \lim_{h \to 0} \frac{f(x + h) - f(x)}{h} + b \lim_{h \to 0} \frac{g(x + h) - g(x)}{h}$$

$$= af'(x) + bg'(x)$$

which concludes the proof. ∎

The theorem we have just proved can be expressed by the following two statements:

(1) If f and g are both differentiable at x, then so is $f + g$ and $(f + g)'(x) = f'(x) + g'(x)$. That is, "the derivative of the sum is the sum of the derivatives."

(2) If f is differentiable at x and a is any constant, then the function af is differentiable at x and $(af)'(x) = af'(x)$. That is, "the derivative of a constant times a function is the constant times the derivative of the function."

Observe that if $f'(2) = 3$ and $g'(2) = -1$, then the function $5f + 4g$ is differentiable at 2 and $(5f + 4g)'(2) = 5f'(2) + 4g'(2) = 5 \cdot 3 + 4(-1) = 11$.

Also, if f and g are both differentiable at x, then so is $f - g$. To see this, observe that $f - g = 1 \cdot f + (-1) \cdot g$. The conclusion is now immediate from the linearity theorem for derivatives. Clearly, $(f - g)'(x) = f'(x) - g'(x)$.

EXAMPLE If $h(x) = 2x^4 - 3x^2$, then find $h'(3)$.

Solution Since the functions $f(x) = x^4$ and $g(x) = x^2$ are both differentiable everywhere, then the linearity of the derivative tells us that for any x, $h'(x) = 2f'(x) - 3g'(x)$. We know that $f'(x) = 4x^3$ and $g'(x) = 2x$. Thus, $h'(x) = 2 \cdot 4x^3 - 3 \cdot 2x = 8x^3 - 6x$. So, $h'(3) = 2 \cdot 4 \cdot 27 - 3 \cdot 2 \cdot 3 = 198$.

Suppose we now wish to differentiate the function $f(x) = 3x^7 + 2x^4 - 3x^2$ at any x. We may begin by noting that the function $f_1(x) = 2x^4 - 3x^2$ is differentiable at x and, as in the example above, $f_1'(x) = 8x^3 - 6x$. Also, the function $f_2(x) = 3x^7$ is differentiable at x and $f_2'(x) = 21x^6$. By the linearity of the derivative, it follows that $f = f_2 + f_1$ is differentiable at x and $f'(x) = f_2'(x) + f_1'(x) = 21x^6 + 8x^3 - 6x$.

In a similar manner we may prove the following:

> **Theorem (The Linearity of the Derivative)** If $f_1, f_2, \cdots, f_n$ are all differentiable at x and $a_1, a_2, \cdots, a_n$ are any constants, then the function $f = a_1 f_1 + a_2 f_2 + \cdots + a_n f_n$ is differentiable at x and $f'(x) = (a_1 f_1 + a_2 f_2 + \cdots + a_n f_n)'(x) = a_1 f_1'(x) + a_2 f_2'(x) + \cdots + a_n f_n'(x)$.

Note. We now know that if f and g are both differentiable at x, then so are the functions $f + g$ and $f - g$ and, furthermore, $(f + g)'(x) = f'(x) + g'(x)$ and $(f - g)'(x) = f'(x) - g'(x)$. In words, "the derivative of the sum is the sum of the derivatives and the derivative of the difference is the difference of the derivatives." One may be tempted to suppose that the same sort of nice rule would also hold true for the derivatives of products and quotients of functions. However, they don't! We shall soon see what rules do apply in these cases.

We are now in a position to apply the linearity of the derivative and the rule for differentiation of positive integral powers to give a rule for the systematic differentiation of polynomials.

Before we do this in the next theorem, we prove a simple, but important, result.

> **Theorem** If $f(x) = c$ is a constant function, then $f'(x) = 0$ for all real numbers x.

Proof   Observe that $\lim\limits_{h \to 0} \dfrac{f(x+h) - f(x)}{h} = \lim\limits_{h \to 0} \dfrac{c - c}{h} = 0.$ ∎

▷ **Theorem**   If $f(x) = a_n x^n + a_{n-1} x^{n-1} + \cdots + a_1 x + a_0$ is any polynomial function, then f is differentiable everywhere and $f'(x) = na_n x^{n-1} + (n-1)a_{n-1} x^{n-2} + \cdots + 2a_2 x + a_1$ for all real numbers x.

Proof   Since the derivative of a constant function is always 0, the linearity of the derivative and the rule for differentiation of positive integral powers tell us that $f'(x) = na_n x^{n-1} + (n-1)a_{n-1} x^{n-2} + \cdots + a_2 x + a_1 + 0$. This completes the proof. ∎

EXAMPLE   Differentiate the polynomial function $f(x) = 2x^5 + 4x^2 - 3x + 2$ at $x = -2$.

Solution   Since $f'(x) = 5 \cdot 2x^4 + 2 \cdot 4x - 3 = 10x^4 + 8x - 3$ for all x, we see that $f'(-2) = 10(-2)^4 + 8(-2) - 3 = 141$.

E X E R C I S E S

1. Find $f'(x)$ if
   (a) $f(x) = 3x + 2$ and $x = 3$
   (b) $f(x) = 2x^2 + 3$ and $x = 4$
   (c) $f(x) = -3x^2 + 2x + 4$ and $x = -2$
   (d) $f(x) = x^3 + x^2 + x + 1$ and $x = 1$
   (e) $f(x) = 3x^4 - 2x^2 + x$ and $x = \dfrac{1}{2}$
   (f) $f(x) = -3x^3 + x^2$ and $x = -1$
   (g) $f(x) = 2x^2 + x - 3$ and $x = -\dfrac{1}{2}$
   (h) $f(x) = x^5 - 3x^4 + x + 2$ and $x = 2$
   (i) $f(x) = 2x^5 + x^3 - 3x$ and $x = -2$
   (j) $f(x) = x^{10}$ and $x = \dfrac{1}{2}$

2. Exhibit two functions, f and g, and an x such that the function $f + g$ is differentiable at x but neither f nor g is differentiable at x.

3. Prove that if $f + g$ is differentiable at x and also f is differentiable at x, then g is differentiable at x.

4 Derivatives of Products and Quotients

▷ **Theorem (The Product Rule)** If f and g are both differentiable at x, then the product function $f \cdot g$ is also differentiable at x and

$$(f \cdot g)'(x) = f(x)g'(x) + g(x)f'(x)$$

Proof   Notice that $(f \cdot g)'(x)$ is defined by

$$\lim_{h \to 0} \frac{f \cdot g(x+h) - f \cdot g(x)}{h} = \lim_{h \to 0} \frac{f(x+h)g(x+h) - f(x)g(x)}{h}$$

$$= \lim_{h \to 0} \left(f(x+h) \frac{g(x+h) - g(x)}{h} + g(x) \frac{f(x+h) - f(x)}{h} \right)$$

$$= \lim_{h \to 0} f(x+h) \lim_{h \to 0} \frac{g(x+h) - g(x)}{h} + g(x) \lim_{h \to 0} \frac{f(x+h) - f(x)}{h}$$

Since $f'(x)$ is finite, f is continuous at x and so $\lim_{h \to 0} f(x+h) = f(x)$. The other limits are just the derivatives $g'(x)$ and $f'(x)$. Thus, $(f \cdot g)'(x) = f(x)g'(x) + g(x)f'(x)$ and the theorem has been proved. ∎

EXAMPLE   Use the Product Rule to differentiate the function $h(x) = (2x+1)(x^2 - 2)$.

Solution   Let $f(x) = 2x + 1$ and $g(x) = x^2 - 2$. Then, by the Product Rule, $h'(x) = (f \cdot g)'(x) = f(x) \cdot g'(x) + g(x) \cdot f'(x) = (2x+1) \cdot 2x + (x^2 - 2) \cdot 2 = 4x^2 + 2x + 2x^2 - 4 = 6x^2 + 2x - 4$.

EXAMPLE   Let $f(x) = 2x^2 + x + 1$ and $g(x) = -x^3 - x^2 + 4$. Use the Product Rule to find the derivative of $f \cdot g$ at $x = 2$.

Solution   We know that $f'(x) = 4x + 1$ and $g'(x) = -3x^2 - 2x$. Thus, $f'(2) = 9$ and $g'(2) = -16$. Also $f(2) = 11$ and $g(2) = -8$. So, since $(f \cdot g)'(x) = f(x)g'(x) + g(x)f'(x)$, we see that $(f \cdot g)'(2) = 11(-16) + (-8)(9) = -248$.

Before we see how to differentiate a quotient of functions, it will be useful to know how to differentiate the reciprocal of a function. We do this in the next theorem.

▷ **Theorem   (The Reciprocal Rule)** Suppose g is differentiable at x and $g(x) \neq 0$. Then $\left(\dfrac{1}{g} \right)'(x) = \dfrac{-g'(x)}{(g(x))^2}$.

Proof   We begin by observing that $\left(\dfrac{1}{g}\right)'(x)$ is defined by

$$\lim_{h \to 0} \frac{\dfrac{1}{g(x+h)} - \dfrac{1}{g(x)}}{h} = \lim_{h \to 0} \frac{g(x) - g(x+h)}{hg(x+h)g(x)}$$

$$= \lim_{h \to 0} \left(-\frac{g(x+h) - g(x)}{h} \cdot \frac{1}{g(x+h)g(x)} \right)$$

But, since g is differentiable at x, g is continuous at x and so

$$\lim_{h \to 0} \frac{1}{g(x+h)g(x)} = \frac{1}{(g(x))^2}$$ (recall that $g(x) \neq 0$). Thus,

$$\left(\frac{1}{g}\right)'(x) = \lim_{h \to 0} \left(-\frac{g(x+h) - g(x)}{h} \cdot \lim_{h \to 0} \frac{1}{g(x+h)g(x)} \right) = \frac{-g'(x)}{(g(x))^2}$$

and the proof is complete. ∎

   We already know that if n is a positive integer, then the function $f(x) = x^n$ is differentiable and $f'(x) = nx^{n-1}$. We can now extend this result to negative integer exponents. If n is a negative integer, then for $f(x) = x^n = \dfrac{1}{x^{-n}}$, we have $f'(x) = \dfrac{nx^{-n-1}}{(x^{-n})^2}$, since the derivative of the function x^{-n} is $-nx^{-n-1}$ because $-n$ is positive. Thus, $f'(x) = \dfrac{nx^{-n-1}}{x^{-2n}} = nx^{-n-1+2n} = nx^{n-1}$, which is expressed in the following theorem:

▷ **Theorem (The Power Rule)**   If n is a nonzero integer, then the function $f(x) = x^n$ is differentiable and $f'(x) = nx^{n-1}$. (If $n < 0$, we assume $x \neq 0$.)

   Thus, if $f(x) = \dfrac{1}{x^5} = x^{-5}$, then $f'(x) = -5x^{-6}$. We are now ready to differentiate quotients.

▷ **Theorem (The Quotient Rule)**   If f and g are both differentiable at x and $g(x) \neq 0$, then $\dfrac{f}{g}$ is differentiable at x and

$$\left(\frac{f}{g}\right)'(x) = \frac{g(x)f'(x) - f(x)g'(x)}{(g(x))^2}$$

Proof The proof is a direct application of the Product Rule and the Reciprocal Rule. Since $\frac{f}{g} = f \cdot \frac{1}{g}$, we regard $\frac{f}{g}$ as the product $f \cdot h$, where $h = \frac{1}{g}$. Thus, $\left(\frac{f}{g}\right)'(x) = (f \cdot h)'(x) = f(x)h'(x) + h(x)f'(x)$. But $h'(x) = \left(\frac{1}{g}\right)'(x) = \frac{-g'(x)}{(g(x))^2}$. Thus,

$$\left(\frac{f}{g}\right)'(x) = f(x)\left(\frac{-g'(x)}{(g(x))^2}\right) + \frac{1}{g(x)}f'(x)$$

$$= \frac{f(x)(-g'(x)) + g(x)f'(x)}{(g(x))^2} = \frac{g(x)f'(x) - f(x)g'(x)}{(g(x))^2}$$

and we are done. ■

EXAMPLE Use the Quotient Rule to differentiate $h(x) = \frac{2x+1}{3x-1}$.

Solution Let $f(x) = 2x + 1$ and $g(x) = 3x - 1$. Then by the Quotient Rule,

$$h'(x) = \frac{g(x)f'(x) - f(x)g'(x)}{(g(x))^2} = \frac{(3x-1)(2) - (2x+1)(3)}{(3x-1)^2}$$

$$= \frac{6x - 2 - 6x - 3}{(3x-1)^2} = \frac{-4x - 5}{(3x-1)^2}$$

EXAMPLE If $h(x) = \frac{x^2 + 3x - 1}{x^2 + 1}$, find $h'(1)$.

Solution If $f(x) = x^2 + 3x - 1$ and $g(x) = x^2 + 1$, then $h(x) = \left(\frac{f}{g}\right)(x)$. Since f and g are polynomials, f and g are both differentiable. Also, $g(1) = 2 \neq 0$. So, we see from the Quotient Rule that $h'(1) = \left(\frac{f}{g}\right)'(1)$ is given by $\frac{g(1)f'(1) - f(1)g'(1)}{(g(1))^2}$. Since $f'(x) = 2x + 3$ and $g'(x) = 2x$, we have $f'(1) = 5$ and $g'(1) = 2$. So, $h'(1) = \frac{2 \cdot 5 - 3 \cdot 2}{2^2} = 1$.

E X E R C I S E S

1. If $f(x) = (x + 1)(x^2 - x - 1)$,

   (a) Use the Product Rule to differentiate f and find $f'(1)$

   (b) Find $f'(1)$ another way.

2. If $f(x) = (-x^2 + x + 2)(x^3 + x)$,

   (a) Use the Product Rule to differentiate f and find $f'(-2)$.

   (b) Find $f'(-2)$ another way.

In 3–6, use the Product Rule to differentiate the function.

   3. $f(x) = (x^2 - 2)(x^2 + 3)$

   4. $g(t) = (t^2 + t)(t^2 - t)$

   5. $g(x) = (2x^2 + 3x - 1)(x + 4)$

   6. $f(s) = (-s^2 - s + 1)(s^2 + 2s - 3)$

   7. Differentiate the function $f(x) = \dfrac{1}{x^n},\ x \neq 0$, if:

     (a) $n = 2$ (b) $n = 3$ (c) $n = 4$ (d) $n = 100$

   8. Find $f'(2)$ if $f(x) = \dfrac{x}{x^2 + 1}$.

   9. Find $g'(-1)$ if $g(x) = \dfrac{-x^2 + x}{x - 1}$.

10. Find $h'(0)$ if $h(x) = \dfrac{x^3 + 3x^2 + 4}{-x^2 - x + 3}$.

In 11–14, use the Quotient Rule to differentiate the function.

11. $f(x) = \dfrac{5x + 3}{-2x + 1}$ **13.** $g(t) = \dfrac{2t^2 + t - 1}{5t + 2}$

12. $g(t) = \dfrac{t^2 + t}{t^2 - t}$ **14.** $f(s) = \dfrac{s^2 + 2s + 1}{s^2 - s - 3}$

In 15–18, find (a) $(f \cdot g)'(x_0)$ and (b) $\left(\dfrac{f}{g}\right)'(x_0)$ using the given values.

15. $f(x_0) = 1;\ g(x_0) = 1;\ f'(x_0) = 1;\ g'(x_0) = 1$

16. $f(x_0) = -1;\ g(x_0) = 1;\ f'(x_0) = 2;\ g'(x_0) = 3$

17. $f(x_0) = 0;\ g(x_0) = 2;\ f'(x_0) = 1;\ g'(x_0) = -1$

18. $f(x_0) = \dfrac{1}{2};\ g(x_0) = -1;\ f'(x_0) = \dfrac{1}{2};\ g'(x_0) = 3$

19. Use the Product Rule (but not the Power Rule) and the fact that if $f(x) = x$, then $f'(x) = 1$ for all x, to show that

   (a) If $f_2(x) = x^2$, then $f_2'(x) = 2x$ for all x.

   (b) If $f_3(x) = x^3$, then $f_3'(x) = 3x^2$ for all x.

   (c) In general, if $f_n(x) = x^n$, for some positive integer n, then $f_n'(x) = nx^{n-1}$ for all x.

20. If $g(x) = (f(x))^2$ and f is differentiable at x, then use the Product Rule to show that $g'(x) = 2f(x)f'(x)$.

21. If $g(x) = (f(x))^3$ and f is differentiable at x, then show that $g'(x) = 3f(x)^2 f'(x)$.

22. If $g(x) = (f(x))^n$, for some nonzero integer n, and f is differentiable at x, then write a formula for $g'(x)$.

23. (a) If f, g, and h are all differentiable at x, then use the Product Rule to show that $(f \cdot g \cdot h)'(x) = f'(x)g(x)h(x) + g'(x)f(x)h(x) + h'(x)f(x)g(x)$.

(b) Generalize this rule to any number of factors.

5 The "Little d" Notation and the Chain Rule

The founding fathers of the calculus were the English mathematician Sir Isaac Newton (1642–1727) and the German mathematician Gottfried Leibnitz (1646–1716). The latter is responsible for a notation which is very widely used today, the "little d" notation.

If y is a function of x, or $y = f(x)$, then the derivative of the function y is written $\dfrac{dy}{dx}$. We read this "$d\,y$, $d\,x$" or "the derivative of y with respect to x." In terms of the "prime" notation, we have $\dfrac{dy}{dx} = y'$. We also often use the symbol $\dfrac{d}{dx}f(x)$ or, more simply, $\dfrac{df}{dx}$, to mean $f'(x)$.

For example, if $y = f(x) = x^3 + 2x$, then $y' = \dfrac{dy}{dx} = f'(x) = 3x^2 + 2$. Also,

$$\frac{d}{dx}f(x) = \frac{df}{dx} = f'(x) = \frac{d}{dx}(x^3 + 2x) = 3x^2 + 2.$$

Recall that at the beginning of this chapter we were concerned with an "instantaneous rate of change" of one quantity with respect to another. This led us to define this rate to be the derivative. More specifically, if $y = f(x)$ is a differentiable function of x, then the "rate of change of y with respect to x" is $\dfrac{dy}{dx}$. We say that "y is changing $\dfrac{dy}{dx}$ times as fast as x."

EXAMPLE Express the Quotient Rule in terms of the "little d" notation and find $\dfrac{dy}{dx}$ if $y = \dfrac{3x^2}{x+2}$.

Solution   Let $y = \dfrac{f(x)}{g(x)}$. The Quotient Rule, phrased in terms of the

"little d" notation, becomes $\dfrac{dy}{dx} = \dfrac{g(x)\dfrac{d}{dx}f(x) - f(x)\dfrac{d}{dx}g(x)}{(g(x))^2}$.

If $f(x) = 3x^2$ and $g(x) = x + 2$, then $\dfrac{dy}{dx} = \dfrac{(x+2)(6x) - 3x^2(1)}{(x+2)^2} =$

$\dfrac{3x^2 + 12x}{(x+2)^2}$.

EXAMPLE   Suppose we start with a square each of whose sides has length 1 and continually magnify the square by increasing the length of its side. Find the rate of change of the area A of the square with respect to its side s when $A = 2$.

Solution A and s are related by the formula $A = s^2$. We are asked to find $\dfrac{dA}{ds}$ when $s = 2$. Clearly $\dfrac{dA}{ds} = 2s$ and, when $s = 2$, this value is 4. Thus, A is changing 4 times as fast as s when $s = 2$.

A word of caution is in order here. The symbols $\dfrac{dy}{dx}, \dfrac{df}{dx}$, etc., are *not* fractions and we are not allowed to blithely manipulate them as though they were such. We will see later (the Chain Rule) that there are times when it would appear that we can manipulate them as fractions, but do not be misled.

E X E R C I S E S

1. Express the linearity of the derivative in terms of the "little d" notation.
2. Express the Reciprocal Rule in terms of the "little d" notation.
3. Express the Product Rule in terms of the "little d" notation.
4. Find $\dfrac{d}{dt}f(t)$ $\left(\text{or } \dfrac{df}{dt}\right)$ if

   (a) $f(t) = t^2 + 2$

   (b) $f(t) = \dfrac{t+1}{t-1}$

   (c) $f(t) = (t-1)(t^2 + 2t + 3) + \dfrac{1}{t}$

   (d) $f(t) = \left(\dfrac{3t+1}{t+2}\right)^2$

5. Find $\dfrac{dy}{dx}$ (or y') if

   (a) $y = x + \dfrac{1}{x}$

   (b) $y = \dfrac{1}{x^3}$

   (c) $y = \dfrac{x+1}{(x-1)^2}$

   (d) $y = -\dfrac{1}{x^2} + \dfrac{x+1}{x^3}$

6. Find the rate of change of the volume of a cube with respect to the side when the side is

(a) 1 (b) 2 (c) 3 (d) $\frac{1}{2}$ (e) $\sqrt{2}$

7. Find the rate of change of the area of a square with respect to the diagonal when the diagonal is

(a) 1 (b) 2 (c) 3 (d) $\frac{1}{2}$ (e) $\sqrt{2}$

8. Find the rate of change of the area of a circle with respect to the radius when the radius is

(a) 1 (b) 2 (c) 3 (d) $\frac{1}{2}$ (e) $\sqrt{2}$

9. Find the rate of change of the area of a circle with respect to the diameter when the diameter is

(a) 1 (b) 2 (c) 3 (d) $\frac{1}{2}$ (e) $\sqrt{2}$

10. Find the rate of change of the area of a circle with respect to the circumference when the radius is

(a) 1 (b) 2 (c) 3 (d) $\frac{1}{2}$ (e) $\sqrt{2}$

11. If $y = 4x^3 + 15x^2 + 6x$, for which values of x is $\dfrac{dy}{dx} = -6$?

12. The volume V and the radius r of a sphere are related by the formula $V = \dfrac{4}{3}\pi r^3$.

(a) Find $\dfrac{dV}{dr}$.

(b) What is the rate of change of V with respect to r when $r = 2$?

(c) For what value of r is the rate of change of the volume with respect to the radius 2?

WE ARE NOW READY to investigate the differentiation of composite functions. Recall that if f and g are functions with f defined on the range of g, then $f \circ g(x) = f(g(x))$. Thus, for example, if $f(x) = x^2 + 1$ and $g(x) = 2x - 3$, then $f \circ g(x) = f(2x - 3) = (2x - 3)^2 + 1 = 4x^2 - 12x + 9 + 1 = 4x^2 - 12x + 10$.

Suppose now that we wish to differentiate the composite function $f \circ g$. Intuitively, the situation is this: g is changing $g'(x)$ times as fast as x and $f(g(x))$ is changing $f'(g(x))$ times as fast as $g(x)$. It seems plausible that $f \circ g(x)$ should therefore be changing $f'(g(x)) \cdot g'(x)$ times as fast as x, that is, $(f \circ g)'(x) = f'(g(x)) \cdot g'(x)$.

In terms of the "little d" notation this becomes $\dfrac{d\,f \circ g}{dx} = \dfrac{d\,f \circ g}{dg} \cdot \dfrac{dg}{dx}$.

It is common practice here to set $u = g(x)$ and $y = f(u) = f \circ g(x)$. So that our equation becomes $\dfrac{dy}{dx} = \dfrac{dy}{du} \cdot \dfrac{du}{dx}$.

It turns out that our intuition is correct. The resulting theorem is called the **Chain Rule** and its proof (which is not very intuitive) may be found in the Appendix. Remember that the symbols $\dfrac{dy}{du}$ and $\dfrac{du}{dx}$ are *not* fractions and, therefore, the Chain Rule *cannot* be proven by "cancelling" the du's in the formula $\dfrac{dy}{dx} = \dfrac{dy}{du} \cdot \dfrac{du}{dx}$. The Chain Rule is of the utmost importance in the differentiation of functions because many of the functions which we need to differentiate are composite functions.

▷ *Theorem (The Chain Rule)* If g is differentiable at x and f is differentiable at $g(x)$, then $f \circ g$ is differentiable at x and $(f \circ g)'(x) = f'(g(x)) \cdot g'(x)$.

Note. If we write $u = g(x)$ and $y = f \circ g(x) = f(u)$, then the Chain Rule becomes $\dfrac{dy}{dx} = \dfrac{dy}{du} \cdot \dfrac{du}{dx}$.

EXAMPLE   Use the Chain Rule to show that if $f(x) = (g(x))^n$, where n is a nonzero integer and g is a differentiable function, then f is differentiable and $f'(x) = n(g(x))^{n-1} \cdot g'(x)$. If $n < 0$, we assume $g(x) \neq 0$.

Solution   Let $h(x) = x^n$, then $f(x) = h \circ g(x)$. By the Chain Rule and the Power Rule, $f'(x) = h'(g(x)) \cdot g'(x) = n(g(x))^{n-1} \cdot g'(x)$.

EXAMPLE   Use the Chain Rule to differentiate the function $f(x) = (x^2 - 7)^{43}$.

Solution   From the preceding example, we see that $f'(x) = 43(x^2 - 7)^{42} \cdot 2x = 86x(x^2 - 7)^{42}$.

Note. You can see that if we had tried to solve this problem without the Chain Rule, we would have had to expand $(x^2 - 7)^{43}$ into a polynomial and then take the derivative; this would have entailed a vast amount of work.

Let us now take another look at the Quotient Rule. We wish to differentiate $\dfrac{f}{g}$. Let us rewrite this quotient as the product $f \cdot (g)^{-1}$. We may now use the Product Rule and the Chain Rule to write

$$\left(\frac{f}{g}\right)'(x) = (f \cdot (g)^{-1})'(x) = f(x)((g)^{-1})'(x) + (g(x))^{-1}f'(x)$$

$$= f(x)(-(g(x))^{-2}(g'(x))) + (g(x))^{-1}f'(x)$$

$$= \frac{-f(x)g'(x)}{(g(x))^2} + \frac{f'(x)}{g(x)} = \frac{-f(x)g'(x)}{(g(x))^2} + \frac{g(x)f'(x)}{(g(x))^2}$$

$$= \frac{g(x)f'(x) - f(x)g'(x)}{(g(x))^2}$$

Sometimes one may find it easier to differentiate a quotient by this technique rather than use the Quotient Rule. Of course, both methods give correct answers that are equal even though they may appear to be different.

EXAMPLE Differentiate $f(x) = \dfrac{(2x + 1)}{(3x - 1)}$.

Solution Write $f(x) = (2x + 1)(3x - 1)^{-1}$. Then

$$f'(x) = (2x + 1)(-(3x - 1)^{-2}(3)) + (3x - 1)^{-1}(2)$$

EXAMPLE Differentiate $g(x) = \dfrac{\left(1 + \dfrac{1}{x}\right)^2}{(1 - x)^3}$.

Solution Write $g(x) = \left(1 + \dfrac{1}{x}\right)^2 (1 - x)^{-3}$. Then

$$g'(x) = \left(1 + \frac{1}{x}\right)^2 (-3(1 - x)^{-4}(-1)) + (1 - x)^{-3}\left(2\left(1 + \frac{1}{x}\right)\left(-\frac{1}{x^2}\right)\right)$$

It would be good practice to work the last two examples by the Quotient Rule and check algebraically that the answers are the same as the ones we have obtained.

Let us now look at an example involving the Chain Rule and the "little d" notation.

EXAMPLE If $u = \dfrac{1}{x^2}$ and $y = \dfrac{u + 1}{u - 2}$, find $\dfrac{dy}{dx}$.

Solution   Recall the following form of the Chain Rule: $\dfrac{dy}{dx} = \dfrac{dy}{du} \cdot \dfrac{du}{dx}$. Now (by the Quotient Rule),

$$\frac{dy}{du} = \frac{(u-2)\cdot 1 - (u+1)(1)}{(u-2)^2} = \frac{-3}{(u-2)^2} = \frac{-3}{\left(\dfrac{1}{x^2} - 2\right)^2} = \frac{-3x^4}{(1-2x^2)^2}$$

Also, $\dfrac{du}{dx} = \dfrac{-2}{x^3}$. Thus, $\dfrac{dy}{dx} = \dfrac{dy}{du}\cdot\dfrac{du}{dx} = \dfrac{-3x^4}{(1-2x^2)^2}\cdot\dfrac{-2}{x^3} = \dfrac{6x}{(1-2x^2)^2}$.

Note. For another solution to this problem, we could have substituted $u = \dfrac{1}{x^2}$ in the equation $y = \dfrac{u+1}{u-2}$, obtaining

$$y = \frac{\dfrac{1}{x^2} + 1}{\dfrac{1}{x^2} - 2}$$

We could then simplify and differentiate. You should work out the answer and see if it is the same as we obtained above.

EXAMPLE Use the Chain Rule repeatedly to differentiate $f(x) = \big((1 + (2 - x^2)^{-2}\big)^{-3}$.

Solution   If $g(x) = 2 - x^2$, $h(y) = 1 + y^{-2}$, and $l(z) = z^{-3}$, then $f(x) = l \circ h \circ g(x)$. Thus, from the Chain Rule (regarding $h \circ g$ as a single function), $f'(x) = l'(h \circ g(x)) \cdot (h \circ g)'(x)$. Now, again, from the Chain Rule, $(h \circ g)'(x) = h'(g(x)) \cdot g'(x)$. Thus, $f'(x) = l'(h \circ g(x)) \cdot h'(g(x)) \cdot g'(x)$. Now,

$$g'(x) = -2x$$
$$h'(g(x)) = h'(2 - x^2) = -2(2 - x^2)^{-3}$$

and

$$l'(h \circ g(x)) = l'\big(1 + (2 - x^2)^{-2}\big) = -3\big(1 + (2 - x^2)^{-2}\big)^{-4}$$

Thus,

$$f'(x) = -3\big(1 + (2 - x^2)^{-2}\big)^{-4} \cdot -2(2 - x^2)^{-3} \cdot -2x$$
$$= -12x\big(1 + (2 - x^2)^{-2}\big)^{-4}(2 - x^2)^{-3}$$

As we shall see in the next example, it is possible to use the Chain Rule without actually introducing the "auxiliary" functions as in the previous examples.

EXAMPLE Without introducing the auxiliary functions of which f is the composite, differentiate $f(x) = ((1 + 2x)^{-2} + x)^{-3}$.

Solution $f'(x) = -3((1 + 2x)^{-2} + x)^{-4} \cdot (-2(1 + 2x)^{-3} \cdot 2 + 1)$
$= -3((1 + 2x)^{-2} + x)^{-4} \cdot (-4(1 + 2x)^{-3} + 1)$

We close this section with an example that shows that, on occasion, the definition of the derivative must be used, since none of the rules we have developed applies.

EXAMPLE If $f(x) = |x|^3$, find $f'(0)$.

Solution We might be tempted to apply the Chain Rule, but since $|x|$ is not differentiable at $x = 0$, this approach does not work. Thus, we resort to the definition:

$$f'(x) = \lim_{h \to 0} \frac{f(x + h) - f(x)}{h} = \lim_{h \to 0} \frac{|x + h|^3 - |x|^3}{h}$$

For $x \geq 0$ and $h > 0$, we have $|x + h| = x + h$ and $|x| = x$, so

$$\lim_{h \to 0^+} \frac{|x + h|^3 - |x|^3}{h} = \lim_{h \to 0^+} \frac{(x + h)^3 - x^3}{h}$$

$$= \lim_{h \to 0^+} \frac{(x^3 + 3x^2h + 3xh^2 + h^3) - x^3}{h}$$

$$= \lim_{h \to 0^+} \frac{3x^2h + 3xh^2 + h^3}{h} = \lim_{h \to 0^+} (3x^2 + 3xh + h^2)$$

If $x = 0$, this limit is 0.

In a similar fashion, for $x \leq 0$ and $h < 0$, we have $|x + h| = -(x + h)$ and $|x| = -x$, so

$$\lim_{h \to 0^-} \frac{|x + h|^3 - |x|^3}{h} = \lim_{h \to 0^-} \frac{-(x + h)^3 + x^3}{h} = \lim_{h \to 0^-} (-3x^2 - 3xh - h^2)$$

If $x = 0$, this limit is also 0.

Thus,

$$\lim_{h \to 0} \frac{f(x + h) - f(x)}{h} = 0$$

if $x = 0$ and so $f'(0) = 0$.

E X E R C I S E S

In 1–16, differentiate the given function.

1. $f(x) = (x + 1)^4$

2. $f(x) = (x + 1)^{-4}$

3. $g(x) = (x + 2)^{23}$

4. $g(x) = \left(x + \dfrac{1}{x}\right)^3$

5. $h(x) = \left(\dfrac{x + 2}{x^2 + 2}\right)^{-2}$

6. $h(x) = (x + x^2)^{-1}$

7. $f(t) = (1 + (t + 1)^3)^7$

8. $f(t) = \left(\dfrac{t}{1 + t}\right)^5$

9. $f(x) = (1 + (2x - 1)^2)^{-3}$

10. $g(x) = (x + (x + 1)^{-3})^{-2}$

11. $g(x) = (x^{-1} - 2x^{-2})^3$

12. $h(x) = \left(\dfrac{1}{x} - (1 + 3x)^{-2}\right)^2$

13. $f(t) = \left(\dfrac{t^2 - 1}{t^2 + 1} + \dfrac{t^3}{2}\right)^4$

14. $g(x) = \left(\left(\dfrac{1}{x} + \dfrac{1}{x + 1}\right)^2 + \dfrac{1}{x}\right)^{-3}$

15. $f(x) = (x^2 + 1)^2 \cdot (x^2 + 2)^3$

16. $g(t) = \dfrac{(t^2 + t)^4}{(t + 1)^6}$

In 17–22, find $(f \circ g)'(x)$

17. $g(x) = x^2 + 1; \; f(x) = x^2$

18. $g(x) = \dfrac{x + 1}{x + 3}; \; f(x) = x^6$

19. $g(x) = \dfrac{2}{x + 2}; \; f(x) = x + x^3$

20. $g(x) = \dfrac{1}{x} + 1; \; f(x) = x^{-2}$

21. $g(x) = \dfrac{x^2 + 1}{x^3 + 1}; \; f(x) = 1 + x^2$

22. $g(x) = x^{-1} + x^{-2} + x^{-3}; \; f(x) = x^5$

In 23–28, find $\dfrac{dy}{dx}$.

23. $y = \dfrac{1}{u^2}; \; u = 3x - 1$

24. $y = \dfrac{v + 1}{2 - v}; \; v = (1 - 2x)^3$

25. $y = u^{-2}; \; u = x^2 + 1$

26. $y = v^2 + 2; \; v = (6x - 5)^3$

27. $y = \dfrac{v + 1}{v^2 + 2}; \; v = u^2 - 1; \; u = 2x + 1$

28. $y = v - 1; \; v = u^3 + u; \; u = \dfrac{1}{t + 1}; \; t = 4x - 1$

In 29–32, differentiate the function by using negative exponents and the Product Rule.

29. $f(x) = \dfrac{x + 1}{x + 2}$

30. $g(x) = \dfrac{(2x - 2)^2}{3x + 1}$

31. $f(t) = \dfrac{\left(2 - \dfrac{2}{t}\right)^3}{\left(1 + \dfrac{1}{t}\right)^2}$

32. $f(x) = \dfrac{(t^2 + t)^4}{(t - t^2)^5}$

6 The Derivatives of Inverse Functions and Roots

We begin this section by recalling that if f is a $1-1$ function, then f has an inverse function, f^{-1}, such that $f^{-1} \circ f(x) = x$ for all x in the domain of f and $f \circ f^{-1}(x) = x$ for all x in the range of f. It is only natural to ask whether if f is a $1-1$ differentiable function, then must f^{-1} also be differentiable. The answer to this question is yes, provided f' is never 0. The proof of this theorem may be found in the Appendix.

Note. It is important to realize here that f^{-1} means the inverse of the function f, *not* $\dfrac{1}{f}$.

The next natural question we may ask is, "How do we calculate the derivative of f^{-1}, provided we are only given f?" The answer is surprisingly simple. First, let us take an intuitive approach. Suppose $y = f(x)$, where f is a $1-1$ differentiable function and f' is never 0 $\left(\text{that is, } \dfrac{dy}{dx} \text{ is never 0}\right)$. Then, y is changing $\dfrac{dy}{dx}$ times as fast as x. So, intuitively, x should be changing $\dfrac{1}{dy/dx}$ times as fast as y. Thus, we should have $\dfrac{dx}{dy} = \dfrac{1}{dy/dx}$.

Now, let us be more rigorous. Suppose f is a $1-1$ differentiable function and f' is never 0. We assume (and prove in the Appendix) that f^{-1} is differentiable. Observe that $f \circ f^{-1}(x) = x$, so that $(f \circ f^{-1})'(x) = 1$. The Chain Rule now tells us that $(f \circ f^{-1})'(x) = f'(f^{-1}(x))(f^{-1})'(x)$, which, therefore, must be 1. So,

$$(f^{-1})'(x) = \frac{1}{f'(f^{-1}(x))}$$

This is the formula for the derivative of an inverse function.

We may express this formula in terms of the "little d" notation as follows: Since $y = f(x)$, we have $x = f^{-1}(y)$. So, $\dfrac{dy}{dx} = f'(x)$ and

$\dfrac{dx}{dy} = (f^{-1})'(y)$. Since $f \circ f^{-1}(y) = y$, $(f \circ f^{-1})'(y) = 1$. By the Chain Rule,

$1 = (f \circ f^{-1})'(y) = f'(f^{-1}(y))\,(f^{-1})'(y) = \dfrac{dy}{dx} \cdot \dfrac{dx}{dy}$ (since $f^{-1}(y) = x$). Thus,

$\dfrac{dx}{dy} = \dfrac{1}{dy/dx}$, which is precisely what our intuition predicted earlier.

Note. One might be tempted to treat $\dfrac{dy}{dx}$ and $\dfrac{dx}{dy}$ as fractions to easily obtain $\dfrac{dx}{dy} = \dfrac{1}{dy/dx}$. However, as we observed earlier, $\dfrac{dy}{dx}$ and $\dfrac{dx}{dy}$ are *not* fractions and so it would be entirely inappropriate to treat them as such.

As an illustration of our work above, observe that for $x > 0$, $f(x) = x^2$ is a $1-1$ differentiable function. Since $f'(x) = 2x$ and $x > 0$, $f'(x)$ is never 0 and $f^{-1}(x) = x^{1/2} = \sqrt{x}$ for all $x > 0$. Thus, we have all the necessary conditions in order to differentiate $x^{1/2}$ as an inverse function.

We have $(f^{-1})'(x) = \dfrac{1}{f'(f^{-1}(x))}$. Here $f'(x) = 2x$. Thus, $(f^{-1})'(x) = \dfrac{1}{2f^{-1}(x)}$. Since $f^{-1}(x) = x^{1/2}$, we have $\dfrac{d}{dx} x^{1/2} = \dfrac{1}{2x^{1/2}} = \dfrac{1}{2} x^{-1/2}$.

Let us now generalize the previous illustration to nth roots for positive integers n. Let $f(x) = x^n$ and $f^{-1}(x) = \sqrt[n]{x} = x^{1/n}$. Notice that for n even f is $1-1$ for the set of values $x > 0$. If n is odd, f is $1-1$ for the set of all real values. Also, for n even and $x > 0$, $f'(x) = nx^{n-1} \neq 0$. For n odd and $x \neq 0$, $f'(x) = nx^{n-1} \neq 0$.

Now, for the above relevant values of x (depending upon whether n is odd or even), $(f^{-1})'(x) = \dfrac{1}{n(f^{-1}(x))^{n-1}}$. Thus, $\dfrac{d}{dx} x^{1/n} = \dfrac{1}{n(x^{1/n})^{n-1}} = \dfrac{1}{n} x^{1/n - 1}$.

Finally, we take the generalization one step further. Suppose m and n are integers with $n > 0$. Then

$$\frac{d}{dx} x^{m/n} = \frac{d}{dx} (x^{1/n})^m = m(x^{1/n})^{m-1} \cdot \frac{d}{dx} x^{1/n} \qquad \text{(by the Power Rule)}$$

$$= m(x^{1/n})^{m-1} \cdot \frac{1}{n} x^{1/n - 1} = \frac{m}{n} x^{m/n - 1}$$

We have just extended the Power Rule to rational exponents:

$\Rightarrow$ **Theorem (The Power Rule)** If $f(x) = x^{m/n}$, then $f'(x) = \dfrac{m}{n}x^{m/n-1}$.

In other words, $\dfrac{d}{dx}x^{m/n} = \dfrac{m}{n}x^{m/n-1}$.

Note. Whenever we have occasion to use the Power Rule, we will assume that the functions involved are all defined on domains which allow the Power Rule to be applied. For example, if we have $\dfrac{d}{dx}x^{1/2}$ or $\dfrac{d}{dx}x^{-3/4}$, we assume $x > 0$.

EXAMPLE Find $f'(x)$ if $f(x) = x^{2/7}$.

Solution $f'(x) = \dfrac{2}{7}x^{2/7-1} = \dfrac{2}{7}x^{-5/7}$.

EXAMPLE Find $\dfrac{d}{dx}3x^{-3/10}$.

Solution $\dfrac{d}{dx}3x^{-3/10} = 3\dfrac{d}{dx}x^{-3/10} = 3 \cdot \left(-\dfrac{3}{10}\right)x^{-3/10-1} = -\dfrac{9}{10}x^{-13/10}$

EXAMPLE Find a function f such that $f'(x) = 2x^3$.

Solution Since $\dfrac{d}{dx}x^4 = 4x^3$, we see that $\dfrac{d}{dx}\dfrac{x^4}{2} = \dfrac{4x^3}{2} = 2x^3$. Notice that if c is any constant, then $f(x) = \dfrac{x^4}{2} + c$ is also a solution, since $\dfrac{d}{dx}c = 0$.

Note. If a function g satisfies the equation $g'(x) = f(x)$, then g is called a **primitive** for f. Later on, we will devote a great deal of space to the study of finding primitives.

EXAMPLE Find a function f such that $\dfrac{d}{dx}f(x) = \dfrac{2}{3}x^{3/4} + x^2$.

That is, find a primitive for $\dfrac{2}{3}x^{3/4} + x^2$.

Solution Since $\dfrac{d}{dx}x^{7/4} = \dfrac{7}{4}x^{3/4}$, we see that $\dfrac{d}{dx}\dfrac{8}{21}x^{7/4} = \dfrac{d}{dx}\left(\dfrac{2}{3} \cdot \dfrac{4}{7}x^{7/4}\right) = \dfrac{2}{3}x^{3/4}$. Also, $\dfrac{d}{dx}x^3 = 3x^2$, so that $\dfrac{d}{dx}\dfrac{1}{3}x^3 = x^2$. Thus, let $f(x) = \dfrac{8}{21}x^{7/4} + \dfrac{1}{3}x^3$. If c is any constant, $f(x) = \dfrac{8}{21}x^{7/4} + \dfrac{1}{3}x^3 + c$ is also a solution

EXAMPLE   Find $\dfrac{d}{dx}(x^2 + 1)^{2/3}$.

Solution   By the Power Rule and the Chain Rule, $\dfrac{d}{dx}(x^2 + 1)^{2/3} =$

$\dfrac{2}{3}(x^2 + 1)^{-1/3} \dfrac{d}{dx}(x^2 + 1) = \dfrac{2}{3}(x^2 + 1)^{-1/3} \cdot 2x = \dfrac{4x}{3}(x^2 + 1)^{-1/3}.$

EXAMPLE   If $f(x) = (2x + 1)^{-1/4} \cdot (3x^2 + x)^{5/3}$, find $f'(x)$.

Solution   From the Product Rule, $f'(x) = (2x + 1)^{-1/4} \cdot \dfrac{d}{dx}(3x^2 + x)^{5/3}$

$+ (3x^2 + x)^{5/3} \cdot \dfrac{d}{dx}(2x + 1)^{-1/4}$. Thus, from the Power Rule and the

Chain Rule, $f'(x) = (2x + 1)^{-1/4} \cdot \dfrac{5}{3}(3x^2 + x)^{2/3} \cdot (6x + 1) + (3x^2 + x)^{5/3} \cdot$

$(-1/4)(2x + 1)^{-5/4} \cdot 2.$

EXAMPLE   If $h(x) = \dfrac{(2x^3 - x^2 + 1)^{5/4}}{\sqrt{x^2 + 3}}$, find $h'(x)$.

First Solution   Write $f(x) = (2x^3 - x^2 + 1)^{5/4} \cdot (x^2 + 3)^{-1/2}$. Then, by the Product Rule, the Chain Rule, and the Power Rule,

$$f'(x) = (2x^3 - x^2 + 1)^{5/4} \cdot \dfrac{d}{dx}(x^2 + 3)^{-1/2} + (x^2 + 3)^{-1/2} \cdot \dfrac{d}{dx}(2x^3 - x^2 + 1)^{5/4}$$

$$= (2x^3 - x^2 + 1)^{5/4}((-1/2)(x^2 + 3)^{-3/2}(2x))$$
$$+ (x^2 + 3)^{-1/2}((5/4)(2x^3 - x^2 + 1)^{1/4}(6x^2 - 2x))$$

Second Solution   If $f(x) = (2x^3 - x^2 + 1)^{5/4}$ and $g(x) = \sqrt{x^2 + 3}$, then the Quotient Rule tells us that $h'(x) = \dfrac{g(x)f'(x) - f(x)g'(x)}{(g(x))^2}$.
Now, by the Chain Rule and the Power Rule,

$$f'(x) = \dfrac{5}{4}(2x^3 - x^2 + 1)^{1/4} \cdot (6x^2 - 2x)$$

Also,

$$g'(x) = \dfrac{d}{dx}(x^2 + 3)^{1/2} = \dfrac{1}{2}(x^2 + 3)^{-1/2}\dfrac{d}{dx}(x^2 + 3) = \dfrac{1}{2}(x^2 + 3)^{-1/2}(2x)$$

Thus,

$$h'(x) = \left[(x^2 + 3)^{1/2} \cdot \frac{5}{4}(2x^3 - x^2 + 1)^{1/4} \cdot (6x^2 - 2x) \right.$$
$$\left. - (2x^3 - x^2 + 1)^{5/4} \cdot 1/2(x^2 + 3)^{-1/2}(2x) \right] \div [x^2 + 3]$$

Earlier in this chapter we saw that the slope of the tangent line to the graph of a function at a point is the derivative of the function at that point (provided the function is differentiable there). We are now in a position to find equations of tangent lines for a wide class of functions.

EXAMPLE Find an equation of the tangent line to the graph of $f(x) = (x^2 + 1)^{1/2}$ at $x = 0$.

Solution Since $f'(x) = (1/2)(x^2 + 1)^{-1/2}(2x)$, we see that $f'(0) = 0$. Thus, the tangent line in question has slope $m = 0$. Since this line clearly passes through $(0, f(0)) = (0,1)$, we may set $m = 0$, $x = 0$, and $y = 1$ in $y = mx + b$ to obtain $b = 1$. Thus, $y = 0 \cdot x + 1$, or $y = 1$, is an answer.

▷ **Definition** The **normal line** to the graph of a function at a given point on its graph is the line through that point perpendicular to the tangent line at that point (provided, of course, that there is a tangent line).

EXAMPLE Find an equation of the normal line to the graph of $f(x) = x\sqrt{x + 3}$ at $x = 1$.

Solution First find $f'(1)$ to find the slope of the tangent line at $x = 1$. We have $f'(x) = x\frac{1}{2}(x + 3)^{-1/2} + (x + 3)^{1/2}$. So, $f'(1) = 1 \cdot 1/2 \cdot 1/2 + 2 = 9/4$. Thus, the normal line must have slope $m = -4/9$ since the product of the slopes of perpendicular lines, each of which has a slope, is -1. Since $f(1) = 2$, we may set $m = -4/9$, $x = 1$, and $y = 2$ in $y = mx + b$ to obtain $b = 22/9$. Thus, $y = -\frac{4}{9}x + \frac{22}{9}$ is an answer.

E X E R C I S E S

In 1-20, find the derivative of the given function. (First convert radicals to rational powers.)

1. $f(x) = (x + 1)^{2/3}$

2. $g(x) = (2x^2 + 1)^{1/4}$

3. $f(x) = \left(\dfrac{2}{x}\right)^{5/3}$

4. $g(x) = (x^2 + x + 1)^{-3/2}$

5. $s(t) = \sqrt{t^2 + 1}$

6. $s(t) = t\sqrt{t^2 + 1}$

7. $s(t) = (t + 1)^{2/3}(t - 1)^{5/4}$

8. $f(x) = \sqrt{x + 1} + \sqrt[3]{x + 1}$

9. $h(x) = \dfrac{1}{\sqrt{x}} - \dfrac{1}{\sqrt{x + 1}}$

10. $g(x) = \sqrt{\dfrac{x + 2}{x - 2}}$

11. $f(x) = \dfrac{(x^2 - 1)^{1/2}}{x}$

12. $g(x) = \dfrac{(x^2 + 1)^{2/3}}{(x + 4)^{3/2}}$

13. $s(t) = \dfrac{\sqrt[4]{t^2 + 1}}{\sqrt[5]{t^2 + 2}}$

14. $h(x) = \sqrt{\sqrt{x} + 1}$

15. $f(x) = (\sqrt{x^2 + x} + \sqrt{x})^{-2/7}$

16. $f(x) = \dfrac{\sqrt{x} + 4}{\sqrt{x + 4}}$

17. $f(x) = \sqrt{\dfrac{\sqrt{x} + 4}{\sqrt{x + 4}}}$

18. $g(x) = (x + 1)^{1/2} \cdot (x + 2)^{2/3} \cdot (x + 3)^{3/4}$

19. $g(x) = \dfrac{(x^2 + 1)^{1/2}(x - 2)^{5/3}}{(x + 1)^{1/4}}$

20. $s(t) = \dfrac{1}{t} + \dfrac{1}{\sqrt{t}} + \dfrac{1}{\sqrt[3]{t}}$

21. If g is a nonzero differentiable function of x, then find a formula for $\dfrac{d}{dx}\sqrt{g(x)}$ in terms of $g(x)$ and $g'(x)$.

22. If g is a nonzero differentiable function of x, then find a formula for $\dfrac{d}{dx}(g(x))^{m/n}$ in terms of $g(x)$ and $g'(x)$.

In 23-36, find a function f whose derivative is the given function. That is, find a primitive, f, for the given function.

23. $f'(x) = x$

24. $f'(x) = x^2$

25. $f'(x) = x^2 + x$

26. $f'(x) = x^2 + x + 1$

27. $f'(x) = \sqrt{x}$

28. $f'(x) = x + \sqrt{x}$

29. $f'(x) = x^{3/2}$

30. $f'(x) = (x + 1)^{3/2}$

31. $f'(x) = (x + 1)^{-3/2}$

32. $f'(x) = (2x + 1)^{3/2}$

33. $f'(x) = \dfrac{1}{2}x^{4/5}$

34. $f'(x) = \dfrac{2}{3}x^{2/3} - x^{-1/2}$

35. $f'(x) = 2\sqrt{x} + 3\sqrt[3]{x}$

36. $f'(x) = \dfrac{\sqrt{3x}}{2} - \sqrt[3]{2x}$

37. Find an equation of the line tangent to the graph of the function $f(x) = x^{2/3} + x^2$ at the point (1,2).

38. Find an equation of the line tangent to the graph of the function $f(x) = 1/x - \sqrt{x}$ at $x = 4$.

39. Find an equation of the normal line to the graph of the function $f(x) = \sqrt{x + 4}$ at the point (0,2).

40. Find an equation of the normal line to the graph of the function $f(x) = (x + 1)x^{2/3}$ at $x = 1$.

41. Let $f(x) = (x + 1)(x + 2)^{2/3}$. What is the slope of the tangent line to the graph of f^{-1} at the point where $f^{-1}(x) = 6$?

42. Let $f(x) = \sqrt{x + 2} - \sqrt[3]{x + 1}$. What is the slope of the normal line to the graph of f^{-1} at the point where $f^{-1}(x) = 0$?

7 Higher-order Derivatives

It often happens that the derivative of a function may again be a differentiable function. Indeed, virtually all the functions with which we will deal in this book have the property that we can continue to differentiate them ad infinitum. Suppose $f(x) = x^2$. Then $f'(x) = 2x$. Clearly $f'(x) = 2x$ is a differentiable function of x and its derivative, written $f''(x)$, is 2. In general, the symbol $f^{(n)}(x)$ or $f'' \cdots '(x)$ (where there are n primes above the f) is called the **nth derivative of f at x** and it is obtained by successively differentiating the function f n times. It is important to understand that, while $f^{(n)}(x)$ is the nth derivative of f at x, $f^n(x)$ is the nth power of f at x.

There is also a corresponding "little d" notation. We write $\dfrac{d^2}{dx^2}f(x) = f''(x)$, $\dfrac{d^3}{dx^3}f(x) = f'''(x)$ and, in general, $\dfrac{d^n}{dx^n}f(x) = f^{(n)}(x)$.

We also use the corresponding symbols $\dfrac{d^2y}{dx^2}$, $\dfrac{d^3y}{dx^3}$ and, in general, $\dfrac{d^ny}{dx^n}$.

Finally, if $y = f(x)$, then we write $y'' = f''(x)$, $y''' = f'''(x)$, etc.

EXAMPLE If $f(x) = \sqrt{x}$, find $f''(x)$ and $f'''(x)$.

Solution Since $f(x) = x^{1/2}$, $f'(x) = \dfrac{1}{2}x^{-1/2}$. Thus, $f''(x) = \dfrac{d}{dx}\dfrac{1}{2}x^{-1/2} = -\dfrac{1}{4}x^{-3/2}$. Also, $f'''(x) = \dfrac{d}{dx}f''(x) = \dfrac{d}{dx}\left(-\dfrac{1}{4}x^{-3/2}\right) = \dfrac{3}{8}x^{-5/2}$.

EXAMPLE Find $\dfrac{d^2}{dx^2}\left(\dfrac{x^2+1}{x+1}\right)$.

Solution   By the Quotient Rule

$$\frac{d}{dx}\left(\frac{x^2+1}{x+1}\right)=\frac{(x+1)2x-(x^2+1)}{(x+1)^2}=\frac{x^2+2x-1}{(x+1)^2}$$

Thus,

$$\frac{d^2}{dx^2}\left(\frac{x^2+1}{x+1}\right)=\frac{d}{dx}\left(\frac{x^2+2x-1}{(x+1)^2}\right)$$

$$=\frac{(x+1)^2(2x+2)-(x^2+2x-1)2(x+1)}{(x+1)^4}$$

$$=\frac{2(x+1)^3-2(x+1)(x^2+2x-1)}{(x+1)^4}$$

$$=\frac{2(x+1)^2-2(x^2+2x-1)}{(x+1)^3}$$

$$=\frac{2x^2+4x+2-2x^2-4x+2}{(x+1)^3}=\frac{4}{(x+1)^3}$$

E X E R C I S E S

In 1–12, find (a) $f'(x)$; (b) $f''(x)$; and (c) $f'''(x)$.

1. $f(x)=x$

2. $f(x)=x^2$

3. $f(x)=x^3$

4. $f(x)=4x^3+x^2$

5. $f(x)=\dfrac{1}{x}$

6. $f(x)=x^3+\dfrac{1}{x^2}$

7. $f(x)=(x-3)^3$

8. $f(x)=(2x+3)^4$

9. $f(x)=\dfrac{x+1}{x+2}$

10. $f(x)=(2x+1)^{1/2}$

11. $f(x)=(x-1)^{-1/3}$

12. $f(x)=x\cdot(x+1)^{1/2}$

13. Find $\dfrac{d^2}{dx^2}\,x^{3/2}(x+1)^{1/3}$

14. If $y=\dfrac{(2x-1)^{1/2}}{(2x+1)^{1/3}}$, find $\dfrac{d^2y}{dx^2}$, i.e., find y''.

15. Find a function f such that $f''(x)=x$. [Hint: Find g such that $g'(x)=x$. Then find f such that $f'(x)=g(x)$.]

16. Find $f(x)$ such that $f''(x)=2x+1$.

17. If $f(x)=a_2x^2+a_1x+a_0$, then show $f'''(x)=0$.

18. If $f(x)=a_nx^n+a_{n-1}x^{n-1}+\cdots+a_1x+a_0$, then show $f^{(n+1)}(x)=0$.

19. If $f(x)=x^n$ for a positive integer n, then show $f^{(n)}(x)=n!$ (Recall that $n!=n(n-1)\cdot\ldots\cdot2\cdot1$ for every positive integer n.)

8 Implicit Differentiation and Differentials

It often happens that an equation involving the variables x and y will define y as a differentiable function of x. For example, $xy = 1$ defines the function $y = \dfrac{1}{x}$. In other cases, for example, $x^3 - xy + y^3 = 0$, it is not clear *which* function of x defines y. However, we will still be able to find $\dfrac{dy}{dx}$ as long as we know that y is *some* differentiable function of x. In general, in such situations, we will make the underlying assumption that y is a differentiable function of x. The differentiation of y as a function of x when we are given an equation in x and y is called **implicit differentiation**. Often, implicit differentiation can be regarded as an application of the Chain Rule.

EXAMPLE   Given that $y^2 x - x + y = 2$, find $\dfrac{dy}{dx}$.

Solution   Since y is a differentiable function of x, so is $y^2 x - x + y$. Therefore, we may differentiate both sides of the given equation with respect to x. We obtain

$$\frac{d}{dx}(y^2 x - x + y) = \frac{d}{dx}2 = 0$$

$$\frac{d}{dx}y^2 x - \frac{d}{dx}x + \frac{d}{dx}y = 0$$

Now,

$$\frac{d}{dx}y^2 x = 2y\frac{dy}{dx}x + y^2\frac{d}{dx}x = 2yx\frac{dy}{dx} + y^2$$

Also,

$$\frac{d}{dx}x = 1 \text{ and } \frac{d}{dx}y = \frac{dy}{dx}$$

Thus,

$$2yx\frac{dy}{dx} + y^2 - 1 + \frac{dy}{dx} = 0$$

So,

$$\frac{dy}{dx}(2yx + 1) = 1 - y^2 \text{ and } \frac{dy}{dx} = \frac{1 - y^2}{2yx + 1}$$

EXAMPLE If $\dfrac{x}{y} + y^3 = xy$, find y'.

Solution We have $\dfrac{d}{dx}\left(\dfrac{x}{y} + y^3 - xy\right) = 0$, so that

$$\frac{y\dfrac{d}{dx}x - x\dfrac{d}{dx}y}{y^2} + 3y^2\frac{dy}{dx} - \left(x\frac{dy}{dx} + y\frac{dx}{dx}\right) = 0$$

We then have

$$\frac{y - x\dfrac{dy}{dx}}{y^2} + 3y^2\frac{dy}{dx} - x\frac{dy}{dx} - y = 0$$

or

$$\frac{1}{y} - y + \left(-\frac{x}{y^2} + 3y^2 - x\right)\frac{dy}{dx} = 0$$

So,

$$y' = \frac{dy}{dx} = \frac{y - \dfrac{1}{y}}{\dfrac{-x}{y^2} + 3y^2 - x} = \frac{y^3 - y}{-x + 3y^4 - xy^2}$$

As the next example shows, we can use the method of implicit differentiation to find higher order derivatives. Also, in the solution, we will use the y' notation instead of the $\dfrac{dy}{dx}$ notation.

EXAMPLE If $xy + x^2 = y^3$, find y''.

Solution We begin by finding y'. Differentiate both sides of the given equation with respect to x to obtain $xy' + y + 2x = 3y^2 y'$. Thus,

$$(x - 3y^2)y' = -y - 2x$$

So,

$$y' = \frac{-y - 2x}{(x - 3y^2)} = (-y - 2x)(x - 3y^2)^{-1}$$

Now, differentiate again with respect to x to obtain $y'' = (-y - 2x) \cdot (-(x - 3y^2)^{-2})(1 - 6yy') + (-y' - 2)(x - 3y^2)^{-1}$.

Finally, substitute $y' = (-y - 2x)(x - 3y^2)^{-1}$ in the last equation to obtain

$$y'' = (-y - 2x)(-(x - 3y^2)^{-2})(1 - 6y(-y - 2x)(x - 3y^2)^{-1})$$
$$+ (y + 2x)(x - 3y^2)^{-2} - 2(x - 3y^2)^{-1}$$

We now introduce a concept which we will later use in Chapter 7. If $y = f(x)$ is a differentiable function of x, then the **differential of y,** written dy, is defined by

$$dy = f'(x)dx$$

At least formally, this notation seems reasonable since it conforms with the equation $\dfrac{dy}{dx} = f'(x)$.

EXAMPLE   Find dy, the differential of y, if (a) $y = \sqrt{x} + x^3$ and (b) $y = \dfrac{x + 2}{\sqrt{x + 1}}$.

Solution   (a) $dy = f'(x)dx$, so that $dy = \left(\dfrac{1}{2\sqrt{x}} + 3x^2\right)dx$.

(b) $dy = \left(\dfrac{\sqrt{x + 1} - (x + 2)\dfrac{1}{2}(x + 1)^{-1/2}}{x + 1}\right)dx$

$= \left(\dfrac{x + 1 - \dfrac{x + 2}{2}}{(x + 1)^{3/2}}\right)dx = \left(\dfrac{x}{2(x + 1)^{3/2}}\right)dx$

E X E R C I S E S

In 1–10, find $\dfrac{dy}{dx}$, i.e., find y'.

1. $x^2 + y^2 = 1$
2. $(x - 1)^2 + (y + 2)^2 = 4$
3. $2x^2 + 3y^2 = 1$
4. $3x^2 - 4y^2 = 2$
5. $\sqrt{x} - \sqrt{y} = 2$
6. $x\sqrt{y} + y\sqrt{x} = 4$

7. $x^2y + y^2x = x + 1$
8. $2x^2 + 3xy + 5y^2 = 2y$
9. $\dfrac{y}{x} + \dfrac{x}{y} = x^2$
10. $\dfrac{x}{y} + \dfrac{x^2}{y^2} = x$

In 11–16, find $\dfrac{d^2y}{dx^2}$, i.e., find y''.

11. $x^2 + y^2 = 1$ **14.** $2y^2 + 5x^2 = 1$

12. $\sqrt{x} + \sqrt{y} = 4$ **15.** $x^2 - y^2 = 3$

13. $2y^2 - 3xy = 10$ **16.** $4x^2 - 2y^2 = 1$

In 17 – 21, find the differential dy.

17. $y = x^2$ **20.** $y = (x + 1)(x + 2)^{1/2}$

18. $y = -x^{-1/2} + x$ **21.** $y = (x - 1)^{2/3}(x + 3)^{1/2}$

19. $y = \dfrac{x + 1}{x - 1}$

Chapter 4
Applications of the Derivative

1 Monotonicity, Maxima, and Minima

In this section we will be primarily concerned with the following problems:

(1) Given a function f, find intervals on which the graph of f is always rising (increasing) as we move from left to right and find intervals on which the graph of f is always falling (decreasing) as we move from left to right.

(2) Given a function f, find points x_0 where the value of f is largest for all points near x_0 (local maximum) and find points x_0 where the value of f is smallest for all points near x_0 (local minimum).

The above questions will be made precise in this section and we will then give methods which enable us to answer them for many functions f. However, before we can proceed to do this, we need to focus our attention on an extremely important theorem of the calculus called the Mean Value Theorem.

> **Mean Value Theorem (MVT)**   Suppose that f is a real-valued function which is defined and continuous on some closed interval $[a,b]$ and that f is differentiable at each point of the open interval $]a,b[$. Then there is at least one number c with $a < c < b$ such that
> $$f'(c) = \frac{f(b) - f(a)}{b - a}$$

Although a rigorous proof of MVT will be given in the Appendix, it will be helpful for us to look at a few graphs in order to get a good intuitive idea of what MVT is saying geometrically.

In Fig. 4-1, we see the graph of a differentiable function f. If we focus our attention on the two points $(a, f(a))$ and $(b, f(b))$ on the graph, then the number $\dfrac{f(b) - f(a)}{b - a}$ represents the slope of the line joining the two points. At the point $(c, f(c))$, the tangent to the graph appears to be parallel to the line joining $(a, f(a))$ and $(b, f(b))$. Since the slope of this tangent is $f'(c)$, it appears that c satisfies the conclusion of MVT for the function f and the interval $[a, b]$, since $a < c < b$ and $f'(c) = \dfrac{f(b) - f(a)}{b - a}$. In Fig. 4-2, we see another illustration of MVT.

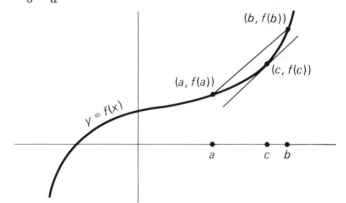

Figure 4–1

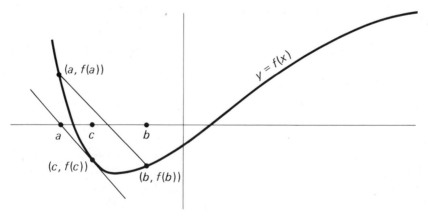

Figure 4–2

EXAMPLE   Verify that MVT holds for the function $f(x) = x^3 + 4x^2 + 4x + 1$ and the interval $[-3,1]$. That is, given the function $f(x) = x^3 + 4x^2 + 4x + 1$ and the values $a = -3$ and $b = 1$, find a number c in $]a,b[$ such that $f'(c) = \dfrac{f(b) - f(a)}{b - a}$.

Solution   Clearly f is continuous on $[-3,1]$ and differentiable on $]-3,1[$. Also, by direct computation

$$\frac{f(b) - f(a)}{b - a} = \frac{1 + 4 + 4 + 1 - (-27 + 36 - 12 + 1)}{1 - (-3)} = \frac{12}{4} = 3$$

and $f'(x) = 3x^2 + 8x + 4$. So, $f'(c) = 3c^2 + 8c + 4$. Setting $f'(c) = \dfrac{f(b) - f(a)}{b - a}$ gives $3c^2 + 8c + 4 = 3$ so that $3c^2 + 8c + 1 = 0$. The quadratic formula now tells us that

$$c = \frac{-8 \pm \sqrt{64 - 12}}{6} = \frac{-4 \pm \sqrt{13}}{3}$$

Since c is to be in the interval $]-3,1[$, we see that both solutions are acceptable. Thus, $c = \dfrac{-4 \pm \sqrt{13}}{3}$.

In Chapter 3 (page 125) we saw that if f is constant on an interval I, then $f'(x) = 0$ for all $x \in I$. MVT allows us to prove the converse of this result:

▷ **Theorem**   If $f'(x) = 0$ for all x in an interval I, then f is constant on I.

Proof   It will certainly be sufficient to show that for any $x_1 < x_2 \in I$, we have $f(x_1) = f(x_2)$. Now, by MVT, there is some $c \in]x_1,x_2[$ such that $f'(c) = \dfrac{f(x_2) - f(x_1)}{x_2 - x_1}$. But, since $f'(c) = 0$, we see that $f(x_1) = f(x_2)$, which completes the proof. ■

We now need the following important definitions.

▷ **Definition**   Suppose f is a function defined on an interval I.
   (1) If $f(x_1) < f(x_2)$ whenever $x_1 < x_2$ are in I, then f is said to be **increasing** on I.
   (2) If $f(x_1) > f(x_2)$ whenever $x_1 < x_2$ are in I, then f is said to be **decreasing** on I.
   (3) If $f(x_1) \leq f(x_2)$ whenever $x_1 < x_2$ are in I, then f is said to be **nondecreasing** on I.

(4) If $f(x_1) \geq f(x_2)$ whenever $x_1 < x_2$ are in I, then f is said to be **nonincreasing** on I.

(5) If f is either nondecreasing or nonincreasing on I, then f is said to be **monotonic** on I.

A function which is constant on an interval is both nonincreasing and nondecreasing on that interval.

The function whose graph is shown in Fig. 4-3 is increasing on each of the intervals $[x_2,x_3]$, $[x_4,x_5]$, and $[x_6,x_7]$. The function is decreasing on each of the intervals $[x_1,x_2]$, $[x_3,x_4]$, and $[x_5,x_6]$.

The following theorem gives a key relationship between the sign of the first derivative and the increasing or decreasing behavior of a differentiable function.

▷ **Theorem** Suppose f is a function which is differentiable on an interval I.

(1) If $f'(x) > 0$ for all x in I, then f is increasing on I.
(2) If $f'(x) < 0$ for all x in I, then f is decreasing on I.
(3) If $f'(x) \geq 0$ for all x in I, then f is nondecreasing on I.
(4) If $f'(x) \leq 0$ for all x in I, then f is nonincreasing on I.

Proof (1) Suppose $f'(x) > 0$ for all x in I. If $x_1 < x_2$ are any two points in I, we must show $f(x_1) < f(x_2)$. By the MVT there is some $c \in]x_1,x_2[$ such that

$$f'(c) = \frac{f(x_2) - f(x_1)}{x_2 - x_1}$$

Since $x_2 - x_1$ is positive and $f'(c)$ is positive by hypothesis, it follows that $f(x_2) - f(x_1)$ is positive, i.e., $f(x_1) < f(x_2)$ and the proof of (1) is complete.

(2) If $f'(x) < 0$ for all $x \in I$, then $(-f)'(x) > 0$ for all $x \in I$. Apply

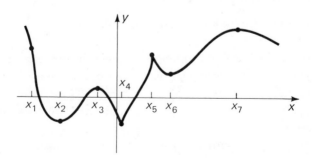

Figure 4–3

part (1) to the function $-f$ to see that $-f$ is increasing on I. Thus, f is decreasing on I.

The proofs of (3) and (4) are left to the reader. They readily follow from the proofs of (1) and (2). ∎

EXAMPLE Determine the interval(s) on which the function $f(x) = x^3 + 2x^2 - 1$ is increasing. Also determine the interval(s) on which it is decreasing.

Solution Since $f'(x) = 3x^2 + 4x$, we want to determine the interval(s) on which $3x^2 + 4x > 0$ and also those on which $3x^2 + 4x < 0$.

Setting $3x^2 + 4x > 0$ gives $x(3x + 4) > 0$. Thus, since the product of two factors is positive if and only if both factors are positive or both factors are negative, we have

or

$x > 0$ and $3x + 4 > 0$	$x < 0$ and $3x + 4 < 0$
$x > 0$ and $x > -4/3$	$x < 0$ and $x < -4/3$
$x > 0$	$x < -4/3$

Thus, f is increasing ($f' > 0$) on $]0,\infty[$ and on $]-\infty, -4/3[$. However, since f is continuous at 0 and $-4/3$, we can actually say that f is increasing on $[0,\infty[$ and on $]-\infty,-4/3]$.

Setting $3x^2 + 4x < 0$ gives $x(3x + 4) < 0$. Thus, since the product of two factors is negative if and only if one factor is positive and the other factor is negative, we have

or

$x > 0$ and $3x + 4 < 0$	$x < 0$ and $3x + 4 > 0$
$x > 0$ and $x < -4/3$	$x < 0$ and $x > -4/3$
impossible	$-4/3 < x < 0$

Thus, f is decreasing ($f' < 0$) on $]-4/3,0[$. Again, since f is continuous at $-4/3$ and 0, we can say that f is decreasing on $[-4/3,0]$.

EXAMPLE Determine the intervals where $f(x) = x + \dfrac{1}{x}$ is increasing and also the intervals where it is decreasing.

Solution $f'(x) = 1 - \dfrac{1}{x^2} = \dfrac{x^2 - 1}{x^2}$. Setting $f'(x) > 0$ gives $\dfrac{x^2 - 1}{x^2} > 0$.

Since $x^2 > 0$ for all $x \neq 0$, we see that $x^2 - 1 > 0$ for all x for which $|x| > 1$. Thus, $x > 1$ or $x < -1$. We conclude that f is increasing on $]1,\infty[$ and $]-\infty,-1[$. Since f is continuous at 1 and -1, we can say further that f is increasing on $[1,\infty[$ and $]-\infty,-1]$.

Setting $f'(x) < 0$ gives us $x^2 - 1 < 0$. Thus, $x^2 < 1$ and so $-1 < x < 1$. However, we must be careful to observe that f *is not defined at 0*. Thus, f is decreasing on $]-1,0[$ and $]0,1[$. Again, since f is continuous at -1 and 1 (but not at 0), we may say that f is decreasing on $[-1,0[$ and $]0,1]$.

A little later on we will again be concerned with the determination of intervals where a function is either increasing or decreasing. Before we proceed we will need the following definition.

▷ **Definition** (1) A function f is said to have a **local** (or **relative**) **maximum at the point** x_0 if there is some open interval I on which f is defined and with $x_0 \in I$ such that $f(x_0) \geq f(x)$ for all $x \in I$. The value $f(x_0)$ is called the **local** (or **relative**) **maximum.**

(2) A function f is said to have a **local** (or **relative**) **minimum at the point** x_0 if there is some open interval I on which f is defined and with $x_0 \in I$ such that $f(x_0) \leq f(x)$ for all $x \in I$. The value $f(x_0)$ is called the **local** (or **relative**) **minimum.**

(3) If f has either a local maximum or local minimum at x_0, we say f has a **local** (or **relative**) **extremum at** x_0. The value $f(x_0)$ is called a **local** (or **relative**) **extremum.**

In Fig. 4-3, the function whose graph is shown has local maxima at x_3, x_5, and x_7. There are local minima at x_2, x_4, and x_6. If we look at each of the values x_2, x_3, x_4, x_5, x_6, and x_7, we observe that for each of them either $f'(x) = 0$ (the tangent to the curve is horizontal) or f is not differentiable there. This leads to the next theorem.

▷ **Theorem** Suppose f has a local extremum at x_0. If f is differentiable at x_0, then $f'(x_0) = 0$. (That is, either $f'(x_0) = 0$ or f is not differentiable at x_0.)

Proof Suppose f has a local maximum at x_0 and that $f(x_0) \geq f(x)$ for all x in the open interval I and $x_0 \in I$. If $f'(x_0)$ exists and is finite, then, by the definition of the derivative, $f'(x_0) = \lim\limits_{x \to x_0} \dfrac{f(x) - f(x_0)}{x - x_0}$. Now, as $x \to x_0$, x must eventually be in the interval I and so for x close to x_0, $f(x) \leq f(x_0)$. As x in I approaches x_0 from the left ($x < x_0$), we see that each of the values $\dfrac{f(x) - f(x_0)}{x - x_0}$ must be nonnegative. On the other hand, as x in I approaches x_0 from the right ($x > x_0$), we see that each of the values $\dfrac{f(x) - f(x_0)}{x - x_0}$ must be nonpositive. In order for the limit

$\lim\limits_{x \to x_0} \dfrac{f(x) - f(x_0)}{x - x_0}$ to exist, it must be that the limit is 0. Thus, $f'(x_0) = 0$.

We will leave it to the reader to complete the proof for the case when f has a local minimum at x_0. ∎

Note. It is important to realize that it is possible to have a function f which is differentiable at a point x_0 with $f'(x_0) = 0$ and yet f does not have a local extremum at x_0. For example, if $f(x) = x^3$ and $x_0 = 0$, then $f'(x) = 3x^2$ and so $f'(0) = 0$. Yet, there is no local extremum at 0 because $f(x) < 0$ if $x < 0$ and $f(x) > 0$ if $x > 0$ (see page 159). In fact, this f is increasing on $]-\infty,\infty[$. In light of the previous theorem, it is reasonable to make the following definition:

▷ **Definition**   If f is defined at x_0 and either $f'(x_0) = 0$ or f is not differentiable at x_0, then x_0 is called a **critical point** of f.

It follows that the critical points of a function f are the only points at which f can possibly have a local extremum. However, f need not have a local extremum at these points.

Note. The function $f(x) = \dfrac{1}{x}$ has derivative $f'(x) = \dfrac{-1}{x^2}$. This derivative is never 0. Also, f is not differentiable at $x = 0$. However, $x = 0$ is *not* a critical point of f because f is not defined at $x = 0$. Remember that a function must be defined at all its critical points. The function $f(x) = \dfrac{1}{x}$ has no critical points. A similar situation exists for the function $f(x) = \dfrac{1}{(x - 2)^4}$.

EXAMPLE   Find the critical points of the following functions:

(a) $f(x) = \dfrac{x^3}{3} - \dfrac{5}{2}x^2 + 6x - 11$

(b) $f(x) = 2x^{1/3} - 3x^2$

(c) $f(x) = |x + 3|$

Solution   (a) Here, $f'(x) = x^2 - 5x + 6$. Clearly, $f'(x)$ exists for all real numbers x. Setting $f'(x) = 0$ gives $(x - 2)(x - 3) = 0$. Thus, $x = 2$ and $x = 3$ are the critical points of f.

(b) Here, $f'(x) = \frac{2}{3}x^{-2/3} - 6x = \frac{2 - 18x^{5/3}}{3x^{2/3}}$. Since f is not differen-

tiable at $x = 0$, we have $x = 0$ as a critical point of f. Also, $f'(x) = 0$

when $18x^{5/3} = 2$. Thus, $x = \left(\frac{1}{9}\right)^{3/5}$ is also a critical point of f.

(c) Here,

$$f(x) = \begin{cases} x + 3 & \text{if } x \geq -3 \\ -(x+3) & \text{if } x < -3 \end{cases}$$

Thus,

$$f'(x) = \begin{cases} 1 & \text{if } x > -3 \\ -1 & \text{if } x < -3 \end{cases}$$

Also, f is not differentiable at $x = -3$. Since f' is never 0, $x = -3$ is the only critical point of f.

EXAMPLE Use the calculus to find the equation of the axis of symmetry of the parabola whose equation is $y = ax^2 + bx + c$, $a \neq 0$.

Solution We know that the axis of symmetry of the parabola, given by an equation $x = x_0$, passes through the vertex (x_0, y_0). At this vertex, we have a local extremum. Thus, since $f(x) = ax^2 + bx + c$ has a derivative for all x, it must be that $f'(x_0) = 0$. Now, $f'(x_0) = 2ax_0 + b$. Setting $2ax_0 + b = 0$ gives $x_0 = \frac{-b}{2a}$. Thus, $x = \frac{-b}{2a}$ is the equation of the axis of symmetry of the parabola whose equation is $y = ax^2 + bx + c$, $a \neq 0$.

We now return to the determination of intervals where certain functions are either increasing or decreasing. It will be proved in the Appendix that if a function g is continuous on an interval and a and b are any two points in the interval, then on that interval, g takes every value between $g(a)$ and $g(b)$. This is the **Intermediate Value Theorem** (IVT), which we first saw in Chapter 2. It follows that a function which is continuous on an interval and never 0 on that interval must be either positive on the entire interval or negative on the entire interval.

Now suppose that a function f has a *continuous* nonzero finite derivative f' on an interval. Then f' must be either positive on the entire interval or negative on the entire interval. It follows that f must be either increasing or decreasing on the interval. Given a function f, we attempt to find such intervals. On such an interval, one way to determine the sign of f' is to evaluate f' at any convenient point in the interval. Since the critical points of f are the points where f' is 0, f' is infinite, or f' does not exist (that is, f' is 0 or f is not differentiable), it is important to find them first. We must also be careful to find the points where f itself is not defined (see part (d) of the next example).

EXAMPLE Determine the intervals upon which the given function is increasing and those upon which it is decreasing.

(a) $f(x) = x^3$

(b) $f(x) = x + \dfrac{1}{\sqrt{x}}$

(c) $f(x) = x^4 - 2x^2$

(d) $f(x) = \dfrac{1}{x^2}$

Solution (a) Since $f'(x) = 3x^2$, 0 is the only critical point of f. Also, f is defined everywhere. Since $f'(x) > 0$ for $x < 0$ and also $f'(x) > 0$ for $x > 0$, we see that f is increasing on $]-\infty,0[$ and $]0,\infty[$ and hence on $]-\infty,0]$ and $[0,\infty[$. It follows that f is increasing on $]-\infty,\infty[$. That is, f is increasing everywhere. See Fig. 4-4(a) for a graph of f.

(b) First of all, observe that f is defined only for $x > 0$. Also, $f'(x) = 1 - \dfrac{1}{2}x^{-3/2}$ for $x > 0$. Setting $f'(x) = 0$ gives $\dfrac{1}{2}x^{-3/2} = 1$ and so $x^{-3/2} = 2$ and $x = 2^{-2/3}$ (which is approximately .63).

For $0 < x < 2^{-2/3}$, $f'(x) < 0$. To see this, we may substitute any convenient value for x in the range $0 < x < 2^{-2/3}$, for example $x = 1/100$. Then $f'(1/100) = 1 - \dfrac{1}{2}(1/100)^{-3/2} = 1 - \dfrac{1}{2} \cdot 1000 = -499$. Thus, f is decreasing on $]0,2^{-2/3}]$.

For $x > 2^{-2/3}$, $f'(x) > 0$. For example, $f'(1) = 1 - \dfrac{1}{2} \cdot 1 = \dfrac{1}{2}$. Thus, f is increasing on $[2^{-2/3},\infty[$. See Fig. 4-4(b) for a graph of f.

(c) Here f is defined everywhere and $f'(x) = 4x^3 - 4x$ for all x. Set $f'(x) = 0$ to obtain the critical points of f:

$$4x^3 - 4x = 0$$
$$4x(x^2 - 1) = 0$$
$$4x(x - 1)(x + 1) = 0$$
$$x = 0,1,-1$$

For $x < -1$, $f'(x) < 0$. For example, $f'(-2) = -32 + 8 = -24$. Thus, f is decreasing on $]-\infty,-1]$.

For $-1 < x < 0$, $f'(x) > 0$. For example, $f'\left(-\dfrac{1}{2}\right) = -\dfrac{1}{2} + 2 = \dfrac{3}{2}$. Thus, f is increasing on $[-1,0]$.

For $0 < x < 1$, $f'(x) < 0$. For example, $f'\left(\frac{1}{2}\right) = \frac{1}{2} - 2 = -\frac{3}{2}$. Thus, f is decreasing on $[0,1]$.

For $x > 1$, $f'(x) > 0$. For example, $f(2) = 32 - 8 = 24$. Thus, f is increasing on $[1,\infty[$. See Fig. 4-4(c) for a graph of f.

(d) The function f is not defined at $x = 0$. Also, $f'(x) = \frac{-2}{x^3}$. Thus, f has no critical points (0 is not a critical point because f is not defined there). For $x < 0$, $f'(x) > 0$ and for $x > 0$, $f'(x) < 0$. Thus, f is increasing on $]-\infty,0[$ and decreasing on $]0,\infty[$. Notice that we cannot extend either of these intervals to include 0 because f is not defined at 0. See Fig. 4-4(d) for a graph of f.

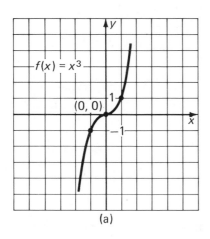

(a)

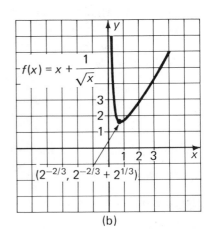

(b)

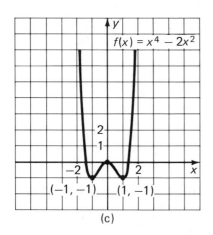

(c)

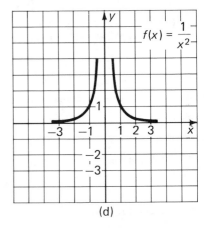

(d)

Figure 4-4

As we have seen, the critical points of a function are the points at which the function may have a local extremum. If we do have a local extremum, we would like to determine whether we have a local maximum or a local minimum. To this end we have the **First Derivative Test**.

> **First Derivative Test (FDT)**   Let x_0 be a critical point of the function f and suppose f is continuous at x_0.

(1) If there is some open interval $]a,b[$ containing x_0 such that $f'(x) < 0$ for $a < x < x_0$ and $f'(x) > 0$ for $x_0 < x < b$, then f has a local maximum at x_0 (see Fig. 4-5).

(2) If there is some open interval $]a,b[$ containing x_0 such that $f'(x) < 0$ for $a < x < x_0$ and $f'(x) > 0$ for $x_0 < x < b$, then f has a local minimum at x_0 (see Fig. 4-6).

(3) If there is some open interval $]a,b[$ containing x_0 such that $f'(x)$ has the same sign in each of the intervals $]a,x_0[$ and $]x_0,b[$, then f has neither a local maximum nor a local minimum at x_0 (see Fig. 4-7).

Proof   We will prove part (1) and leave it to the reader to supply proofs for parts (2) and (3). Since $f'(x) > 0$ for all $x \in]a,x_0[$, we see by the theorem on page 154, that f is increasing on $]a,x_0[$. Since f is continuous at x_0, it follows that $f(x_0) > f(x)$ for all $x \in]a,x_0[$. Also, since $f'(x) < 0$ for all $x \in]x_0,b[$, we see that f is decreasing on $]x_0,b[$. We conclude, then, from the continuity of f at x_0, that $f(x_0) > f(x)$ for all $x \in]x_0,b[$. Thus, f has a local maximum at x_0. ∎

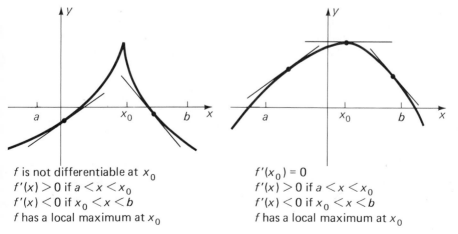

f is not differentiable at x_0
$f'(x) > 0$ if $a < x < x_0$
$f'(x) < 0$ if $x_0 < x < b$
f has a local maximum at x_0

$f'(x_0) = 0$
$f'(x) > 0$ if $a < x < x_0$
$f'(x) < 0$ if $x_0 < x < b$
f has a local maximum at x_0

Figure 4–5

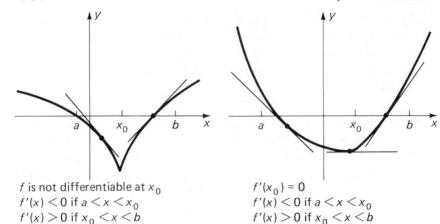

f is not differentiable at x_0
$f'(x) < 0$ if $a < x < x_0$
$f'(x) > 0$ if $x_0 < x < b$
f has a local minimum at x_0

$f'(x_0) = 0$
$f'(x) < 0$ if $a < x < x_0$
$f'(x) > 0$ if $x_0 < x < b$
f has a local minimum at x_0

Figure 4-6

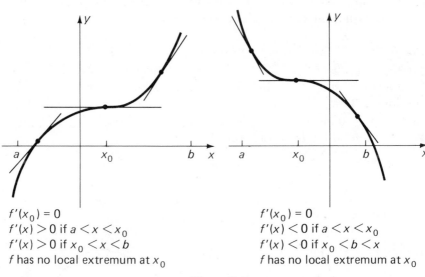

$f'(x_0) = 0$
$f'(x) > 0$ if $a < x < x_0$
$f'(x) > 0$ if $x_0 < x < b$
f has no local extremum at x_0

$f'(x_0) = 0$
$f'(x) < 0$ if $a < x < x_0$
$f'(x) < 0$ if $x_0 < b < x$
f has no local extremum at x_0

Figure 4-7

EXAMPLE   Find the critical point(s) of the function $f(x) = x^2 - 2x + 1$ and decide whether there is a local maximum, a local minimum, or neither at each critical point.

Solution   Since f is a polynomial function, it is differentiable everywhere. The only critical points occur where f' is 0. Since $f'(x) = 2x - 2$, we see that $f'(x) = 0$ if and only if $x = 1$. For $x < 1, f'(x) < 0$ and for $x > 1, f'(x) > 0$. Thus, by part(2) of FDT, f has a local minimum at $x = 1$. See Fig. 4-8 for a graph of f.

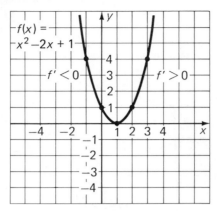

Figure 4–8

EXAMPLE Find the critical point(s) of the function $f(x) = 2x^3 - 3x^2 - 12x$ and decide whether there is a local maximum, a local minimum, or neither at each critical point.

Solution Since f is a polynomial function, it is differentiable everywhere. The only critical points occur where f' is 0. We find that $f'(x) = 6x^2 - 6x - 12$. Setting $6x^2 - 6x - 12 = 0$ gives $x^2 - x - 2 = 0$, or $x = 2$, $x = -1$. Thus, the critical points are $x = 2$ and $x = -1$.

   Now, for $x < -1$, $f'(x) = 6(x - 2)(x + 1) > 0$, and for $-1 < x < 2$, $f'(x) < 0$. Thus, f has a local maximum at $x = -1$ by part (1) of FDT. Also, for $x > 2$, $f'(x) > 0$ so that f has a local minimum at $x = 2$ by part (2) of FDT. See Fig. 4-9 for a graph of f.

EXAMPLE Find the critical point(s) of the function $f(x) = x^3$ and decide whether there is a local maximum, local minimum, or neither at each critical point.

Solution The function f, being a polynomial function, is differentiable everywhere. Thus, the critical points of f occur where $f' = 0$. Setting $f'(x) = 0$ gives $3x^2 = 0$. Thus, $x = 0$ is the only critical point. Now, for $x < 0$, $f'(x) > 0$, and also for $x > 0$, $f'(x) > 0$; thus, by part (3) of FDT, f has no local extremum at $x = 0$. See Fig. 4-10 for a graph of f.

EXAMPLE Find the critical point(s) of the function $h(x) = |x|$ and decide whether there is a local maximum, a local minimum, or neither at each critical point.

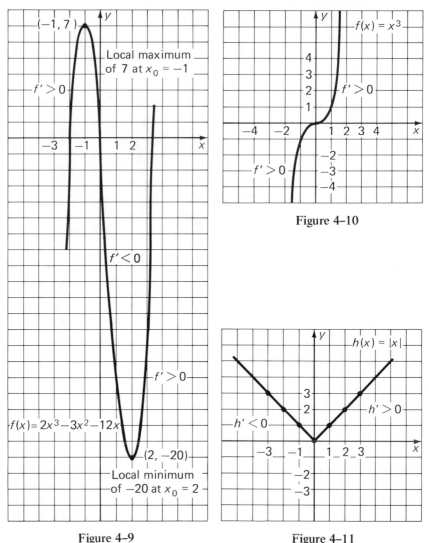

Figure 4-10

Figure 4-9

Figure 4-11

Solution We have seen that since

$$|x| = \begin{cases} x & \text{if } x \geq 0 \\ -x & \text{if } x < 0 \end{cases}$$

x is differentiable except at $x = 0$. Thus, $x = 0$ is a critical point. Also, for $x < 0$, $h'(x) = -1$, and for $x > 0$, $h'(x) = 1$. Thus, $h'(x)$ is never 0, and so 0 is the only critical point of h. Finally, by part (2) of FDT, h has a local minimum at $x = 0$. See Fig. 4-11 for a graph of h.

There is another test which, under suitable conditions, enables us to determine local extrema of a function. This test, called the **Second Derivative Test (SDT)**, involves only the sign of the second derivative at a point. Specifically, we have the following:

▷ **Second Derivative Test (SDT)**   Let f' be differentiable at x_0 and suppose $f'(x_0) = 0$.
   (1) If $f''(x_0) > 0$, then f has a local minimum at x_0.
   (2) If $f''(x_0) < 0$, then f has a local maximum at x_0.

Note. If $f''(x_0) = 0$ or if f' is not differentiable at x_0, then the test does not apply. Also, since any polynomial function is differentiable everywhere and its derivative is itself a polynomial, SDT certainly applies to all polynomials whenever the first derivative at a point is 0.

Proof   (1) We have that $f''(x_0) > 0$. Thus, $\lim\limits_{x \to x_0} \dfrac{f'(x) - f'(x_0)}{x - x_0} > 0$. Thus there is some interval $]a,b[$ containing x_0 such that

$$\frac{f'(x) - f'(x_0)}{x - x_0} > 0$$

for all $x \in \,]a,b[$, $x \neq x_0$. Thus, $f'(x) - f'(x_0)$ and $x - x_0$ have the same sign for all $x \in \,]a,b[$, $x \neq x_0$. Now, if $a < x < x_0$, then $x - x_0 < 0$ so that $f'(x) - f'(x_0) < 0$. Thus, $f'(x) < f'(x_0) = 0$. Similarly, if $x_0 < x < b$, then $f'(x) > f'(x_0) = 0$. By part (2) of **FDT**, we see that f has a local minimum at x_0.

(2) This part may be proven in a similar fashion, using part (1) of FDT. Also, this part may be proven by applying part (1) of SDT to the function $-f$. ■

EXAMPLE   Use SDT to find the local extrema of the function $f(x) = 2x^2 - x + 3$.

Solution   Since f is a polynomial function, it is differentiable everywhere. Its only critical points occur where $f'(x) = 0$. Setting $f'(x) = 0$ gives $4x - 1 = 0$, or $x = 1/4$. Since $f''(x) = 4$, we see that $f''(1/4) = 4 > 0$, so that by part (1) of SDT, there is a local minimum at $x = 1/4$.

EXAMPLE   Use SDT to find the local extrema of the function $f(x) = 2x^3 - 3x^2 - 12x$ (see the first example on page 163).

Solution   Since $f'(x) = 6x^2 - 6x - 12$, setting $f'(x) = 0$ gives $6x^2 - 6x - 12 = 0$, or $x^2 - x - 2 = 0$. Thus, $x = 2$ and $x = -1$ are the only critical points of the polynomial function f. Now, $f''(x) = 12x - 6$, so that $f''(2) = 18$ and $f''(-1) = -18$. By part (1) of SDT, f has a local minimum at 2. By part (2) of SDT, f has a local maximum at -1.

It often happens that on an interval (finite or infinite) a particular function has more than one local maximum or more than one local minimum (see Fig. 4-3). However, as the following definition shows, a given function has at most one **absolute maximum** and at most one **absolute minimum** on a given interval.

▷ **Definition** Let f be a function defined on an interval I.

(1) If $x_0 \in I$ and $f(x_0) \geq f(x)$ for all $x \in I$, then f is said to have an **absolute maximum** (or **maximum**) on I at the point x_0. The value $f(x_0)$ is called the **absolute maximum** (or **maximum**) of f on I.

(2) If $x_0 \in I$ and $f(x_0) \leq f(x)$ for all $x \in I$, then f is said to have an **absolute minimum** (or **minimum**) on I at the point x_0. The value $f(x_0)$ is called the **absolute minimum** (or **minimum**) of f on I.

(3) If $f(x_0)$ is either an absolute maximum or an absolute minimum of f on I, then $f(x_0)$ is called an **absolute extremum** (or **extremum**) of f on I.

Note. It is possible for a function to have an absolute extremum on an interval at more than one point. For example, the function $f(x) = x^2$ has an absolute maximum of 1 on the interval $[-1,1]$. This maximum value occurs at the two points $x_0 = 1$ and $x_0 = -1$. The absolute minimum of this function on this interval is 0, which occurs at the point $x_0 = 0$ (see Fig. 4-12).

The following theorem will be proven in the Appendix:

▷ **Extreme Value Theorem (EVT)** If f is continuous on the **closed** interval $[a,b]$, then f has an absolute maximum and an absolute minimum on $[a,b]$.

However, an arbitrary function on an arbitrary interval need not have either an absolute maximum or an absolute minimum. For example, the function $f(x) = x$ on the interval $]-1,1[$ has neither an absolute maximum nor an absolute minimum.

In order to find the absolute extrema of a continuous function f on a closed interval I, we evaluate f at each of its critical points and at each endpoint of I. The largest value of f found is the absolute maximum of f on I. The smallest value of f found is the absolute minimum of f on I.

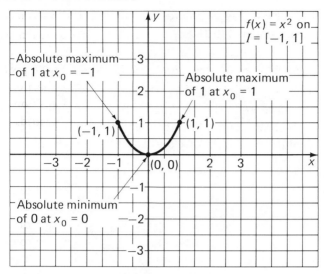

Figure 4-12

EXAMPLE Find the absolute extrema of the function $f(x) = 2x^2 + 2x - 1$ on the interval $[-1,1]$.

Solution Since $f'(x) = 4x + 2$ exists and is finite for all x, the critical points occur where $f'(x) = 0$, i.e., $x = -1/2$. Here, $f(-1/2) = -3/2$. Also, $f(-1) = -1$ and $f(1) = 3$. Thus, we may conclude that the absolute minimum of f on $[-1,1]$ is $-3/2$ and the absolute maximum of f on $[-1,1]$ is 3. A graph of f may be found in Fig. 4-13.

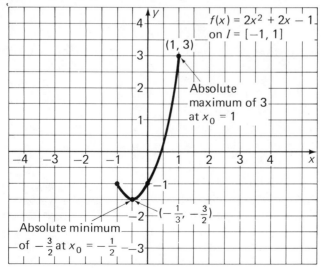

Figure 4-13

EXAMPLE Find the absolute extrema of the function $f(x) = (x - 1)^{2/3}$ on the interval [0,3].

Solution Since $f'(x) = \dfrac{2}{3}(x - 1)^{-1/3} = \dfrac{2}{3(x - 1)^{1/3}}$, we see that $f'(x)$ is never 0. However, f is not differentiable at $x = 1$, and so we have a critical point there and $f(1) = 0$. Also, $f(0) = 1$ and $f(3) = 2^{2/3}$ (which is approximately 1.59). Thus, the absolute minimum of f on [0,3] is 0 and the absolute maximum of f on [0,3] is $2^{2/3}$. A graph of f may be found in Fig. 4-14.

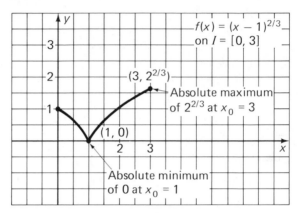

Figure 4-14

E X E R C I S E S

In 1-6, verify that MVT holds for the given function on the given interval.

1. $f(x) = x^2 + 2$ on [1,4]
2. $f(x) = 2x^2 + 3x - 1$ on [-2,2]
3. $f(x) = x^3$ on [0,1]
4. $f(x) = x^3 + x^2 + x$ on [-1,2]
5. $f(x) = \sqrt{x}$ on [1,4]
6. $f(x) = x^{2/3}$ on [0,8]

7. For the function in exercise 6 above, suppose we ask the same question for the interval [-8,8]. What goes wrong? Why?

In 8-26, (a) find the critical points of the function, (b) find the intervals on which it is increasing, (c) find the intervals on which it is decreasing, (d) find the local maxima, (e) find the local minima, and (f) try to sketch a graph of the function.

8. $f(x) = 2x^2 + x - 1$

9. $f(x) = x^3 - x^2$

10. $f(x) = x^4 + 4x$

11. $f(x) = -x^4 + 32x$

12. $f(x) = 3x^4 - 4x^3 + 6$

13. $f(x) = x^3 + 2x^2 + x - 3$

14. $f(x) = (x + 2)^3$

15. $f(x) = \sqrt{x}$

16. $f(x) = \sqrt[3]{x}$

17. $f(x) = x - \sqrt{x}$

18. $f(x) = \sqrt{x} - \dfrac{1}{\sqrt{x}}$

19. $f(x) = \dfrac{x + 1}{x - 1}$

20. $f(x) = x\sqrt{x + 1}$

21. $f(x) = (x + 1)^2(x - 1)^2$

22. $f(x) = (x - 2)^3(x + 1)^2$

23. $f(x) = 8x^2 + x^{-1/2}$

24. $f(x) = x^{3/2} + 6x^{1/2}$

25. $f(x) = x^{4/3} - 8x^{1/3}$

26. $f(x) = \begin{cases} x \text{ if } x \le 1 \\ 2 - x \text{ if } x > 1 \end{cases}$

In 27–32, find the (absolute) minimum and the (absolute) maximum of the function on the given intervals. (One or both may not exist.)

27. $f(x) = x^2$

    (a) $[-2,2]$ (b) $[-4,4]$ (c) $]-\infty,\infty[$

28. $f(x) = -2x^2 + 4x - 1$

    (a) $[0,2]$ (b) $[-2,-1]$ (c) $]-\infty,\infty[$

29. $f(x) = x^3 + 4x^2 - 3x + 2$

    (a) $[-5,-2]$ (b) $[0,1]$ (c) $[-5,1]$

30. $f(x) = \dfrac{x - 1}{x + 1}$

    (a) $[-1,1]$ (b) $[-3,3]$

31. $f(x) = \dfrac{x^2}{x - 1}$

    (a) $[0,3]$ (b) $[2,4]$

32. $f(x) = (x - 2)^{2/3}$

    (a) $[-1,3]$ (b) $]-\infty,\infty[$

2 Concavity, Points of Inflection, and Graphing Equations

Later in this section we will be concerned with graphing equations. In preparation for that, it will be very helpful for us to investigate two notions of concavity which we now define.

▷ **Definition** Suppose a function f is differentiable on an interval I.

(a) We say f is **concave upward** on I if f' is an increasing function on I.

(b) We say f is **concave downward** on I if f' is a decreasing function on I.

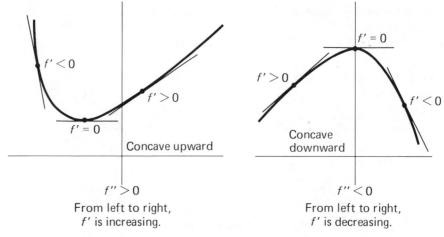

Figure 4–15

If we think of $f'(x)$ as being the slope of the tangent line to the graph of f at the point $(x, f(x))$, then upward concavity on I means that this tangent line turns counterclockwise (positive direction) as x moves from left to right through I, while downward concavity means that it turns in the clockwise (negative) direction (see Fig. 4-15).

The following theorem will help us locate intervals of concavity for many functions.

▷ **Theorem** Let f' be differentiable on I.
   (a) If $f''(x) > 0$ for all $x \in I$, then f is concave upward on I.
   (b) If $f''(x) < 0$ for all $x \in I$, then f is concave downward on I.

Proof (a) Since $f''(x) > 0$ for all $x \in I$, we see (since f'' is the derivative of f') that f' is an increasing function on I. Thus, f is concave upward on I.

   (b) The proof of this part is similar to part (a) and is left to the reader. ∎

EXAMPLE Find the intervals of concavity of (the graph of) the function

$$f(x) = \frac{(x + 1)(x - 2)}{(x - 1)}$$

Solution First we differentiate f:

$$f'(x) = \frac{(2x - 1)(x - 1) - (x^2 - x - 2)}{(x - 1)^2} = \frac{x^2 - 2x + 3}{(x - 1)^2}$$

Next, we differentiate f':

$$f''(x) = \frac{(2x-2)(x-1) - 2(x^2 - 2x + 3)}{(x-1)^3} = \frac{-4}{(x-1)^3}$$

Now, $f''(x) > 0$ when $x - 1 < 0$, i.e., when $x < 1$. Thus, f is concave upward on $]-\infty,1[$. Also, $f''(x) < 0$ when $x - 1 > 0$, i.e., when $x > 1$. Thus, f is concave downward on $]1,\infty[$. A graph of f can be seen in Fig. 4-16.

EXAMPLE   Find the intervals of concavity of $f(x) = x^3 + 2x^2 - 3x - 1$.

Solution $f'(x) = 3x^2 + 4x - 3$, and $f''(x) = 6x + 4$. Now, $f''(x) > 0$ when $x > -2/3$. Thus, f is concave upward on $]-2/3,\infty[$. Also, $f''(x) < 0$ when $x < -2/3$. Thus, f is concave downward on $]-\infty,-2/3[$. A graph of f may be found in Fig. 4-17.

You will notice in the last example (see Fig. 4-17) that the point $(-2/3,43/27)$ plays an important role in the graph of the function $f(x) = x^3 + 2x^2 - 3x - 1$ because it is the point where the graph of $f(x)$ changes from concave upward to concave downward. Such a point is called a **point of inflection** (or **inflection point**) of the graph. We make this precise as follows:

Definition   The point $(x_0,f(x_0))$ on the graph of f is called a **point of inflection** of the graph if $f'(x_0)$ exists and there are numbers a and b with $a < x_0 < b$ such that either

(1) f is concave upward on $]a,x_0[$ and concave downward on $]x_0,b[$, or

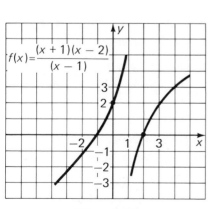

Figure 4-16

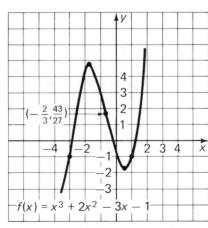

Figure 4-17

(2) f is concave downward on $]a,x_0[$ and concave upward on $]x_0,b[$.

Note. In this definition we allow the possibility that $f'(x_0)$ is infinite. We will shortly investigate such an example when we look at the function $f(x) = x^{1/3}$.

The next theorem is helpful in searching for points of inflection.

▷ **Theorem**   If $(x_0,f(x_0))$ is a point of inflection of the graph of f, then either $f''(x_0) = 0$ or f' is not differentiable at x_0.

Proof   If $f''(x_0)$ exists and is finite and $(x_0,f(x_0))$ is a point of inflection of the graph of f, then because the concavity of the graph of f changes at $(x_0,f(x_0))$, we see that f' must be increasing on one side of x_0 and decreasing on the other. Thus, it must be that $f''(x_0) = 0$. We conclude that either $f''(x_0) = 0$ or f' is not differentiable at x_0. ■

If $(x_0,f(x_0))$ is a point of inflection of the graph of f, then we also may say that "the graph of f has a point of inflection at x_0," or, more simply, "f has a point of inflection at x_0." The theorem we just proved tells us that we may search for the points of inflection of a function f among those points x_0 such that $f''(x_0) = 0$, $f''(x_0) = \pm\infty$, or $f''(x_0)$ does not exist. However, it is important to realize that just because $f''(x_0) = 0$, we may not conclude that x_0 is a point of inflection of f. For example, if $f(x) = x$, then $f''(x) = 0$ for all x, yet f has no points of inflection. Similarly, you should find it easy to give an example of a function f defined at a number x_0 such that f' is not differentiable at x_0 and yet f does not have a point of inflection at x_0.

We get a little more help in our search for points of inflection from the following:

▷ **Point of Inflection Test (PIT)**   If f'' is differentiable at x_0 and $f''(x_0) = 0$ and $f'''(x_0) \neq 0$, then f has a point of inflection at x_0.

The proof of PIT is left as an exercise. Notice that if $f'''(x_0) = 0$ or f'' is not differentiable at x_0, then PIT simply does not apply.

EXAMPLE   Find the points of inflection of the graphs of (a) $f(x) = x^3$, (b) $f(x) = x^5$, (c) $f(x) = x^{1/3}$, and (d) $f(x) = ax^3 + bx^2 + cx + d$, $a \neq 0$.

Solution   (a) $f'(x) = 3x^2$, $f''(x) = 6x$, and $f'''(x) = 6$. Since $f''(x)$ exists and is finite for all x, the only points of inflection can occur where $f''(x) = 6x = 0$. This gives us $x = 0$. PIT now tells us that, since

$f'''(0) = 6 \neq 0$, f has a point of inflection at $x = 0$. Thus, $(0,0)$ is the only point of inflection of the graph of $f(x) = x^3$. A graph of f may be seen in Fig. 4-18.

(b) $f'(x) = 5x^4$, $f''(x) = 20x^3$, and $f'''(x) = 60x^2$. We need search only where $f''(x) = 0$, and thus, we see that $x = 0$ gives us the only possible point of inflection. However, since $f'''(0) = 0$, PIT gives us no information. Instead, we check that for $x < 0$, $f''(x) = 20x^3 < 0$ and for $x > 0$, $f''(x) > 0$. Thus, f is concave downward on $]-\infty,0[$ and concave upward on $]0,\infty[$, and f does have a point of inflection at 0 and $(0,0)$ is the only point of inflection of the graph of f. A graph of f may be seen in Fig. 4-18.

(c) $f'(x) = \dfrac{1}{3}x^{-2/3}$ and $f''(x) = -\dfrac{2}{9}x^{-5/3}$. Here, f'' is never 0 (so PIT does not apply), but at $x = 0$, f' is not differentiable. Hence $(0,0)$ is

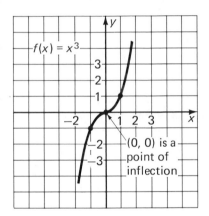

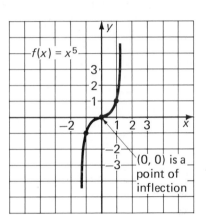

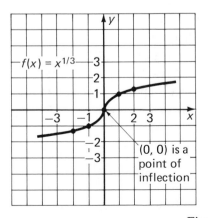

Figure 4–18

the only possible point of inflection of the graph of f. Since $f''(x) > 0$ for $x < 0$ and $f''(x) < 0$ for $x > 0$, we see that f is concave upward on $]-\infty,0[$ and concave downward on $]0,\infty[$. Since $f'(0)$ exists (even though $f'(0) = \infty$), we see that $(0,0)$ is indeed a point of inflection of the graph of $f(x) = x^{1/3}$. A graph of f may be seen in Fig. 4-18.

(d) $f'(x) = 3ax^2 + 2bx + c$, $f''(x) = 6ax + 2b$, and $f'''(x) = 6a$. The only possible point of inflection occurs when $f''(x) = 0$, i.e., at $x_0 = \dfrac{-b}{3a}$. Since $f'''(x_0) = 6a \neq 0$, PIT tells us that f has a point of inflection at $\dfrac{-b}{3a}$.

E X E R C I S E S

In 1–10, find the intervals of concavity and find the points of inflection (if there are any) of the given function.

1. $f(x) = x^3 + x^2 + x + 1$
2. $g(x) = 1/x$
3. $f(x) = 2x^2 + x + 2$
4. $g(x) = -x^2 + 2x + 3$
5. $f(x) = x + 1/x$
6. $g(x) = \dfrac{x+1}{x-1}$

7. $f(x) = x^{5/3}$
8. $g(x) = x^{4/3}$
9. $f(x) = \dfrac{x}{x^2 - 1}$
10. $g(x) = \dfrac{x}{x^2 + 1}$

11. Prove PIT.

WE ARE NOW READY to formalize a procedure for graphing equations in x and y. We should emphasize from the outset that some of these equations may not represent functions. Nevertheless, we will be able to apply the techniques which we have developed in this chapter. By the way, graphing an equation is also called "graphing a curve." Also, it is worthwhile recalling here that in Chapter 1, sections 3 to 6, we already saw how to graph certain quadratic equations.

The procedure consists in examining the following ten characteristics:

(1) Extent
(2) Intercepts
(3) Symmetry
(4) Critical points
(5) Local (or relative) extrema

(6) Intervals of monotonicity
(7) Points of inflection
(8) Intervals of concavity
(9) Vertical asymptotes
(10) Horizontal asymptotes

(1) *Extent.* This is a first approximation to finding where the graph lies. We usually look for values of the variables for which the equation makes no sense. For example, we can't take square roots of negative numbers, we can't divide by zero, etc.

(2) *Intercepts.* We find the points where the graph crosses the axes. Substitute $x = 0$ to find where the graph crosses the y-axis. Substitute $y = 0$ to find where the graph crosses the x-axis. If intercepts cannot be found precisely, try to approximate them.

(3) *Symmetry.* We will be concerned with three types of symmetry. If whenever (x,y) satisfies the equation, $(-x,y)$ also does, then the graph is **symmetric about the y-axis.** That is, if the plane were folded on the y-axis, the graph would be cut into two pieces which exactly matched each other. To check for symmetry about the y-axis, substitute $-x$ for x and see if the resulting equation is equivalent to the original. Thus, $y = x^2$ is symmetric about the y-axis because $y = (-x)^2$ and $y = x^2$ are equivalent. Recall that if our equation represents a function, then the graph is symmetric about the y-axis if the function is even.

Similarly, if whenever (x,y) satisfies the equation, $(x,-y)$ also does, then the graph is **symmetric about the x-axis.** To check for symmetry about the x-axis, substitute $-y$ for y and see if the resulting equation is equivalent to the original. Thus, $y^2 = x$ is symmetric about the x-axis because $(-y)^2 = x$ and $y^2 = x$ are equivalent.

The graph is **symmetric about the origin** if whenever (x,y) satisfies the equation, so does $(-x,-y)$. To check for symmetry about the origin, substitute $-x$ for x and $-y$ for y and see if the resulting equation is equivalent to the original. Thus, $y = x$ is symmetric about the origin because $-y = -x$ and $y = x$ are equivalent. Recall that if our equation represents a function, then the graph is symmetric about the origin if the function is odd.

(4) *Critical points.* These are the points (x,y) on the curve where $\dfrac{dy}{dx} = 0$, $\dfrac{dy}{dx} = \pm\infty$, or $\dfrac{dy}{dx}$ does not exist.

(5) *Local extrema.* For functions $y = f(x)$ we search among the critical points for local maxima and local minima. We may be able to use SDT here.

(6) *Intervals of monotonicity.* For functions $y = f(x)$, we find the intervals on which f is increasing and the intervals on which f is decreasing.

(7) *Points of inflection.* For functions $y = f(x)$, we calculate $y'' = f''(x)$ to locate the points of inflection. PIT may be used here.

(8) *Intervals of concavity.* For functions $y = f(x)$, we calculate $y'' = f''(x)$ to determine the intervals on which the graph of f is concave upward and those intervals on which the graph of f is concave downward.

(9) *Vertical asymptotes.* For functions $y = f(x)$, it may happen that for a fixed $x = x_0$, $\lim_{x \to x_0^-} f(x) = \pm\infty$ or $\lim_{x \to x_0^+} f(x) = \pm\infty$. In this case we say that the graph of f has the vertical line $x = x_0$ as a **vertical asymptote.** For example, the graph of $y = \dfrac{1}{x}$ has the line $x = 0$ as a vertical asymptote. In a graph, we usually show a vertical asymptote as a dotted line. It, of course, is not actually part of the graph of the equation.

(10) *Horizontal asymptotes.* For functions $y = f(x)$, it may happen that $\lim_{x \to \infty} f(x) = y_0$ or $\lim_{x \to -\infty} f(x) = y_0$ for some finite y_0. In this case we say that the graph of f has the horizontal line $y = y_0$ as a **horizontal asymptote.** For example, $y = \dfrac{1}{x}$ has the line $y = 0$ as a horizontal asymptote. In a graph, we usually show a horizontal asymptote as a dotted line. As with a vertical asymptote, it is not actually part of the graph of the equation.

Note. Of course, it almost goes without saying that as one plots more and more points of the graph (these are usually found by substituting convenient values of the variables), the better one's idea of the appearance of the graph.

EXAMPLE   Graph the equation $y = x^3 + x^2 - x$.

Solution   (1) *Extent.* Both x and y may assume any real value. [*Note.* In general, any odd degree polynomial in x assumes all real values.]

(2) *Intercepts.* If $x = 0$, then $y = 0$. Thus, $(0,0)$ is an intercept. If $y = 0$, then $x^3 + x^2 - x = 0$. So $x(x^2 + x - 1) = 0$. If $x = 0$, we again get $(0,0)$. If $x^2 + x - 1 = 0$, we get $x = \dfrac{-1 \pm \sqrt{5}}{2}$. Thus, $\left(\dfrac{-1 + \sqrt{5}}{2}, 0\right)$ and $\left(\dfrac{-1 - \sqrt{5}}{2}, 0\right)$ are x-intercepts.

(3) *Symmetry.* The graph has no symmetry.

(4) *Critical points.* $\dfrac{dy}{dx} = 3x^2 + 2x - 1$ for all x. Setting $\dfrac{dy}{dx} = 0$ gives $3x^2 + 2x - 1 = 0$. So $(3x - 1)(x + 1) = 0$. Thus, $x = 1/3$ and $x = -1$ are the critical points.

(5) *Local extrema.* Since $\dfrac{d^2y}{dx^2} = 6x + 2$, we have by SDT a relative maximum at $x = -1$ and a relative minimum at $x = 1/3$. Thus, the point $(-1,1)$ is a relative maximum on the graph and $(1/3,-5/27)$ is a relative minimum.

(6) *Intervals of monotonicity.* Since $y' > 0$ for $x < -1$ (for example, when $x = -2$, $y' = 7$), y is increasing on $]-\infty,-1]$. Since $y' < 0$ for $-1 < x < 1/3$ (for example, when $x = 0$, $y' = -1$), y is decreasing on $[-1,1/3]$. Since $y' > 0$ for $x > 1/3$ (for example, when $x = 1$, $y' = 4$), y is increasing on $[1/3,\infty[$.

(7) *Points of inflection.* Since $y'' = 6x + 2$ and $y''' = 6$, PIT tells us that we have a point of inflection at $x = -1/3$ (where $y'' = 0$). Thus, $(-1/3,11/27)$ is the only point of inflection.

(8) *Intervals of concavity.* For $x < -1/3$, $y'' < 0$, and so the graph is concave downward on $]-\infty,-1/3[$. For $x > -1/3$, $y'' > 0$, and so the graph is concave upward on $]-1/3,\infty[$.

(9) *Vertical asymptotes.* There are no vertical asymptotes.

(10) *Horizontal asymptotes.* There are no horizontal asymptotes. See Fig. 4-19 for a graph of $y = x^3 + x^2 - x$.

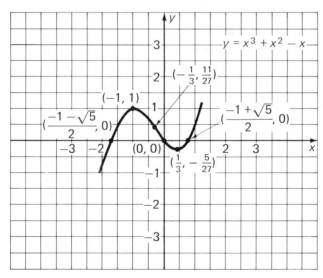

Figure 4-19

EXAMPLE   Graph the curve $y = (x + 2)^2(x - 1)^2$.

Solution   (1) *Extent.* x may assume any real value, but since

$(x + 2)^2 \geq 0$ and $(x - 1)^2 \geq 0$ for all x, we see that always y must be nonnegative ($y \geq 0$ for all x).

(2) *Intercepts.* When $x = 0$, we have $y = 4$ and so (0,4) is the y-intercept. When $y = 0$, $x = -2$ or $x = 1$. Thus, $(-2,0)$ and $(1,0)$ are the x-intercepts.

(3) *Symmetry.* The graph has no symmetry.

(4) *Critical points.* Since y is a polynomial in x, the only critical points occur where $y' = 0$. We have

$$\begin{aligned} y' &= (x + 2)^2 \cdot 2(x - 1) + (x - 1)^2 \cdot 2(x + 2) \\ &= 2(x + 2)(x - 1)(2x + 1) \\ &= (2x + 4)(2x^2 - x - 1) \\ &= 4x^3 + 6x^2 - 6x - 4 \end{aligned}$$

so $x = -2$, $x = -1/2$, and $x = 1$ give us the critical points $(-2,0)$, $(-1/2,81/16)$, and $(1,0)$ on the graph.

(5) *Local extrema.* Since $y'' = 12x^2 + 12x - 6 = 6(2x^2 + 2x - 1)$, we have $y'' > 0$ when $x = -2$, $y'' < 0$ when $x = -1/2$, and $y'' > 0$ when $x = 1$. Thus, we learn from SDT that $(-2,0)$ and $(1,0)$ are local minima, while $(-1/2,81/16)$ is a local maximum.

(6) *Intervals of monotonicity.* For $x < -2$, $y' < 0$ so y is decreasing on $]-\infty,-2]$. For $-2 < x < -1/2$, $y' > 0$ so y is increasing on $[-2,-1/2]$. For $-1/2 < x < 1$, $y' < 0$ so y is decreasing on $[-1/2,-1]$. For $x > 1$, $y' > 0$ so y is increasing on $[1,\infty[$.

(7) *Points of inflection.* We have $y'' = 0$ if and only if $2x^2 + 2x - 1 = 0$; that is, $x = (-1 \pm \sqrt{3})/2$. Now, $y''' = 6(4x + 2)$, which is nonzero at both of these values of x. According to PIT, the points of inflection on our graph are the points having x-coordinates $x_1 = (-1 - \sqrt{3})/2$ and $x_2 = (-1 + \sqrt{3})/2$. These points are approximately $(-1.37,2.25)$ and $(.37,2.25)$.

(8) *Intervals of concavity.* If $x = -2$, then $y'' = 18 > 0$ so $y'' > 0$ and our graph is concave upward on $]-\infty,x_1]$. For $x = 0$, $y'' = -6 < 0$ so our graph is concave downward on $[x_1,x_2]$. If $x = 1$, then $y'' = 18 > 0$ so we also have upward concavity on $[x_2,\infty[$.

(9) *Vertical asymptotes.* There are no vertical asymptotes.

(10) *Horizontal asymptotes.* There are no horizontal asymptotes.

See Fig. 4-20 for a graph of $y = (x + 2)^2(x - 1)^2$.

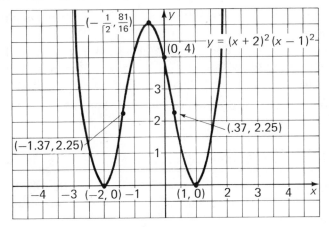

Figure 4–20

EXAMPLE   Graph the equation $y = (x - 4)x^{2/3}$.

Solution

    (1) *Extent.* x and y may assume any values.

    (2) *Intercepts.* Intercepts are $(0,0)$ and $(4,0)$.

    (3) *Symmetry.* The graph has no symmetry.

    (4) *Critical points.*

$$y' = (x - 4) \cdot \frac{2}{3}x^{-1/3} + x^{2/3} = x^{-1/3}\left(x + \frac{2}{3}(x - 4)\right) = x^{-1/3} \cdot \frac{1}{3}(5x - 8)$$

Thus, the only critical points occur for $x = 0$ and $x = \frac{8}{5}$. The critical

points on the curve are $(0,0)$ and $\left(\frac{8}{5}, \frac{-12}{5} \cdot \left(\frac{8}{5}\right)^{2/3}\right)$.

    Note. $\frac{-12}{5}\left(\frac{8}{5}\right)^{2/3}$ is approximately -3.28.

    (5) *Local extrema.*

$$y'' = \frac{1}{3}\left[-\frac{1}{3}x^{-4/3}(5x - 8) + 5x^{-1/3}\right] = \frac{1}{3}x^{-1/3}\left[-\frac{1}{3}x^{-1}(5x - 8) + 5\right]$$

SDT tells us that, since when $x = \frac{8}{5}$, $y'' = \frac{5}{3}\left(\frac{8}{5}\right)^{-1/3} > 0$, we have a

local minimum at approximately $\left(\frac{8}{5}, -3.28\right)$. However, SDT tells us

nothing when $x = 0$, since there y is not differentiable. Thus, we proceed to (6) to get the needed information.

(6) *Intervals of monotonicity.* For $x < 0$, $y' > 0$ (for example, when $x = -1$, $y' = 13/3$), and so y is increasing on $]-\infty,0]$.

For $0 < x < 8/5$, $y' < 0$ (for example, when $x = 1$, $y' = -8/3$), and so y is decreasing on $[0,8/5]$.

This tells us that at $x = 0$, the curve has a local maximum.

For $x > 8/5$, $y' > 0$ $\left(\text{for example, when } x = 9/5, y' = (9/5)^{-1/3} \cdot \frac{1}{3} > 0\right)$, and so y is increasing on $[8/5, \infty[$.

(7) *Points of inflection.* Since $y'' = \frac{1}{3}x^{-1/3}\left[-\frac{1}{3}x^{-1}(5x - 8) + 5\right]$, we see that there is a possible point of inflection when $x = 0$. We will check this when we check concavity in step (8). Also, setting $y'' = 0$ gives (for $x \neq 0$)

$$5x^{-1/3} = \frac{1}{3}x^{-4/3}(5x - 8)$$

$$15 = x^{-1}(5x - 8)$$

$$15x = 5x - 8$$

$$x = -.8$$

For $x = -.8$, we will check whether we have a point of inflection in step (8).

(8) *Intervals of concavity.* For $x < -.8$, $y'' < 0$ (for example, $y'' = \frac{-2}{9}$ when $x = -1$), and so the curve is concave downward on $]-\infty,-.8[$.

For $-.8 < x < 0$, $y'' > 0$ $\left(\text{for example, } y'' = \frac{56}{3} \text{ when } x = -\frac{1}{8}\right)$, and so the curve is concave upward on $]-.8,0[$.

This shows that there is a point of inflection when $x = -.8$. When $x = -.8$, y is approximately -4.14, so the point of inflection is approximately $(-.8,-4.14)$.

For $x > 0$, $y'' > 0$ $\left(\text{for example, } y'' = \frac{14}{9} \cdot 2^{-1/3} > 0 \text{ when } x = 2\right)$, and so the curve is concave upward on $]0,\infty[$.

This shows that we *do not* have a point of inflection when $x = 0$.

(9) *Vertical asymptotes.* There are no vertical asymptotes.

(10) *Horizontal asymptotes.* There are no horizontal asymptotes.

See Fig. 4-21 for a graph of $y = (x - 4)x^{2/3}$.

EXAMPLE Graph the equation $y = \dfrac{1}{x^2 - 1}$.

Solution   (1) *Extent.* x may not take the values 1 or −1. Also, y may not take the value 0, since $0 = \dfrac{1}{x^2 - 1}$ is impossible.

(2) *Intercepts.* If $x = 0$, then $y = -1$, so that $(0,-1)$ is the y-intercept. Since y can't be 0, there is no x-intercept.

(3) *Symmetry.* If we substitute $-x$ for x, we get an equivalent equation, and so the graph is symmetric about the y-axis and the function is even.

(4) *Critical points.* $y' = \dfrac{-2x}{(x^2 - 1)^2}$. The only critical point occurs when $x = \overset{.}{0}$. The critical point on the graph is $(0,-1)$.

(5) *Local extrema.* $y'' = \dfrac{-2(3x^2 + 1)}{(1 - x^2)^3}$, so that $y'' = -2 < 0$ when $x = 0$. Thus, by SDT, $(0,-1)$ is a relative maximum of the graph.

(6) *Intervals of monotonicity.* Remember that at $x = -1$ and $x = 1$, there are no points on the graph.

For $x < -1$, $y' > 0$, so that the graph is increasing on $]-\infty,-1[$.
For $-1 < x < 0$, $y' > 0$, so that the graph is increasing on $]-1,0]$.
For $0 < x < 1$, $y' < 0$, so that the graph is decreasing on $[0,1[$.
For $x > 1$, $y' < 0$, so that the graph is decreasing on $]1,\infty[$.

(7) *Points of inflection.* The only possible points of inflection can occur when $y'' = 0$. This gives $\dfrac{-2(3x^2 + 1)}{(1 - x^2)^3} = 0$ and so we must have $3x^2 + 1 = 0$. This is impossible and so there are no points of inflection.

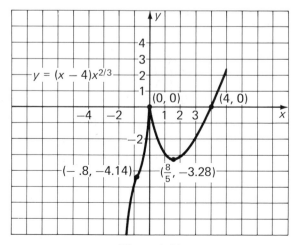

Figure 4–21

(8) *Intervals of concavity.* $y'' = \dfrac{-2(3x^2 + 1)}{(1 - x^2)^3}$, so that for $x < -1$,

$y'' > 0$ and the graph is concave upward on $]-\infty,-1[$.

For $-1 < x < 1$, $y'' < 0$, so that the graph is concave downward on $]-1,1[$.

For $x > 1$, $y'' > 0$, and the graph is concave upward on $]1,\infty[$.

(9) *Vertical asymptotes.* Notice that $\lim\limits_{x \to 1^+} \dfrac{1}{x^2 - 1} = \infty$ and

$\lim\limits_{x \to 1^-} \dfrac{1}{x^2 - 1} = -\infty$. Thus, the graph has the vertical asymptote $x = 1$.

Also, $\lim\limits_{x \to -1^+} \dfrac{1}{x^2 - 1} = -\infty$ and $\lim\limits_{x \to -1^-} \dfrac{1}{x^2 - 1} = \infty$, so that the graph also

has the vertical asymptote $x = -1$.

(10) *Horizontal asymptotes.* Since $\lim\limits_{x \to \infty} \dfrac{1}{x^2 - 1} = 0$ and $\lim\limits_{x \to -\infty} \dfrac{1}{x^2 - 1} = 0$,

we see that the graph has the horizontal asymptote $y = 0$.

See Fig. 4-22 for a graph of $y = \dfrac{1}{x^2 - 1}$.

EXAMPLE   Graph the equation $x^2 + 4y^2 + 8y = 1$.

Solution   We begin by completing the square in y to obtain

$$x^2 + 4y^2 + 8y + 4 = 5$$

$$\text{or} \qquad x^2 + (2y + 2)^2 = 5$$

$$\text{or} \qquad x^2 + 4(y + 1)^2 = 5$$

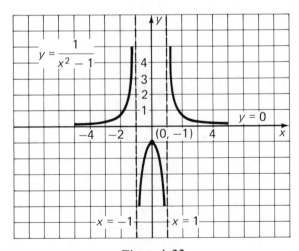

Figure 4-22

In section 5 of Chapter 1 we learned how to graph such an ellipse, but we'll proceed here using our ten-step approach.

If we try to solve for y, we obtain $(y+1)^2 = \dfrac{5-x^2}{4}$. Now, y is *not* a function of x here, but we can write

$$y + 1 = \pm\sqrt{\frac{5-x^2}{4}}$$

or

$$y = -1 \pm \frac{1}{2}\sqrt{5-x^2}$$

Thus, the graph of our original equation is the union of the graphs of the two functions $y = -1 + \dfrac{1}{2}\sqrt{5-x^2}$ and $y = -1 - \dfrac{1}{2}\sqrt{5-x^2}$. We proceed with $y = -1 + \dfrac{1}{2}\sqrt{5-x^2}$.

(1) *Extent.* Since $5 - x^2$ must be nonnegative, we must have $-\sqrt{5} \le x \le \sqrt{5}$.

Also, we must have $-1 \le y \le -1 + \dfrac{\sqrt{5}}{2}$.

(2) *Intercepts.* When $x = 0$, $y = -1 + \dfrac{\sqrt{5}}{2}$. Thus, the y-intercept is $\left(0, -1 + \dfrac{\sqrt{5}}{2}\right)$. When $y = 0$, we have $\sqrt{5-x^2} = 2$ and so $x = 1$ or $x = -1$. Thus, the x-intercepts are $(1,0)$ and $(-1,0)$.

(3) *Symmetry.* We have symmetry about the y-axis.

(4) *Critical points.* $y' = \dfrac{1}{4}(5-x^2)^{-1/2} \cdot (-2x) = \dfrac{-x}{2\sqrt{5-x^2}}$.

Thus, the critical points occur at $x = 0$ and the endpoints $x = \pm\sqrt{5}$. The critical points on the graph are $\left(0, -1 + \dfrac{\sqrt{5}}{2}\right)$, $(\sqrt{5}, -1)$, and $(-\sqrt{5}, -1)$.

(5) *Local extrema.* Since $2y'' = (5-x^2)^{-1/2}(-x^2(5-x^2)^{-1} - 1)$, we see that when $x = 0$, $y'' < 0$, so that the graph has a relative maximum at $\left(0, -1 + \dfrac{\sqrt{5}}{2}\right)$.

Also, since we have already observed in step (1) that $y \ge -1$, it must be that $(\sqrt{5}, -1)$ and $(-\sqrt{5}, -1)$ are relative minima.

(6) *Intervals of monotonicity.* For $-\sqrt{5} < x < 0$, $y' > 0$, so that the graph is increasing on $[-\sqrt{5}, 0]$.

For $0 < x < \sqrt{5}$, $y' < 0$, so that the graph is decreasing on $[0,\sqrt{5}]$.

(7) *Points of inflection.* The only possible points of inflection can occur here where $y'' = 0$.

Setting $y'' = 0$ gives $(5 - x^2)^{-1/2}(-x^2(5 - x^2)^{-1} - 1) = 0$. Since y'' is defined only for $-\sqrt{5} < x < \sqrt{5}$, we have $5 - x^2 \neq 0$ and we get

$$-x^2(5 - x^2)^{-1} - 1 = 0$$

or

$$-x^2 = 5 - x^2$$

which is impossible. Thus, there are no points of inflection.

(8) *Intervals of concavity.* Since $y'' < 0$ for $-\sqrt{5} < x < \sqrt{5}$, we see that the graph is concave downward on $]-\sqrt{5},\sqrt{5}[$.

(9)–(10) *Asymptotes.* There are no asymptotes.

In Fig. 4-23 we see a graph of the function $y = -1 + \dfrac{1}{2}\sqrt{5 - x^2}$. We leave it to the reader to work out the steps (1)–(10) for the graph of the function $y = -1 - \dfrac{1}{2}\sqrt{5 - x^2}$. In Fig. 4-23 we see a graph of this function also and, in addition, a graph of the ellipse $x^2 + 4y^2 + 8y = 1$.

EXAMPLE   Graph the equation $y^2 = x^2 \cdot \dfrac{x + 1}{x - 1}$.

Solution   The graph is the union of the graphs of $y = \sqrt{x^2 \cdot \dfrac{x + 1}{x - 1}}$ and $y = -\sqrt{x^2 \cdot \dfrac{x + 1}{x - 1}}$.

We will run through steps (1)–(10) for the function $y = \sqrt{x^2 \cdot \dfrac{x + 1}{x - 1}}$ and leave it to the reader to analyze the function $y = -\sqrt{x^2 \cdot \dfrac{x + 1}{x - 1}}$.

(1) *Extent.* Clearly $(0,0)$ is on the graph and $x = 1$ is impossible. Also, if $x \neq 0$, then $x^2 > 0$ and so we must have $\dfrac{x + 1}{x - 1} \geq 0$. Thus, we must have $x \leq -1$ or $x > 1$. y may assume any nonnegative value.

(2) *Intercepts.* When $x = 0$, $y = 0$. Thus, $(0,0)$ is an intercept. If $y = 0$, then $x = 0$ or $x = -1$, so that $(-1,0)$ is an x-intercept.

(3) *Symmetry.* The graph of $y = \sqrt{x^2 \cdot \dfrac{x + 1}{x - 1}}$ has no symmetry. (However, the graph of $y^2 = x^2 \cdot \dfrac{x + 1}{x - 1}$ is symmetric about the x-axis.)

(4) *Critical points.* Since $y' = \dfrac{x^2 - x - 1}{(x-1)\sqrt{x^2-1}}$, we have $x = -1$ as

a critical point. Also, we have critical points where $x^2 - x - 1 = 0$, or

$x = \dfrac{1 \pm \sqrt{5}}{2}$. However, $\dfrac{1 - \sqrt{5}}{2}$ is *not* in the domain of our function

(see step (1)) and so we have only the additional critical point

$x = \dfrac{1 + \sqrt{5}}{2}$. Thus, the critical points on the curve are $(-1,0)$ and,

approximately, $(1.62, 3.33)$.

(5) *Local extrema.* Since $y'' = \dfrac{x+2}{(x-1)(x^2-1)^{3/2}}$, we see that when

$x = \dfrac{1 + \sqrt{5}}{2}$, y'' is approximately 2.84. Thus, by SDT, we have a rela-

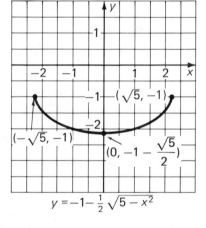

$$y = -1 + \frac{1}{2}\sqrt{5 - x^2}$$

$$y = -1 - \frac{1}{2}\sqrt{5 - x^2}$$

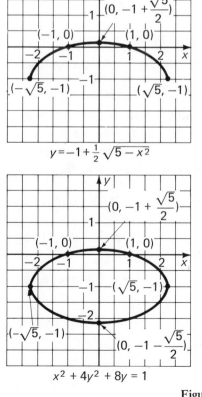

$$x^2 + 4y^2 + 8y = 1$$

Figure 4–23

tive minimum at $x = \dfrac{1 + \sqrt{5}}{2}$. The local minimum on the graph is, approximately, (1.62,3.33).

In step (6) we will see whether or not we have a relative extremum at $x = -1$.

(6) *Intervals of monotonicity.* For $x < -1$, $x - 1$ is negative. Also, $x^2 - x - 1$ and $\sqrt{x^2 - 1}$ are both positive so that $y' = \dfrac{x^2 - x - 1}{(x - 1)\sqrt{x^2 - 1}} < 0$. Thus, the graph is decreasing on $]-\infty,-1]$. We see that $(-1,0)$ is a relative minimum on the graph.

We could also have seen that y' is negative on $]-\infty,-1[$ by substituting any convenient value in $]-\infty,-1[$ for x in the equation for y'.

For $1 < x < \dfrac{1 + \sqrt{5}}{2}$, $y' < 0$ because $x^2 - x - 1$ is negative and both $x - 1$ and $\sqrt{x^2 - 1}$ are positive. Thus, the graph is decreasing on $\left]1,\dfrac{1 + \sqrt{5}}{2}\right]$.

For $x > \dfrac{1 + \sqrt{5}}{2}$, $y' > 0$ because $x^2 - x - 1$, $x - 1$, and $\sqrt{x^2 - 1}$ are all positive. Thus, the graph is increasing on $\left[\dfrac{1 + \sqrt{5}}{2},\infty\right[$.

(7)–(8) *Points of inflection and intervals of concavity.* Since $y'' = \dfrac{x + 2}{(x - 1)(x^2 - 1)^{3/2}}$, we see that $y'' = 0$ for $x = -2$.

For $x < -2$, $y'' > 0$ because $x + 2$ and $x - 1$ are both negative and $(x^2 - 1)^{3/2}$ is positive. Thus, the graph is concave upward on $]-\infty,-2[$.

For $-2 < x < -1$, $y'' < 0$ because $x - 1$ is negative and both $x + 2$ and $(x^2 - 1)^{3/2}$ are positive. Thus, the graph is concave downward on $]-2,-1[$.

Also, we have a point of inflection at $x = -2$. This point is, approximately, $(-2,2.58)$.

For $x > 1$, $y'' > 0$ because $x + 2$, $x - 1$, and $(x^2 - 1)^{3/2}$ are all positive so that the graph is concave upward on $]1,\infty[$.

(9) *Vertical asymptotes.* Since $\lim\limits_{x \to 1^+} \sqrt{x^2 \cdot \dfrac{x + 1}{x - 1}} = \infty$, we have a vertical asymptote at $x = 1$.

(10) *Horizontal asymptotes.* There are no horizontal asymptotes.

See Fig. 4-24 for graphs of both $y = \sqrt{x^2 \cdot \dfrac{x + 1}{x - 1}}$ and $y^2 = x^2 \cdot \dfrac{x + 1}{x - 1}$.

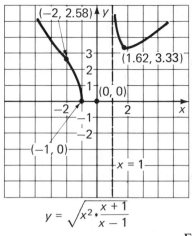

$$y = \sqrt{x^2 \cdot \frac{x+1}{x-1}}$$

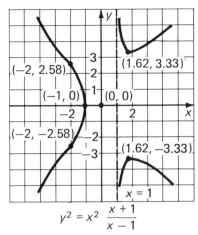

$$y^2 = x^2 \frac{x+1}{x-1}$$

Figure 4–24

Note. You will notice that the point $(0,0)$ is an "isolated point" of the graph. This is an example of a particular variety of "singular point." Singular points may be isolated, or the graph may cross itself at a singular point, or some other strange behavior may take place at a singular point.

EXERCISES

In 1–32, use the ten-step procedure for graphing the equation.

1. $y = x^2 + 3x + 1$
2. $y = (x-3)^2$
3. $y = x^3 + x^2 - 5x$
4. $y = x^3 - x^2 + x + 4$

[Find the x-intercept to the nearest tenth.]

5. $y = (x-1)(x+1)(x+2)$
6. $y = 3x^4 - 4x^3 + 1$
7. $y = x^4 - 2x^3$
8. $y = x^4 + 2x^2$
9. $y = (x-1)^2 \cdot (x-2)^2$
10. $y = (x+1)^5$
11. $y = \sqrt{x+1}$
12. $y^2 = x + 1$
13. $y = \sqrt{x^2 + 1}$
14. $y^2 = x^2 + 1$
15. $y = \sqrt{1 - x^2}$
16. $y^2 = 1 - x^2$
17. $y^2 = x^4$
18. $y = x^2(x+2)^3$

[Find the x-coordinate of the point of inflection to the nearest tenth.]

19. $y = x^{2/3}(x+1)$
20. $y = 3x^{2/3} - 2x$
21. $y = 3x^{4/3} - 4x$
22. $y = x\sqrt{x+1}$
23. $y = \dfrac{x+1}{x-1}$
24. $y = \dfrac{x}{x^2+1}$

25. $y = \dfrac{(x-1)^2}{x^2+1}$

26. $y = x^2\sqrt{1-x}$

27. $y = \dfrac{x}{1-x^2}$

28. $y^2 = x^2$

29. $xy^2 = x^2 + y^2$

30. $y^2(1-x^2) = x^4$

31. $y^2 = x(4-x)^2$

32. $xy^2 + 2x^3 - y^2 = 0$

3 Distance, Velocity, and Acceleration

We saw, at the beginning of Chapter 3, that if $s(t)$ is the directed distance from a starting point that an object travels along a line in time t, and if s is a differentiable function of t, then $s'(t)$ represents the **velocity** (instantaneous velocity) of the object at time t. The derivative $s'(t)$ represents the rate of change of s, with respect to t. Suppose we write $v(t) = s'(t)$, where v is velocity. Then we may wish to investigate the rate of change of v with respect to t. The derivative $v'(t)$ is called the **acceleration** of the object at time t. It is customary to write $a(t) = v'(t) = s''(t)$. Also, it is customary to write $\dot{s}(t) = v(t)$ and $\ddot{s}(t) = \dot{v}(t) = a(t)$. The dot signifies a derivative with respect to time.

Note. Velocity is measured in units like feet per second or meters per second. Acceleration is measured in units like feet per second per second or meters per second per second.

EXAMPLE If $s(t) = t^3 + 6t - 1$ is a distance function, then calculate the velocity function v and the acceleration function a.

Solution $v(t) = \dot{s}(t) = 3t^2 + 6$
$a(t) = \dot{v}(t) = 6t$

One of the classical problems in the calculus is to investigate the motion of a freely falling body, subject only to the force of gravity (friction, wind, etc., are ignored). The basic equation which we shall use is

$$s(t) = \frac{1}{2}gt^2 + v_0 t + s_0$$

In this equation, $s(t)$ is the height above ground after time t, s_0 represents the original height of the object when free fall begins, v_0 represents the initial velocity when free fall begins, and g is a constant, called the **gravitational constant**, which represents the acceleration due to gravity. We will take the value of g to be -32 feet per second per second (−32 ft/sec²) or, in the metric system, −9.8 meters per second per second (−9.8 m/sec²). The value of this constant has been determined experimentally.

EXAMPLE   Suppose an object is dropped from a building 1200 feet above ground level.
   (a) How long does it take to hit the ground?
   (b) What is its velocity when it hits the ground?
   (c) What is its velocity when it is 200 feet from the ground?

Solution   (a) Since the object is dropped (as opposed to hurled down), we have $v_0 = 0$. Also, $s_0 = 1200$ and $g = -32$. We are asked to find t such that $s(t) = 0$. Thus,

$$0 = -16t^2 + v_0 t + s_0$$

So,

$$0 = -16t^2 + 1200$$
$$16t^2 = 1200$$
$$t^2 = 75$$
$$t = \sqrt{75} = 5\sqrt{3} \approx 8.66 \text{ seconds}$$

Of course, we reject the solution $t = -\sqrt{75}$ because, since we start at $t = 0$, we must have $t \geq 0$.
   (b) Since $\dot{s}(t) = gt + v_0 = gt$, we have $\dot{s}(3\sqrt{5}) = -32 \cdot 5\sqrt{3} = -160\sqrt{3}$ ft/sec ≈ -277.13 ft/sec. Notice that since height from the ground (up) is measured in a positive direction and since the object is falling, s is a decreasing function. This is why $\dot{s}$ is negative.
   (c) When $s(t) = 200$, we have

$$200 = -16t^2 + 1200$$
$$16t^2 = 1000$$
$$t = \frac{5\sqrt{10}}{2} \approx 7.91 \text{ seconds}$$

Therefore, since $\dot{s}(t) = -32t$, we have $\dot{s}\left(\frac{5\sqrt{10}}{2}\right) = -80\sqrt{10} \approx -252.98$ ft/sec.

If an object is thrown directly upward from ground level with an initial velocity v_0, then the equation $s(t) = \frac{1}{2}gt^2 + v_0 t = -16t^2 + v_0 t$ (in the English system) gives its height in feet after t seconds.

EXAMPLE   A ball is thrown directly upward from ground level with an initial velocity of 48 ft/sec.

   (a) How long does it take to reach its maximum height?

   (b) What is its maximum height?

   (c) How long does it take to hit the ground?

   (d) What is its velocity when it hits the ground?

Solution   (a) We wish to find the absolute maximum of the function $s(t) = -16t^2 + 48t$.

   Since $\dot{s}(t) = -32t + 48$ and $\ddot{s}(t) = -32$, we have $\dot{s}(t) = 0$ when $t = 1.5$ seconds. Also, SDT tells us this gives a maximum.

   (b) When $t = 1.5$, $s(t) = 36$. Thus, the maximum height is 36 feet at time $t = 1.5$ seconds.

   (c) When it hits the ground, we have $s(t) = 0$ and so we solve the equation $0 = -16t^2 + 48t$ to get $t = 0$ and $t = 3$. Since $t = 0$ was the starting time, we see that the ball hits the ground after 3 seconds.

   (d) When $t = 3$, $\dot{s}(t) = -32t + 48 = -48$ ft/sec. The fact that 48 ft/sec is the initial velocity is no accident. See exercise 8, on page 192.

EXAMPLE   A particle is traveling along a horizontal line. Suppose distance to the right of some fixed point O is called positive and distance to the left is called negative. If the **equation of motion,** that is, the distance function that gives the directed distance of the object from O at time t, is given by $s(t) = t^3 - 6t^2 + 3t$, analyze the motion of the particle. Make sure to indicate when the particle reverses its direction, when its velocity increases, and when its velocity decreases.

Solution   It may be helpful to refer to Fig. 4-25 as you follow the solution. We have $\dot{s}(t) = 3t^2 - 12t + 3 = 3(t^2 - 4t + 1)$. Thus, $\dot{s}(t) = 0$, when $t = 2 \pm \sqrt{3}$.

   Between $t = 0$ and $t = 2 - \sqrt{3}$, $\dot{s}(t) > 0$ and so the particle is moving to the right.

   Between $t = 2 - \sqrt{3}$ and $t = 2 + \sqrt{3}$, $\dot{s}(t) < 0$ and so the particle is moving back to the left. It reversed its direction at $t = 2 - \sqrt{3}$.

   For $t > 2 + \sqrt{3}$, $\dot{s}(t) > 0$ and so the particle is moving to the right again. It reversed its direction at $t = 2 + \sqrt{3}$.

   Also, $a(t)$ is given by $a(t) = 6t - 12$. The acceleration is negative for $0 < t < 2$ and positive for $t > 2$. This means that the velocity decreases up to $t = 2$ and, after $t = 2$, it then increases. That is, on the time interval $]0,2[$ the particle is **decelerating** and on $]2,\infty[$ the particle is **accelerating**.

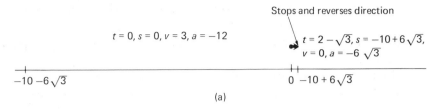

(a)

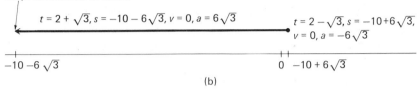

(b)

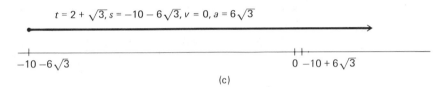

(c)

Figure 4-25

(a) Since, when $t = 0$ and $v > 0$, the particle is moving to the right. Since $a < 0$, the particle is slowing down. It stops when $v(t) = 0$. This happens first when $t = 2 - \sqrt{3}$. At that time, $s = -10 + 6\sqrt{3}$ and $a = -6\sqrt{3}$. Since $a < 0$, the object reverses direction.

(b) The particle stops again when $v(t) = 0$. This happens when $t = 2 + \sqrt{3}$. At that time, $s = -10 - 6\sqrt{3}$ and $a = 6\sqrt{3}$. Since $a > 0$, the particle reverses direction.

(c) The particle keeps moving to the right for all $t > 2 + \sqrt{3}$.

E X E R C I S E S

In 1-4, find $\dot{s}(t)(= v(t))$ and $\dot{v}(t)(= a(t))$.

1. $s(t) = t^2 + 4t - 3$

2. $s(t) = t^3 + 3t^2 - 9t + 6$

3. $s(t) = \sqrt{t + 3}$

4. $s(t) = \dfrac{t + 1}{t^2 + 1}$

5. A rock is thrown down from a helicopter hovering at a height of 400 meters. Suppose its initial velocity is -20 meters/sec. [*Note.* $g = -9.8$ meters/sec².]

   (a) How long does it take the rock to hit the ground?

   (b) What is its velocity when it hits the ground?

   (c) What is its velocity when it is 200 meters from the ground?

6. An object is thrown down from a height s_0 with an initial velocity v_0.

(a) Express, in terms of g, v_0, and s_0, the time it takes to hit the ground.

(b) Use part (a) to find its velocity when it hits the ground.

(c) Express, in terms of g, v_0, s_0, and h, the time it takes to reach a height h $(0 \leq h \leq s_0)$.

(d) Use part (c) to find its velocity when it has a height h.

7. A high-powered rifle is fired directly upward into the air from ground level. The muzzle velocity is 2400 ft/sec.

(a) How long does the bullet take to reach its maximum height?

(b) What is its maximum height?

(c) How long does it take to hit the ground?

(d) What is its velocity when it hits the ground?

8. An object is projected straight up from ground level with an initial velocity v_0.

(a) How long does it take (in terms of v_0) to reach its maximum height?

(b) Use part (a) to express its maximum height.

(c) How long does it take (in terms of v_0) to hit the ground?

(d) Use part (c) to express its velocity when it hits the ground.

In 9–12, a particle moves along a horizontal line and motion to the right is called positive while motion to the left is called negative. Analyze the given equation of motion, making sure to indicate when (if ever) the particle reverses its direction, when (if ever) it is decelerating, and when (if ever) it is accelerating. [In order to analyze the acceleration in exercise 12, you should use trial and error to approximate the time to the nearest tenth.]

9. $s(t) = 3t^2 + 8t$ **11.** $s(t) = \sqrt{t + 4} - 2$

10. $s(t) = t^3 + 3t^2 - 9t$ **12.** $s(t) = \dfrac{t + 1}{t^2 + 1} - 1$

4   Miscellaneous Problems on Maxima and Minima

In this section we will look at a variety of problems in which we will want to find the absolute maximum or the absolute minimum of certain functions on certain intervals. As we have noted earlier, the absolute maximum is often called the **maximum** and the absolute minimum is often called the **minimum**.

EXAMPLE Of all the rectangles with perimeter 100 feet, find the one with maximum area.

Solution The area A is given by the formula $A = l \cdot w$, where l is the length and w is the width. We know that $2l + 2w = 100$. Thus, $w = 50 - l$ and $A = A(l) = l(50 - l) = 50l - l^2$. Since $A'(l) = 50 - 2l$, the only critical point occurs for $l = 25$.

Since $A''(l) = -2$, we have a maximum for $l = 25$. Also, at the endpoints, $l = 0$ and $l = 50$, the area is clearly 0. Thus, the maximum area is $A(25) = 625$ ft², which occurs for a 25 ft by 25 ft square.

EXAMPLE A cylindrical can is to be manufactured to hold 50 cubic inches. Find the height and radius of the base of the can so that the smallest amount of metal is used in the can.

Solution In Fig. 4-26, the area of each base (top or bottom) is πr^2. Also the lateral (side) area is $2\pi rh$. Thus, the surface area A of the can is $2\pi r^2 + 2\pi rh$. This is the quantity we must minimize.

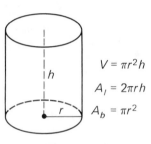

$V = \pi r^2 h$

$A_l = 2\pi rh$

$A_b = \pi r^2$

Since the volume is 50, we have $50 = \pi r^2 h$, so that $h = 50/\pi r^2$. We have $A = A(r) = 2\pi r^2 + 2\pi r(50/\pi r^2) = 2\pi r^2 + 100/r$. Thus, $A'(r) = 4\pi r - 100/r^2$. Setting $A'(r) = 0$ yields $100/r^2 = 4\pi r$ or $r = \sqrt[3]{25/\pi}$.

Figure 4-26

Since $A'(r) < 0$ for $0 < r < \sqrt[3]{25/\pi}$ and $A'(r) > 0$ for $r > \sqrt[3]{25/\pi}$, we see that the minimum surface area occurs when $r = \sqrt[3]{25/\pi}$. Here, $h = 50/\pi r^2 = 50/[\pi \cdot (25/\pi)^{2/3}]$. These values are approximately, $r = 2.00$ in. and $h = 4.00$ in.

EXAMPLE A tall building which has n stories costs $2n^2 + 600n + 1500$ (in thousands of dollars) to build. How many floors should the building have in order to minimize the average cost per floor?

Solution The average cost per floor, $A(n)$, is

$$\frac{2n^2 + 600n + 1500}{n} \qquad (n > 0)$$

Thus,

$$A'(n) = \frac{(4n + 600)n - (2n^2 + 600n + 1500)}{n^2} = \frac{2n^2 - 1500}{n^2}$$

Setting $A'(n) = 0$ gives $n = \sqrt{750} \approx 27.39$. Since, for $0 < n < \sqrt{750}$, $A'(n) < 0$ and for $n > \sqrt{750}$, $A'(n) > 0$, we have a minimum at $\sqrt{750}$.

However, since we cannot build $\sqrt{750}$ floors, we must check the two values $n = 27$ and $n = 28$ to see which gives the smaller value.

$$\text{For } n = 27, A(n) \approx 709.56$$
$$\text{For } n = 28, A(n) \approx 709.57$$

Thus, the average cost per floor is minimal when we have 27 floors.

EXAMPLE   A club sells memberships for $400 if 50 people or fewer join. For each person in excess of 50 who joins, the membership fee of each member will be reduced by $2. The club can accept no more than 150 members. How many memberships should be sold to maximize the club's receipts?

Solution   Let $R(n)$ = the club's receipts if n memberships are sold ($0 \le n \le 150$). Now, if $0 \le n \le 50$, then $R(n) = 400n$. For $50 < n \le 150$, each member will pay $400 - 2(n - 50) = 500 - 2n$ dollars. The club's receipts will be $(500 - 2n)n = 500n - 2n^2$. Thus,

$$R(n) = \begin{cases} 400n & \text{if } 0 \le n \le 50 \\ 500n - 2n^2 & \text{if } 50 < n \le 150 \end{cases}$$

Clearly, for $0 \le n \le 50$, the maximum receipts are $R(50) = \$20{,}000$. For, $50 < n < 150$, $R'(n) = 500 - 4n$. Setting $R'(n) = 0$ gives $n = 125$. By SDT, and the continuity of $R(n)$, this is a maximum for $50 \le n \le 150$ because $R''(n) = -4 < 0$ for $50 < n < 150$. Thus, we have the maximum revenue of $31,250 for 125 members.

EXAMPLE   A fence b feet high stands on level ground parallel to a very high vertical wall. The distance from the fence to the wall is a feet. What is the length of the shortest ladder that will reach from the ground, across the fence, and to the wall?

Solution   In Fig. 4-27, let x feet be the distance from the foot of the wall to the foot of the ladder and let y feet be the height of the ladder's top above the ground. Considering the two similar right triangles shown in Fig. 4-27, we see that

$$\frac{y}{x} = \frac{b}{x - a}$$

so

$$y = \frac{bx}{x - a}$$

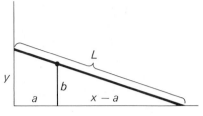

Figure 4-27

By the Pythagorean Theorem, the length L of the ladder satisfies

$$L^2 = x^2 + \left(\frac{bx}{x-a}\right)^2$$

We shall find the value x_0 of x that minimizes L^2 for that value also minimizes L. We have

$$\frac{dL^2}{dx} = 2x + 2\left(\frac{bx}{x-a}\right)\left(\frac{-ba}{(x-a)^2}\right) = 2x\left(1 - \frac{b^2a}{(x-a)^3}\right)$$

Setting this equal to 0 and solving for $x > a$, we obtain

$$x_0 = a + b^{2/3}a^{1/3}$$

We have as the corresponding value of L^2

$$L^2 = (a + b^{2/3}a^{1/3})^2 + \left(\frac{ba + b^{5/3}a^{1/3}}{b^{2/3}a^{1/3}}\right)^2$$
$$= a^{2/3}(a^{2/3} + b^{2/3})^2 + b^{2/3}(a^{2/3} + b^{2/3})^2$$
$$= (a^{2/3} + b^{2/3})^3$$

Since it is evident that there is a minimum for L^2, this is it. Now take square roots.

$$L = (a^{2/3} + b^{2/3})^{3/2} \text{ feet } \quad Answer$$

E X E R C I S E S

1. Find two positive numbers whose sum is 60 and whose product is as large as possible.
2. Find two positive numbers whose product is 100 and whose sum is as small as possible.
3. Of all rectangles with area 100 square feet, find the one with smallest perimeter.
4. Show that among all rectangles with fixed area A, the square with side $\sqrt{A}$ is the one with smallest perimeter.

5. Show that among all rectangles with fixed perimeter P, the square with side $P/4$ has largest area.

6. A rectangular box with a square bottom and a volume of 20 cubic feet is to be made (see Fig. 4-28). The top and bottom cost $.10 per square foot to make and the four sides each cost $.05 per square foot to make. Find the dimensions of the box which will minimize the cost of the box.

7. If the cost of constructing a building of n floors (measured in thousands of dollars) is $3n^2 + 400n + 1200$, how many floors should be built to minimize the cost of the average floor?

8. A club sells memberships for $420 if 50 people or fewer join. For each person in excess of 50 who joins, the membership fee of each member is reduced by $2. The club can accept no more than 150 members. How many memberships should be sold to maximize the club's receipts?

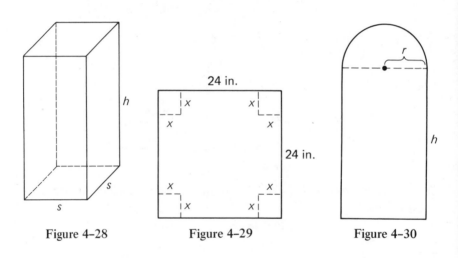

Figure 4-28   Figure 4-29   Figure 4-30

9. An open rectangular box is to be constructed from a square sheet of metal of side 24 inches by cutting out square corners and folding up the sides (see Fig. 4-29). What size square corners should be cut out to maximize the volume of the box?

10. Do exercise 9 if the square sheet of metal has side s.

11. A Norman window is one in the shape of a rectangle topped by a semicircular region (see Fig. 4-30). If the perimeter of such a window is to be 12 feet, find the dimensions of the window which maximize its area.

12. A rectangular corral is to be built along the side of a long building (see Fig. 4-31). If 150 feet of fencing is available, what dimensions should the corral be to maximize its area?

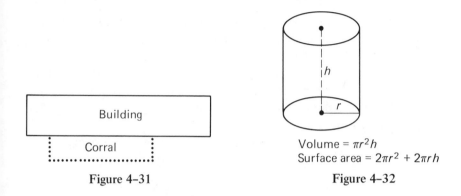

Volume $= \pi r^2 h$
Surface area $= 2\pi r^2 + 2\pi r h$

Figure 4–31   Figure 4–32

13. A can (right circular cylinder) with its top is to be made from 100 square inches of metal (see Fig. 4-32). What are the dimensions of the can with maximum volume?

14. Do exercise 13 if we start with s square inches of metal.

15. A farmer has a crop weighing 10,000 pounds in his field. This can be sold for 20 cents per pound. If he waits to pick his crop, its weight will increase 800 pounds per week but the price will fall 1 cent per pound per week. When should he harvest the crop to maximize his income?

16. Suppose that, in a certain city of p people, the rate that the flu spreads is (directly) proportional to the product of the number of people who have it and the number of people who don't have it. Show that the flu is spreading the fastest when $p/2$ people have the flu.

17. In a certain period of time, a tree farm planted with 400 trees per acre will yield a revenue of $500 per tree. If more trees are planted per acre, then the crowding of the trees will retard growth so that for each new tree the revenue per tree is reduced by $1. How many trees per acre will maximize the revenue from the tree farm?

18. Postal regulations require that the sum of the length, width and girth of a rectangular box which is to be shipped cannot exceed 64 inches. If the box is to have a square base, find the dimensions of the box with maximum volume which may be shipped.

19. A right circular cone is to be made from s square centimeters of material (see Fig. 4-33). Find the dimensions of the cone which will have maximum volume.

20. A rectangular sheet of paper is to be used for a rectangular printed notice. The page must contain 30 square inches of print and there must be margins of 2 inches on each side and 1 inch on the top and bottom. Find the dimensions of the sheet of smallest area which will suffice.

21. A rectangular plot of area 1000 square feet is to be made into a rectangular garden surrounded by a 3-foot-wide walkway. What should be the dimensions of the 1000 square foot plot so that the garden has maximal area?

22. Which quadrant I point on the hyperbola $y^2 = x^2 - 1$ is closest to the point $(4,0)$?

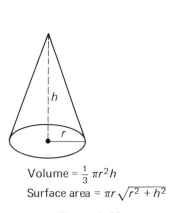

Volume $= \frac{1}{3}\pi r^2 h$

Surface area $= \pi r \sqrt{r^2 + h^2}$

Figure 4–33

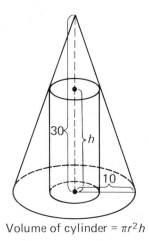

Volume of cylinder $= \pi r^2 h$

Figure 4–34

23. Suppose a right circular cone has height 30 inches and base radius 10 inches (see Fig. 4-34). Find the dimensions of the right circular cylinder of maximum volume which can be inscribed in the cone.

24. A company ships from a mainland plant to an island (see Fig. 4-35). The plant is located at point A. The island is 24 miles from the shore at point B and A is 36 miles from B. The company wants to build a shipping station at a point X somewhere along the shore where the goods will be transferred from truck to boat. It costs $1 per ton per mile to ship by truck and $1.25 per ton per mile to

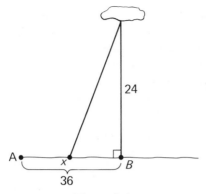

Figure 4–35

ship by boat. Where should the shipping station be built in order to minimize the shipping costs?

25. Ohm's Law states that, in a battery cell, the relationship between the current I (in amperes), the electromotive force, E (in volts), the external resistance R (in ohms), and the internal resistance r (in ohms), is given by the formula

$$I = \frac{E}{R + r}$$

Suppose E and r are fixed but that R can be varied. The power P generated by the battery is given by the formula $P = RI^2$. Show that P is maximal when $R = r$.

5 Some Applications of the Derivative to Business

A primary concern in the operation of any business is the cost of production. It often happens that the cost of production for two identical items is not the same. For example, suppose an aircraft manufacturer designs a new jet. There are tremendous design and start-up costs, so that the first jet costs the manufacturer an astronomical amount to produce. However, if the manufacturer produces 100 jets, you can see that the initial, or **fixed,** costs are then averaged over 100 planes. It costs considerably less to produce the hundredth plane than to produce the first, even though the two planes are identical.

In the other direction, consider the following situation: Suppose an electric utility has a contract with an oil supplier to purchase a fixed amount of oil at a fixed price. It may be that if the utility wishes to increase its production, it must purchase additional oil on the open market at much higher prices. You can see that it will cost more to produce each additional unit of electrical power than it did to produce the power from the oil bought on contract.

Throughout our discussion, we will assume that we have a **cost function** $C(x)$ which is the total cost of producing the first x units. It should be clear, for example, that the cost of producing the fifth unit is $C(5) - C(4)$, that is, the cost of producing the first five units less the cost of producing the first four units. In general, $C(x + 1) - C(x)$ is the cost of producing the $(x + 1)$st unit.

Now, if $C(x)$ is differentiable, then $C'(x) = \lim_{h \to 0} \dfrac{C(x + h) - C(x)}{h}$. If $h = 1$, the difference quotient becomes $\dfrac{C(x + 1) - C(x)}{1} = C(x + 1) - C(x)$, which is the cost of producing the $(x + 1)$st unit. Thus, if the cost function $C(x)$, is reasonably well behaved, then $C'(x)$ is close to the cost of production of the $(x + 1)$th unit. $C'(x)$ is called the **marginal cost at x units of production.**

EXAMPLE Suppose the cost function for x units of a chemical fertilizer is given by $C(x) = 6x^2 + x + 30$. Find the cost of producing the 101st unit. Also, find the marginal cost of production at 100 units.

Solution The cost of producing the 101st unit is $C(101) - C(100) = 6(101)^2 + 101 + 30 - (6(100)^2 + 100 + 30) = 1207$.

The marginal cost of production at x is $C'(x) = 12x + 1$. Thus, $C'(100) = 1201$.

A notion analogous to that of marginal cost is that of **marginal revenue.** If $R(x)$ is a differentiable function representing the revenue from the sale of x units of an item, then $R'(x)$ is called the **marginal revenue at x units of sales.** Also, the revenue from the sale of the $(x + 1)$st unit is $R(x + 1) - R(x)$. If $R(x)$ is reasonably well behaved, then $R'(x)$ is close to the revenue from the sale of the $(x + 1)$st unit.

EXAMPLE If $R(x) = 4x^2 - \dfrac{500}{x + 1} + \dfrac{10,000}{\sqrt{x + 2}}$ is the revenue function for a bicycle manufacturer, find, to the nearest integer, the marginal revenue at 50 units of sales and find to the nearest integer, the revenue from the sale of the 51st unit.

Solution Since $R'(x) = 8x + \dfrac{500}{(x+1)^2} - \dfrac{10,000}{2(x+2)^{3/2}}$,

$$R'(50) = 400 + \frac{500}{51^2} - \frac{10,000}{2(52)^{3/2}}$$

which is approximately 386.8. Thus, to the nearest integer, the marginal revenue at 50 units of sales is 387.

Also, the revenue from the sale of the 51st unit is

$$R(51) - R(50) = 4 \cdot 51^2 - \frac{500}{52} + \frac{10,000}{\sqrt{53}} - \left(4 \cdot 50^2 - \frac{500}{51} + \frac{10,000}{\sqrt{52}}\right)$$

which is approximately 391.

Sometimes a producer is able to predict the **demand** (how many units purchasers will buy) for his product in terms of the price, p, per unit. This is expressed by a **demand function, $D(p)$.**

EXAMPLE Suppose a producer determines that the demand function for his product is given by $D(p) = 400 - 2p$, where $0 \le p \le 200$ and p is measured in dollars. Suppose his cost function, measured in dollars, is $C(x) = 1000 + 10x$, $x \ge 0$.

(a) Express the price p as a function of the number x of units sold.

(b) Find the revenue function, $R(x)$. That is, express the revenue as a function of x.

(c) How many units, x, must be sold to maximize the revenue? What price should be charged to maximize the revenue?

(d) Find the profit function, $P(x)$. That is, express the profit as a function of x.

(e) How many units, x, must be sold to maximize the profit? What price should be charged to maximize the profit?

Solution (a) Since $D(p) = 400 - 2p$, we may write $x = 400 - 2p$ and so

$$p = \frac{400 - x}{2} = 200 - \frac{x}{2}$$

(b) The revenue is the number of units sold multiplied by the price per unit. Thus,

$$R(x) = xp = x\left(200 - \frac{x}{2}\right) = 200x - \frac{x^2}{2}$$

(c) Since $R'(x) = -x + 200$, $R'(x) = 0$ when $x = 200$. Since $R''(200) = -1 < 0$, R has a relative maximum at $x = 200$. Also, $x \geq 0$ and (since $p \geq 0$), $x \leq 400$. Checking at the endpoints, we see that $R(0) = R(400) = 0$ and so R has an absolute maximum at $x = 200$. When $x = 200$, the price $p = 200 - \dfrac{x}{2} = \$100$ and R has the maximum value $R(200) = \$20,000$.

(d) The profit is the revenue less the cost. That is,

$$P(x) = R(x) - C(x)$$

Thus, $P(x) = 200x - \dfrac{x^2}{2} - (1000 + 10x) = \dfrac{-x^2}{2} + 190x - 1000$.

(e) Since $P'(x) = -x + 190$, $P'(x) = 0$ when $x = 190$. Since $P''(190) = -1 < 0$, $P(x)$ has a relative maximum at $x = 190$. Also, since $0 \leq x \leq 400$, we check the endpoints to find

$$P(0) = -1000 \qquad \text{(a \$1000 loss)}$$

and

$$P(400) = -5000 \qquad \text{(a \$5000 loss)}$$

Thus, P has an absolute maximum at 190. When $x = 190$, the price $p = 200 - \dfrac{x}{2} = \$105$ and P has the maximum value $P(190) = \$17,050$.

EXERCISES

In 1–4, (a) find, to the nearest integer, the marginal cost at 40 units of production, and (b) find, to the nearest integer, the cost of production of the 41st unit.

1. $C(x) = x^2 + 3x + 10$

2. $C(x) = 3x^3 - x^2 + \dfrac{1}{x}$

3. $C(x) = \sqrt{x} - \dfrac{1}{x+1}$

4. $C(x) = 2x^2 + x^{3/2} + 10$

In 5–8, (a) find, to the nearest integer, the marginal revenue at 30 units of sales, and (b) find, to the nearest integer, the revenue from the sale of the 31st unit.

5. $R(x) = 5x^2 - x + 20$

6. $R(x) = x^3 + 2x^2 - \dfrac{10}{x}$

7. $R(x) = 2\sqrt{x} + \dfrac{1}{x^2}$

8. $R(x) = 3x^3 + x^{5/2} + 100$

9. Let $P(x) = \dfrac{-x^2}{2} + 50x$ be the profit function for a manufacturer of digital watches; that is, $P(x)$ is the profit in dollars from the sale of the first x units.

(a) Write a formula for the **marginal profit** at x units of sales.

(b) Find the marginal profit at 30 units of sales.

(c) Find the profit from the sale of the 31st unit.

(d) How many watches should be sold to maximize the profit?

10. Let $P(x) = \dfrac{x^3}{3} + 5x^2 - 2000x$ be the profit function for an electric utility.

(a) For what volume of sales is the marginal profit 0?

(b) For which volumes of sales is the marginal profit negative?

(c) For which volumes of sales is the marginal profit positive? (Remember we must have $x \geq 0$.)

11. The demand function for a producer is given by $D(p) = 500 - p$, where $0 \leq p \leq 500$ and p is measured in dollars. Also, the cost function, measured in dollars, is $C(x) = 2000 + 5x$, $x \geq 0$.

(a) Express the price p as a function of the number of units sold x.

(b) Find the revenue function, $R(x)$.

(c) How many units must be sold in order to maximize the revenue? What price should be charged to maximize the revenue?

(d) Find the profit function, $P(x)$.

(e) How many units must be sold in order to maximize the profit? What price should be charged to maximize the profit?

12. Do the previous problem if $D(p) = 400 - p^2$, $0 \leq p \leq 20$, and $C(x) = 2000 + 20x$, $x \geq 0$.

13. Prove that if the revenue function and the cost function are both differentiable, then whenever the profit is maximal, the marginal cost is equal to the marginal revenue.

14. If $x = D(p)$ is a demand function which depends only on price p, then we define $E(p)$, the **price elasticity of demand at price p,** to be $\dfrac{p}{x}\dfrac{dx}{dp}$. Recall that the revenue function R is the product of the demand function and the price per unit function, that is, $R = x \cdot p$.

(a) Demand is called **inelastic** on some price interval if $E(p) > -1$ on that interval. Show that the revenue, as a function of price, is increasing when the demand is inelastic. [*Hint:* First write $R(p) = D(p) \cdot p$.]

(b) Demand has **unit elasticity** on some price interval if $E(p) = -1$ on that interval. Show that the revenue, as a function of price, is constant when the demand has unit elasticity.

(c) Demand is called **elastic** on some price interval if $E(p) < -1$ on that interval. Show that the revenue, as a function of price, is decreasing when the demand is elastic.

(d) Suppose $x = D(p) = 200 - \dfrac{p}{4}$, where p is measured in dollars, $0 \leq p \leq 800$. For which price interval is the demand inelastic? For which price interval is the demand elastic? What conclusion can you draw concerning maximizing the revenue?

15. The owner of a large wine store wishes to develop an optimal ordering policy for a popular wine which she carries. Each bottle costs her $10. In addition, each time she places an order, the distributor charges an ordering fee of $20. She estimates that **inventory costs** per bottle per year are $8; that is, it costs $8 per year to store and process each bottle. She plans to sell 2000 bottles in a year. We will assume that the demand for the wine is constant throughout the year and that her supply is exhausted just as the next shipment arrives.

(a) If she places x orders of equal size and equally spaced per year, write a formula for $C(x)$, the total cost to her. [*Hint:* When you compute her inventory cost, use the fact that in the time between consecutive orders, the average bottle is in her store only one-half the time.]

(b) How many orders should she place per year to minimize her yearly cost? How many bottles per order?

(c) If, in general, the ordering fee is $A per order, the inventory cost per item per year is $B, and D items which cost $E each are to be sold each year, find (in terms of A, B, D and E) the **optimal reorder quantity**. That is, find the number of items per order (all orders are of equal size and are equally spaced) which minimizes the yearly cost.

6   Related Rates and Parametric Equations

It may happen that we are interested in the rate of change of one quantity with respect to a second but we are not given a direct functional relationship between the two quantities. If, however, we are given information about other quantities which are related to both quantities, we may be able to obtain the desired information, usually via the Chain Rule.

EXAMPLE Suppose water is being poured into a cubical tank at the rate of 100 cubic feet per minute (ft³/min). Suppose the side of the cube measures 20 feet. Find the rate at which the depth of the water in the tank is changing with respect to time.

Solution Let $V = V(t)$ be the volume of water in the tank at time t, when the water has been flowing for t minutes (see Fig. 4-36). We are given $\dfrac{dV}{dt} = 100$ ft³/min. If $h = h(t)$ is the depth of the water at time t,

we are asked to find $\dfrac{dh}{dt}$. We know that $V = 20 \cdot 20 \cdot h = 400\,h$ ft³. Thus,

$$\frac{dV}{dt} = \frac{d}{dt}400h = 400\frac{dh}{dt}. \text{ Thus, } \frac{dh}{dt} = \frac{1}{400}\frac{dV}{dt} = \frac{1}{400} \cdot 100 = \frac{1}{4}\text{ft/min.}$$

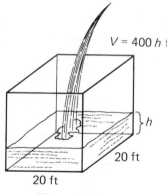

$V = 400\,h$ ft.³

h

20 ft

20 ft

Figure 4–36

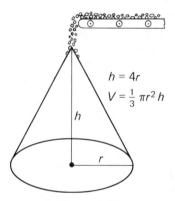

$h = 4r$

$V = \dfrac{1}{3}\pi r^2 h$

h

r

Figure 4–37

EXAMPLE Suppose coal is being dropped from a conveyor belt into a (right circular) conical pile at the rate of 1200 ft³/min (see Fig. 4-37). Suppose also that the height of the conical pile is always four times its radius. Find the rate at which the radius is changing (with respect to time) when the height is 80 feet.

Solution If $V = V(t)$ is the volume of the conical pile at time t, then we know $\dfrac{dV}{dt} = 1200$ ft³/min. Let $r = r(t)$ be the radius of the cone at time t and let $h = h(t)$ be the height of the cone at time t. We are given $h = 4r$ and we are asked to find $\dfrac{dr}{dt}$ when $h = 80$ ft. Now, V is given by the formula $V = \dfrac{1}{3}\pi r^2 h$ and, since $h = 4r$, $V = \dfrac{4}{3}\pi r^3$. Thus,

$$\frac{dV}{dt} = \frac{4}{3}\pi \cdot 3r^2 \frac{dr}{dt} = 4\pi r^2 \frac{dr}{dt}$$

So, since $\dfrac{dV}{dt} = 1200$, we have

$$1200 = 4\pi r^2 \frac{dr}{dt}$$

or

$$\frac{dr}{dt} = \frac{1200}{4\pi r^2} = \frac{300}{\pi r^2}$$

Now, when $h = 80$, $r = 20$, and so $\dfrac{dr}{dt} = \dfrac{300}{400\pi} = \dfrac{3}{4\pi}$ ft/min (which is approximately 2.86 inches per minute).

EXAMPLE Two ships, A and B, leave a port at midnight. Ship A sails due east at 20 miles per hour and ship B sails due north at 15 miles per hour. Find the rate at which the ships are separating.

Solution If $s = s(t)$ is the distance between A and B after t hours of travel (see Fig. 4-38), then we are asked to find $\dfrac{ds}{dt}$. Notice that, by the Pythagorean Theorem, $(15t)^2 + (20t)^2 = (s(t))^2$ so that $(s(t))^2 = (25t)^2$ and $s(t) = 25t$. Then, $\dfrac{ds}{dt} = 25$ miles per hour.

EXAMPLE The top of a 12-meter ladder which is leaning against a vertical wall begins to slide down the wall at the rate of 3 meters per second (m/sec). Find the rate at which the bottom of the ladder is moving away from the wall when the top of the ladder is 8 meters from the ground.

Solution Let $x = x(t)$ represent the distance from the top of the ladder to the ground at time t seconds and let $y = y(t)$ represent the distance from the bottom of the ladder to the wall (see Fig. 4-39). Then, we are given $\dfrac{dx}{dt} = -3$m/sec. Notice that $\dfrac{dx}{dt}$ is negative because x is decreasing as t increases. We must find $\dfrac{dy}{dt}$ when $x = 8$ meters. Now, the Pythagorean Theorem tells us that $y = \sqrt{144 - x^2} =$

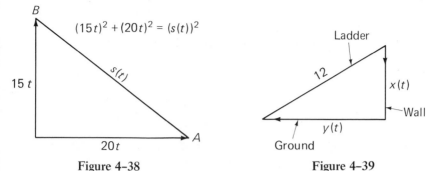

Figure 4–38   Figure 4–39

$(144 - x^2)^{1/2}$ and so $\dfrac{dy}{dt} = \dfrac{1}{2}(144 - x^2)^{-1/2}\left(-2x\,\dfrac{dx}{dt}\right)$. When $x = 8$,

$$\frac{dy}{dt} = \frac{1}{2}(80)^{-1/2}(-16 \cdot -3) = \frac{48}{2\sqrt{80}} = \frac{6}{\sqrt{5}} = \frac{6\sqrt{5}}{5}\ \text{m/sec}$$

which is approximately 2.68 m/sec.

EXAMPLE   Two straight roads leave a town and form a 45° angle. Car A leaves town and travels along one road at 50 kilometers per hour (km/hr) and car B leaves town and travels along the other road at 60 km/hr. If car B leaves town one hour after car A, find the rate at which the cars are separating when car A is 100 km from the town.

Solution   Let $s = s(t)$, $t \geq 1$, be the distance between A and B after car A has traveled t hours (see Fig. 4-40). We must find $\dfrac{ds}{dt}$ when $t = 2$ hours. The Law of Cosines tells us that

$$(s(t))^2 = (50t)^2 + (60(t - 1))^2 - 2 \cos 45° \cdot 50t \cdot 60(t - 1)$$

Thus,

$$(s(t))^2 = 2500t^2 + 3600(t^2 - 2t + 1) - 2 \cdot \frac{\sqrt{2}}{2}(3000t^2 - 3000t)$$

$$= (6100 - 3000\sqrt{2})t^2 - (7200 - 3000\sqrt{2})t + 3600$$

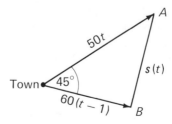

Figure 4–40

Differentiation of both sides with respect to t gives

$$2s\frac{ds}{dt} = 2(6100 - 3000\sqrt{2})t - (7200 - 3000\sqrt{2})$$

and so

$$\frac{ds}{dt} = \frac{(6100 - 3000\sqrt{2})t}{s} - \frac{3600 - 1500\sqrt{2}}{s}$$

Now, when $t = 2$, $s^2 = 10,000 + 3600 - 6000\sqrt{2} = 13,600 - 6000\sqrt{2}$. Thus, $s = \sqrt{13,600 - 6000\sqrt{2}} = 20\sqrt{34 - 15\sqrt{2}}$ km. Finally, then, when $t = 2$ hours,

$$\frac{ds}{dt} = \frac{(6100 - 3000\sqrt{2})2}{20\sqrt{34 - 15\sqrt{2}}} - \frac{3600 - 1500\sqrt{2}}{20\sqrt{34 - 15\sqrt{2}}} = \frac{430 - 225\sqrt{2}}{\sqrt{34 - 15\sqrt{2}}} \text{ km/hr}$$

(which is approximately 31.27 km/hr).

A problem closely related to that of related rates is that of finding derivatives when the variables are defined **parametrically**. Specifically, suppose x and y are each defined in terms of a third variable (parameter), t. Then the problem is to find $\dfrac{dy}{dx}$.

EXAMPLE Suppose x and y are defined parametrically by $x = t^2 - 1$ and $y = t^3 + 2$. Find $\dfrac{dy}{dx}$ and $\dfrac{d^2y}{dx^2}$.

Solution $\dfrac{dx}{dt} = 2t$ and $\dfrac{dy}{dt} = 3t^2$. The Chain Rule tells us that $\dfrac{dy}{dt} = \dfrac{dy}{dx} \cdot \dfrac{dx}{dt}$ or $\dfrac{dy}{dx} = \dfrac{dy/dt}{dx/dt}$. Thus, $\dfrac{dy}{dx} = \dfrac{3t^2}{2t} = \dfrac{3t}{2}$.

Also,

$$\frac{d^2y}{dx^2} = \frac{d}{dx}\left(\frac{dy}{dx}\right) = \frac{d}{dx}\left(\frac{3t}{2}\right) = \frac{d}{dt}\left(\frac{3t}{2}\right) \cdot \frac{dt}{dx} \quad \text{(by the Chain Rule)}$$

$$= \frac{3}{2} \cdot \frac{1}{dx/dt} = \frac{3}{2} \cdot \frac{1}{2t} = \frac{3}{4t} \quad \text{(differentiation of an inverse function)}$$

EXAMPLE If $x = \sqrt{t^2 + 5}$ and $y = t^3 - 2t^2$, find $\dfrac{dy}{dx}$ when $t = 2$.

Solution $\dfrac{dy}{dx} = \dfrac{dy/dt}{dx/dt}$. Now,

$$\frac{dy}{dt} = 3t^2 - 4t$$

and

$$\frac{dx}{dt} = \frac{1}{2}(t^2 + 5)^{-1/2} \cdot 2t = \frac{t}{\sqrt{t^2 + 5}}$$

Thus, $\dfrac{dy}{dx} = \dfrac{3t^2 - 4t}{t/\sqrt{t^2 + 5}}$. When $t = 2$, $\dfrac{dy}{dx} = \dfrac{3 \cdot 4 - 4 \cdot 2}{2/\sqrt{4 + 5}} = 6$.

E X E R C I S E S

1. A spherical balloon is being inflated so that the volume is increasing by 10 cubic inches per second (in.³/sec). What is the rate of change of the radius when the radius is 10 inches? (Recall that the volume of a sphere is given by the formula $V = \dfrac{4}{3}\pi r^3$, where r is the radius.)

2. An inflated spherical balloon is punctured and the volume decreases by 12 in.³/sec. What is the rate of change of the diameter when the diameter is 3 inches?

3. A 26-foot ladder is leaning against a vertical wall. The bottom of the ladder, which is on the horizontal, is being pulled away from the wall at the rate of 2 ft/sec. Find the rate at which the top of the ladder is moving down the wall when the bottom of the ladder is 10 ft from the wall.

4. A water tank in the shape of an inverted right circular cone is being emptied at the rate of 20 ft³/min. Suppose the radius of the cone is 10 feet and the height of the cone is 30 feet. Find the rate at which the water level is falling when the water is 15 feet deep. [*Hint:* If $r = r(t)$ is the radius of the water surface at time t and if $h = h(t)$ is the height of the water at time t, then the dimensions of the tank determine a simple relationship between r and h.]

5. A particle is moving counterclockwise around the circular path whose equation is $x^2 + y^2 = 100$. If the abscissa (*x*-coordinate) of the particle is increasing by 72 in./sec at a point where $x = 8$, find the rate of change of the ordinate (*y*-coordinate) at this point.

6. A particle moves clockwise around the ellipse whose equation is $x^2 + 4y^2 = 9$. If the ordinate of the particle is increasing by 100 cm/sec at a point where $y = 1$, find the rate of change of the abscissa at this point.

7. A boy standing in one place is flying a kite at a height of 60 feet. Suppose the kite is moving in a straight line parallel to the level ground at a rate of .5 ft/sec. If the kite string is taut and there is 100 feet of string paid out, at what rate is the string being paid out?

8. A man who is 6 feet tall walks in a straight line at 20 ft/min and passes under a light which is 16 feet above the ground. Find the rate at which the man's shadow is increasing. [*Hint:* Use similar triangles to relate the length of his shadow to his distance to the point directly under the light.]

9. One ship is traveling in a straight line to a port at 20 mph. A second ship is traveling in a straight line away from the port at 25 mph. If the angle between the two paths is 60°, find the rate at which the distance between the two ships is changing when the slower ship is 200 miles from port and the faster ship is 100 miles from port. [*Hint:* Use the Law of Cosines to relate the distance between the ships to the distances of the ships from port.]

10. The formula for the surface area of a sphere is $A = 4\pi r^2$, where r is the radius. If the volume of a sphere is increasing by 100 cm³/sec, find the rate of change of the surface area when the radius is 5 cm.

11. One particle moves along the x-axis with equation of motion $s_1(t) = t^2 + t^{1/2}$, that is, $s_1(t)$ is its position on the x-axis at time t. Another particle moves along the y-axis with equation of motion $s_2(t) = t^3 - t + 1$. At time $t = 3$, what is the rate of change with respect to t of the distance between the two particles?

12. One particle moves along the x-axis with equation of motion $s_1(t) = t^3 + 3t - 1$, that is, $s_1(t)$ is its position on the x-axis at time t. Another particle moves along the y-axis with equation of motion $s_2(t) = t^2 - t + 2$. At time $t = 2$, what is the rate of change with respect to t of the distance between the two particles?

13. If x and y are defined parametrically in terms of t, then find $\dfrac{dy}{dx}$ and $\dfrac{d^2y}{dx^2}$ if

   (a) $x = 2t^2 - t;\ y = 1/t$
   (b) $x = \sqrt{t};\ y = t^2$
   (c) $x = (t + 1)^{3/2};\ y = (t^2 - 1)^{-1/2}$
   (d) $x = t + \sqrt{t};\ y = t^3$

14. Suppose a curve is defined parametrically by the equations $x = x(t)$ and $y = y(t)$. The curve is actually the set of ordered pairs $(x(t),y(t))$. Find an equation of the tangent to the curve at the point $(x(4),y(4))$ corresponding to $t = 4$ if

(a) $x = x(t) = t^2$ and $y = y(t) = \sqrt{t}$

(b) $x = x(t) = \dfrac{1}{t^2 - 15}$ and $y = y(t) = t^3 + 2t$

[*Hint:* First find the slope of the tangent to the curve and then find an equation of the tangent.]

Chapter 5

Trigonometric, Exponential, and Logarithmic Functions and Indeterminate Forms

1 The Trigonometric Functions

If a number $\theta \geqq 0$ is given, then the **angle**, $\angle POQ$, of θ **radians** (in "standard position") is obtained as follows. Start at the point $P = (1,0)$ on the unit circle (whose equation is $x^2 + y^2 = 1$) and travel around the circle in a counterclockwise (**positive**) direction stopping at the point Q such that the total length of circular arc that has been traversed (distance traveled) is exactly θ (see Fig. 5-1). If

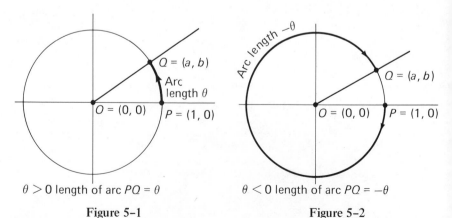

$\theta > 0$ length of arc $PQ = \theta$

Figure 5–1

$\theta < 0$ length of arc $PQ = -\theta$

Figure 5–2

$\theta < 0$, the description of how to locate Q is the same except that one goes from P in the clockwise (**negative**) direction and the total arc length traversed is to be $-\theta > 0$ (see **Fig. 5-2**). In either case, when a number θ is given, this locates a point $Q = (a,b)$ on the unit circle and we **define** $\cos\theta = a$ and $\sin\theta = b$. Since Q is on the unit circle ($a^2 + b^2 = 1$), we have the identity

$$\cos^2\theta + \sin^2\theta = 1 \tag{1}$$

[We adopt here the usual convention of writing $\cos^2\theta$ instead of $(\cos\theta)^2$.] We denote by π the length of the upper half of the unit circle from $(1,0)$ to $(-1,0)$. Thus 2π is the length (circumference) of the entire unit circle. It is apparent that the point Q determined by any given number θ is the same as the point determined by $\theta + 2\pi n$ for any integer n. Thus we have

$$\cos(\theta + 2n\pi) = \cos\theta \quad \text{and} \quad \sin(\theta + 2n\pi) = \sin\theta \tag{2}$$

for any integer n and any real number θ. For any θ, the line segment QQ' joining the point Q determined by θ to the point Q' determined by $-\theta$ is vertical and bisected by the x-axis (see **Fig. 5-3**), and so we have the identities

$$\cos(-\theta) = \cos\theta \quad \text{and} \quad \sin(-\theta) = -\sin\theta \tag{3}$$

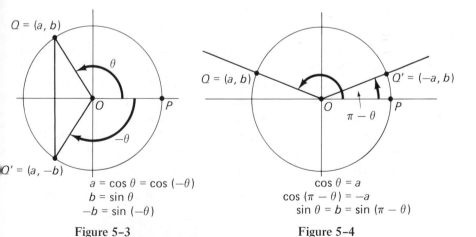

$a = \cos\theta = \cos(-\theta)$
$b = \sin\theta$
$-b = \sin(-\theta)$

Figure 5-3

$\cos\theta = a$
$\cos(\pi - \theta) = -a$
$\sin\theta = b = \sin(\pi - \theta)$

Figure 5-4

It is also clear from **Fig. 5-4** (at least for $0 \le \theta \le \pi$) that

$$\cos(\pi - \theta) = -\cos\theta \quad \text{and} \quad \sin(\pi - \theta) = \sin\theta \tag{4}$$

By using (2)–(4), the cosine and sine of any number can be expressed in terms of those for some number between 0 and $\pi/2$ (inclusive).

EXAMPLE   Express $\cos\left(\dfrac{36\pi}{7}\right)$ in terms of the cosine of some number between 0 and $\pi/2$.

Solution   We have

$$\cos\left(\frac{36\pi}{7}\right) = \cos\left(\frac{36\pi}{7} - 6\pi\right) = \cos\left(-\frac{6\pi}{7}\right)$$

$$= \cos\frac{6\pi}{7} = -\cos\left(\pi - \frac{6\pi}{7}\right) = -\cos\frac{\pi}{7}$$

where we first used (2) to change $36\pi/7$ to some number between $-\pi$ and π and then we used (3) and (4).

Of course, we all know that angles are frequently measured in degrees instead of radians. All that needs to be known in order to convert from one system of angle measurement to the other is that the straight angle ($Q = (-1,0)$) contains 180°, which is π radians. Thus we have

$$\boxed{\theta \text{ radians} = \left(\frac{180\theta}{\pi}\right)^\circ}$$

and

$$\boxed{d^\circ = \frac{\pi d}{180} \text{ radians}}$$

It must be clearly understood that the functions sin (sine) and cos (cosine) that we discuss in calculus are functions of a real number variable. The θ that appears in the symbol $\cos\theta$ is a real number with *no* "units" attached. These functions can be used to discuss angles *provided* that θ is interpreted to refer to an angle of measure θ radians *(not degrees)*. For instance, we recall that the sine of an angle of 30° is 1/2, *but* $\sin 30 \neq 1/2$. In fact, $9\pi < 30 < 10\pi, -\pi < 30 - 10\pi < 0$, and so $\sin 30 = \sin(30 - 10\pi) < 0$. We do have $30° = \pi/6$ radians and it is true that $\sin\dfrac{\pi}{6} = \dfrac{1}{2}$. In Table 5-1 we list the sines and cosines of some commonly occurring angles ($d° = \theta$ radians).

The not entirely obvious entries for 30°, 45°, and 60° can be easily verified by considering a square of diagonal 1 and an equilateral triangle of side 1 along with the Pythagorean Theorem (see Fig. 5-5). Of course, we can compute the values of $\sin\theta$ and $\cos\theta$ only for a few

Table 5-1

$d°$	θ	Q	$\cos \theta$	$\sin \theta$
0°	0	$(1,0)$	1	0
30°	$\pi/6$	$\left(\dfrac{\sqrt{3}}{2},\dfrac{1}{2}\right)$	$\sqrt{3}/2$	$1/2$
45°	$\pi/4$	$\left(\dfrac{1}{\sqrt{2}},\dfrac{1}{\sqrt{2}}\right)$	$1/\sqrt{2}$	$1/\sqrt{2}$
60°	$\pi/3$	$\left(\dfrac{1}{2},\dfrac{\sqrt{3}}{2}\right)$	$1/2$	$\sqrt{3}/2$
90°	$\pi/2$	$(0,1)$	0	1
180°	π	$(-1,0)$	-1	0
270°	$3\pi/2$	$(0,-1)$	0	-1
360°	2π	$(1,0)$	1	0

special values of θ by simple geometrical constructions. Later on after having studied about power series (pages 487–493), we shall see how these values can be computed to any desired degree of accuracy for any given θ at all. This will answer at last the gnawing question as to the source of the trigonometric tables.

All of what has been said in the preceding material depends on our having a firm grasp on what is *meant* by "the length of a circular arc." Of course, we have a very good intuitive idea of what this means, but, in this book, so far we have only *defined* "length" for line segments by using the distance formula. Later on, after we have studied the definite integral, we shall *define* "arc length" for very general

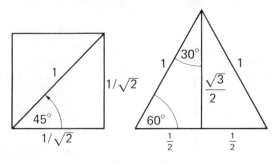

Figure 5-5

curves in the plane. In the meantime, we shall sketch briefly a time-honored geometrical method of handling circular arc length and area.

Suppose that P and Q are two distinct points on a circle of radius r centered at O. Let n be any positive integer. Divide the arc from P to Q (taken counterclockwise) into n congruent arcs. In each of these small arcs, draw the chord joining its endpoints. Also join each such endpoint to O by a radial line. In this way we form n isosceles triangles each having base b_n and height h_n (see Fig. 5-6 for the case $n = 4$). The n chords form a polygonal line having perimeter (total length) $p_n = nb_n$ and it, along with the segments OP and OQ, forms a closed polygon surrounding a region whose area A_n is exactly n times the area of any one of the isosceles triangles. Thus,

$$A_n = n\left(\frac{1}{2}b_n h_n\right) = \frac{p_n h_n}{2}$$

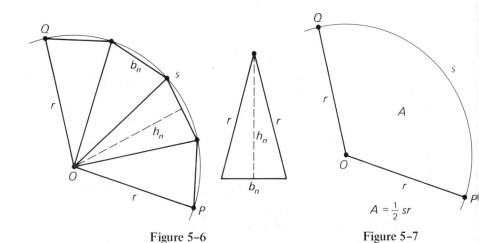

Figure 5-6   Figure 5-7

It can be proved that there exists a unique number s such that

$$\lim_{n \to \infty} p_n = s$$

This seems intuitively evident. We call this number s the **length** of the circular arc PQ. It also seems clear and it can be proved that

$$\lim_{n \to \infty} h_n = r$$

From this, we obtain

$$\lim_{n \to \infty} A_n = \lim_{n \to \infty} \frac{p_n h_n}{2} = \frac{sr}{2}$$

Thus we define the area A of the circular sector OPQ shown in Fig. 5-7 by

$$A = \frac{1}{2}sr \qquad (5)$$

Notice that if the above constructions are carried out for another radius $r' > 0$ and if the number c is defined by $c = r'/r$, a consideration of similar triangles (see Fig. 5-8) shows that the new chords have lengths $b'_n = cb_n$ and so the length s' of the circular arc $P'Q'$ is given by $s' = \lim_{n \to \infty} nb'_n = \lim_{n \to \infty} ncb_n = c \cdot \lim_{n \to \infty} nb_n = cs$ from which we see that

$$\frac{s'}{r'} = \frac{cs}{cr} = \frac{s}{r}$$

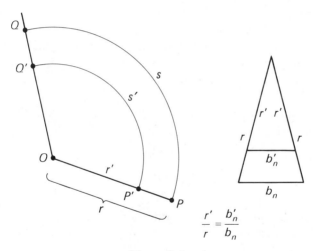

Figure 5–8

It follows from this that the value of the ratio s/r does not depend on r but merely on the angle POQ. Thus, we define the radian measure of the angle POQ to be the number

$$\theta = \frac{s}{r} \qquad (6)$$

Now (5) and (6) yield $s = r\theta$ and so

$$A = \frac{1}{2}\theta r^2 \qquad (7)$$

It is essential in applying this formula for the area of sector POQ that the number θ be the measure of angle POQ in *radians, not degrees.* For example, if $r = 1$ and POQ is a right angle, then sector POQ has area $A = \dfrac{1}{2} \cdot \dfrac{\pi}{2} \cdot 1^2 = \dfrac{\pi}{4}$, *not* $\dfrac{1}{2} \cdot 90 \cdot 1^2 = 45$. The maxim is:

When applying calculus to geometry, always measure angles in radians.

In case $\theta = 2\pi$, (6) and (7) yield the familiar formulas

$$\boxed{\quad s = 2\pi r \qquad \text{and} \qquad A = \pi r^2 \quad}$$

for the circumference and area of a circle of radius r.

Returning to the case $r = 1$ and Fig. 5-1, we see from (7) that, for $0 \le \theta \le \pi$, the point Q determined by θ is just the point on the upper half of the unit circle such that the area of the sector OPQ is $\theta/2$ where π denotes the area of the disc bounded by the unit circle. Thus we see that the functions sin and cos can be defined in terms of areas of circular sectors with no mention of arc length at all. We take this viewpoint in Chapter 6, section 8, where we give an analytically precise definition of these two functions. It is precise because we give earlier in that chapter a precise definition of "area."

The number π is known to be irrational; it is not equal to any number of the form m/n where m and n are integers. The decimal expansion of π contains no repeating block of digits (any number that does is rational). The rational number

$$\frac{22}{7} = 3.142857\ 142857 \cdots$$

is often used as an "approximation" to π. The actual decimal expansion of π (carried out to 15 digits) is $\pi = 3.14159265358979 \cdots$. Thus

$$.00126448 < \frac{22}{7} - \pi < .00126450$$

Methods for computing rational approximations to π that are as accurate as desired will be found in Chapter 10.

The remaining four trigonometric functions that are commonly used are the tangent (tan), cotangent (cot), secant (sec), and cosecant (csc). They are defined by the formulas

$$\boxed{\begin{array}{ll} \tan \theta = \dfrac{\sin \theta}{\cos \theta} & \cot \theta = \dfrac{\cos \theta}{\sin \theta} \\[2ex] \sec \theta = \dfrac{1}{\cos \theta} & \csc \theta = \dfrac{1}{\sin \theta} \end{array}}$$

for all real numbers θ that do not force division by 0. Thus tan and sec are defined except at odd multiples of $\pi/2$ (where cos is 0) while cot and csc are defined except at multiples of π (where sin is 0).

The portions of the graphs of the functions sin, cos, tan, and sec corresponding to $-\pi/2 \leq x \leq 3\pi/2$ are shown in Fig. 5-9. The remainders of the graphs are obtained by repeating these pictures on successive adjacent intervals of length 2π as the identities (2) show.

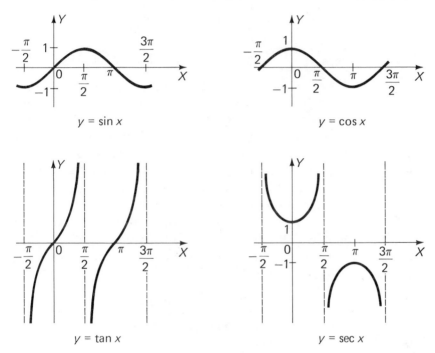

Figure 5–9

2 Trigonometric Identities

Beyond identities (1)–(4) of the preceding section, the most important identities satisfied by sin and cos are the **addition formulas**, which are

$$\cos (\alpha + \beta) = \cos \alpha \cos \beta - \sin \alpha \sin \beta \qquad (1)$$

and

$$\sin (\alpha + \beta) = \sin \alpha \cos \beta + \cos \alpha \sin \beta \qquad (2)$$

These formulas are valid for any two real numbers α and β. Geometrical proofs of these formulas can be found in any trigonometry book. We prove them analytically in Chapter 6. Taking $\beta = \alpha$, we obtain the **double-angle formulas**

$$\cos 2\alpha = \cos^2 \alpha - \sin^2 \alpha \qquad\qquad (3)$$

and

$$\sin 2\alpha = 2 \sin \alpha \cos \alpha \qquad\qquad (4)$$

Since $\sin^2 \alpha + \cos^2 \alpha = 1$, it follows from (3) that $1 - 2 \sin^2 \alpha = \cos 2\alpha = 2 \cos^2 \alpha - 1$ and so we obtain the **half-angle formulas**

$$\sin^2 \alpha = \frac{1}{2}(1 - \cos 2\alpha) \qquad\qquad (5)$$

and

$$\cos^2 \alpha = \frac{1}{2}(1 + \cos 2\alpha) \qquad\qquad (6)$$

Replacing β by $-\beta$ in (1) and (2) and using $\cos(-\beta) = \cos \beta$ and $\sin(-\beta) = -\sin \beta$, we obtain

$$\cos(\alpha - \beta) = \cos \alpha \cos \beta + \sin \alpha \sin \beta \qquad\qquad (7)$$

and

$$\sin(\alpha - \beta) = \sin \alpha \cos \beta - \cos \alpha \sin \beta \qquad\qquad (8)$$

Adding (1) and (7) gives

$$2 \cos \alpha \cos \beta = \cos(\alpha + \beta) + \cos(\alpha - \beta) \qquad\qquad (9)$$

while subtracting (1) from (7) gives

$$2 \sin \alpha \sin \beta = \cos(\alpha - \beta) - \cos(\alpha + \beta) \qquad\qquad (10)$$

Adding (2) and (8) yields

$$2 \sin \alpha \cos \beta = \sin(\alpha + \beta) + \sin(\alpha - \beta) \qquad\qquad (11)$$

These last three identities express products as sums (or differences). If we make the substitutions $u = \alpha + \beta$ and $v = \alpha - \beta$ in them, we obtain

$$\cos u + \cos v = 2 \cos \frac{u + v}{2} \cos \frac{u - v}{2} \qquad\qquad (12)$$

$$\cos u - \cos v = -2 \sin \frac{u+v}{2} \sin \frac{u-v}{2} \qquad (13)$$

and

$$\sin u + \sin v = 2 \sin \frac{u+v}{2} \cos \frac{u-v}{2} \qquad (14)$$

Replacing v by $-v$ in (14) gives

$$\sin u - \sin v = 2 \cos \frac{u+v}{2} \sin \frac{u-v}{2} \qquad (15)$$

Formulas (12) − (15) express a sum (or difference) as a product.

By dividing (2) by (1) and (8) by (7) we obtain the useful formulas

$$\tan (\alpha + \beta) = \frac{\tan \alpha + \tan \beta}{1 - \tan \alpha \tan \beta} \qquad (16)$$

and

$$\tan (\alpha - \beta) = \frac{\tan \alpha - \tan \beta}{1 + \tan \alpha \tan \beta} \qquad (17)$$

where each is valid whenever its right side is meaningful.

Of the above seventeen identities, we strongly recommend that the first two be memorized. We have seen how the other fifteen follow easily from them and so we see no compelling reason that they be committed to memory. We have listed them here for handy reference.

Another identity which we will use later is

$$\sec^2 \theta = 1 + \tan^2 \theta \qquad (18)$$

It is valid whenever $\cos \theta \neq 0$ and it is obtained from the Pythagorean identity $1 = \cos^2 \theta + \sin^2 \theta$ by division by $\cos^2 \theta$.

EXAMPLE   Find the exact value of each of (a) $\sin (\pi/8)$, (b) $\cos (\pi/8)$, and (c) $\cos (7\pi/12)$.

Solution   (a) By formula (5) we have

$$\sin^2 (\pi/8) = \frac{1}{2}[1 - \cos (\pi/4)] = \frac{1}{2}\left[1 - \frac{\sqrt{2}}{2}\right] = \frac{2 - \sqrt{2}}{4}$$

so

$$|\sin (\pi/8)| = \frac{1}{2}\sqrt{2 - \sqrt{2}}$$

But $0 < \pi/8 < \pi$, so that $\sin (\pi/8) > 0$. Thus,

$$\sin (\pi/8) = \frac{1}{2}\sqrt{2 - \sqrt{2}}$$

(b) Using (a) we have

$$\cos^2 (\pi/8) = 1 - \sin^2 (\pi/8) = 1 - \frac{2 - \sqrt{2}}{4} = \frac{2 + \sqrt{2}}{4}$$

Since $\cos x > 0$ for $-\pi/2 < x < \pi/2$, we have

$$\cos (\pi/8) = \frac{1}{2}\sqrt{2 + \sqrt{2}}$$

(c) By (1) of this section, we have

$$\cos (7\pi/12) = \cos (\pi/3 + \pi/4) = \left(\frac{1}{2}\right)\left(\frac{\sqrt{2}}{2}\right) - \left(\frac{\sqrt{3}}{2}\right)\left(\frac{\sqrt{2}}{2}\right) = \frac{\sqrt{2} - \sqrt{6}}{4}$$

EXAMPLE Prove the identities (a) $\cos 3\theta = 4 \cos^3 \theta - 3 \cos \theta$, and (b) $\sin 3\theta = 3 \sin \theta - 4 \sin^3 \theta$.

Solution (a) We have

$$
\begin{aligned}
\cos 3\theta &= \cos \theta \cos 2\theta - \sin \theta \sin 2\theta &\text{(by (1))} \\
&= \cos \theta(2 \cos^2 \theta - 1) - 2 \sin^2 \theta \cos \theta &\text{(by (3) and (4))} \\
&= \cos \theta[(2 \cos^2 \theta - 1) - 2(1 - \cos^2 \theta)] \\
&= \cos \theta(4 \cos^2 \theta - 3) \\
&= 4 \cos^3 \theta - 3 \cos \theta
\end{aligned}
$$

(b) We have

$$
\begin{aligned}
\sin 3\theta &= \sin \theta \cos 2\theta + \cos \theta \sin 2\theta &\text{(by (2) and (4))} \\
&= \sin \theta(1 - 2 \sin^2 \theta) + 2 \sin \theta \cos^2 \theta \\
&= \sin \theta[(1 - 2 \sin^2 \theta) + 2(1 - \sin^2 \theta)] \\
&= \sin \theta[3 - 4 \sin^2 \theta] \\
&= 3 \sin \theta - 4 \sin^3 \theta
\end{aligned}
$$

A function of the form $f(t) = a \cos \omega t + b \sin \omega t$, where a, b, and ω are real constants with $a^2 + b^2 \neq 0$ and $\omega > 0$, is called a **pure harmonic** (or is said to describe **simple harmonic motion**). If we write $r = \sqrt{a^2 + b^2}$, then $(a/r)^2 + (b/r)^2 = 1$ and so there is a unique number t_0, such that $0 \leq t_0 < 2\pi/\omega$, $\cos \omega t_0 = a/r$, and $\sin \omega t_0 = b/r$. In terms of these new constants t_0 and r, we can now write

$$f(t) = r \cos \omega t \cos \omega t_0 + r \sin \omega t \sin \omega t_0$$
$$= r \cos [\omega(t - t_0)] \qquad (19)$$

Since $f(t + 2\pi/\omega) = f(t)$ for all t, we say that f is periodic of **period** $T = 2\pi/\omega$. This number T is also called the **wavelength** of f. The number $1/T = \omega/2\pi$ counts the number of complete oscillations that f makes in each t-interval of length 1, and so we call $\omega/2\pi$ the **frequency** of f. Since as cos oscillates between the values 1 and -1, f oscillates between r and $-r$, the number r is called the **amplitude** of f. The number t_0 is the smallest value of $t > 0$ at which f attains its maximum value r. We call t_0 the **phase displacement** of f. Notice that we can also write f in the form $f(t) = r \sin [\omega(t - t_1)]$ if we take $t_1 = t_0 - \pi/(2\omega)$, since then

$$\sin [\omega(t - t_1)] = \sin \left[\omega(t - t_0) + \frac{\pi}{2} \right] = \cos [\omega(t - t_0)]$$

EXAMPLE Find the period, frequency, amplitude, and phase displacement of the pure harmonic $f(t) = -\cos 4\pi t + \sqrt{3} \sin 4\pi t$. Write f in the form (19) above. Also, sketch a graph of this function.

Solution Here we have $a = -1$, $b = \sqrt{3}$, and $\omega = 4\pi$. The amplitude is $r = \sqrt{a^2 + b^2} = 2$. The period is $T = 2\pi/\omega = 1/2$. The frequency is $1/T = 2$. We want $0 \le t_0 < 2\pi/\omega = T = 1/2$ such that $\cos 4\pi t_0 = a/r = -1/2$ and $\sin 4\pi t_0 = b/r = \sqrt{3}/2$. We must have $4\pi t_0 = 2\pi/3$ and so $t_0 = 1/6$. Filling these answers into (19), we obtain

$$f(t) = 2 \cos [4\pi(t - 1/6)]$$

To graph f, it may be easiest to first graph $g(t) = 2 \cos (4\pi t)$, which is obtained from f by replacing t_0 by 0. The graph of g is like the graph of the cosine function, shown in Fig. 5-9, except that its maximum is $r = 2$ and its minimum is $-r$ while one complete wave occurs on the interval $0 \le t \le 1/2$ (see Fig. 5-10). To obtain the graph of

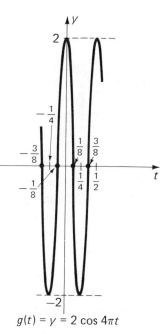

$g(t) = y = 2 \cos 4\pi t$

Figure 5–10

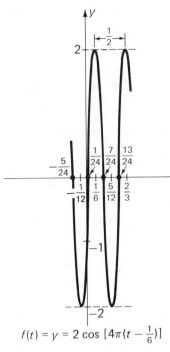

$$f(t) = y = 2 \cos \left[4\pi \left(t - \tfrac{1}{6} \right) \right]$$

Figure 5–11

f, we copy the graph of g except that the y-axis is placed 1/6 unit further to the left. Equivalently, the graph of g is moved 1/6 unit to the right while the axes remain fixed (see Fig. 5-11).

E X E R C I S E S

In 1–6, (a) express the cosine of the given number in terms of the cosine of some number between 0 and $\pi/2$, and (b) express the sine of the given number in terms of the sine of some number between 0 and $\pi/2$.

1. $37\pi/7$ **3.** $-58\pi/5$ **5.** 45

2. $11\pi/9$ **4.** $-7\pi/11$ **6.** 2

In 7–12, express the given function of x in terms of $\sin x$ and/or $\cos x$.

7. $\cos \left(x - \dfrac{\pi}{2} \right)$ **9.** $\cos \left(\dfrac{\pi}{2} - x \right)$ **11.** $\cos \left(x + \dfrac{\pi}{4} \right)$

8. $\sin \left(x - \dfrac{\pi}{2} \right)$ **10.** $\sin \left(\dfrac{\pi}{2} - x \right)$ **12.** $\sin \left(x + \dfrac{\pi}{4} \right)$

In 13–18, (a) find the exact value of the sine of the given number, and (b) find the exact value of the cosine of the given number.

13. $\dfrac{13\pi}{12}$ **15.** $-\dfrac{11\pi}{12}$ **17.** $\dfrac{5\pi}{8}$

14. $-\dfrac{19\pi}{12}$ **16.** $\dfrac{3\pi}{8}$ **18.** $\dfrac{7\pi}{24}$

19. (a) Prove the identity $\cos 5\theta = 16 \cos^5 \theta - 20 \cos^3 \theta + 5 \cos \theta$.

    (b) Prove the identity $(x + 1)(4x^2 - 2x - 1)^2 = 16x^5 - 20x^3 + 5x + 1$.

    (c) Prove that $\cos \dfrac{\pi}{5} = \dfrac{1 + \sqrt{5}}{4}$.

In 20–25, find the period, frequency, amplitude, and phase displacement of the given pure harmonic. Write f in the form (19) of this section and sketch a graph of f.

20. $f(t) = 3 \sin 2t$

21. $f(t) = -\sin 2\pi t$

22. $f(t) = \cos 2t - \sin 2t$

23. $f(t) = \sqrt{3} \cos \pi t + \sin \pi t$

24. $f(t) = -\sqrt{2} \cos 2\pi t - \sqrt{2} \sin 2\pi t$

25. $f(t) = -\cos \pi t$

3 The Derivatives of Trigonometric Functions

It follows from the very definition of derivative given in Chapter 3 that the derivative $\sin' x$ of the function sin at any fixed real number x is equal to the limit as $\theta \to 0$ of the difference quotient

$$\frac{\sin (x + \theta) - \sin x}{\theta}$$

Since the addition formula for sin shows that

$$\sin (x + \theta) - \sin x = \sin x \cos \theta + \cos x \sin \theta - \sin x$$
$$= \cos x \sin \theta - \sin x[1 - \cos \theta]$$

we have

$$\frac{\sin (x + \theta) - \sin x}{\theta} = \cos x \cdot \frac{\sin \theta}{\theta} - \sin x \cdot \frac{1 - \cos \theta}{\theta}$$

Thus, we see that

$$\sin' x = \lim_{\theta \to 0} \left(\cos x \cdot \frac{\sin \theta}{\theta} - \sin x \cdot \frac{1 - \cos \theta}{\theta} \right)$$
$$= \cos x \cdot \lim_{\theta \to 0} \frac{\sin \theta}{\theta} - \sin x \cdot \lim_{\theta \to 0} \frac{1 - \cos \theta}{\theta} \qquad (1)$$

provied that these last two limits exist. We shall show that

$$\lim_{\theta \to 0} \frac{\sin \theta}{\theta} = 1 \qquad (2)$$

and

$$\lim_{\theta \to 0} \frac{1 - \cos \theta}{\theta} = 0 \qquad (3)$$

Once this is done, it will then follow from (1) that

$$\sin' x = \cos x \qquad \text{for all } x \qquad (4)$$

Since

$$\frac{\sin(-\theta)}{-\theta} = \frac{\sin\theta}{\theta}$$

for all $\theta \neq 0$, it is sufficient to consider only those θ for which $0 < \theta < \pi/2$ in order to prove (2).

Fix any θ with $0 < \theta < \pi/2$ and consider Fig. 5-12 in which the radian measure of the angle POQ is θ, $O = (0,0)$, $P = (1,0)$, $Q = (\cos\theta, \sin\theta)$, and segments $\overline{SQ}$ and $\overline{PR}$ are both perpendicular to $\overline{OP}$. For any two points A and B, recall that AB denotes the length of the seg-

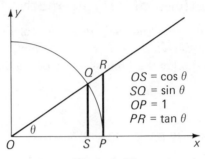

$OS = \cos\theta$
$SQ = \sin\theta$
$OP = 1$
$PR = \tan\theta$

Figure 5-12

ment $\overline{AB}$. Thus we have $OS = \cos\theta$, $SQ = \sin\theta$, $OP = 1$, and, by a consideration of the similar right triangles $\triangle OSQ$ and $\triangle OPR$,

$$PR = \frac{PR}{OP} = \frac{SQ}{OS} = \frac{\sin\theta}{\cos\theta} = \tan\theta$$

Therefore

$$\text{area of } \triangle OSQ = \frac{1}{2}OS \cdot SQ = \frac{1}{2}\cos\theta\sin\theta$$

and

$$\text{area of } \triangle OPR = \frac{1}{2}OP \cdot PR = \frac{1}{2}\frac{\sin\theta}{\cos\theta}$$

According to formula (7) of section 1 (page 217),

$$\text{area of circular sector } OPQ = \frac{\theta}{2}$$

A glance at Fig. 5-12 shows that these three areas stand in the relation

$$\frac{1}{2}\cos\theta\sin\theta < \frac{1}{2}\theta < \frac{1}{2}\frac{\sin\theta}{\cos\theta}$$

These inequalities imply (upon multiplication by $\dfrac{2}{\sin \theta}$ and taking reciprocals) that

$$\frac{1}{\cos \theta} > \frac{\sin \theta}{\theta} > \cos \theta \tag{5}$$

Since (5) is true whenever $0 < \theta < \pi/2$ and since $\lim\limits_{\theta \to 0} \cos \theta = 1$, it is now clear that equality (2) is correct.

To see that (3) is also correct, notice that

$$\frac{1 - \cos \theta}{\theta} = \frac{1 - \cos^2 \theta}{\theta(1 + \cos \theta)} = \frac{\sin^2 \theta}{\theta(1 + \cos \theta)} = \sin \theta \cdot \frac{\sin \theta}{\theta} \cdot \frac{1}{1 + \cos \theta}$$

whenever $0 < |\theta| < \pi/2$ and so

$$\lim_{\theta \to 0} \frac{1 - \cos \theta}{\theta} = 0 \cdot 1 \cdot \frac{1}{2} = 0$$

This completes the proofs of (2) and (3) and hence of (4).

Using the addition formula for cos, we have

$$\frac{\cos (x + \theta) - \cos x}{\theta} = -\cos x \cdot \frac{1 - \cos \theta}{\theta} - \sin x \cdot \frac{\sin \theta}{\theta}$$

from which (2) and (3) yield

$$\cos' x = \lim_{\theta \to 0} \frac{\cos (x + \theta) - \cos x}{\theta} = -\sin x \qquad \text{for all } x \tag{6}$$

We now use the rule for differentiating quotients to find the derivatives of the other four trigonometric functions:

$$\frac{d}{dx} \tan x = \frac{d}{dx} \frac{\sin x}{\cos x} = \frac{\cos x \sin' x - \sin x \cos' x}{\cos^2 x}$$

$$= \frac{\cos^2 x + \sin^2 x}{\cos^2 x} = \frac{1}{\cos^2 x} = \sec^2 x$$

$$\frac{d}{dx} \cot x = \frac{d}{dx} \frac{1}{\tan x} = \frac{0 - 1 \cdot \tan' x}{\tan^2 x} = -\frac{\sec^2 x}{\tan^2 x} = -\csc^2 x$$

$$\frac{d}{dx} \sec x = \frac{d}{dx} \frac{1}{\cos x} = \frac{0 - 1 \cdot \cos' x}{\cos^2 x} = \frac{1}{\cos x} \cdot \frac{\sin x}{\cos x} = \sec x \tan x$$

$$\frac{d}{dx} \csc x = \frac{d}{dx} \frac{1}{\sin x} = \frac{0 - 1 \cdot \sin' x}{\sin^2 x} = -\frac{1}{\sin x} \cdot \frac{\cos x}{\sin x} = -\csc x \cot x$$

We summarize the six differentiation formulas just obtained:

$\dfrac{d}{dx}\sin x = \cos x$	$\dfrac{d}{dx}\cos x = -\sin x$
$\dfrac{d}{dx}\tan x = \sec^2 x$	$\dfrac{d}{dx}\cot x = -\csc^2 x$
$\dfrac{d}{dx}\sec x = \sec x \tan x$	$\dfrac{d}{dx}\csc x = -\csc x \cot x$

We urge the reader to memorize these formulas.

EXAMPLE   In each of the following find $y'\left(=\dfrac{dy}{dx}\right)$.

(a) $y = \sin(3x - 1)$

(b) $y = \dfrac{\sin x}{1 + \cos x}$

(c) $y = \sec^3(2x + 1)$

(d) $y = \csc x \sin 2x$

(e) $y = \cos 7x \cos^7 x$

(f) $\sin x - \cos y = x^2 - y^2$

Solution   (a) The Chain Rule gives $y' = \sin'(3x - 1) \cdot \dfrac{d}{dx}(3x - 1) = 3 \cos(3x - 1)$.

(b) The Quotient Rule gives

$$\frac{dy}{dx} = \frac{(1 + \cos x)\dfrac{d}{dx}\sin x - \sin x\dfrac{d}{dx}(1 + \cos x)}{(1 + \cos x)^2}$$

$$= \frac{(1 + \cos x) \cdot \cos x - \sin x \cdot (-\sin x)}{(1 + \cos x)^2}$$

$$= \frac{\cos x + \cos^2 x + \sin^2 x}{(1 + \cos x)^2} = \frac{1 + \cos x}{(1 + \cos x)^2} = \frac{1}{1 + \cos x}$$

(c) Again we use the Chain Rule. If we write $u = 2x + 1$ and $v = \sec u$, then $y = v^3$ so that

$$\frac{dy}{dx} = \frac{dy}{dv} \cdot \frac{dv}{du} \cdot \frac{du}{dx} = 3v^2 \cdot \sec u \tan u \cdot 2$$

$$= 3 \sec^2(2x + 1) \cdot \sec(2x + 1) \tan(2x + 1) \cdot 2$$
$$= 6 \sec^3(2x + 1) \tan(2x + 1)$$

(d) We can first simplify by writing

$$y = \csc x \sin 2x = \frac{1}{\sin x} \cdot 2 \sin x \cos x = 2 \cos x$$

and obtain $y' = -2 \sin x$ or we can differentiate the product directly and get

$$y' = \csc x \cdot 2 \cos 2x + \sin 2x \cdot (-\csc x \cot x)$$
$$= \csc x \, (2 \cos 2x - \cot x \sin 2x)$$
$$= 2 \csc x \, [(\cos^2 x - \sin^2 x) - \cos^2 x] = -2 \sin x$$

(e) Here we differentiate the product $y = \cos 7x \cos^7 x$ directly and then simplify to get

$$y' = (\cos 7x)(7 \cos^6 x)(-\sin x) + (\cos^7 x)(-\sin 7x)(7)$$
$$= -7 \cos^6 x \, (\sin x \cos 7x + \cos x \sin 7x)$$
$$= -7 \cos^6 x \cdot \sin 8x$$

(f) Differentiate $\sin x - \cos y = x^2 - y^2$ implicitly to get $\cos x - (-\sin y)y' = 2x - 2yy'$. So, $(2y + \sin y)y' = 2x - \cos x$ and $y' = \dfrac{2x - \cos x}{2y + \sin y}$.

Because of the multitude of trigonometric identities, there are often many different forms in which the correct answer to a problem can be expressed. In part (d) we saw that it was much easier to simplify the original expression before differentiating it than it was to proceed in the opposite order. This is the easiest procedure in most cases (even for algebraic functions), but not in all cases, as part (e) shows.

EXAMPLE If a particle moves along a straight line and its (directed) distance from the starting point (displacement) at time t is given by an equation $s(t) = r \sin (kt + b)$ (where r, k, and b are constants), then the motion of the particle is called **simple harmonic motion** (see page 222). Find the velocity $v(t)$ and the acceleration $a(t)$ of the particle at time t.

Solution Since $v(t) = s'(t)$, we have $v(t) = rk \cos (kt + b)$. Since $a(t) = v'(t)$, we have $a(t) = -rk^2 \sin (kt + b)$.

EXAMPLE Find the radius, height, and volume of the right circular cone of greatest volume that can be inscribed in a sphere of radius a.

Solution In Fig. 5-13 we show a plane cross-section of the picture that contains the axis of symmetry of the cone. Here θ is the radian measure of a central angle of the sphere that subtends a radius of the circular base of the cone. This base radius is $r = a \sin \theta$ and the height of the cone is $h = a + a \cos \theta$. Thus, the volume V of our typical inscribed cone is given by

$$V = \frac{1}{3}\pi r^2 h = \frac{1}{3}\pi a^3 \sin^2 \theta \, (1 + \cos \theta)$$

and we have

$$\frac{3}{\pi a^3} \cdot \frac{dV}{d\theta} = (\sin^2 \theta)(-\sin \theta) + (1 + \cos \theta)(2 \sin \theta \cos \theta)$$

$$= (\sin \theta)(3 \cos^2 \theta + 2 \cos \theta - 1)$$

$$= (\sin \theta)(\cos \theta + 1)(3 \cos \theta - 1)$$

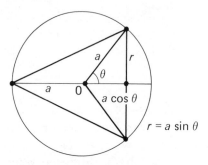

Figure 5-13

In our problem, we want $0 < \theta < \pi$ and we see that the only θ in this interval for which $\dfrac{dV}{d\theta} = 0$ is $\theta = \theta_0$ where $\cos \theta_0 = \dfrac{1}{3}$. This θ_0 must give the required maximum. Since $\sin^2 \theta_0 = 1 - \cos^2 \theta_0 = 1 - \left(\dfrac{1}{3}\right)^2 = \dfrac{8}{9}$ and $\sin \theta_0 > 0$, we have $\sin \theta_0 = \dfrac{2}{3}\sqrt{2}$. Therefore, the required answers are

$$\text{radius} = r_0 = a \sin \theta_0 = \frac{2}{3}\sqrt{2}\, a$$

$$\text{height} = h_0 = a + a \cos \theta_0 = \frac{4}{3}a$$

$$\text{volume} = V_0 = \frac{1}{3}\pi a^3 \sin^2 \theta_0 (1 + \cos \theta_0)$$

$$= \frac{1}{3}\pi a^3 \cdot \frac{8}{9} \cdot \frac{4}{3} = \frac{32\pi a^3}{81}$$

EXAMPLE A steel pole L meters long is to be carried horizontally along a hallway w meters in width ($w < L$) and into a corridor at right angles to the hallway. Neglecting the thickness of the pole, how wide must the corridor be in order that this turn can be made?

Solution   Fig. 5-14 shows a line segment of length L with endpoints on the coordinate axes and x-intercept greater than w. A moment's thought shows that our problem is to determine the maximum value of the y-coordinate of the point P having x-coordinate w on such a segment. If θ is the radian measure of the acute angle between the segment and the x-axis then we have

$$y = L \sin \theta - w \tan \theta$$

and so

$$\frac{dy}{d\theta} = L \cos \theta - w \sec^2 \theta$$

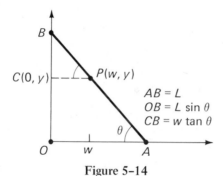

$$AB = L$$
$$OB = L \sin \theta$$
$$CB = w \tan \theta$$

Figure 5–14

This derivative is 0 if and only if $\cos^3 \theta = w/L$. Thus the maximum y_0 is attained when $\theta = \theta_0$, where $0 < \theta_0 < \pi/2$ and $\cos \theta_0 = (w/L)^{1/3}$. We have $\sin \theta_0 = [1 - (w/L)^{2/3}]^{1/2}$ and so

$$y_0 = L \sin \theta_0 - w \tan \theta_0 = (\sin \theta_0)\left(L - \frac{w}{\cos \theta_0}\right)$$
$$= [L^{-1/3}(L^{2/3} - w^{2/3})^{1/2}](L - L^{1/3}w^{2/3}) = [L^{2/3} - w^{2/3}]^{3/2}$$

We conclude that the corridor must be at least y_0 meters wide.

The limit formulas (2) and (3) of this section can sometimes be used to evaluate other limits, as we now show.

EXAMPLE   Evaluate the limits (where $a \neq 0$ is a constant):
(a) $\lim\limits_{x \to 0} x \cot x$

(b) $\lim\limits_{x \to 0} \dfrac{1 - \cos x}{\sin ax}$

(c) $\lim\limits_{x \to 0} \dfrac{1 - \cos x}{\sin^2 ax}$

(d) $\lim\limits_{x \to \infty} x\left(1 - \cos \dfrac{1}{x}\right)$

Solution   (a) $\lim\limits_{x\to 0} x \cot x = \lim\limits_{x\to 0} \dfrac{\cos x}{(\sin x)/x}$

$$= \left(\lim\limits_{x\to 0} \dfrac{\sin x}{x}\right)^{-1} (\lim\limits_{x\to 0} \cos x) = \dfrac{1}{1} = 1$$

(b) Rearranging, we have

$$\dfrac{1 - \cos x}{\sin ax} = \dfrac{1 - \cos x}{x} \cdot \dfrac{1}{a} \cdot \dfrac{ax}{\sin ax}$$

Since $x \to 0$ is equivalent to $\theta = ax \to 0$, and since

$$\lim\limits_{\theta\to 0} \dfrac{\theta}{\sin \theta} = \lim\limits_{\theta\to 0} \left(\dfrac{\sin \theta}{\theta}\right)^{-1} = 1^{-1} = 1$$

we have

$$\lim\limits_{x\to 0} \dfrac{1 - \cos x}{\sin ax} = 0 \cdot \dfrac{1}{a} \cdot 1 = 0$$

(c) We have

$$\dfrac{1 - \cos x}{\sin^2 ax} = \dfrac{1 - \cos^2 x}{(1 + \cos x) \sin^2 ax} = \dfrac{\sin^2 x}{(1 + \cos x) \sin^2 ax}$$

$$= \dfrac{1}{1 + \cos x} \cdot \left(\dfrac{ax}{\sin ax}\right)^2 \cdot \left(\dfrac{\sin x}{x}\right)^2 \cdot \dfrac{1}{a^2}$$

and so

$$\lim\limits_{x\to 0} \dfrac{1 - \cos x}{\sin^2 ax} = \dfrac{1}{2} \cdot 1^2 \cdot 1^2 \cdot \dfrac{1}{a^2} = \dfrac{1}{2a^2}$$

(d) Since $x \to \infty$ is equivalent to $\theta = 1/x \to 0^+$, we have

$$\lim\limits_{x\to \infty} x\left(1 - \cos \dfrac{1}{x}\right) = \lim\limits_{\theta\to 0^+} \dfrac{1 - \cos \theta}{\theta} = 0$$

EXERCISES

In 1–10, first simplify and then find $y' \left(= \dfrac{dy}{dx}\right)$.

1. $y = (\cos x + \sin x)^2$

2. $y = \dfrac{2 \cot x}{1 + \cot^2 x}$

3. $y = \cos \left(x + \dfrac{\pi}{4}\right) + \sin \left(x + \dfrac{\pi}{4}\right)$

4. $y = 2 \csc 2x \sin x$

5. $y = \sin 2x \cos 2x$

6. $y = \cos^4 x - \sin^4 x$

7. $y = \dfrac{\sin 3x}{\cos x} + \dfrac{\cos 3x}{\sin x}$

8. $y = 1 - 2 \sin^2\left(x - \dfrac{\pi}{2}\right)$

9. $y = \dfrac{1}{\sec x - \tan x} - \dfrac{1}{\sec x + \tan x}$

10. $y = 3 \sin^2 2x + \cos 4x + \cos^2 2x$

In 11–24, find $y' \left(= \dfrac{dy}{dx} \right)$.

11. $y = \sin (x^2 + 1)$

12. $y = 3 \cot (1 - 2x)$

13. $y = \sin^2 (x^2)$

14. $y = 2x \sin x + (2 - x^2) \cos x$

15. $y = \tan x - x$

16. $y = \dfrac{1 - \cos 2x}{1 + \cos 2x}$

17. $y = (1 - \tan^2 x) \sec^2 x$

18. $y = 2 \sin (ax + b) \cos (ax - b)$

19. $y \sin x + x \sin y = 1$

20. $y = \cot (x + y)$

21. $x = \sin^2 y$

22. $\sin (x - y) + \sin (x + y) = 1$

23. $y - \sin^2 y = \cos^2 y + x$

24. $x^2 + \tan^2 y = \sec^2 y - y$

In 25–27, find the differential, dy.

25. $y = \sin x \cos x$

26. $y = \dfrac{\tan x}{1 + \sin x}$

27. $y = \sqrt{x} - \sec x + \csc x$

28. Find an equation of the tangent to the curve $\sin y = \cos x$ at the point $(\pi/2, 0)$.

29. If a and b are constants, what are the maximum and minimum values attained by the function $f(x) = a \sin x + b \cos x$?

30. Suppose that the range of a projectile fired from a cannon is given by the formula $r = c \sin 3\theta$, where θ is the angle of elevation and c is a constant depending upon the muzzle velocity. Assuming that $0 < \theta < \pi/2$, find the angle of elevation which will give the maximum range.

31. Use Fig. 5-13 to show that the isosceles triangle of largest area that can be inscribed in a circle of radius a is equilateral. What is that largest area?

32. A wall of height h feet stands parallel to and w feet from a very high building on level ground. A ladder with its foot on the ground is to pass over the wall and lean against the building. Find the length (in terms of h and w) of the shortest ladder with which this can be done. (See Fig. 5-15.)

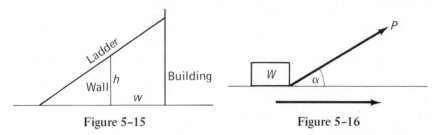

Figure 5–15   Figure 5–16

33. The angle of elevation of the sun is increasing at a rate of 15°/hour. When this angle is 30°, what is the rate of change of the length of the shadow cast by a building h meters in height? (In solving calculus problems, always measure angles in radians.)

34. A statue s feet tall stands atop a pillar p feet tall. At what distance x should a woman whose eyes are w feet above the level ground stand from the foot of the pillar in order that the angle θ between her lines of sight to the foot and to the top of the statue be the greatest? [*Hint:* Maximize $\tan \theta$; notice that $\tan \alpha = (p - w)/x$ and $\tan \beta = (p + s - w)/x$ where α and β are the angles of elevation of the foot and top of the statue, respectively.]

35. The light beam from a lighthouse which stands 1/2 mile from a straight shoreline turns at the rate of 3 revolutions/minute. At what rate is the light traveling along the shoreline as it passes a point on the shore that is 1/4 mile from the point on shore nearest the lighthouse?

36. A weight of W pounds is being dragged in a straight line along a horizontal floor (see Fig. 5-16). The magnitude of the force is given by the equation

$$P = \frac{kW}{k \sin \alpha + \cos \alpha}$$

where α is the angle at which the force is being exerted and k is a nonnegative constant called the coefficient of friction. For which angle α is P a minimum? What is the minimum value of P?

In 37–44, evaluate the indicated limit.

37. $\lim\limits_{x \to 0} \dfrac{\tan x}{x}$

38. $\lim\limits_{x \to 0} \dfrac{1 - \cos x}{x^2}$

39. $\lim\limits_{x \to 0} \dfrac{\sin ax}{bx}$

40. $\lim\limits_{x \to 0} \dfrac{\sin ax}{\sin bx}$

41. $\lim\limits_{x \to 0} \dfrac{\sin^2 x \cos x}{1 - \cos x}$

42. $\lim\limits_{x \to \infty} x \sin \dfrac{1}{x}$

43. $\lim\limits_{x \to 0} \left(\dfrac{1}{\sin x} - \dfrac{1}{\tan x} \right) \cdot \dfrac{1}{x}$ **44.** $\lim\limits_{x \to 0} \left(\dfrac{1}{\sin x} - \dfrac{1}{\tan x} \right)$

45. (a) Consider graphs of $y = \tan x$ and $y = x$ on the same coordinate plane to show that there is exactly one number x_0 satisfying $\pi < x_0 < 3\pi/2$ and $\tan x_0 = x_0$.

(b) Show that $\cos x < \dfrac{\sin x}{x}$ if $0 < x < x_0$.

(c) Show that $\sin x < x$ for every $x > 0$.

(d) Show that the function f defined by $f(0) = 1$ and $f(x) = (\sin x)/x$ for $x \neq 0$ is strictly decreasing on the interval $[0, x_0]$.

(e) Show that the function f defined in (d) attains an absolute minimum value at $x = x_0$.

(f) Show that $f(x_0) = \cos x_0$.

(g) On a single coordinate plane, sketch graphs of the two equations $y = f(x)$ and $y = \cos x$ for $-2\pi \leq x \leq 2\pi$. Label their points of intersection.

4   Inverse Trigonometric Functions

Recall from our discussion of inverse functions in Chapter 1, section 7, that the inverse of a function f is the function f^{-1} whose domain is the range of f and whose range is the domain of f *provided that*, for each given number x in the range of f, the equation $f(y) = x$ has just one solution y in the domain of f. If this proviso is satisfied, then we write $f^{-1}(x) = y$ for that one y satisfying $f(y) = x$ and we say that f is a one-to-one function. If there is some x in the range of f for which the equation $f(y) = x$ has two or more different solutions y *in the domain of f*, then f has *no* inverse function. For instance, the function f defined on the domain $]{-\infty}, \infty[$ by the formula $f(y) = y^2$ has range $[0, \infty[$. Taking $x = 4$, we see that the equation $y^2 = 4$ has the two solutions, $y = -2$ and $y = 2$, in the domain of f and so f has *no* inverse function.

However, it is possible to restrict f to the smaller domain $[0, \infty[$ to obtain a one-to-one function F having the same range that f has. That is, the function F having domain $[0, \infty[$ defined by $F(y) = f(y) = y^2$ for $y \geq 0$ has an inverse function F^{-1}. Indeed, given x in range $F = $ range $f = [0, \infty[$, the *only* solution y in domain $F = [0, \infty[$ of the equation $y^2 = x$ is the nonnegative square root $\sqrt{x}$ of x and so $F^{-1}(x) = \sqrt{x}$ for each x in range F. It is only by tradition that we chose to restrict f to $[0, \infty[$ to obtain a one-to-one function F. The function g defined on the domain $]-\infty,0]$ by $g(y) = y^2$ also has an inverse function g^{-1} given by $g^{-1}(x) = -\sqrt{x}$ for each x in range g = range f.

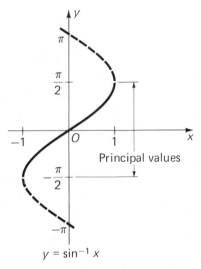

$$y = \sin^{-1} x$$

Figure 5–17

The graph of the equation $x = \sin y$, which we also write as $y = \sin^{-1} x$, is shown in Fig. 5-17. The part of this curve corresponding to $-\pi/2 \leq y \leq \pi/2$ is the graph of a continuous function Sin^{-1} which we call the **principal branch** of the **inverse sine.** Since there are infinitely many numbers y for which $\sin y = 1/2$ ($y = \pi/6 + 2k\pi$ and $y = 5\pi/6 + 2k\pi$ where k is any integer), the symbol $\sin^{-1} \dfrac{1}{2}$ does not denote just one specific number, and so it is ambiguous. However, we have $\text{Sin}^{-1} \dfrac{1}{2} = \dfrac{\pi}{6}$ because $\dfrac{\pi}{6}$ is the one number in the interval $\left[-\dfrac{\pi}{2}, \dfrac{\pi}{2}\right]$ whose sine is $\dfrac{1}{2}$. The function Sin^{-1} is the inverse of the *one-to-one* function Sin defined on $\left[-\dfrac{\pi}{2}, \dfrac{\pi}{2}\right]$ by

$$\text{Sin } y = \sin y \qquad \text{for } -\frac{\pi}{2} \leq y \leq \frac{\pi}{2}$$

We see that $\text{Sin}^{-1} x$ is defined for those and only those x for which $-1 \leq x \leq 1$ and we always have $-\dfrac{\pi}{2} \leq \text{Sin}^{-1} x \leq \dfrac{\pi}{2}$. Thus

$$\text{Sin}^{-1} x = y$$
means
$$-1 \leq x \leq 1, -\frac{\pi}{2} \leq y \leq \frac{\pi}{2}, \text{ and } x = \sin y$$

The restriction of cos to $[-\pi/2, \pi/2]$ is not one-to-one $[\cos(-y) = \cos y]$, and so we define Cos on $[0, \pi]$ by

$$\text{Cos } y = \cos y \qquad \text{for } 0 \leq y \leq \pi$$

We note that Cos is one-to-one and we obtain

$$y = \text{Cos}^{-1} x$$
means
$$-1 \leq x \leq 1, 0 \leq y \leq \pi, \text{ and } x = \cos y$$

We define Tan on $\left]-\dfrac{\pi}{2}, \dfrac{\pi}{2}\right[$ by

$$\text{Tan } y = \tan y \qquad \text{for } -\frac{\pi}{2} < y < \frac{\pi}{2}$$

We note that Tan is one-to-one and takes on any given real value x for exactly one y in $\left]-\dfrac{\pi}{2}, \dfrac{\pi}{2}\right[$. Thus

$$y = \text{Tan}^{-1} x$$
means
$$x \text{ is a real number, } -\frac{\pi}{2} < y < \frac{\pi}{2}, \text{ and } x = \tan y$$

The graphs of the functions Sin, Cos, Tan, and their inverses are shown in Fig. 5-18.

EXAMPLE Evaluate:

(a) $\text{Sin}^{-1}(1)$

(b) $\text{Cos}^{-1}\left(\dfrac{\sqrt{2}}{2}\right)$

(c) $\text{Tan}^{-1}\left(-\dfrac{\sqrt{3}}{3}\right)$

(d) $\text{Sin}^{-1}\left(-\dfrac{\sqrt{3}}{2}\right)$

(e) $\text{Cos}^{-1}(0)$

(f) $\text{Tan}^{-1}(1)$

Solution   (a) We want the number y such that $-\pi/2 \le y \le \pi/2$ and $\sin y = 1$. Clearly, $y = \pi/2$ is the solution. Thus, $\text{Sin}^{-1}(1) = \pi/2$.

(b) We want the number y such that $0 \le y \le \pi$ and $\cos y = \dfrac{\sqrt{2}}{2}$. Clearly, $y = \pi/4$. Thus, $\text{Cos}^{-1}\left(\dfrac{\sqrt{2}}{2}\right) = \pi/4$.

(c) We want the number y such that $-\pi/2 < y < \pi/2$ and $\tan y = \dfrac{-\sqrt{3}}{3}$. Clearly, $y = -\pi/6$. Thus, $\text{Tan}^{-1}\left(\dfrac{-\sqrt{3}}{3}\right) = -\pi/6$.

(d) Since $\sin(-\pi/3) = \dfrac{-\sqrt{3}}{2}$ and $-\pi/2 \le -\pi/3 \le \pi/2$, we have $\text{Sin}^{-1}\left(\dfrac{-\sqrt{3}}{2}\right) = -\pi/3$.

(e) Since $\cos(\pi/2) = 0$ and $0 < \pi/2 < \pi$, we have $\text{Cos}^{-1}(0) = \pi/2$.

(f) Since $\tan(\pi/4) = 1$ and $-\pi/2 < \pi/4 < \pi/2$, we have $\text{Tan}^{-1}(1) = \pi/4$.

EXAMPLE   Evaluate (a) $\text{Sin}^{-1}\left(\sin \dfrac{3\pi}{4}\right)$, (b) $\text{Cos}^{-1}\left(\cos \dfrac{3\pi}{4}\right)$, (c) $\text{Tan}^{-1}\left(\tan \dfrac{3\pi}{4}\right)$, and (d) $\text{Tan}^{-1}\left(\dfrac{1}{2}\right) + \text{Tan}^{-1}\left(\dfrac{1}{3}\right)$.

Solution   (a) Since $\sin \dfrac{3\pi}{4} = \dfrac{\sqrt{2}}{2}$, we are seeking the number y such that $-\dfrac{\pi}{2} \le y \le \dfrac{\pi}{2}$ and $\sin y = \dfrac{\sqrt{2}}{2}$. The only such number is $y = \dfrac{\pi}{4}$. Thus $\text{Sin}^{-1}\left(\sin \dfrac{3\pi}{4}\right) = \dfrac{\pi}{4}$.

(b) Since $0 \le \dfrac{3\pi}{4} \le \pi$, we have $\cos \dfrac{3\pi}{4} = \text{Cos} \dfrac{3\pi}{4}$ and so

$$\text{Cos}^{-1}\left(\cos \dfrac{3\pi}{4}\right) = \text{Cos}^{-1}\left(\text{Cos} \dfrac{3\pi}{4}\right) = \dfrac{3\pi}{4}$$

(c) Since $\tan \dfrac{3\pi}{4} = -1$, we are seeking the number y such that $-\dfrac{\pi}{2} < y < \dfrac{\pi}{2}$ and $\tan y = -1$. The only such number is $y = -\dfrac{\pi}{4}$ and so $\text{Tan}^{-1}\left(\tan \dfrac{3\pi}{4}\right) = -\dfrac{\pi}{4}$.

(d) Write $\alpha = \text{Tan}^{-1}\left(\dfrac{1}{2}\right)$ and $\beta = \text{Tan}^{-1}\left(\dfrac{1}{3}\right)$. Then α and β are both between 0 and $\pi/4 = \text{Tan}^{-1}\ 1$. Also, $\tan\ (\alpha + \beta) = \dfrac{\tan\ \alpha + \tan\ \beta}{1 - \tan\ \alpha\ \tan\ \beta} =$

$\dfrac{1/2 + 1/3}{1 - \dfrac{1}{6}} = 1$. Since $-\dfrac{\pi}{2} < \alpha + \beta < \dfrac{\pi}{2}$ and $\text{Tan}\ (\alpha + \beta) = 1$, we have

$$\text{Tan}^{-1}\left(\frac{1}{2}\right) + \text{Tan}^{-1}\left(\frac{1}{3}\right) = \alpha + \beta = \text{Tan}^{-1}\ (1) = \frac{\pi}{4}$$

It is possible to define principal values for the inverses of the other three trigonometric functions, but they are so seldom used or needed that we relegate them to the exercises as good tests of the reader's understanding of what is presented in the main text. We give just one of these as the second example below.

Since the one-to-one functions Sin, Cos, and Tan are differentiable with nonzero derivatives on the *open* intervals $\left]-\dfrac{\pi}{2}, \dfrac{\pi}{2}\right[$, $]0,\pi[$, and

$\left]-\dfrac{\pi}{2}, \dfrac{\pi}{2}\right[$, respectively, it follows from our general discussion of differentiation of inverse functions (Chapter 3, page 139) that their inverses Sin^{-1}, Cos^{-1}, and Tan^{-1} are differentiable on the image intervals $]-1,1[$, $]-1,1[$, and $]-\infty,\infty[$, respectively. We now compute these three derivatives.

If $y = \text{Sin}^{-1}\ x$, where $-1 < x < 1$ and $-\dfrac{\pi}{2} < y < \dfrac{\pi}{2}$, then $x = \sin\ y$ and so

$$\frac{dx}{dy} = \cos\ y = \sqrt{1 - \sin^2\ y} = \sqrt{1 - x^2}$$

and

$$\frac{d}{dx}\text{Sin}^{-1}\ x = \frac{dy}{dx} = \frac{1}{\sqrt{1 - x^2}}$$

where we have taken the *positive* square root because $\cos\ y > 0$ for $-\dfrac{\pi}{2} < y < \dfrac{\pi}{2}$. Also notice in Fig. 5-18 that Sin^{-1} is an increasing function and so its derivative cannot be negative.

If $y = \text{Cos}^{-1}\ x$, where $-1 < x < 1$ and $0 < y < \pi$, then $x = \cos\ y$ and so

$$\frac{dx}{dy} = -\sin\ y = -\sqrt{1 - \cos^2\ y} = -\sqrt{1 - x^2}$$

and

$$\frac{d}{dx}\mathrm{Cos}^{-1}\,x = \frac{dy}{dx} = -\frac{1}{\sqrt{1-x^2}}$$

where the positive square root is taken because $\sin y > 0$ for $0 <$

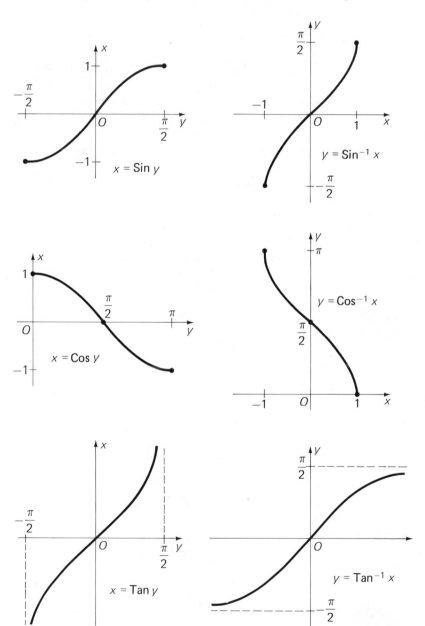

Figure 5–18

$y < \pi$. The negativity of this derivative is in harmony with the fact that Cos^{-1} is a decreasing function (see Fig. 5-18).

If $y = \mathrm{Tan}^{-1} x$, where $-\infty < x < \infty$ and $-\dfrac{\pi}{2} < y < \dfrac{\pi}{2}$, then $x = \tan y$ and so

$$\frac{dx}{dy} = \sec^2 y = 1 + \tan^2 y = 1 + x^2$$

and

$$\frac{d}{dx} \mathrm{Tan}^{-1} x = \frac{dy}{dx} = \frac{1}{1 + x^2}$$

It is interesting to observe that the derivative of each of these three inverse trigonometric functions turned out to be an algebraic function. We summarize these results:

$$\frac{d}{dx} \mathrm{Sin}^{-1} x = -\frac{d}{dx} \mathrm{Cos}^{-1} x = \frac{1}{\sqrt{1 - x^2}} \qquad \text{for } -1 < x < 1$$

$$\frac{d}{dx} \mathrm{Tan}^{-1} x = \frac{1}{1 + x^2} \qquad \text{for } -\infty < x < \infty$$

These formulas should be memorized.

It is not at all surprising that the derivatives of Sin^{-1} and Cos^{-1} are negatives of each other in view of our next example.

EXAMPLE   Prove that if $-1 \leqq x \leqq 1$, then

$$\mathrm{Cos}^{-1} x = \frac{\pi}{2} - \mathrm{Sin}^{-1} x$$

Solution   Given any such x, write $y = \mathrm{Sin}^{-1} x$. Then $-\dfrac{\pi}{2} \leqq y \leqq \dfrac{\pi}{2}$ and so $0 \leqq \dfrac{\pi}{2} - y \leqq \pi$. Therefore, $\dfrac{\pi}{2} - y$ is in the domain of Cos and hence

$$\mathrm{Cos} \left(\frac{\pi}{2} - y \right) = \cos \left(\frac{\pi}{2} - y \right) = \sin y = \mathrm{Sin}\, y = x$$

Thus,

$$\frac{\pi}{2} - y = \mathrm{Cos}^{-1} x$$

and

$$\text{Sin}^{-1} x = y = \frac{\pi}{2} - \text{Cos}^{-1} x$$

This completes the proof. ■

EXAMPLE For $0 \leq y < \dfrac{\pi}{2}$ and for $\dfrac{\pi}{2} < y \leq \pi$, define Sec $y =$ sec y. Prove the following statements:

(a) If x is a given number with $|x| \geq 1$, then there is exactly one number y such that $0 \leq y \leq \pi$, $y \neq \dfrac{\pi}{2}$, and $x = \text{Sec } y$. (We write this unique y as $y = \text{Sec}^{-1} x$.)

(b) For $|x| \geq 1$, we have $\text{Sec}^{-1} x = \text{Cos}^{-1} (x^{-1})$.

(c) For $|x| > 1$, we have

$$\frac{d}{dx} \text{Sec}^{-1} x = \frac{1}{|x|\sqrt{x^2 - 1}}$$

Solution   Given a fixed x with $|x| \geq 1$, we have $-1 \leq x^{-1} \leq 1$ and so x^{-1} is in the domain of Cos^{-1}. Write $y = \text{Cos}^{-1} (x^{-1})$. Then $0 \leq y \leq \pi$ and, since $x^{-1} \neq 0$, $y \neq \dfrac{\pi}{2}$. Also, $x^{-1} = \cos y = (\sec y)^{-1}$ and so $x = \sec y = \text{Sec } y$. Thus, we have found one number y satisfying (a). If z were another number satisfying the same conditions for our fixed x $\left(0 \leq z \leq \pi, z \neq \dfrac{\pi}{2}, \text{ and Sec } z = x\right)$, we would have $\text{Cos } z = x^{-1} = \text{Cos } y$ and so, since Cos is one-to-one on $[0,\pi]$, $z = y$. Therefore, the y we found is unique, (a) is proven, and Sec^{-1} is well-defined. We also have equality (b) because both sides are our unique y. To prove (c), just differentiate equality (b) using the Chain Rule and noticing that $|x^{-1}| < 1$:

$$\frac{d}{dx} \text{Sec}^{-1} x = \frac{-1}{\sqrt{1 - (x^{-1})^2}} \cdot (-x^{-2}) = \frac{\sqrt{x^2}}{\sqrt{x^2 - 1}} \cdot \frac{1}{x^2}$$

$$= \frac{|x|}{\sqrt{x^2 - 1}} \cdot \frac{1}{|x|^2} = \frac{1}{|x|\sqrt{x^2 - 1}}$$

Note. We remark that textbooks are about equally divided over how to define $\text{Sec}^{-1} x$ for $x \leq -1$. In many books one finds the requirement $\pi \leq \text{Sec}^{-1} x < \dfrac{3\pi}{2}$ if $x \leq -1$. This alternative definition has the advantage that formula (c) of the last example becomes true when the absolute value signs are removed, but it has the disadvantage that formula (b) becomes false for $x \leqq -1$. Since inverse secants are seldom used, this point should be of little or no concern to the reader. It is only an instance of a piece of general advice. *Always learn the definitions of the terms being used in the book being read.*

EXAMPLE In each of the following, find $y' \left(= \dfrac{dy}{dx} \right)$:

(a) $y = \text{Tan}^{-1} \dfrac{1 + x}{1 - x}$

(b) $y = \text{Cos}^{-1} (\sin x)$

(c) $y = x\sqrt{a^2 - x^2} + a^2 \, \text{Sin}^{-1} \dfrac{x}{a}$ (where $|x| < a$)

(d) $\text{Tan}^{-1} \dfrac{x}{y} = y$

Solution (a) $y' = \dfrac{1}{1 + \left(\dfrac{1 + x}{1 - x} \right)^2} \cdot \dfrac{d}{dx} \left(\dfrac{1 + x}{1 - x} \right)$

$= \dfrac{(1 - x)^2}{(1 - x)^2 + (1 + x)^2} \cdot \dfrac{(1 - x)(1) - (1 + x)(-1)}{(1 - x)^2}$

$= \dfrac{(1 - x)^2}{2 + 2x^2} \cdot \dfrac{2}{(1 - x)^2} = \dfrac{1}{1 + x^2}$

(b) $y' = \dfrac{-1}{\sqrt{1 - \sin^2 x}} \cdot \dfrac{d}{dx} \sin x = \dfrac{-\cos x}{|\cos x|}$

and so $y' = -1$ if $\cos x > 0$, $y' = 1$ if $\cos x < 0$, and y' does not exist if $\cos x = 0$.

(c) $\circ y' = x \cdot \dfrac{1}{2}(a^2 - x^2)^{-1/2}(-2x) + \sqrt{a^2 - x^2} \cdot 1 + a^2 \cdot \dfrac{1}{\sqrt{1 - (x/a)^2}} \cdot \dfrac{1}{a}$

$= \dfrac{-x^2}{\sqrt{a^2 - x^2}} + \dfrac{a^2 - x^2}{\sqrt{a^2 - x^2}} + \dfrac{a^2}{\sqrt{a^2 - x^2}} = 2\sqrt{a^2 - x^2}$

(d) Differentiating implicitly gives

$$\dfrac{1}{1 + \left(\dfrac{x}{y} \right)^2} \cdot \dfrac{d}{dx} \dfrac{x}{y} = y'.$$

Thus,

$$\dfrac{y^2}{y^2 + x^2} \cdot \dfrac{y - xy'}{y^2} = y'$$

Solving for y' gives $y' = \dfrac{y}{y^2 + x^2 + x}$.

E X E R C I S E S

In 1–12, evaluate or simplify the given expression.

1. $\text{Tan}^{-1} \sqrt{3}$

2. $\text{Sin}^{-1} \left(-\dfrac{1}{2}\right)$

3. $\text{Sin}^{-1} \left(-\dfrac{1}{\sqrt{2}}\right)$

4. $\text{Cos}^{-1} \left(-\dfrac{\sqrt{3}}{2}\right)$

5. $\text{Sin}^{-1} \left(\cos \dfrac{7\pi}{6}\right)$

6. $\text{Cos}^{-1} \left(\sin \dfrac{7\pi}{6}\right)$

7. $\cos \left(\text{Sin}^{-1} \dfrac{3}{5}\right)$

8. $\sin (\text{Tan}^{-1} 2)$

9. $\cos (\text{Tan}^{-1} (-3))$

10. $\cos \left(\text{Cos}^{-1} \dfrac{1}{8}\right)$

11. $\text{Tan}^{-1} 2 - \text{Tan}^{-1} (-3)$

12. $\tan \left(\text{Sin}^{-1} \dfrac{3}{5} + \text{Tan}^{-1} \dfrac{5}{12}\right)$

In 13–25, find $y' \left(=\dfrac{dy}{dx}\right)$.

13. $y = \text{Sin}^{-1} (\cos x)$
14. $y = \text{Tan}^{-1} \sqrt{x}$
15. $y = (\text{Cos}^{-1} 2x)^2$
16. $y = \text{Cos}^{-1} (1 - x)$

17. $y = \text{Tan}^{-1} x + \text{Tan}^{-1} \dfrac{1}{x}$

18. $y = \dfrac{\sqrt{1 - x^2}}{x} + \text{Sin}^{-1} x$

19. $y = \dfrac{x}{\sqrt{1 - x^2}} - \text{Sin}^{-1} x$

20. $y = \text{Tan}^{-1} \dfrac{x}{1 - \sqrt{1 - x^2}}$
21. $y = \text{Sin}^{-1} x + \text{Cos}^{-1} \sqrt{1 - x^2}$
22. $(\text{Tan}^{-1} y)^2 = x^2$
23. $\text{Sin}^{-1} \sqrt{x^2 + y^2}$
    $= \sqrt{1 - (x^2 + y^2)}$
24. $y = \sin (\text{Sin}^{-1} x^2)$
25. $y = \dfrac{\text{Sin}^{-1} x}{\text{Cos}^{-1} x}$

26. For $0 < y < \pi$, define $\text{Cot } y = \cot y$. Prove the following statements:
    (a) If x is any given real number, then there exists exactly one number y such that $0 < y < \pi$ and $\text{Cot } y = x$. (We write this unique y as $y = \text{Cot}^{-1} x$.)

    (b) For each real number x, we have $\text{Cot}^{-1} x = \dfrac{\pi}{2} - \text{Tan}^{-1} x$.

    (c) $\dfrac{d}{dx} \text{Cot}^{-1} x = \dfrac{-1}{1 + x^2}$ for all x.

    Sketch graphs of the functions Cot and Cot^{-1}.

27. Sketch graphs of the functions Sec and Sec^{-1} defined in the example on page 242.

28. For each real number y satisfying $0 < |y| \leq \dfrac{\pi}{2}$, define $\text{Csc } y = \csc y$. Prove the following statements:

(a) If x is a given real number with $|x| \geqq 1$, then there is exactly one number y such that $-\dfrac{\pi}{2} \leqq y \leqq \dfrac{\pi}{2}$, $y \neq 0$, and $x = \mathrm{Csc}\ y$. (We write this unique y as $y = \mathrm{Csc}^{-1}\ x$.)

(b) If $|x| \geqq 1$, then $\mathrm{Csc}^{-1}\ x = \mathrm{Sin}^{-1}\ (x^{-1})$.

(c) $\dfrac{d}{dx}\mathrm{Csc}^{-1}\ x = \dfrac{-1}{|x|\ \sqrt{x^2 - 1}}$ if $|x| > 1$.

Sketch graphs of the functions Csc and Csc^{-1}.

5 Exponentials and Logarithms

An **exponential function** is a function f of the form $f(x) = a^x$, where the base a is a positive constant and the exponent x is the variable. Actually, we have defined a^x only for rational values of x [if $x = m/n$, where m and n are integers with $n > 0$, then $a^x = a^{m/n} = (\sqrt[n]{a})^m$], but it is possible to use limiting processes to define a^x for irrational values of x in such a way that the above function f becomes a *continuous* function defined for all real values of x and such that the usual laws of exponents still hold.

LAWS OF EXPONENTS
If a, b, u, and v are real numbers with $a > 0$ and $b > 0$, then

$$a^u a^v = a^{u+v}$$
$$a^u b^u = (ab)^u$$
$$(a^u)^v = a^{uv}$$

From these, we deduce that

$$b^u b^{-u} = b^0 = 1 \qquad b^{-u} = \frac{1}{b^u}$$

$$\left(\frac{a}{b}\right)^u = (ab^{-1})^u = a^u b^{-u} = \frac{a^u}{b^u}$$

Analytical details of all of this are somewhat complicated and so we have placed them in the Appendix.

As an example, consider the problem of computing a decimal approximation to the number $3^{\sqrt{2}}$. The decimal expansion of the exponent is $\sqrt{2} = 1.414213\cdots$. We will sandwich the desired number between numbers that are a bit too small and a bit too large. The authors used a pocket calculator to obtain

$3^{1.4} = 4.65554\cdots$ $\qquad\qquad$ $3^{1.5} = 5.19615\cdots$

$3^{1.41} = 4.70696\cdots$ $\qquad\qquad$ $3^{1.42} = 4.75896\cdots$

$3^{1.414} = 4.72770\cdots$ $\qquad\qquad$ $3^{1.415} = 4.73289\cdots$

$3^{1.4142} = 4.72873\cdots$ $\qquad\qquad$ $3^{1.4143} = 4.72925\cdots$

$3^{1.41421} = 4.72879\cdots$ $\qquad\qquad$ $3^{1.41422} = 4.72884\cdots$

$3^{1.414213} = 4.72880\cdots$ $\qquad\qquad$ $3^{1.414214} = 4.72881\cdots$

If $a > 1$, then a^x is a strictly increasing function of x with $\lim_{x \to \infty} a^x = \infty$ and $\lim_{x \to -\infty} a^x = 0$. If $0 < a < 1$, then a^x is a strictly decreasing function of x with $\lim_{x \to \infty} a^x = 0$ and $\lim_{x \to -\infty} a^x = \infty$. These facts are indicated by the graphs in Fig. 5-19. Of course, $1^x = 1$ for all x. For any positive constant $a \neq 1$, the corresponding exponential function a^x attains each given value $y > 0$ for exactly one value of x. Geometrically speaking,

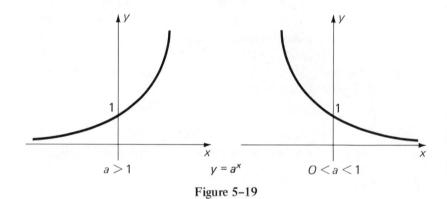

Figure 5-19

this says that each horizontal line above the x-axis is intersected by the graph of $y = a^x$ at exactly one point. For given $a > 0$, $a \neq 1$, and given $y > 0$, the unique solution x of the equation $a^x = y$ is called the **logarithm of y to the base a** and we write $x = \log_a y$. For instance, $\log_2 16 = 4$ because $x = 4$ is the unique solution of the equation $2^x = 16$. Since $a^x > 0$ for all x, only positive numbers y have logarithms.

$$\log_a y = x \qquad \text{means} \qquad a^x = y$$

It is immediately apparent from this definition that

$$\log_a a^x = x \qquad \text{and} \qquad a^{\log_a y} = y$$

In other words, $\log_a$ is the inverse of the function f defined by $f(x) = a^x$. Thus $f^{-1} = \log_a$, and so $f^{-1}(y) = \log_a y$ for $y > 0$. The graph of the equation $x = \log_a y$ is obtained by flipping the graph of $y = a^x$ about the line $y = x$. Compare the graphs in Fig. 5-20 with those in Fig. 5-19.

Corresponding to the laws of exponents, we have the following:

LAWS OF LOGARITHMS

If a, b, s, and t are positive numbers with $a \neq 1$ and $b \neq 1$, and x is any real number, then

$$\log_a (st) = \log_a s + \log_a t$$
$$\log_a (s^x) = x \cdot \log_a s$$
$$\log_b s = \frac{\log_a s}{\log_a b}$$

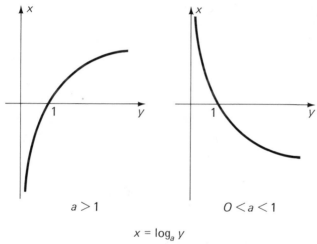

$$a > 1 \qquad\qquad\qquad 0 < a < 1$$

$$x = \log_a y$$

Figure 5–20

From these we obtain

$$\log_a \left(\frac{s}{t}\right) = \log_a (st^{-1}) = \log_a s + \log_a (t^{-1}) = \log_a s - \log_a t$$

To prove the three laws above, let $u = \log_a s$, $v = \log_a t$, and $w = \log_a b$. Then

$$a^{u+v} = a^u a^v = st$$

so

$$u + v = \log_a (st)$$

Also,

$$a^{xu} = (a^u)^x = s^x$$

so that

$$xu = \log_a (s^x)$$

Finally,

$$a^{w \cdot \log_b s} = (a^w)^{\log_b s} = b^{\log_b s} = s$$

so

$$w \cdot \log_b s = \log_a s.$$

Logarithms to the base 10 are called **common logarithms.** When expressing common logarithms, it is customary to omit the subscript 10 and write simply $\log x$ instead of $\log_{10} x$ for the number y for which $10^y = x$. According to the third law above, we have

$$\log_b s = \frac{\log s}{\log b}$$

for any positive numbers b and s with $b \neq 1$.

EXAMPLE   Find (a) $\log_2 8$; (b) $\log_3 \dfrac{1}{27}$; (c) $\log .1$; (d) $\log 10^8$; and (e) $\log (\log 10)$.

Solution   (a) Since $2^3 = 8$, we have $\log_2 8 = 3$.

(b) Since $3^{-3} = \dfrac{1}{27}$, we have $\log_3 \dfrac{1}{27} = -3$.

(c) Since $10^{-1} = .1$, we have $\log .1 = -1$.

(d) Since $10^8 = 10^8$, we have $\log 10^8 = 8$.

(e) Since $\log 10 = 1$, we have $\log (\log 10) = \log 1 = 0$.

EXAMPLE   Find all solutions x of the equation $3^{x^2-3x} = \dfrac{1}{9}$.

Solution   This equation is equivalent (upon taking base 3 logarithms of both sides) to $x^2 - 3x = \log_3 (1/9)$. But $\log_3 (1/9) = -2$ because $3^{-2} = 1/9$. Thus we are to solve $x^2 - 3x = -2$, which is equivalent to $(x - 1)(x - 2) = 0$. The solutions are $x = 1$ and $x = 2$.

EXAMPLE   If $\log_2 x = 3 \log_2 3 + \dfrac{1}{2} \log_2 5 - 2 \log_2 7$, find x.

Solution   We have

$$\log_2 x = \log_2 (3^3) + \log_2 (5^{1/2}) - \log_2 (7^2)$$
$$= \log_2 \frac{3^3 \cdot 5^{1/2}}{7^2} = \log_2 \frac{27\sqrt{5}}{49}$$

and so

$$x = \frac{27\sqrt{5}}{49}$$

EXAMPLE   Solve the equation $y = 2^x + 2^{-x}$ for x in terms of y. Express the answer in terms of common logarithms.

Solution   Multiply through by 2^x and rearrange to get

$$(2^x)^2 - y \cdot 2^x + 1 = 0$$

The quadratic formula (regarding 2^x as the variable) gives

$$2^x = \frac{y \pm \sqrt{y^2 - 4}}{2}$$

so

$$x = \log_2 \left(\frac{y \pm \sqrt{y^2 - 4}}{2} \right) = \log_2 (y \pm \sqrt{y^2 - 4}) - 1$$
$$= \frac{\log (y \pm \sqrt{y^2 - 4})}{\log 2} - 1$$

EXERCISES

Solve each of the following equations for x. Express answers in terms of common logarithms if not expressible without logarithms.

1. $\log_4 x = \dfrac{3}{2}$

2. $\log_9 x = -\dfrac{3}{2}$

3. $\log x = -2$

4. $\log (x^2) = 1$

5. $\log_x 3 = 2$

6. $\log_x 2 = 3$

7. $\log_2 (2x - 1) + \log_2 x = \log_2 6$

8. $\log x = 2 - \log 5$

9. $2^{3x-2} = 4^x$

10. $3^{x+2} = 5^{x-1}$

11. $2^{2x+1} = 3^{x-2}$

12. $2^x + 4^x = 8^x$

13. $3^x - 4 = 5 \cdot 3^{-x}$

14. $5^x + 5^{-x} = 5$

15. $\log_2 x + \log_3 x = 1$

16. $4^{\log_2 x} = 9$

17. $9^{\log_3 x} = 4$

18. $\log x + \dfrac{6}{\log x} = 5$

19. $y = \log (x^2 + 1)$

20. $y = \log x + \log (x - 2)$

21. $y = \text{Tan}^{-1} (\log_3 2x)$

22. $y = \text{Sin } (\log x^2)$ **26.** $\log (10^x) = x^2 - 2$
23. $3^{\log_3 x^2} = 4$ **27.** $\log (10^{-x}) = 5$
24. $\log_6 (6^{(x^2 - 7)}) = 6x$ **28.** $3^x = 3^{\log_2 8}$
25. $(1/2)^{\log_2 x} = 13$

6 Derivatives of Exponential and Logarithmic Functions and Some Applications

Let us consider the problem of finding the derivative f' of an exponential function f defined by

$$f(x) = a^x$$

where a is a given positive constant. For $h \neq 0$ we have

$$\frac{f(x + h) - f(x)}{h} = \frac{a^{x+h} - a^x}{h} = a^x \cdot \frac{a^h - 1}{h} = f(x) \cdot \frac{a^h - 1}{h}$$

Thus, according to the very definition of derivative,

$$f'(x) = f(x) \cdot \lim_{h \to 0} \frac{a^h - 1}{h} \tag{1}$$

if this limit exists. Notice that this limit, if it exists, depends only on a, not on x. Notice also that $(a^h - 1)/h$ is the slope of the line through the two points $(0,1)$ and (h,a^h) which lie on the graph of f. Thus, we see that the value of the above limit is the slope $f'(0)$ of the tangent line to the graph of f at the point $(0,1)$. It seems geometrically evident that such a tangent line exists and hence that the above limit does indeed exist. Formula (1) can be rewritten

$$f'(x) = f(x) f'(0) \qquad \text{for all } x \tag{2}$$

if $f'(0)$ exists. We will see below that there is a certain number e (between 2 and 3) that does not depend on a for which

$$f'(0) = \frac{1}{\log_a e} = \log_e a$$

for every choice of a.

Let us put this matter a different way. Does there exist a positive number e for which the function $f(x) = e^x$ satisfies $f'(0) = 1$? If so, equation (2) would imply that f is its own derivative. For this e to exist, it would be necessary and sufficient that it satisfy

$$\lim_{h \to 0} \frac{e^h - 1}{h} = 1$$

We write ≈ for "approximately equal," and thus we have

$$\frac{e^h - 1}{h} \approx 1$$

$$e^h \approx 1 + h$$

$$e \approx (1 + h)^{1/h}$$

for values of h "very close" to 0. In particular, taking $h = \frac{1}{n}$ for "large" integers n, this says

$$e \approx \left(1 + \frac{1}{n}\right)^n$$

In the Appendix it is *proved* that

$$e = \lim_{n \to \infty} \left(1 + \frac{1}{n}\right)^n \tag{3}$$

does exist and that

$$\frac{d}{dx} e^x = e^x \tag{4}$$

The accompanying table shows values of $\left(1 + \frac{1}{n}\right)^n$ for a few values of n.

n	$\left(1+\frac{1}{n}\right)^n$
10	2.5937···
100	2.7048···
1000	2.7169···
−1000	2.7196···
−100	2.7320···
−10	2.8680···

The decimal expansion of e is given by

$$e = 2.718281828459045 \cdots$$

From here on we shall reserve the letter e to denote this number. This letter is used to honor the great Swiss mathematician Leonhard

Euler (1707–1783), who discovered this number and many of its important properties. For typographical reasons we sometimes write $\exp(u)$ instead of e^u, particularly when u is a complicated function, that is,

$$\exp(u) = e^u$$

EXAMPLE   If $y = \exp\left(\dfrac{\sin x}{x + \cos x}\right)$, find $\dfrac{dy}{dx}$.

Solution   Writing $u = \dfrac{\sin x}{x + \cos x}$, we have

$$\frac{du}{dx} = \frac{(x + \cos x)\cos x - (\sin x)(1 - \sin x)}{(x + \cos x)^2} = \frac{x \cos x - \sin x + 1}{(x + \cos x)^2}$$

Since $y = e^u$, $\dfrac{dy}{du} = e^u$ and so the Chain Rule gives

$$\frac{dy}{dx} = \frac{dy}{du} \cdot \frac{du}{dx} = e^u \cdot \frac{du}{dx} = \exp\left(\frac{\sin x}{x + \cos x}\right) \cdot \frac{x \cos x - \sin x + 1}{(x + \cos x)^2}$$

The function $\log_e$ will be denoted by $\ln$. It is called the **natural logarithm function.** Thus, for $x > 0$, $y = \ln x$ means $e^y = x$. In this case, we have (differentiating with respect to y) $\dfrac{dx}{dy} = e^y = x$, so that $\dfrac{dy}{dx} = \dfrac{1}{x}$. This shows that

$$\boxed{\frac{d}{dx} \ln x = \frac{1}{x} \qquad \text{for } x > 0}$$

If $y = u^v$, then $\ln y = v \ln u$ and so $y = e^{v \ln u}$. This simple fact, together with the last two boxed formulas, can be used to differentiate any function of the form $f(x) = u(x)^{v(x)}$. One simply writes $f(x) = \exp[v(x) \ln u(x)]$ and then uses previously known rules of differentiation.

EXAMPLE   If $y = x^b$ for $x > 0$, where b is any real constant, find $\dfrac{dy}{dx}$.

Solution   Since $y = e^{b \ln x}$, we have

$$\frac{dy}{dx} = e^{b \ln x} \cdot \frac{d}{dx}(b \ln x) = x^b \cdot \frac{b}{x} = bx^{b-1}$$

which is a formula that we knew before only for *rational* constants b.

EXAMPLE   If $y = a^x$, where a is a positive constant, find $\dfrac{dy}{dx}$.

Solution   Since $y = e^{x \ln a}$, $\dfrac{dy}{dx} = e^{x \ln a} \cdot \dfrac{d}{dx}(x \ln a) = a^x \ln a$. Since $(\ln a)(\log_a e) = 1$ if $a \neq 1$, we also have

$$\frac{dy}{dx} = \frac{a^x}{\log_a e}$$

We emphasize the results of the preceding two examples. If b is a constant (not depending on x), then

$$\boxed{\dfrac{d}{dx}x^b = bx^{b-1} \qquad \text{for } x > 0}$$

If a is a positive constant (not depending on x) with $a \neq 1$, then

$$\boxed{\dfrac{d}{dx}a^x = a^x \ln a = \dfrac{a^x}{\log_a e}}$$

Notice carefully that

$$\frac{d}{dx}a^x \neq xa^{x-1}$$

EXAMPLE   If $y = x^x$ for $x > 0$, find $\dfrac{dy}{dx}$.

Solution   We have $y = e^{x \ln x}$, so that

$$\frac{dy}{dx} = e^{x \ln x} \cdot \frac{d}{dx}(x \ln x) = x^x \cdot (1 + \ln x)$$

The answer is *not* $x \cdot x^{x-1}$.

EXAMPLE   Find all points on the graph of the equation $y = e^x - x$ at which y attains a relative maximum or a relative minimum.

Solution   Since $e^x - x$ is differentiable everywhere, the only critical points occur when $y' = 0$. Setting $y' = 0$ gives $e^x - 1 = 0$. Thus, $x = 0$

is the only critical point. Since $y'' = e^x$ is positive when $x = 0$ (indeed for all x), we see by the Second Derivative Test that there is a relative minimum when $x = 0$. The point on the graph is $(0,1)$.

EXAMPLE   If $y = (x^2 + 1)^{\sin x}$, what is $\dfrac{dy}{dx}$?

Solution   We have $y = \exp[(\sin x) \ln (x^2 + 1)]$ so that

$$\frac{dy}{dx} = y \cdot \frac{d}{dx}[(\sin x) \ln (x^2 + 1)] = y[\sin x \cdot \frac{2x}{x^2 + 1} + \cos x \cdot \ln(x^2 + 1)]$$

$$= (x^2 + 1)^{\sin x} \cdot \left[\frac{2x \sin x}{x^2 + 1} + \ln (x^2 + 1) \cos x\right]$$

In general we have

$$\frac{d}{dx} u(x)^{v(x)} = \frac{d}{dx} e^{v(x) \ln u(x)} = e^{v(x) \ln u(x)} \cdot \frac{d}{dx}[v(x) \ln u(x)]$$

$$= u(x)^{v(x)} \left[\frac{v(x)u'(x)}{u(x)} + v'(x) \ln u(x)\right]$$

Another technique that is sometimes useful in simplifying the differentiation of a function which is a quotient of two products of other functions is the so-called method of **logarithmic differentiation**. We illustrate this method with the next two examples.

EXAMPLE   If $y = \dfrac{(x - 1)^7(x + 1)^8}{(x^2 + 1)^3}$, find y'.

Solution   First take natural logarithms to get

$$\ln y = 7 \ln(x - 1) + 8 \ln (x + 1) - 3 \ln (x^2 + 1)$$

Now differentiate implicitly with respect to x to get

$$\frac{y'}{y} = \frac{7}{x - 1} + \frac{8}{x + 1} - 3 \cdot \frac{2x}{x^2 + 1}$$

and solve for y' to get

$$y' = \frac{(x - 1)^7(x + 1)^8}{(x^2 + 1)^3} \left(\frac{7}{x - 1} + \frac{8}{x + 1} - \frac{6x}{x^2 + 1}\right)$$

EXAMPLE   If $y = \dfrac{x^{\ln x}}{(\ln x)^x}$ for $x > 1$, find y'.

Solution   Since $\ln y = (\ln x)(\ln x) - x \ln(\ln x)$, we have

$$\frac{y'}{y} = 2(\ln x) \cdot \frac{1}{x} - x\left(\frac{1}{\ln x} \cdot \frac{1}{x}\right) - \ln(\ln x) \cdot 1$$

So,

$$y' = y \cdot \left(\frac{2}{x}\ln x - \frac{1}{\ln x} - \ln \ln x\right)$$

It often happens that problems involving rates of growth or decay involve exponential functions. We will now investigate several examples.

Suppose a sum of money P (called the **principal**) is deposited in an interest-paying account. If the rate of annual interest is r and interest is compounded n times per year, then we have the formula

$$A(t) = P\left(1 + \frac{r}{n}\right)^{nt}$$

where $A(t)$ is the total amount in the account after t years. We, of course, assume that no money is withdrawn from or deposited in the account after the initial deposit.

Thus, if \$2000 is deposited in an account paying 10% per year compounded quarterly ($n = 4$), then the total amount in the account after two years is

$$A(2) = 2000(1 + .025)^{4 \cdot 2} = 2000(1.025)^8$$

which is, to the nearest cent, \$2436.80. We see that the total interest is $A - P = \$436.80$.

If interest were compounded daily ($n = 365$), instead of quarterly, we would have

$$A(2) = 2000(1 + .000273972)^{365 \cdot 2} = 2000(1.000273972)^{730}$$
$$= \$2442.74, \text{ to the nearest cent}$$

Today, interest is sometimes compounded "continuously." That is, shorter and shorter periods of compounding are used. In other words, we let $n \to \infty$ and we take the limit of $P\left(1 + \frac{r}{n}\right)^{nt}$. It can be shown (see exercise 54, page 261) that if this is done, then we have the formula

$$A(t) = P \cdot e^{rt}$$

when interest is compounded continuously at an annual rate r.

For example, if the annual passbook rate is 5.5% and interest is compounded continuously, then after one year an original deposit of one dollar will be worth $A = 1 \cdot e^{.055} = 1.0564$ dollars. The interest per dollar per year is .0564, or 5.64%. That is why you will often see an "effective annual yield" of 5.64% advertised.

EXAMPLE   A sum of $10,000 is deposited in an account paying 12% interest per year.

(a) Find the total amount after 3 years if interest is compounded annually. What is the amount of interest?

(b) Answer the same question if interest is compounded semi-annually.

(c) Answer the same question if interest is compounded quarterly.

(d) Answer the same question if interest is compounded continuously.

(e) If interest is compounded continuously, at what rate is A changing after 3 years?

Solution   (a) Here $P = 10,000$, $r = .12$, $n = 1$, and $t = 3$. Thus,

$$A(3) = 10,000\left(1 + \frac{.12}{1}\right)^{1 \cdot 3} = 10,000(1.12)^3 = \$14,049.30$$

The interest is $A - P = \$4049.30$.

(b) Here, $P = 10,000$, $r = .12$, $n = 2$, and $t = 3$. Thus,

$$A(3) = 10,000\left(1 + \frac{.12}{2}\right)^{2 \cdot 3} = 10,000(1.06)^6 = \$14,185.20$$

The interest is $A - P = \$4185.20$.

(c) Here $P = 10,000$, $r = .12$, $n = 4$, and $t = 3$. Thus,

$$A(3) = 10,000\left(1 + \frac{.12}{4}\right)^{4 \cdot 3} = 10,000(1.03)^{12} = \$14,257.60$$

The interest is $A - P = \$4257.60$.

(d) Here we use the formula $A(t) = Pe^{rt}$. Thus,

$$A(3) = 10,000 \cdot e^{.12 \cdot 3} = 10,000 \cdot e^{.36} = \$14,333.30$$

The interest is $A - P = \$4333.30$.

(e) Here we want to find $A'(3)$. Since $A'(t) = Pre^{rt}$, we have $A'(3) = 10,000 \cdot .12 \cdot e^{.36} = 1719.996$ dollars per year. *Note.* You can see that t does not have to be very large before $A(t)$ is a very rapidly increasing function. The moral of the story is that funds left to accumulate interest really do add up. Unfortunately, there is a hitch: the government makes us pay tax on the interest we earn and, therefore, we can't just "let the money ride."

Let us assume that interest is being compounded continuously. The **present value of A dollars in t years** is the principal P such that an investment now of P dollars will yield an amount A in t years. If the interest rate is r, then we have

$$A = A(t) = Pe^{rt}$$

Thus,

$$P = Ae^{-rt}$$

EXAMPLE Find the present value of $1000 in 5 years if the interest rate is 8% annually compounded continuously.

Solution We have $A = 1000$, $t = 5$, and $r = .08$. Thus, $P = Ae^{-rt} = 1000e^{-.08 \cdot 5} = \$670.32$, to the nearest cent.

Here is an example from biology involving an exponential function.

EXAMPLE Suppose the population function during a certain time period for a colony of bacteria is given by

$$P(t) = 100{,}000(2)^{t/5}$$

where t, $0 \leq t \leq 1000$, is measured in seconds.
  (a) How many bacteria are there after 10 seconds?
  (b) After how many seconds are there 1,000,000 bacteria?
  (c) When $t = 10$ seconds, how fast is the population changing?

Solution (a) Here $t = 10$. Thus, $P(10) = 100{,}000(2)^{10/5} = 100{,}000 \cdot 2^2 = 400{,}000$.
  (b) We want to solve $1{,}000{,}000 = 100{,}000(2)^{t/5}$. Thus, we have $2^{t/5} = 10$ and

$$(t/5)\log 2 = 1$$
$$t = \frac{5}{\log 2}$$
$$t \approx 16.61 \text{ seconds}$$

  (c) $P'(t) = 100{,}000 \cdot \dfrac{\ln 2}{5} \cdot (2)^{t/5}$. Thus, $P'(10) = 80{,}000 \ln 2$ bacteria per second.

EXAMPLE A radioactive isotope has a **half-life** of 1000 years. This means that in 1000 years, half of a given quantity of the isotope will decay and half will remain.
  (a) If we start with a sample of 100 grams of the isotope, write an equation for the amount $A(t)$ of isotope left after t years.
  (b) How much isotope will be left after 400 years?
  (c) After how many years will there be 10 grams of the isotope sample left?

(d) When $t = 50$ years, how rapidly is the sample decaying?

Solution   (a) After one half-life, there will be one half of the original sample left. After two half-lives, there will be one fourth of the original sample left, etc. Thus,

$$A(1000) = 100 \cdot \frac{1}{2}$$

$$A(2000) = 100 \cdot \left(\frac{1}{2}\right)^2$$

In general, $A(1000t) = 100\left(\frac{1}{2}\right)^t$, or $A(t) = 100\left(\frac{1}{2}\right)^{\frac{t}{1000}}$.

Note. More generally, if the half-life is H and the original sample contained G grams, then after time t the amount left is given by

$$A(t) = G\left(\frac{1}{2}\right)^{\frac{t}{H}}$$

Here, H and t must be measured in the same time unit.

(b) $A(400) = 100\left(\frac{1}{2}\right)^{\frac{400}{1000}} = 75.79$ grams

(c) We set $A(t) = 10$ and solve $10 = 100\left(\frac{1}{2}\right)^{\frac{t}{1000}}$. We obtain

$$\left(\frac{1}{2}\right)^{t/1000} = 1/10$$

$$(t/1000)\log .5 = \log .1$$

$$t/1000 = \frac{-1}{\log .5}$$

$$t = \frac{-1000}{\log .5}$$

$$t \approx 3321.93 \text{ years}$$

(d) We want to find $A'(t)$ when $t = 50$. Since $A(t) = 100e^{(\ln .5)t/1000}$, we have

$$A'(t) = \frac{100 \cdot \ln .5}{1000}e^{(\ln .5)t/1000} = \frac{100 \cdot \ln .5}{1000}\left(\frac{1}{2}\right)^{t/1000}$$

Thus, $A'(50) \approx -.067$ g/yr. The sample is decaying at a rate of approximately .067 grams per year.

E X E R C I S E S

In 1–32, find $y' \left(= \dfrac{dy}{dx} \right)$.

1. $y = \ln (x + 1)^4$

2. $y = \ln (x^2 + 5x)$

3. $y = \ln \left(\dfrac{x}{1 + x} \right)$

4. $y = \ln (x + \sqrt{x^2 + 1})$

5. $y = x \operatorname{Tan}^{-1} x - \ln \sqrt{x^2 + 1}$

6. $y = \ln (\cos 4x)$

7. $y = \log_a (x^2 - x)$

8. $y = (\log x)^{1/3}$

9. $y = e^{2 \ln x}$

10. $y = \ln (\ln x)$

11. $y = \ln \sqrt{\dfrac{x - 1}{x + 1}}$

12. $y = \dfrac{x}{\ln x}$

13. $y = \dfrac{\ln x}{x}$

14. $y = \ln (\sec x + \tan x)$

15. $y = \exp (\sin x)$

16. $y = \exp (2 \ln x + \ln x^2)$

17. $y = \ln \dfrac{e^x + 1}{e^x - 1}$

18. $y = e^{x + \ln x}$

19. $y = x^6 e^{-3 \ln x}$

20. $y = (x^2 - 2x + 2)e^x$

21. $y = (\sin x)^x$

22. $y = \ln 2^x$

23. $y = x^{(x^2)}$

24. $y = \sqrt{\dfrac{2x + 1}{(x + 1)(x + 2)}}$

25. $y = \dfrac{(x + 1)^7}{(x^2 + 2x + 3)^2}$

26. $y = x^{\ln x}$

27. $y = (1 + x)^{1/x}$

28. $e^y = \ln x$

29. $\ln y = x^2$

30. $\ln xy = y^2$

31. $\sin xy + \ln y = 2^x$

32. $\cos \dfrac{y}{x} = \ln \dfrac{x}{y}$

In 33–36, find the differential dy.

33. $y = e^x \ln x$

34. $y = \ln x$

35. $y = \sec x - 3^x$

36. $y = \exp (\cos x + \sin x)$

In 37–44, find all points on the graph (i.e., the x value and the y value) of the given equation at which y attains a relative maximum or relative minimum value.

37. $y = xe^{-x}$

38. $y = \dfrac{1 - \ln x}{x}$

39. $y = \ln x - x$

40. $y = x(\ln x)^2$

41. $y = x \ln x$

42. $y = e^x(x^2 - 3)$

43. $y = x^x$

44. $y = \ln \dfrac{x}{1 + x^2}$

45. Find an equation of the tangent to the curve $\ln y = x^2 + x$ at the point $(0,1)$.

46. The sum of \$5000 is deposited in an account paying 8% annual interest.

(a) If interest is compounded semiannually, find the total amount in the account after two years. How much interest has been earned?

(b) If interest is compounded quarterly, find the total amount in the account after four years. How much interest has been earned?

(c) If interest is compounded continuously, find the total amount in the account after five years. How much interest has been earned? After five years, at what rate is the total amount changing? After ten years, at what rate is the total amount changing?

47. Do exercise 46 if the annual interest rate is 4%. Is the interest earned in each part half the interest earned at an annual rate of 8% as in exercise 46? Explain.

48. (a) Find the present value of $2000 in ten years if interest is accumulated at a rate of 10% annually compounded continuously.

(b) Find the present value of $2000 in five years if interest is accumulated at a rate of 10% annually compounded continuously.

(c) Find the present value of $2000 in ten years if interest is accumulated at a rate of 5% annually compounded continuously.

(d) Is either of the values found in parts (b) and (c) twice the value found in part (a)? Explain.

49. The population function during a certain time $(0 \leq t \leq 200)$ for a colony of bacteria is given by $P(t) = 20{,}000 + 40{,}000(2)^{t/4} - 10{,}000t$, where t is measured in minutes.

(a) How many bacteria are there after four minutes?

(b) How many bacteria are there after one hour?

(c) When $t = 40$ minutes, how fast is the population changing?

(d) When $t = 3$ hours, how fast is the population changing?

(e) When $t = 1$ second, how fast is the population changing?

(f) What do parts (c), (d), and (e) indicate about the size of the population?

50. A certain radioactive isotope has a half-life of 20 seconds. Suppose we start with a sample of 80 grams.

(a) Write an equation for the amount, $A(t)$, left after t seconds.

(b) How much isotope will be left after one minute?

(c) After how many seconds will there be 2 grams left?

(d) When $t = 10$ seconds, how rapidly is the sample decaying?

(e) How fast is the sample decaying when $t = 2$ minutes?

51. Suppose $P(x) = e^{-.1x}$ approximates the proportion of refrigerators still in use x years after production, $0 \leq x \leq 15$.

(a) What proportion of refrigerators made today will be in service 3 years from now?

(b) In how many years will 60% of the refrigerators made today still be in use?

(c) Find $P'(2)$.

(d) Find $P'(12)$.

(e) Interpret the results found in parts (c) and (d).

52. A large manufacturer of a new kind of gum estimates that during the tth month of production ($t \geq 1$) his sales will be given by

$$S(t) = e^{\left(-\frac{12}{t} - \frac{t}{48}\right)} + 1$$

where t is measured in months and $S(t)$ is measured in millions of packages. During which month will his sales be maximal? How many packages of gum will he sell during that month?

53. Suppose a city estimates that its population t years from now will be given by the formula $P(t) = 50{,}000 \ln \left(\frac{t}{4} + 3\right)$, $t \geq 0$.

(a) What is its present population?

(b) What will be the population in four years?

(c) In how many years will the population be 200,000?

(d) Find $P'(2)$.

(e) Find $P'(8)$.

(f) Interpret the results found in parts (d) and (e).

54. Use the fact that $\lim\limits_{x \to \infty} \left(1 + \frac{1}{x}\right)^x = e$ and the formula $A(t) = P\left(1 + \frac{r}{n}\right)^{nt}$

for interest compounded n times a year to derive the formula $A(t) = Pe^{rt}$ for interest compounded continuously.

$\left[\text{Hint: Let } n \to \infty \text{ in the formula } A(t) = P\left(1 + \frac{r}{n}\right)^{nt}.\right]$

55. In science and engineering, certain functions called **hyperbolic functions** sometimes arise. They are defined as follows:

$$\sinh x = \frac{e^x - e^{-x}}{2} \qquad\qquad \operatorname{csch} x = \frac{2}{e^x - e^{-x}}, \; x \neq 0$$

$$\cosh x = \frac{e^x + e^{-x}}{2} \qquad\qquad \operatorname{sech} x = \frac{2}{e^x + e^{-x}}$$

$$\tanh x = \frac{e^x - e^{-x}}{e^x + e^{-x}} \qquad\qquad \coth x = \frac{e^x + e^{-x}}{e^x - e^{-x}}, \; x \neq 0$$

Their inverse functions are defined as follows:

$$\sinh^{-1} x = \ln\left(x + \sqrt{1 + x^2}\right)$$
$$\cosh^{-1} x = \ln\left(x + \sqrt{x^2 - 1}\right), \; x \geq 1$$

$$\tanh^{-1} x = \frac{1}{2} \ln \frac{1+x}{1-x}, \ |x| < 1$$

$$\operatorname{csch}^{-1} x = \ln \left(\frac{1}{x} + \frac{\sqrt{1+x^2}}{|x|} \right), \ x \neq 0$$

$$\operatorname{sech}^{-1} x = \ln \left(\frac{1+\sqrt{1-x^2}}{x} \right), \ 0 < x \leq 1$$

$$\coth^{-1} x = \frac{1}{2} \ln \frac{x+1}{x-1}, \ |x| > 1$$

Prove each of the following differentiation rules:

(a) $\sinh' x = \cosh x$

(b) $\cosh' x = \sinh x$

(c) $\tanh' x = \operatorname{sech}^2 x$

(d) $\operatorname{csch}' x = -\operatorname{csch} x \coth x$

(e) $\operatorname{sech}' x = -\operatorname{sech} x \tan h x$

(f) $\coth' x = -\operatorname{csch}^2 x$

(g) $\dfrac{d}{dx} \sinh^{-1} x = \dfrac{1}{\sqrt{1+x^2}}$

(h) $\dfrac{d}{dx} \cosh^{-1} x = \dfrac{1}{\sqrt{x^2-1}}, \ x > 1$

(i) $\dfrac{d}{dx} \tanh^{-1} x = \dfrac{1}{1-x^2}, \ |x| < 1$

(j) $\dfrac{d}{dx} \operatorname{csch}^{-1} x = -\dfrac{1}{|x|\sqrt{1+x^2}}, \ x \neq 0$

(k) $\dfrac{d}{dx} \operatorname{sech}^{-1} x = -\dfrac{1}{x\sqrt{1-x^2}}, \ 0 < x < 1$

(l) $\dfrac{d}{dx} \coth^{-1} x = \dfrac{1}{1-x^2}, \ |x| > 1$

56. When we suspend a uniform rope from its endpoints, the curve
   which the rope makes is a section of a curve called a **catenary**.
   The equation of a catenary is $y = a \cosh bx$, where a and b are
   constants with $a > 0$. If $b \neq 0$, prove that the catenary is concave
   upward on $]-\infty,\infty[$. What can you say about the catenary if $b = 0$?

7 The Indeterminate Forms $\dfrac{0}{0}$ and $\dfrac{\infty}{\infty}$

Earlier in this chapter, when proving that the derivative of $\sin x$ is $\cos x$, we were faced with the task of evaluating the limits

$$\lim_{h \to 0} \frac{\sin h}{h} \quad \text{and} \quad \lim_{h \to 0} \frac{\cos h - 1}{h}$$

We found their values to be 1 and 0, respectively. In each of these cases, the top and bottom of the quotient both have limit 0 and so, since $\dfrac{0}{0}$ is a meaningless symbol, the value of the required limit is not obvious. In these two cases we were able to find the values of the limits by using certain geometrical arguments.

Consider now the problem of evaluating the two limits

$$\lim_{x \to \frac{\pi}{2}} \frac{(2x - \pi)^2}{\ln (\sin x)} \quad \text{and} \quad \lim_{x \to \infty} \frac{\ln \dfrac{1}{x}}{\sqrt{x}}$$

In the first of these both top and bottom of the quotient have limit 0 as $x \to \pi/2$. In the second one the top has limit $-\infty$ and the bottom has limit ∞ as $x \to \infty$. Since neither $\dfrac{0}{0}$ nor $\dfrac{-\infty}{\infty}$ is meaningful, the values of these limits, if they exist, are not obvious. We present below a method for evaluating these limits.

More generally, consider a function of the form

$$\phi(x) = \frac{f(x)}{g(x)}$$

and an extended real number a (a is either a real number or $\pm\infty$). If

$$\lim_{x \to a} f(x) = \lim_{x \to a} g(x) = 0$$

we say that ϕ has the **indeterminate form** $\dfrac{0}{0}$ at a. If $\lim_{x \to a} f(x)$ and $\lim_{x \to a} g(x)$ are each either ∞ or $-\infty$, we say that ϕ has the **indeterminate form** $\dfrac{\infty}{\infty}$ at a. It often happens in these cases that $\phi(x)$ actually has a perfectly good limit as $x \to a$. The following theorem, which is named in honor of the French mathematician G.F.A. de L'Hôpital (1661–1704), in whose calculus book it first appeared, is frequently useful in evaluating limits of indeterminate forms. The proof of this theorem is somewhat involved so we place it in the Appendix.

▷ **L'Hôpital's Rule**   Let a be an extended real number and let f and g be real-valued functions which are defined and differentiable, with $g' \neq 0$, in some (possibly one-sided) deleted neighborhood I of a. Suppose that either

$$\text{(i)} \quad \lim_{x \to a} f(x) = \lim_{x \to a} g(x) = 0$$

or

$$\text{(ii)} \quad \left| \lim_{x \to a} f(x) \right| = \left| \lim_{x \to a} g(x) \right| = \infty$$

Then, if L is an extended real number and $\lim_{x \to a} \dfrac{f'(x)}{g'(x)} = L$, it then follows that

$$\lim_{x \to a} \frac{f(x)}{g(x)} = L$$

Remarks. In this theorem a or L may be ∞ or $-\infty$ or a real number. The *deleted* neighborhood I of a can be an open interval having a as an endpoint, in which case the limits in the theorem must all be considered as one-sided limits, or I can consist of an open interval containing a with the point a itself removed (that is, deleted). The functions f and g need not be defined at a itself.

EXAMPLE   Evaluate $\lim_{x \to \pi/2} \dfrac{(2x - \pi)^2}{\ln (\sin x)}$.

Solution   The functions $f(x) = (2x - \pi)^2$ and $g(x) = \ln (\sin x)$ both have limit 0 at $\pi/2$ and so (i) holds. We have $f'(x) = 4(2x - \pi)$ and $g'(x) = (\cos x)/(\sin x)$ so that

$$\frac{f'(x)}{g'(x)} = \frac{(4\pi - 8x) \sin x}{-\cos x}$$

which again has the meaningless form $\dfrac{0}{0}$ at $\pi/2$. Taking derivatives of top and bottom once more yields

$$\frac{f''(x)}{g''(x)} = \frac{(4\pi - 8x) \cos x - 8 \sin x}{\sin x} = (4\pi - 8x) \cot x - 8$$

which approaches $0 \cdot 0 - 8 = -8$ as $x \to \dfrac{\pi}{2}$.

Thus, two applications of L'Hôpital's Rule yield

$$\lim_{x \to \pi/2} \frac{f(x)}{g(x)} = \lim_{x \to \pi/2} \frac{f'(x)}{g'(x)} = \lim_{x \to \pi/2} \frac{f''(x)}{g''(x)} = -8$$

EXAMPLE   Evaluate $\displaystyle\lim_{x \to \infty} \frac{\ln \dfrac{1}{x}}{\sqrt{x}}$.

Solution   Writing $f(x) = \ln \dfrac{1}{x} = -\ln x$ and $g(x) = \sqrt{x}$, we have

$f'(x) = -x^{-1}$, $g'(x) = \dfrac{1}{2}x^{-1/2}$, and $f'(x)/g'(x) = -2\sqrt{x}/x = -2/\sqrt{x}$. Since

$f(x) \to -\infty$ and $g(x) \to \infty$, L'Hôpital's Rule yields

$$\lim_{x \to \infty} \frac{\ln \dfrac{1}{x}}{\sqrt{x}} = \lim_{x \to \infty} \frac{-2}{\sqrt{x}} = 0$$

In practice we seldom introduce the names f and g for the top and bottom of the fraction. Instead we successively write

$$\lim_{x \to a} \frac{f(x)}{g(x)} = \lim_{x \to a} \frac{f'(x)}{g'(x)} = \lim_{x \to a} \frac{f''(x)}{g''(x)} = \cdots = \lim_{x \to a} \frac{f^{(n)}(x)}{g^{(n)}(x)}$$

until we reach a limit which can be evaluated (if we ever do). Be *extremely careful* in doing this that the function on the left of each equality sign is actually indeterminate of the form $\dfrac{0}{0}$ or $\dfrac{\infty}{\infty}$ before writing that equality.

For instance, it is *false* that

$$\lim_{x \to \pi} \frac{\sin x}{x} = \lim_{x \to \pi} \frac{\cos x}{1}$$

because the limit on the left is $\dfrac{0}{\pi} = 0$ while that on the right is $\dfrac{-1}{1} = -1$. Sometimes repeated application of L'Hôpital's Rule leads nowhere, as the next two examples show.

EXAMPLE   Evaluate $\displaystyle\lim_{x \to 0^+} \frac{e^{-1/x}}{x}$.

Solution   If we successively differentiate top and bottom separately we obtain

$$\frac{e^{-1/x}}{x},$$

$$\frac{x^{-2}e^{-1/x}}{1} = \frac{e^{-1/x}}{x^2},$$

$$\frac{x^{-2}e^{-1/x}}{2x} = \frac{e^{-1/x}}{2x^3},$$

$$\cdots,$$

$$\frac{e^{-1/x}}{n!x^{n+1}}$$

and all of these have the form $\dfrac{0}{0}$ as $x \to 0^+$. This is discouraging, but observe that a change of variable $(t = 1/x)$ and a single application of L'Hôpital's Rule yield

$$\lim_{x \to 0^+} \frac{e^{-1/x}}{x} = \lim_{t \to \infty} \frac{t}{e^t} = \lim_{t \to \infty} \frac{1}{e^t} = 0$$

Notice that this middle equality is justified because $\dfrac{t}{e^t}$ has the indeterminate form $\dfrac{\infty}{\infty}$ as $t \to \infty$.

EXAMPLE   If $\phi(x) = \dfrac{1}{x}\left(\dfrac{1}{\tan x} - \dfrac{1}{x}\right)$, find $\lim_{x \to 0} \phi(x)$.

Solution   As $x \to 0$, $\phi(x)$ has the form $\infty - \infty$, which is meaningless. Let us write $\phi(x)$ as a quotient of two functions and hope that L'Hôpital's Rule will come to the rescue.

We have

$$\phi(x) = \frac{x - \tan x}{x^2 \tan x}$$

which has the $\dfrac{0}{0}$ form at 0. Differentiating top and bottom separately gives

$$\frac{1 - \sec^2 x}{x^2 \sec^2 x + 2x \tan x}$$

which is still $\dfrac{0}{0}$ at 0. Doing it again yields

$$\frac{-2 \sec^2 x \tan x}{2x^2 \sec^2 x \tan x + 4x \sec^2 x + 2 \tan x}$$

This expression also has the limit form $\dfrac{0}{0}$, and the situation gets worse and worse. However, we also have

$$\phi(x) = \frac{x \cos x - \sin x}{x^2 \sin x}$$

so that

$$\lim_{x \to 0} \phi(x) = \lim_{x \to 0} \frac{-x \sin x}{x^2 \cos x + 2x \sin x}$$

$$= \lim_{x \to 0} \frac{-\sin x}{x \cos x + 2 \sin x} = \lim_{x \to 0} \frac{-\cos x}{-x \sin x + 3 \cos x}$$

$$= \frac{-1}{0 + 3} = -\frac{1}{3}$$

The moral of these examples is that one should not necessarily depend on L'Hôpital's Rule alone. It may be prudent to use it in concert with certain algebraic or trigonometric simplifications or with certain changes of variable.

E X E R C I S E S

Evaluate the following limits.

1. $\lim\limits_{x \to 1} \dfrac{x^{10} - 1}{x - 1}$

2. $\lim\limits_{x \to 0} \dfrac{e^x - e^x}{\tan x}$

3. $\lim\limits_{x \to 0} \dfrac{a^x - b^x}{x}$

4. $\lim\limits_{x \to 0} \dfrac{x - \tan x}{x - \sin x}$

5. $\lim\limits_{x \to \pi} \dfrac{(x - \pi)^2}{\ln(\cos 2x)}$

6. $\lim\limits_{x \to 0} \dfrac{\sin x - x}{x^3}$

7. $\lim\limits_{x \to 0} \dfrac{x - \mathrm{Sin}^{-1} x}{x^3}$

8. $\lim\limits_{x \to 0} \dfrac{e^x - e^{-x}}{\ln(1 + x)}$

9. $\lim\limits_{x \to \pi} \dfrac{\sec^2 (x/4) - \tan (x/4)}{1 + \cos x}$

10. $\lim\limits_{x \to 0} \dfrac{\ln (\sec x)}{x^2}$

11. $\lim\limits_{x \to 0} \dfrac{x^2 - 2 \mathrm{Tan}^{-1} x}{x}$

12. $\lim\limits_{x \to \infty} \dfrac{\ln (3 + e^x)}{2x}$

13. $\lim\limits_{x \to 0} \dfrac{\sin x}{x - 1}$

14. $\lim\limits_{x \to 0} \left(\dfrac{1}{x} - \dfrac{1}{\sin x} \right)$

15. $\lim\limits_{x \to 1} \dfrac{x^3 - e^{1-x}}{1 - x + \ln x}$

16. $\lim\limits_{x \to 1} \dfrac{\ln x}{(x - 1)^2}$

17. $\lim\limits_{x \to 0^+} \dfrac{\ln (\sin^2 x)}{\ln x}$

18. $\lim\limits_{x \to \infty} \dfrac{\sqrt{x^2 + 1}}{x}$

19. $\lim\limits_{x \to \pi/2^-} \dfrac{e^{-\tan x}}{\cos x}$

20. $\lim\limits_{x \to \pi/2^+} \dfrac{e^{-\tan x}}{\cos x}$

21. $\lim\limits_{x \to 0^+} \dfrac{1 - \ln x}{e^{1/x}}$

22. $\lim\limits_{x \to \infty} \dfrac{2^x}{3^{x^2}}$

8 Limits of Other Indeterminate Forms

In order to evaluate limits that lead to any of the forms $0 \cdot \infty$, $\infty - \infty$, 0^0, ∞^0 and 1^∞, it is often useful to rewrite the function ϕ whose limit is to be taken (or else $\ln \phi$) as a quotient of functions and then to apply L'Hôpital's Rule. For instance, we may write

$$f(x)g(x) = \frac{f(x)}{1/g(x)}$$

or

$$f(x) - g(x) = \frac{\dfrac{1}{g(x)} - \dfrac{1}{f(x)}}{\dfrac{1}{f(x)g(x)}}$$

or

$$\ln (f(x)^{g(x)}) = g(x) \ln f(x) = \frac{\ln f(x)}{1/g(x)}$$

We give examples to illustrate each of these forms.

EXAMPLE   Evaluate $\lim\limits_{x \to 0^+} (\sin x) \ln (\tan x)$.

Solution   Since $\sin x = \dfrac{1}{\csc x}$, the required limit is

$$\lim_{x \to 0^+} \frac{\ln(\tan x)}{\csc x} = \lim_{x \to 0^+} \frac{\sec^2 x/\tan x}{-\csc x \cot x} = \lim_{x \to 0^+} \frac{\sec^2 x}{-\csc x}$$

$$= \lim_{x \to 0^+} \frac{-\sin x}{\cos^2 x} = \frac{0}{1} = 0$$

EXAMPLE   Evaluate $\lim\limits_{x \to 1^+} \phi(x)$, where $\phi(x) = \dfrac{1}{x - 1} - \dfrac{1}{\ln x}$.

Solution   As given, ϕ has the form $\infty - \infty$ as $x \to 1^+$. But we also have $\phi(x) = \dfrac{\ln x - x + 1}{(x - 1)\ln x}$ and this has the form $\dfrac{0}{0}$ as $x \to 1^+$. Thus L'Hôpital's Rule yields

$$\lim_{x \to 1^+} \phi(x) = \lim_{x \to 1^+} \frac{\dfrac{1}{x} - 1}{\dfrac{x - 1}{x} + \ln x} = \lim_{x \to 1^+} \frac{1 - x}{x - 1 + x \ln x}$$

$$= \lim_{x \to 1^+} \frac{-1}{1 + 1 + \ln x} = \frac{-1}{2}$$

EXAMPLE Evaluate $\lim_{x \to 0^+} \phi(x)$, where $\phi(x) = (x + 2\sqrt{x})^{a/\ln x}$ and a is any constant.

Solution Here ϕ has the form 0^0 as $x \to 0^+$. We have

$$\ln \phi(x) = \frac{a \ln (x + 2\sqrt{x})}{\ln x}$$

which is indeterminate of the form $\frac{\infty}{\infty}$ as $x \to 0^+$, so that we may apply L'Hôpital's Rule to get

$$\lim_{x \to 0^+} \ln \phi(x) = \lim_{x \to 0^+} a \cdot \frac{\dfrac{1 + x^{-1/2}}{x + 2\sqrt{x}}}{\dfrac{1}{x}} = \lim_{x \to 0^+} a \cdot \frac{\sqrt{x} + 1}{\sqrt{x} + 2} = \frac{a}{2}$$

It follows that

$$\lim_{x \to 0^+} \phi(x) = \lim_{x \to 0^+} \exp (\ln \phi(x)) = e^{a/2}$$

This shows that there are functions which are indeterminate of type 0^0 and which have any given positive limit.

EXAMPLE Evaluate $\lim_{x \to \infty} \phi(x)$, where $\phi(x) = (a^x + x)^{1/x}$ and a is any constant greater than 1.

Solution Here ϕ is indeterminate of the form ∞^0 as $x \to \infty$. Since $\ln \phi(x) = \dfrac{\ln (a^x + x)}{x}$ has the form $\dfrac{\infty}{\infty}$ as $x \to \infty$, we may apply L'Hôpital's Rule to obtain (after three applications)

$$\lim_{x \to \infty} \ln \phi(x) = \lim_{x \to \infty} \frac{\dfrac{a^x \ln a + 1}{a^x + x}}{1} = \lim_{x \to \infty} \frac{a^x (\ln a)^2}{a^x \ln a + 1}$$

$$= \lim_{x \to \infty} \frac{a^x (\ln a)^3}{a^x (\ln a)^2} = \ln a$$

Therefore

$$\lim_{x \to \infty} \phi(x) = \lim_{x \to \infty} \exp (\ln \phi(x)) = e^{\ln a} = a$$

EXAMPLE Evaluate $\lim_{x \to \infty} \phi(x)$, where $\phi(x) = \left(1 + \dfrac{a}{x}\right)^x$ and a is any constant.

Solution Here ϕ has the form 1^∞ as $x \to \infty$. Since

$$\ln \phi(x) = \frac{\ln (1 + a/x)}{1/x}$$

has the form $\dfrac{0}{0}$ at ∞, we obtain

$$\lim_{x \to \infty} \ln \phi(x) = \lim_{x \to \infty} \frac{\dfrac{-ax^{-2}}{1 + ax^{-1}}}{-x^{-2}} = \lim_{x \to \infty} \frac{a}{1 + a/x} = a$$

and hence

$$\lim_{x \to \infty} \phi(x) = \lim_{x \to \infty} \exp (\ln \phi(x)) = e^a$$

E X E R C I S E S

In 1–22, evaluate the limits.

1. $\lim_{x \to \infty} (1 + x)^{1/x}$

2. $\lim_{x \to 0^+} (1 + x)^{\ln x}$

3. $\lim_{x \to \infty} (1 + x)^{\ln x}$

4. $\lim_{x \to 0^+} x \cot 2x$

5. $\lim_{x \to 0^+} x \ln x$

6. $\lim_{x \to 1} x^{\frac{1}{x-1}}$

7. $\lim_{x \to 0} (\cos x)^{1/x}$

8. $\lim_{x \to 0^+} x^{2/\ln x}$

9. $\lim_{x \to \infty} \left(\tan \dfrac{3}{x} - \tan \dfrac{1}{x}\right)$

10. $\lim_{x \to 0^+} x^{(x^2)}$

11. $\lim_{x \to 0} (\sec 3x)(\cos 4x)$

12. $\lim_{x \to \infty} [\ln (2x + 3) - \ln x]$

13. $\lim_{x \to 1} \left(\dfrac{x}{\ln x} - \dfrac{1}{x \ln x}\right)$

14. $\lim_{x \to 0} \left(\dfrac{1}{x \sin x} - \dfrac{1}{x^2}\right)$

15. $\lim_{x \to 0} \left(\dfrac{1}{\sin^2 x} - \dfrac{1}{x^2}\right)$

16. $\lim_{x \to 0} (\csc x) \tan^{-1} x$

17. $\lim_{x \to \infty} (\ln x)^{1/x}$

18. $\lim_{x \to 0} (\cos x)^{\sin x}$

19. $\lim_{x \to 0^-} (1 - 3^x)^{\sin x}$

20. $\lim_{x \to 0^+} x^{\pi/(1 + \ln x)}$

21. $\lim_{x \to 0} \left(\dfrac{\sin^{-1} x}{x}\right)^{1/x^2}$

22. $\lim_{x \to 1} (2 - x)^{\tan(\pi x/2)}$

23. The number e is often defined by $e = \lim_{x \to \infty} \left(1 + \dfrac{1}{x}\right)^x$. Check this limit using L'Hôpital's Rule.

9 Graphing Equations Involving Exponentials and Logarithms

We begin this section by proving two theorems which give us useful information about the orders of magnitude of exponential and logarithmic functions as compared to power functions. We then give three examples in which these results are applied.

Our first theorem shows that any exponential function a^x (with $a > 1$) tends to ∞ much more rapidly than does any power function x^b as $x \to \infty$.

Theorem 1 Let a and b be given real numbers with $a > 1$. Then

$$\lim_{x \to \infty} \frac{x^b}{a^x} = 0$$

Proof We shall use L'Hôpital's Rule. First choose a positive integer $n > b$. Since

$$0 < \frac{x^b}{a^x} < \frac{x^n}{a^x} \qquad \text{for } x > 1$$

we need only prove that

$$\lim_{x \to \infty} \frac{x^n}{a^x} = 0$$

This is indeterminate of the form $\dfrac{0}{0}$ and so n applications of L'Hôpital's Rule yield

$$\lim_{x \to \infty} \frac{x^n}{a^x} = \lim_{x \to \infty} \frac{nx^{n-1}}{a^x(\ln a)} = \lim_{x \to \infty} \frac{n(n-1)x^{n-2}}{a^x(\ln a)^2} = \cdots = \lim_{x \to \infty} \frac{n!}{a^x(\ln a)^n} = 0$$

This completes the proof. ∎

Our next theorem says that as $x \to \infty$, the function $\ln x$ tends to ∞ more slowly than does any power function x^c no matter how small the positive exponent c.

Theorem 2 If c is any given positive constant, then

$$\lim_{x \to \infty} \frac{\ln x}{x^c} = 0$$

Proof The given limit is indeterminate of the form $\dfrac{\infty}{\infty}$ and so L'Hôpital's Rule yields

$$\lim_{x \to \infty} \frac{\ln x}{x^c} = \lim_{x \to \infty} \frac{1/x}{cx^{c-1}} = \lim_{x \to \infty} \frac{1}{cx^c} = 0$$

completing the proof. ∎

EXAMPLE Evaluate the limit $\lim_{x \to \infty} \dfrac{\ln(\ln x)}{\ln x}$.

Solution Writing $t = \ln x$, we have $t \to \infty$ as $x \to \infty$ and

$$\frac{\ln (\ln x)}{\ln x} = \frac{\ln t}{t}$$

It now follows from Theorem 2 that the value of the required limit is 0.

In the remaining two examples we use our ten-step procedure for graphing equations given in Chapter 4 (pages 174–176).

EXAMPLE Discuss and sketch the graph of the equation $y = x \ln x$.

Solution (1) *Extent.* Since $\ln x$ is defined only for $x > 0$, the graph lies entirely to the right of the y-axis. Also, $y < 0$ if $0 < x < 1$ and $y > 0$ if $x > 1$.

(2) *Intercepts.* The only x-intercept is at $x = 1$.

(3) *Symmetry.* There is no symmetry.

(4) *Critical points.* We have $y' = 1 + \ln x$ and so y' exists for all $x > 0$ and $y' = 0$ if and only if $x = e^{\ln x} = e^{-1}$. Thus the only critical point on the graph is $\left(\dfrac{1}{e}, -\dfrac{1}{e}\right)$.

(5) *Local extrema.* When $x = \dfrac{1}{e}$, we obtain $y'' = \dfrac{1}{x} = e > 0$ and so $\left(\dfrac{1}{e}, -\dfrac{1}{e}\right)$ is a relative minimum.

(6) *Monotonicity.* We have $y' = 1 + \ln x > 0$ for $x > e^{-1}$ and so y is strictly increasing on $\left[\dfrac{1}{e}, \infty\right[$. For $0 < x < e^{-1}$, $y' = 1 + \ln x < 1 + \ln e^{-1} = 0$ and so y is strictly decreasing on $\left]0, \dfrac{1}{e}\right]$.

(7)–(8) *Points of inflection and concavity.* Since $y'' = \dfrac{1}{x} > 0$ for every $x > 0$, this function is concave upward on its domain $]0, \infty[$ and there are no points of inflection.

(9)–(10) *Asymptotes.* There are no asymptotes but we do have

$$\lim_{x \to 0^+} x \ln x = \lim_{t \to \infty} \frac{1}{t} \ln \frac{1}{t} = \lim_{t \to \infty} -\frac{\ln t}{t} = 0$$

by Theorem 2. Also, $\lim_{x \to \infty} x \ln x = \infty$ and $\lim_{x \to 0^+} y' = -\infty$.

The graph is shown in Fig. 5-21.

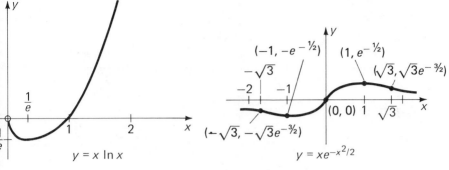

Figure 5-21   Figure 5-22

EXAMPLE Discuss and sketch a graph of the function $f(x) = xe^{-x^2/2}$.

Solution (1) *Extent.* This function is defined at every x. If $x > 0$, then $f(x) > 0$. If $x < 0$, then $f(x) < 0$.

(2) *Intercepts.* The origin is the only intercept on either axis.

(3) *Symmetry.* Since $f(-x) = -f(x)$, the graph is symmetric with respect to the origin.

(4) *Critical points.* Since $f'(x) = (1 - x^2)e^{-x^2/2}$, we have $f'(x) = 0$ just when $x = 1$ or -1. The only critical points on the graph are $(1, e^{-1/2})$ and $(-1, -e^{-1/2})$.

(5)–(6) *Local extrema and monotonicity.* We have $f'(x) > 0$ for $-1 < x < 1$ while $f'(x) < 0$ if $x < -1$ or $x > 1$. Thus f is strictly increasing on $[-1,1]$ while it is strictly decreasing on each of $]-\infty,-1]$ and $[1,\infty[$. Accordingly f takes its minimum value at -1 and its maximum value at 1.

(7)–(8) *Points of inflection and concavity.* Since $f''(x) = (x^3 - 3x)e^{-x^2/2}$, the graph has points of inflection at $(0,0)$, and $(-\sqrt{3},-\sqrt{3}e^{-3/2})$, and $(\sqrt{3},\sqrt{3}e^{-3/2})$. It is concave upward on each of $[-\sqrt{3},0]$ and $[\sqrt{3},\infty[$ and it is concave downward on each of $]-\infty,-\sqrt{3}]$ and $[0,\sqrt{3}]$.

(9)–(10) *Asymptotes.* The x-axis is the only asymptote. By Theorem 1, we have $\lim_{x \to \infty} f(x) = 0$ and $\lim_{x \to -\infty} f(x) = 0$.

The graph of f appears in Fig. 5-22.

EXERCISES

In 1–24, use the ten-step procedure of Chapter 4 (pages 174–176) to discuss and sketch a graph of the given equation. (For 21–24, you may wish to consult the exercises on page 261.)

1. $y^2 = e^x$

2. $y^2 = \ln x$

3. $y = \ln (x^2)$

4. $y = (\ln x)^2$

5. $y = \dfrac{\ln x}{x}$

6. $y = \dfrac{e^x}{x^2}$

7. $y = \dfrac{x^2}{e^x}$

8. $y = \dfrac{\ln x}{e^x}$

9. $y = \ln (\ln x)$

10. $y = \ln (e^x)$

11. $y = \ln (\sin x)$

12. $y = e^{\sin x}$

13. $y = e^{-1/x}$

14. $y = \dfrac{1 - \ln x}{x}$

15. $y = x^x \qquad (x > 0)$

16. $y = e^{-x^2/2}$

17. $y = \ln \dfrac{2x - 1}{x^2}$

18. $y = (x^2 - 3)e^x$

19. $y = xe^{1/x}$

20. $y = e^{x^2 - 4x}$

21. $y = \sinh x \left(= \dfrac{e^x - e^{-x}}{2} \right)$

22. $y = \cosh x \left(= \dfrac{e^x + e^{-x}}{2} \right)$

23. $y = \tanh x \left(= \dfrac{e^x - e^{-x}}{e^x + e^{-x}} \right)$

24. $y = \sinh^{-1} x \ (= \ln (x + \sqrt{1 + x^2}))$

10 Polar Coordinates

The position of a point P in the plane is completely determined by its distance r from the origin and any one of its **polar angles** θ (see Fig. 5-23). Such an ordered pair (r,θ) is called a set of **polar coordinates** for P. These are related to the rectangular coordinates (x,y) of P by the formulas

$$\boxed{\begin{array}{ll} x = r \cos \theta & y = r \sin \theta \\ |r| = \sqrt{x^2 + y^2} & \tan \theta = y/x \end{array}}$$

$\qquad$ (1)

$\qquad$ (2)

Unlike rectangular coordinates, polar coordinates of a given point are not unique. This is because the θ is not unique and because we do allow r to be negative.

When r is positive, the point is on the ray which is the terminal side of angle θ. When r is negative, the point is in the opposite direction from the ray which is the terminal side of angle θ. For instance,

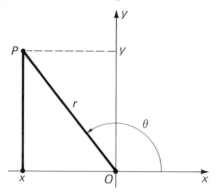

Figure 5-23

the point whose rectangular coordinates are (1,1) has as polar coordinates $(\sqrt{2}, \pi/4 + 2n\pi)$ and $(-\sqrt{2}, 5\pi/4 + 2n\pi)$, where n is any integer. Of course the origin has polar coordinates $(0, \theta)$ for any θ.

EXAMPLE   Change the equation $x\sqrt{x^2 + y^2} = 2y$ from rectangular to polar coordinates.

Solution   Using (1) and (2), we have $x\sqrt{x^2 + y^2} = (r \cos \theta)\,|r|$ and $2y = 2r \sin \theta$ and so the desired polar equation is

$$|r|r \cos \theta = 2r \sin \theta$$

This equation is equivalent to

$$|r| = 2 \tan \theta$$

Notice that the origin is the only point on the y-axis for which the original equation is satisfied. This point is still on the graph of the last equation, since $r = 0$ if $\theta = 0$.

EXAMPLE   Change the equation $r = 3 \cos 2\theta$ from polar coordinates to rectangular coordinates.

Solution   We have $r = 3 \cos 2\theta = 3 \cos^2 \theta - 3 \sin^2 \theta$ or, equivalently, $r^3 = 3(r \cos \theta)^2 - 3(r \sin \theta)^2$. Thus the required equation is

$$\pm(x^2 + y^2)^{3/2} = 3(x^2 - y^2)$$

or, equivalently,

$$(x^2 + y^2)^3 = 9(x^2 - y^2)^2$$

EXAMPLE   Sketch a graph of the polar equation $r = 3 \cos 2\theta$.

Solution   We begin by making a table of values of r that correspond to various values of θ (see Fig. 5-24). It is often useful in sketching polar curves to think of a directed line through the origin which is turning through an ever-increasing angle θ. As it turns, the graph is traced out by a moving point P on this line whose position (positive or negative distance) relative to the origin is determined by the r that arises through the equation from the value of θ. In this example, as θ increases from 0 to $\pi/4$, r decreases from 3 to 0 and then, as θ moves from $\pi/4$ to $\pi/2$, r decreases from 0 to -3, etc.

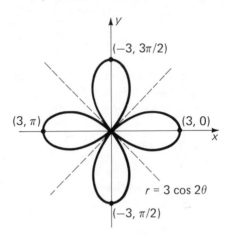

Figure 5-24

θ	0	$\pi/6$	$\pi/4$	$\pi/3$	$\pi/2$	$2\pi/3$	$3\pi/4$	$5\pi/6$	π
r	3	3/2	0	$-3/2$	-3	$-3/2$	0	3/2	3

$7\pi/6$	$5\pi/4$	$4\pi/3$	$3\pi/2$	$5\pi/3$	$7\pi/4$	$11\pi/6$	2π
3/2	0	$-3/2$	-3	$-3/2$	0	3/2	3

Sometimes the nonuniqueness of the polar coordinates of a point can cause some difficulty in finding the points of intersection of two given polar curves.

EXAMPLE   Find all points of intersection of the curves $r = -\sqrt{3}\cos\theta$ and $r = 3\cos 2\theta$.

Solution   The first of these curves has the equation $x^2 + y^2 = -x\sqrt{3}$ in rectangular coordinates, which is equivalent to $(x + \sqrt{3}/2)^2 + y^2 = (\sqrt{3}/2)^2$. Thus, this curve is the circle of radius $\sqrt{3}/2$ with center $(-\sqrt{3}/2, 0)$. The second curve is shown in Fig. 5-24. In Fig. 5-25 we show the circle and the part of the second curve to the left of the

y-axis. It is evident that these curves intersect in exactly the five points which are marked. Let us try to find these points by solving the given equations simultaneously. We have

$$-\sqrt{3}\ \cos\theta = r = 3\ \cos 2\theta = 6\ \cos^2\theta - 3$$

or

$$6\ \cos^2\theta + \sqrt{3}\ \cos\theta - 3 = 0$$

which gives

$$(2\ \cos\theta + \sqrt{3})(3\ \cos\theta - \sqrt{3}) = 0$$

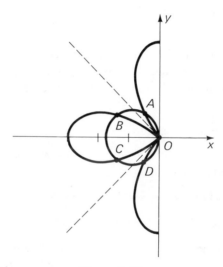

Figure 5–25

and

$$\cos\theta = -\sqrt{3}/2 \qquad \text{or} \qquad \cos\theta = \sqrt{3}/3$$

For $\cos\theta = -\sqrt{3}/2$, we have $r = -\sqrt{3}\ \cos\theta = 3/2$ on the circle and $r = 3\ \cos 2\theta = 6\ \cos^2\theta - 3 = 9/2 - 3 = 3/2$ on the other curve. This yields the points $B(3/2,5\pi/6)$ and $C(3/2,7\pi/6)$. For $\cos\theta = \sqrt{3}/3$, we have $r = -\sqrt{3}\ \cos\theta = -1$ on the circle and $r = 6\ \cos^2\theta - 3 = 2 - 3 = -1$ on the other curve. This yields the points $D(-1,\alpha)$ and $A(-1,-\alpha)$, where α is the first-quadrant angle $\text{Cos}^{-1}\ (\sqrt{3}/3)$. Notice that we have failed to discover the origin O by this procedure. All this means is that there is no one value of θ that gives $r = 0$ in both equations. However, $(0,\pi/2)$ satisfies the first equation while $(0,\pi/4)$ satisfies the second.

A general analytical procedure which will always detect *all* points of intersection of two given polar curves $f(r,\theta) = 0$ and $g(r,\theta) = 0$ is as follows. First, check to see whether or not the origin is on both curves by attempting to solve $f(0,\theta)=0$ and $g(0,\theta)=0$ *separately*. Next, notice that the equations

$$f((-1)^n r,\theta + n\pi) = 0 \qquad n = 0,\pm 1,\pm 2, \ldots$$

all have the same graph, and so do the equations

$$g((-1)^m r,\theta + m\pi) = 0 \qquad m = 0,\pm 1,\pm 2, \ldots$$

Finally, for each choice of m and n, solve the system of two equations so obtained simultaneously.

EXAMPLE Find all points of intersection of the polar curves $r = \cos\theta$ and $r^2 = 2 + \cos\theta$.

Solution Notice first that for $r = 0$, the second equation becomes $\cos\theta = -2$, which is impossible. Thus the origin is not a point of intersection. Considering an arbitrary integer n, the first equation has the equivalent forms

$$(-1)^n r = \cos(\theta + n\pi) = (-1)^n \cos\theta$$

which is the same as $r = \cos\theta$. For integers m, the second equation has the equivalent forms

$$r^2 = [(-1)^m r]^2 = 2 + \cos(\theta + m\pi) = 2 + (-1)^m \cos\theta$$

Thus we must solve the two systems

$$\begin{cases} r = \cos\theta \\ r^2 = 2 + \cos\theta \end{cases} \qquad \begin{cases} r = \cos\theta \\ r^2 = 2 - \cos\theta \end{cases}$$

The first one yields

$$(\cos\theta + 1)(\cos\theta - 2) = 0$$

while the second yields

$$(\cos\theta - 1)(\cos\theta + 2) = 0$$

Thus, we obtain the single point $(-1,\pi)$ from the first system and the single point $(1,0)$ from the second. These, however, are simply different polar coordinates for the same point. We conclude that the only point of intersection is $(1,0)$.

For many purposes it is useful to know the slope of the tangent line at a point on a given polar curve $r = f(\theta)$. For this we need to know dy/dx at the point in question. Using the transformation formulas (1) and letting r' denote $dr/d\theta$, we have

$$\frac{dy}{d\theta} = \frac{d}{d\theta}(r \sin \theta) = r \cos \theta + r' \sin \theta$$

and

$$\frac{dx}{d\theta} = \frac{d}{d\theta}(r \cos \theta) = -r \sin \theta + r' \cos \theta$$

Thus, we obtain the formula

$$\frac{dy}{dx} = \left(\frac{dy}{d\theta}\right) \Big/ \left(\frac{dx}{d\theta}\right) = \frac{r \cos \theta + r'\sin \theta}{r'\cos \theta - r \sin \theta}$$

EXAMPLE   Find the slope of the tangent line to $r = 1 + \cos \theta$ at $(1,\pi/2)$. Also find the points on this curve having largest and smallest y-coordinates and those having smallest and largest x-coordinates. Finally, sketch a graph of the curve.

Solution   We have $r' = -\sin \theta$ so that

$$\frac{dy}{dx} = \frac{(1 + \cos \theta)\cos \theta - \sin^2 \theta}{-\sin \theta \cos \theta - (1 + \cos \theta)\sin \theta} = \frac{(2 \cos \theta - 1)(\cos \theta + 1)}{-(\sin \theta)(2 \cos \theta + 1)}$$

For $\theta = \pi/2$, we get $dy/dx = 1$. To find the extreme values for y, we solve $dy/dx = 0$, which is equivalent to $\cos \theta = 1/2$, so that $\theta = \pm\pi/3$. (Notice that our formula for dy/dx takes the meaningless form $0/0$ if $\cos \theta = -1$ and that $\lim_{\theta \to \pi} dy/dx = 0$.) To find the extreme values for x, we solve $dx/dy = 0$, which is equivalent to $\cos \theta = -1/2$ or else $\sin \theta = 0$ *and* $\cos \theta \neq -1$. This yields $\theta = \pm 2\pi/3$ and $\theta = 0$. We conclude that the extreme y-values are taken at $(r,\theta) = (3/2,\pm\pi/3)$ and are $y =$

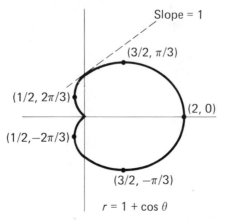

Figure 5–26

$r \sin \theta = \pm 3\sqrt{3}/4$. The extreme x-values are taken at $(r,\theta) = (1/2, \pm 2\pi/3)$ and $(2,0)$ and they are $x = r \cos \theta = -\sqrt{3}/4$ and 2. The graph is shown in Fig. 5-26.

EXERCISES

In 1–8, convert the given equation in rectangular coordinates to an equivalent equation in polar coordinates. Here a is a positive constant.

1. $x = a$

2. $x^2 + y^2 = a^2$

3. $y = ax^2$

4. $x = y$

5. $xy = a$

6. $x^2 - y^2 = a^2$

7. $(x^2 + y^2)^2 = a(x^2 - y^2)$

8. $(x^2 + y^2)^2 = axy$

In 9–16, convert the given polar equation to an equivalent equation in rectangular coordinates. Again $a > 0$.

9. $r = a$

10. $\theta = a$

11. $r^2 = \theta$

12. $r = 1 + \cos \theta$

13. $r^2 = a^2 \cos 2\theta$

14. $r^2 = a^2 \sin 2\theta$

15. $r^2 = \cos^2 \theta$

16. $r^3 = a \sec \theta$

In 17–24, sketch the given polar curve.

17. $r = \theta$

18. $r = 1 - \sin 2\theta$

19. $r = \cos 3\theta$

20. $r^2 = \sin 2\theta$

21. $r = 1 + 2 \cos \theta$

22. $r = \tan \theta \sec \theta$

23. $r = \cos \frac{1}{2}\theta$

24. $r^2 \sin 2\theta = 2$

In 25–30, find all points of intersection of the given pair of polar curves. Sketch graphs to show these intersections.

25. $r = 1 + \cos \theta$; $r^2 = 4 \cos 2\theta$

26. $r = 2 \sin 2\theta$; $r = 1$

27. $r^2 \sin 2\theta = 4$; $r = 2 \csc \theta$

28. $r = \sin 2\theta$; $r = 1 + \cos 2\theta$

29. $r^2 = \cos \theta$; $r = \sin \theta$

30. $r = \tan \theta$; $r = \cot \theta$

Chapter 6

Integration

THE SUBJECT *calculus* consists of two parts: differential calculus and integral calculus. To this point in the book, we have been studying the first of these two parts. In this chapter we take up a study of the second and we show in the Fundamental Theorem of Calculus (FTC) and the Existence of Primitives Theorem (EPT) just how these two parts are related to each other. The definite integral is used to reconstruct a function from its derivative or to construct a function having a given derivative.

The precise definition of the definite integral and the theorems giving its basic properties tend to be somewhat theoretical, but it is necessary to understand these matters in order that the numerous applications of the integral be meaningful. The mathematical theory presented in this chapter is kept to the minimum that is necessary for an intelligent use of integration. We recommend that this small amount of theory be studied and digested because of its usefulness later.

We lead into the study of integral calculus by a consideration of the problem of finding the areas of certain regions in the plane that are bounded by certain curves.

1 An Area Problem

Let a, b, and p be any three fixed positive real numbers with $a < b$. We consider the problem of finding a number A that can reasonably be called the "area" of the plane region R (shown in Fig. 6-1a) that lies under the graph of the function $f(x) = x^p$, above the x-axis, and between the vertical lines $x = a$ and $x = b$. We surely want A to be between the areas of the largest rectangle contained in R (Fig. 6-1b) and the smallest rectangle containing R (Fig. 6-1c) and so we insist that

$$a^p(b - a) \leqq A \leqq b^p(b - a)$$

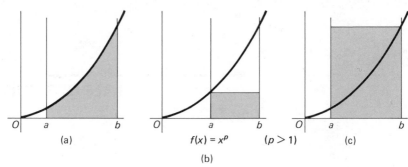

(a)

$f(x) = x^p$ $(p > 1)$ (c)

(b)

Figure 6-1

To get better (closer) bounds for a reasonable choice of A, we fix any positive integer n and divide the base interval $[a,b]$ into n subintervals by means of the points $a = x_0 < x_1 < x_2 < \cdots < x_n = b$ which we define by $x_k = ar^k$ where $r = \sqrt[n]{b/a}$ $(k = 0,1,2,\ldots,n)$. For each k, we consider the largest rectangle having the kth subinterval $[x_{k-1},x_k]$ as base that lies in R. The area of this kth rectangle is

$$f(x_{k-1})(x_k - x_{k-1}) = (ar^{k-1})^p(ar^k - ar^{k-1}) = a^{p+1}r^{(p+1)(k-1)}(r - 1)$$

It is clear that A should not be less than the sum, L_n, of the areas of these n rectangles (see Fig. 6-2). The reason for our particular choice of the division points x_k is that we can use the formula

$$1 + u + u^2 + \cdots + u^{n-1} = \frac{u^n - 1}{u - 1} \qquad (u \neq 1)$$

for the sum of a geometric progression to calculate L_n. We have (taking $u = r^{p+1}$) that

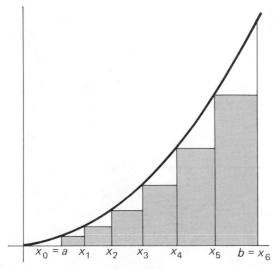

Figure 6-2

$$L_n = a^{p+1}u^0(r-1) + a^{p+1}u^1(r-1) + a^{p+1}u^2(r-1) + \cdots + a^{p+1}u^{n-1}(r-1)$$
$$= a^{p+1}(1 + u + u^2 + \cdots + u^{n-1})(r-1)$$
$$= a^{p+1} \cdot \frac{r^{n(p+1)} - 1}{r^{p+1} - 1} \cdot (r-1)$$

Since $r^n = b/a$, we have $a^{p+1}(r^{n(p+1)} - 1) = b^{p+1} - a^{p+1}$ and so

$$L_n = (b^{p+1} - a^{p+1}) \cdot \frac{r-1}{r^{p+1} - 1} \qquad (1)$$

To get an upper estimate for A, we increase the height of the kth rectangle to the largest value of f on the interval $[x_{k-1}, x_k]$ (see Fig. 6-3). This new height is $f(x_k) = (ar^k)^p = r^p(ar^{k-1})^p = r^p f(x_{k-1})$ and so the sum U_n of the areas of these n new rectangles satisfies $U_n = r^p L_n$. We surely want to insist that A satisfy

$$L_n \leq A \leq U_n = r^p L_n \qquad (2)$$

and that this should be true for every integer $n \geq 1$. Also, we have

$$\lim_{n \to \infty} r = \lim_{n \to \infty} \left(\frac{b}{a}\right)^{1/n} = \left(\frac{b}{a}\right)^0 = 1 \qquad (3)$$

Therefore, since the function g defined by $g(x) = x^{p+1}$ satisfies $g'(1) = p + 1$, the definition of derivative yields

$$\lim_{n \to \infty} \frac{r-1}{r^{p+1} - 1} = \lim_{r \to 1} \frac{r-1}{g(r) - g(1)} = \frac{1}{g'(1)} = \frac{1}{p+1}$$

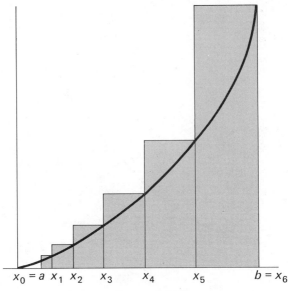

Figure 6–3

Thus, (1), (2), and (3) show that

$$\lim_{n \to \infty} L_n = \frac{b^{p+1} - a^{p+1}}{p+1} = (\lim_{n \to \infty} r^p)(\lim_{n \to \infty} L_n) = \lim_{n \to \infty} U_n$$

Since inequalities (2) are supposed to hold for each n, it seems that we ought to choose

$$A = \frac{b^{p+1} - a^{p+1}}{p+1} \tag{4}$$

for the area of R. Notice that if $p = 1$, then (4) conforms to the usual formula for the area of a trapezoid of height $b - a$ with the parallel sides of lengths a and b.

Now let us consider the same problem except that we fix $p < 0$. Then f is decreasing on $[a,b]$ so that $f(x_{k-1}) \geq f(x) \geq f(x_k)$ for $x_{k-1} \leq x \leq x_k$. Hence, using the same rectangles as above to compute L_n and U_n, we should now have

$$L_n \geq A \geq U_n \tag{2'}$$

if $p \neq -1$, the calculations of L_n and U_n proceed exactly as before and we are again led to (4). The special case that $p = -1$ is exceptional because then $u = r^{p+1} = r^0 = 1$ and so, in place of (1), we obtain

$$L_n = a^{p+1}(1 + u + u^2 + \cdots + u^{n-1})(r - 1) = n(\sqrt[n]{b/a} - 1) \tag{1'}$$

Since the function $h(x) = (b/a)^x$ satisfies $h'(0) = \ln(b/a) = \ln b - \ln a$, we have, for $p = -1$,

$$\lim_{n \to \infty} L_n = \lim_{n \to \infty} \frac{h(1/n) - h(0)}{1/n} = \ln b - \ln a \qquad (4')$$

The equalities (2) and (3) still hold, and so our only reasonable choice is

$$A = \lim_{n \to \infty} U_n = \lim_{n \to \infty} L_n = \ln b - \ln a \quad \text{for} \quad p = -1$$

EXAMPLE   Find the most reasonable choice for the area A in the following cases:

(a) $f(x) = x^2$; $a = 1, b = 2$

(c) $f(x) = \dfrac{1}{\sqrt[3]{x}}$; $a = \dfrac{1}{8}, b = 1$

(b) $f(x) = \sqrt[3]{x}$; $a = \dfrac{1}{8}, b = 1$

(d) $f(x) = \dfrac{1}{x}$; $a = 1, b = 3$

Solution   (a) Since $p = 2$, (4) yields $A = \dfrac{2^3 - 1^3}{3} = \dfrac{7}{3}$.

(b) Since $p = \dfrac{1}{3}$, (4) yields $A = \dfrac{1^{4/3} - (1/8)^{4/3}}{4/3} = \dfrac{3}{4}\left(1 - \dfrac{1}{16}\right) = \dfrac{45}{64}$.

(c) Here $p = -\dfrac{1}{3}$ and so $A = \dfrac{1^{2/3} - \left(\dfrac{1}{8}\right)^{2/3}}{2/3} = \dfrac{3}{2}\left(1 - \dfrac{1}{4}\right) = \dfrac{9}{8}$.

(d) Here $p = -1$ and so (4') gives $A = \ln 3 - \ln 1 = \ln 3$.

EXERCISES

In 1–20, find the most reasonable number A to assign as the "area" of the region R that lies between the x-axis and the graph of f and between the lines $x = a$ and $x = b$. In each case, draw a sketch of the region R.

1. $f(x) = x$; $a = 1, b = 4$

2. $f(x) = x^3$; $a = 1, b = 2$

3. $f(x) = x^3$; $a = \dfrac{1}{2}, b = 2$

4. $f(x) = x^3$; $a = \dfrac{1}{4}, b = 2$

5. $f(x) = x^3$; $a = 0, b = 2$

6. $f(x) = \sqrt{x}$; $a = 1, b = 4$

7. $f(x) = \sqrt{x}$; $a = 0, b = 1$

8. $f(x) = \dfrac{1}{\sqrt{x}}$; $a = \dfrac{1}{4}, b = 1$

9. $f(x) = \dfrac{1}{\sqrt{x}}$; $a = \dfrac{1}{n^2}, b = 1$

10. $f(x) = \dfrac{1}{\sqrt{x}}$; $a = 0, b = 1$

11. $f(x) = \dfrac{1}{x^2}$; $a = 1, b = 2$

12. $f(x) = \dfrac{1}{x^2}$; $a = 1, b = 100$

13. $f(x) = \dfrac{1}{x^2}$; $a = 1, b = \infty$

14. $f(x) = \dfrac{1}{x}$; $a = 1, b = 2$ **18.** $f(x) = \dfrac{1}{x}$; $a = e^{-n}, b = 1$

15. $f(x) = \dfrac{1}{x}$; $a = 1, b = e$ **19.** $f(x) = \dfrac{1}{x}$; $a = 0, b = 1$

16. $f(x) = \dfrac{1}{x}$; $a = 1, b = e^n$ **20.** $f(x) = \dfrac{1}{x}$; $a = 1, b = \infty$

17. $f(x) = \dfrac{1}{x}$; $a = \dfrac{1}{e}, b = 1$

21. Let $0 < b \leq \pi/2$ be given and fixed. Imitate the reasoning of this section to find the number A that can most reasonably be called the "area" of the region R that is bounded by the graph of $f(x) = \sin x$, the x-axis, $x = 0$, and $x = b$. Do this by obtaining estimates L_n and U_n corresponding to a subdivision $0 = x_0 < x_1 < \cdots < x_n = b$, where $x_k = 2kh$ and $h = \dfrac{b}{2n}$. Illustrate your analysis of the problem with sketches analogous to Figs. 6-1 to 6-3. [*Hint:* Prove and use the formula $2 \sin x_k \sin h = \cos(x_{k-1} + h) - \cos(x_k + h)$ (since $x_{k-1} + h = x_k - h$) to show that $(2 \sin h)L_n = 2h[\cos(x_0 + h) - \cos(x_{n-1} + h)]$.]

2 The Summation Symbol

In extending the ideas of the preceding section to more general functions f, we shall be faced with writing out sums of large numbers of terms (areas of rectangles) which, fortunately, all have the same form. Thus, it is desirable (and possible) to introduce a condensed notation for such sums. This summation notation will also be used in later chapters.

The idea is simple. Suppose that m and n are given integers with $m \leq n$ and that for each integer k with $m \leq k \leq n$ some number u_k has been specified. Then, instead of writing

$$u_m + u_{m+1} + u_{m+2} + \cdots + u_{n-1} + u_n \tag{1}$$

for the sum of these numbers, we write

$$\sum_{k=m}^{n} u_k \tag{2}$$

to denote this sum. Here $\sum$, the capital Greek letter sigma, is called the **summation symbol**, m is called the **lower limit of summation**, n is called the **upper limit of summation**, u_k is called the **kth term**, and k is called the **dummy index**. The term "dummy" is used for the k in (2) because it can be replaced by any other uncommitted symbol without affecting the meaning of (2). Thus, the symbols

$$\sum_{j=m}^{n} u_j, \quad \sum_{r=m}^{n} u_r, \quad \sum_{\alpha=m}^{n} u_\alpha, \quad \sum_{\text{cat}=m}^{n} u_{\text{cat}}$$

each denote the sum (1). The symbol (2) is read "the sum from $k = m$ to $k = n$ of u sub k."

Thus, instead of writing $1 + 4 + 9 + 16 + 25 + 36 + 49 + 64 + 81 + 100$ for the sum of the first ten perfect squares, we can write

$$\sum_{k=1}^{10} k^2 \quad \text{or} \quad \sum_{s=1}^{10} s^2$$

Also,

$$\sum_{j=-2}^{3} \frac{1}{j^2 + 1} = \frac{1}{5} + \frac{1}{2} + \frac{1}{1} + \frac{1}{2} + \frac{1}{5} + \frac{1}{10}$$

In addition, the sum of the first 100 positive integers can be denoted $\sum_{k=1}^{100} k$.

The **value** of a sum is the number obtained by adding up all its terms. Check that the values of the sums in the above three examples are respectively 385, $\frac{5}{2}$, and 5050. Just as we write $1 + 4 + 9 = 14$, we regard any sum as being equal to its value.

E X E R C I S E S

1. Evaluate (find the value of) the following sums:

(a) $\displaystyle\sum_{k=2}^{6} \frac{1}{k}$ (b) $\displaystyle\sum_{k=0}^{4} (k^2 - 1)$ (c) $\displaystyle\sum_{j=0}^{6} 2^{-j}$

(d) $\displaystyle\sum_{r=7}^{7} (r^3 + r)$ (e) $\displaystyle\sum_{j=-3}^{2} 2^j$ (f) $\displaystyle\sum_{t=10}^{99} 2^t$

2. Show that if $c_0, c_1, \cdots, c_n$ are given numbers, then

$$\sum_{k=1}^{n} (c_k - c_{k-1}) = c_n - c_0 \quad \text{and} \quad \sum_{k=0}^{n-1} (c_k - c_{k+1}) = c_0 - c_n$$

3. Use summation symbol notation to express:

(a) the sum of the first n perfect cubes: $1, 8, 27, 64, \cdots, n^3$.

(b) the sum of the reciprocals of the first n positive integers.

4. Show that $\displaystyle\sum_{k=1}^{n} k^{-2} < 2$ for every positive integer n. [*Hint:* Write $c_k = (k+1)^{-1}$, check that $(k+2)^{-2} < c_k - c_{k+1}$ for $k \geqq 0$, and use the results of exercise 2.]

3   The Definition of Area

In elementary geometry courses, one learns various formulas for finding the "area" of certain plane regions. These regions are ordinarily bounded by a finite number of line segments and/or arcs of circles. These formulas are usually justified by a few properties of "area" that we readily accept. These properties are

(1) If R is a region, then area (R) is a nonnegative number.

(2) If R is a rectangle of length l and width w, then area $(R) = lw$.

(3) If a region R is divided into a finite number of nonoverlapping subregions $R_1, R_2, \cdots, R_n$, then area $(R) = \displaystyle\sum_{k=1}^{n}$ area (R_k).

(4) If S is a subregion of a region R, then area $(S) \leqq$ area (R).

(5) If R_1 and R_2 are congruent regions, then area $(R_1) =$ area (R_2).

In section 1 we were guided implicitly by the first four of these in coming to a "reasonable solution" to the problem stated there. Here we shall use the same guidelines to develop a definition of exactly what we *mean* by the *area* of R for a fairly large class of regions R.

Let $a < b$ be given (and fixed) real numbers and let f be a given function that is defined, nonnegative, and continuous on $[a,b]$. Let R be the region bounded by the vertical lines $x = a$ and $x = b$, the graph of f, and the x-axis. More precisely, R consists of those points (x,y) for which $a \leqq x \leqq b$ and $0 \leqq y \leqq f(x)$. Fig. 6-4 shows such an R. Con-

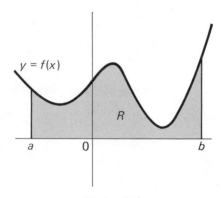

Figure 6–4

sider *any* finite set $P = \{x_0, x_1, \cdots, x_n\}$ of points of $[a,b]$ where $a = x_0 < x_1 < x_2 < \cdots < x_n = b$. This is called a **subdivision** of $[a,b]$. For each k $(1 \leq k \leq n)$ consider the smallest number M_k and the largest number m_k such that

$$m_k \leq f(x) \leq M_k \qquad \text{for all } x \text{ in } [x_{k-1}, x_k]$$

[Since f is continuous, there exist points s_k and t_k in $[x_{k-1}, x_k]$ for which $f(s_k) = m_k$ and $f(t_k) = M_k$.] Write $\Delta x_k = x_k - x_{k-1}$ for the length of the interval $[x_{k-1}, x_k]$. The rectangles of heights M_k and m_k having $[x_{k-1}, x_k]$ as base have the respective areas $M_k \Delta x_k$ and $m_k \Delta x_k$. These rectangles are shown in Fig. 6-5a and b, respectively. The numbers

$$U_a^b(f,P) = \sum_{k=1}^{n} M_k \Delta x_k$$

and

$$L_a^b(f,P) = \sum_{k=1}^{n} m_k \Delta x_k$$

are the areas of two polygonal regions (indicated in Fig. 6-5) having vertical and horizontal sides, the first of which contains R and the

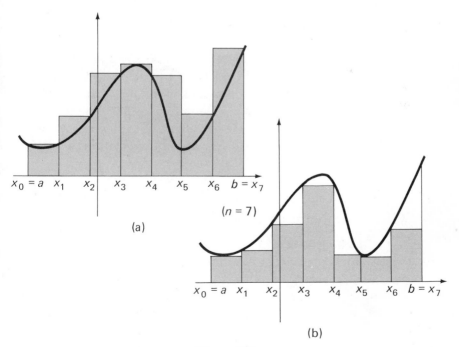

Figure 6–5

second of which is contained in R. We call these two numbers the
upper sum and the **lower sum** for f corresponding to P, respectively.
It seems intuitively reasonable that whatever number A we choose
to call the "area" of R should fall between these two sums. The following theorem, which is a special case of the first theorem in the next
section, removes our quandary as to how to select A.

$\Rightarrow$ **Theorem** If f is a function which is defined, nonnegative, and continuous on a closed interval $[a,b]$, then there exists exactly one number A having the property that

$$L_a^b(f,P) \leqq A \leqq U_a^b(f,P)$$

for every subdivision P of $[a,b]$.

$\Rightarrow$ **Definition** By the **area** of the region R described above, we mean
that unique number A of the preceding theorem.

We are assured by the theorem that we can now speak of *the* area
of R unambiguously, but the theorem gives us little information on
how to actually compute the number A. It might happen, as it did in
section 1, that f, a, and b are such that we can somehow find a sequence P_1, P_2, P_3, $\cdots$ of subdivisions of $[a,b]$ for which

$$\lim_{n \to \infty} L_a^b(f,P_n) = \lim_{n \to \infty} U_a^b(f,P_n)$$

and for which we can actually evaluate these sums and limits. In
general, this is not possible and we must be content with approximation methods, some of which are studied in later chapters. Hap-
pily though, there is a profound theorem called the Fundamental
Theorem of Calculus (FTC) whose use allows us to evaluate A easily
and exactly for many (but not all) functions f and intervals $[a,b]$. We
take up a discussion of FTC a little later.

4   The Definite Integral

Much of what was said in section 3 can be repeated ver-
batim without requiring that f be either continuous or nonnegative.
The discussion may then lose something in geometrical significance
(since some of the m_k's or M_k's may be negative), but, as we shall
see later, there is a wide variety of other applications of the resulting
integration theory.

Let $a < b$ be fixed real numbers and let f be a real-valued function that is defined and **bounded** on $[a,b]$. This means that there exist real numbers m and M such that

$$m \leq f(x) \leq M \qquad \text{for all } x \text{ satisfying } a \leq x \leq b \qquad (1)$$

Given a subdivision

$$P = \{a = x_0 < x_1 < \cdots < x_n = b\} \qquad (2)$$

of $[a,b]$, define m_k, M_k, Δx_k, $L_a^b(f,P)$, and $U_a^b(f,P)$ just as in section 3: m_k is the largest number and M_k is the smallest number such that

$$\left. \begin{array}{l} m_k \leq f(x) \leq M_k \qquad \text{for all } x \text{ satisfying } x_{k-1} \leq x \leq x_k \\ \Delta x_k = x_k - x_{k-1} \\ L_a^b(f,P) = \displaystyle\sum_{k=1}^{n} m_k \Delta x_k \qquad \text{and} \qquad U_a^b(f,P) = \sum_{k=1}^{n} M_k \Delta x_k \end{array} \right\} \qquad (3)$$

Before defining what we mean by the definite integral of f, we present two easy lemmas about upper and lower sums.

▷ **Lemma 1** Let P and Q be subdivisions of $[a,b]$ such that each point of P is also a point of Q. Then

$$L_a^b(f,P) \leq L_a^b(f,Q) \leq U_a^b(f,Q) \leq U_a^b(f,P)$$

That is, adding points to a subdivision cannot decrease lower sums and cannot increase upper sums.

Proof Write P as in (2). Suppose first that Q contains just one more point than P, call it u, and that $x_{k_0-1} < u < x_{k_0}$. Let us write m' and m'' for the largest numbers satisfying

$$m' \leq f(x) \qquad \text{for all } x \text{ satisfying } x_{k_0-1} \leq x \leq u$$

and

$$m'' \leq f(x) \qquad \text{for all } x \text{ satisfying } u \leq x \leq x_{k_0}$$

and also M' and M'' for the smallest numbers satisfying

$$f(x) \leq M' \qquad \text{for all } x \text{ satisfying } x_{k_0-1} \leq x \leq u$$

and

$$f(x) \leq M'' \qquad \text{if } u \leq x \leq x_{k_0}$$

We see that

$$m_{k_0} \leq m', \; m_{k_0} \leq m'', \; M' \leq M_{k_0}, \; M'' \leq M_{k_0}$$

and so

$$L_a^b(f,Q) - L_a^b(f,P) = m'(u - x_{k_0-1}) + m''(x_{k_0} - u) - m_{k_0}(x_{k_0} - x_{k_0-1})$$
$$\geqq m_{k_0}[(u - x_{k_0-1}) + (x_{k_0} - u) - (x_{k_0} - x_{k_0-1})] = 0$$

while

$$U_a^b(f,P) - U_a^b(f,Q) = M_{k_0}(x_{k_0} - x_{k_0-1}) - M'(u - x_{k_0-1}) - M''(x_{k_0} - u)$$
$$\geqq M_{k_0}[(x_{k_0} - x_{k_0-1}) - (u - x_{k_0-1}) - (x_{k_0} - u)] = 0$$

This proves the first and third inequalities of the lemma (while the second one is obvious) in the case that P and Q differ by just one point. Since we can get from P to Q in a finite number of steps by adding just one point at each step, the general case follows by a finite number of applications of the special case just proved. ∎

▷ **Lemma 2**   If P_1 and P_2 are any two subdivisions of $[a,b]$, then

$$L_a^b(f,P_1) \leqq U_a^b(f,P_2)$$

That is, no lower sum can exceed an upper sum whether or not the subdivisions have common points.

Proof   Let Q be the subdivision consisting of all the points that are in either P_1 or P_2. By Lemma 1, we have

$$L_a^b(f,P_1) \leqq L_a^b(f,Q) \leqq U_a^b(f,Q) \leqq U_a^b(f,P_2) \blacksquare$$

Let us think of all of the numbers $L_a^b(f,P)$ and $U_a^b(f,P)$ for all conceivable subdivisions P of $[a,b]$ as being plotted on a single horizontal number line (see Fig. 6-6). According to Lemma 2, every L is to the left of every U and so there is at least one number (point) γ which

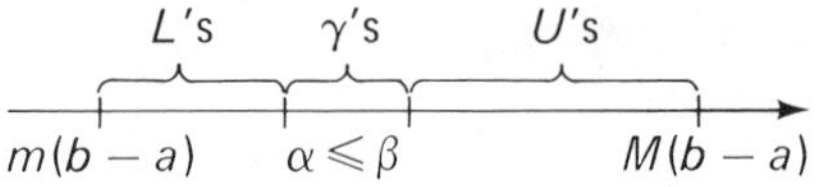

Figure 6–6

separates the L's from the U's. Indeed, the smallest number α that is not less than any L is such a γ and so is the largest number β not exceeding any U. Clearly, α is the smallest such separating number γ and β is the largest one. These two special numbers α and β (which are determined by f and $[a,b]$) may or may not be equal. They are the only two numbers which satisfy the following conditions:

   (i) $L_a^b(f,P) \leqq \alpha \leqq \beta \leqq U_a^b(f,P)$ for every subdivision P of $[a,b]$.
   (ii) If $L_a^b(f,P) \leqq \gamma \leqq U_a^b(f,P)$ for every such P, then $\alpha \leqq \gamma \leqq \beta$.
   We are interested in the functions f (and intervals $[a,b]$) for which

the corresponding numbers α and β are equal, and so we make the following definition.

▷ **Definition** A bounded real-valued function f defined on a closed interval $[a,b]$ is said to be **integrable over** $[a,b]$ if there is *only one* number γ such that $L_a^b(f,P) \leq \gamma \leq U_a^b(f,P)$ for every subdivision P of $[a,b]$ (that is, $\alpha = \beta$). If this is so, then we call the number γ the **definite integral** of f over $[a,b]$ and we denote this unique number by

$$\int_a^b f = \gamma \tag{4}$$

Even though the number $\int_a^b f$ (if it exists) depends only on $[a,b]$ and f, most functions f that we consider in calculus are defined by some formula for $f(x)$ in terms of the "independent variable x." In such cases we write

$$\int_a^b f(x)\,dx = \gamma \tag{5}$$

instead of (4). The elongated S in (4) and (5) is called the **integral sign** while the numbers a and b are called the **lower and upper limits of integration,** respectively. The letter x that appears in (5) is called the **dummy variable of integration** and the symbol dx is called the **differential of the dummy variable.** The expression $f(x)$ is called the **integrand.** In (5), the x can be replaced by any other uncommitted symbol without affecting the meaning. Thus,

$$\int_a^b f(x)\,dx = \int_a^b f(\theta)\,d\theta = \int_a^b f(t)\,dt$$

The dx is *not* a number or a function. It can be regarded for now as merely a good way of keeping track of which symbol is being used as the variable of integration. We will see later that it plays an important role in certain techniques for evaluating integrals. Our work in section 1 *proves* that if p is a real number and $f(x) = x^p$ for all $x > 0$, then f is integrable over any closed interval $[a,b]$ with $b > a > 0$. This is because the special upper and lower sums U_n and L_n that we used there had the same limit and so, by (i) above,

$$\beta \leq \lim_{n \to \infty} U_n = \lim_{n \to \infty} L_n \leq \alpha \leq \beta$$

whence

$$\alpha = \beta = \lim_{n \to \infty} L_n = \lim_{n \to \infty} U_n = \int_a^b f.$$

Since we were able to evaluate this limit, we also *proved* that

$$\int_a^b x^p \, dx = \frac{b^{p+1} - a^{p+1}}{p + 1} \qquad \text{if } p \neq -1$$

and

$$\int_a^b \frac{dx}{x} = \int_a^b x^{-1} \, dx = \ln b - \ln a$$

Here, now, is an example of a function that is *not* integrable. Fix any $a < b$ and define $f(x) = 1$ if x is a rational number (cx is an integer for some positive integer c), and $f(x) = 0$ otherwise. For any P defined as in (2), we have $m_k = 0$ and $M_k = 1$ for all k (because each $[x_{k-1}, x_k]$ contains both rational and irrational numbers) and so $L_a^b(f, P) = 0$ while

$$U_a^b(f, P) = \sum_{k=1}^n \Delta x_k = b - a$$

Therefore $\alpha = 0$ and $\beta = b - a$. Since $\alpha < \beta$, f is not integrable over $[a, b]$. The reason for this nonintegrability is that f is "too" discontinuous. Though many discontinuous functions are integrable, we shall find the next theorem adequate for our study of calculus.

▷ ***Existence Theorem for Integrals (ETI)***   Suppose that f is a real-valued function that is defined and *continuous* on some closed interval $[a, b]$. Then f is integrable over $[a, b]$. Moreover, given any number $\epsilon > 0$, there exists some $\delta > 0$ having the following property: If P defined as in (2) satisfies $\Delta x_k < \delta$ for all k ($1 \leq k \leq n$), then

$$U_a^b(f, P) - L_a^b(f, P) < \epsilon$$

and any sum S of the form

$$S = \sum_{k=1}^n f(\xi_k) \Delta x_k$$

where $x_{k-1} \leq \xi_k \leq x_k$ ($1 \leq k \leq n$) satisfies

$$\left| S - \int_a^b f \right| < \epsilon$$

Proof   Let α and β be as in (i) and (ii) above and let $\epsilon > 0$ be given.

According to the Uniform Continuity Theorem in the Appendix, there is a $\delta > 0$ for which

$$|f(s) - f(t)| < \frac{\epsilon}{b-a} \qquad \text{if } s \text{ and } t \text{ are in } [a,b] \text{ and } |s - t| < \delta \qquad (6)$$

Now let P be given with $\Delta x_k < \delta$ for all k. Use the Extreme Value Theorem (page 166) to obtain s_k and t_k in $[x_{k-1}, x_k]$ such that

$$m_k = f(s_k) \leq f(x) \leq f(t_k) = M_k \qquad \text{for all } x \text{ in } [x_{k-1}, x_k]$$

Then $|s_k - t_k| < \delta$ for all k and so, using (i),

$$0 \leq \beta - \alpha \leq U_a^b(f,P) - L_a^b(f,P) = \sum_{k=1}^{n} f(t_k)\Delta x_k - \sum_{k=1}^{n} f(s_k)\Delta x_k$$

$$= \sum_{k=1}^{n} [f(t_k) - f(s_k)]\Delta x_k < \sum_{k=1}^{n} \frac{\epsilon}{b-a} \Delta x_k = \frac{\epsilon}{b-a} \sum_{k=1}^{n} \Delta x_k = \epsilon$$

which proves that $\alpha = \beta$ (otherwise we could have started with $0 < \epsilon < \beta - \alpha$). Also, $f(s_k) \leq f(\xi_k) \leq f(t_k)$ for all k and so both S and $\int_a^b f$ are in the closed interval $[L_a^b(f,P), U_a^b(f,P)]$ whose length is less than ϵ. This completes the proof. ■

The importance of ETI is that it assures us that if f is a continuous function on $[a,b]$, then it is meaningful to speak of $\int_a^b f$; this integral is a precisely defined definite real number. The theorem, however, gives us little information on how to calculate this number. For example, ETI assures us that $\int_0^1 \frac{dx}{1 + x^2}$ is a number which can be approximated as closely as desired (closer than ϵ) by sums of the form S provided that the subdivision P is fine enough ($\Delta x_k < \delta$ for all k where δ is small enough so that (6) holds). We shall see later that

$$\int_0^1 \frac{dx}{1 + x^2} = \frac{\pi}{4}$$

Sums of the above form S are known as **Riemann sums** (pronounced *ree'mahn*) in honor of the nineteenth-century German mathematician G. F. B. Riemann who first used such sums to give a precise definition of the integral. The integral that we have defined here is usually called the **Riemann integral** to distinguish it from other integrals that are studied in more advanced courses.

For any subdivision P of $[a,b]$ as in (2), we define the **mesh** of P to be the number

$$|P| = \max \{\Delta x_k : 1 \le k \le n\}$$

That is, $|P|$ is the length of the longest of the n subintervals determined by P.

▷ **Corollary** Suppose that f is continuous on $[a,b]$ and that P_1, P_2, P_3, $\cdots$ are subdivisions of $[a,b]$ for which

$$\lim_{j \to \infty} |P_j| = 0$$

For each j, let S_j be any Riemann sum for f corresponding to P_j. Then

$$\lim_{j \to \infty} S_j = \int_a^b f$$

Proof Given any $\epsilon > 0$, let δ be as in ETI above. Choose j_0 such that $|P_j| < \delta$ for $j > j_0$. By ETI, we have

$$\left| S_j - \int_a^b f \right| < \epsilon \qquad \text{if } j > j_0$$

which completes the proof. ∎

EXAMPLE Evaluate the limit

$$\lim_{n \to \infty} \frac{1}{n} \sum_{k=1}^{n} \sqrt{1 + \frac{k}{n}}$$

Solution Letting $P_n = \{1 = x_0 < x_1 < \cdots < x_n = 2\}$, where $x_k = 1 + k/n$, and choosing $\xi_k = x_k$, we see that $\Delta x_k = 1/n$, $|P_n| \to 0$ as $n \to \infty$, and

$$S_n = \frac{1}{n} \sum_{k=1}^{n} \sqrt{1 + \frac{k}{n}} = \sum_{k=1}^{n} f(\xi_k) \Delta x_k$$

is a Riemann sum corresponding to P_n for the function $f(x) = \sqrt{x}$ on the interval $[1,2]$. Thus, by the integrability of $f(x) = x^{1/2}$ and the corollary,

$$\lim_{n \to \infty} S_n = \int_1^2 x^{1/2}\, dx = \frac{2^{3/2} - 1^{3/2}}{3/2} = \frac{2}{3}(2\sqrt{2} - 1)$$

We next show that the integral acts additively over adjacent intervals.

▷ **Theorem** Suppose that f is continuous on $[a,b]$ and that $a < c < b$. Then

$$\int_a^c f + \int_c^b f = \int_a^b f$$

Proof Let $\epsilon > 0$ be given. Now ETI provides a subdivision P of $[a,b]$ such that

$$U_a^b(f,P) - L_a^b(f,P) < \epsilon$$

If c is not already in P, then we add it to P without damaging this inequality (see Lemma 1): say $c = x_r$. Writing

$$P_1 = \{a = x_0 < x_1 < \cdots < x_r = c\}$$

and

$$P_2 = \{c = x_r < x_{r+1} < \cdots < x_n = b\}$$

we see that

$$U_a^c(f,P_1) + U_c^b(f,P_2) = U_a^b(f,P)$$

and the same with L in place of U. Thus, abbreviating in an obvious way, we have

$$-\epsilon < L_a^b - U_a^b = L_a^c + L_c^b - U_a^b \leq \int_a^c + \int_c^b - \int_a^b \leq U_a^c + U_c^b - L_a^b$$
$$= U_a^b - L_a^b < \epsilon$$

and so

$$\left| \left(\int_a^c + \int_c^b \right) - \int_a^b \right| < \epsilon$$

Since $\epsilon > 0$ was arbitrary, this proves the desired equality. ∎

In case $a \geq b$, the symbol $\int_a^b f$ has not yet been assigned any meaning. We now *define* this symbol in such a way that the very useful conclusion of the preceding theorem remains true regardless of the ordering of the three numbers a, b, and c.

▷ **Definition** If $a > b$ and f is integrable over $[b,a]$, we define

$$\int_a^b f = -\int_b^a f$$

We also define

$$\int_a^a f = 0$$

for any a and any f.

With these definitions, the preceding theorem can now be extended as follows.

▷ **Corollary** If f is continuous on an interval I and a, b, and c are *any* numbers in I, then

$$\int_a^c f + \int_c^b f = \int_a^b f$$

Proof One easily checks this formula in the three cases $a = b$, $b = c$, and $c = a$. The case $a < c < b$ is the preceding theorem. If $a < b < c$, then

$$\int_a^c = \int_a^b + \int_b^c = \int_a^b - \int_c^b$$

and so

$$\int_a^c + \int_c^b = \int_a^b$$

If $b < a < c$, then

$$\int_b^c = \int_b^a + \int_a^c$$

and so

$$\int_a^b = -\int_b^a = \int_a^c - \int_b^c = \int_a^c + \int_c^b$$

The remaining three cases, $b < c < a$, $c < a < b$, and $c < b < a$, are left for the reader to check. ∎

E X E R C I S E S

1. By subdividing $[1,2]$ into n subintervals of length $1/n$ and considering upper and lower sums for $f(x) = 1/x$, show that

$$\sum_{j=n}^{2n-1} \frac{1}{j} > \ln 2 > \sum_{j=n+1}^{2n} \frac{1}{j}$$

and so

$$0 < \ln 2 - \left(\frac{1}{n+1} + \frac{1}{n+2} + \frac{1}{n+3} + \cdots + \frac{1}{n+n} \right) < \frac{1}{2n}$$

for every positive integer n.

2. Using $\int_0^b = \int_0^a + \int_a^b$, prove that if $p \geq 0$ and $b > 0$, then

$$\frac{b^{p+1} - a^{p+1}}{p+1} \leq \int_0^b x^p \, dx \leq a^{p+1} + \frac{b^{p+1} - a^{p+1}}{p+1}$$

whenever $0 < a < b$ and so

$$\int_0^b x^p \, dx = \frac{b^{p+1}}{p+1}$$

3. Use upper and lower sums corresponding to subdivisions into subintervals of length 1 to show that if $p > 0$ is a real number and $n > 0$ is an integer, then:

(a) $\dfrac{n^{p+1}}{p+1} = \int_0^n x^p \, dx < \sum_{k=1}^{n} k^p < \int_1^{n+1} x^p \, dx = \dfrac{(n+1)^{p+1} - 1}{p+1}$

(b) $\dfrac{(1+n)^{1-p} - 1}{1-p} = \int_1^{n+1} \dfrac{dx}{x^p} < \sum_{k=1}^{n} \dfrac{1}{k^p} \leq 1 + \int_1^n \dfrac{dx}{x^p} = \dfrac{n^{1-p} - p}{1-p}$

provided that $p \neq 1$

(c) $\ln(n+1) = \int_1^{n+1} \dfrac{dx}{x} < \sum_{k=1}^{n} \dfrac{1}{k} \leq 1 + \int_1^n \dfrac{dx}{x} = 1 + \ln n$

Conclude from (b) and (c) that:

(d) $p \leq 1$ implies $\displaystyle\lim_{n \to \infty} \sum_{k=1}^{n} \dfrac{1}{k^p} = \infty$

(e) $p > 1$ implies $\displaystyle\lim_{n \to \infty} \sum_{k=1}^{n} \dfrac{1}{k^p} \leq \dfrac{p}{p-1} < \infty$

4. Let $a < b$ and $c > 0$ with $c \neq 1$ be given real numbers. Define f by $f(x) = c^x$. Verify each of the following statements.

(a) If n is a positive integer and $h = (b-a)/n$, then

$$S_n = \sum_{k=0}^{n-1} c^{a+kh} \cdot h$$

is a Riemann sum for f over $[a,b]$.

(b) $S_n = hc^a \cdot \dfrac{c^{hn} - 1}{c^h - 1} = \dfrac{h}{c^h - 1}(c^b - c^a)$

(c) $\displaystyle\lim_{h \to 0} \dfrac{h}{c^h - 1} = \dfrac{1}{\ln c}$

$\left[\text{Hint: } \ln c = f'(0) = \displaystyle\lim_{h \to 0} \dfrac{f(h) - f(0)}{h}. \right]$

(d) $\displaystyle\int_a^b c^x \, dx = \lim_{n \to \infty} S_n = \dfrac{c^b - c^a}{\ln c}$

5. Let f and g be any two functions that are continuous on $[a,b]$ and

satisfy $f(x) \leq g(x)$ for every x in $[a,b]$. Prove the following two assertions.

(a) $\displaystyle\int_a^b f \leq \int_a^b g$ $\left[Hint:\ L_a^b(f,P) \leq L_a^b(g,P) \leq \displaystyle\int_a^b g. \right]$

(b) If $\displaystyle\int_a^b f = \int_a^b g$, then $f(x) = g(x)$ for every x in $[a,b]$. [Hint: Assuming that $f(x^*) < y_1 < y_2 < g(x^*)$ for some x^* with $a < x^* < b$, choose $P = \{a = x_0 < x_1 < x_2 < x_3 = b\}$ where $x_1 < x^* < x_2$ are such that $f(x) \leq y_1$ and $g(x) \geq y_2$ whenever $x_1 \leq x \leq x_2$ and then show that $L_a^b(g,P) - U_a^b(f,P) \geq (y_2 - y_1)(x_2 - x_1) > 0.]$

6. Prove that if there are subdivisions P_1 and P_2 of $[a,b]$ for which $L_a^b(f,P_1) = U_a^b(f,P_2)$, then $f(x) = f(a)$ for every x in $[a,b]$. [Hint: Let Q be defined as in the proof of Lemma 2 and show that f must be constant on each of the subintervals determined by Q.]

7. Suppose that f is a nondecreasing function on $[a,b]$: $f(s) \leq f(t)$ if $a \leq s \leq t \leq b$. Let $P_n = \{a = x_0 < x_1 \cdots < x_n = b\}$, where $\Delta x_k = (b - a)/n$ for all k ($1 \leq k \leq n$), be the subdivision of $[a,b]$ into n subintervals of equal length.

(a) Show that $U_a^b(f,P_n) - L_a^b(f,P_n) = \dfrac{b - a}{n} \cdot \displaystyle\sum_{k=1}^n [f(x_k) - f(x_{k-1})] = \dfrac{b-a}{n}[f(b) - f(a)]$ and deduce that f is integrable over $[a,b]$.

(b) Give an example of a function f that is nondecreasing on $[0,1]$ and is discontinuous at $x = 1/n$ for every positive integer n.

(c) Conclude from parts (a) and (b) that the converse of ETI is false.

8. Let f be a strictly increasing continuous function on $[a,b]$. Write $c = f(a)$, $d = f(b)$, and define the inverse function g on $[c,d]$ by $g(y) = x$ if $f(x) = y$.

(a) Prove, as Fig. 6-7 suggests, that if

$$P = \{a = x_0 < x_1 < \cdots < x_n = b\}, y_k = f(x_k) \qquad \text{for } k = 0, 1, \cdots, n$$

and

$$Q = \{c = y_0 < y_1 < \cdots < y_n = d\},$$

then

$$L_a^b(f,P) + U_c^d(g,Q) = \sum_{k=1}^n y_{k-1}\Delta x_k + \sum_{k=1}^n x_k \Delta y_k$$

$$= \sum_{k=1}^n (x_k y_k - x_{k-1} y_{k-1}) = bd - ac$$

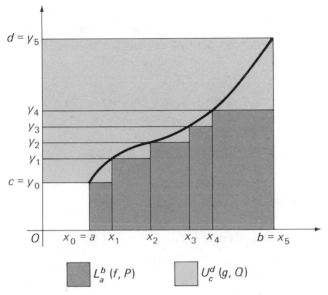

$d = y_5$
y_4
y_3
y_2
y_1
$c = y_0$

O | $x_0 = a$ x_1 | x_2 | x_3 x_4 | $b = x_5$

☐ $L_a^b (f, P)$ ☐ $U_c^d (g, Q)$

Figure 6–7

(b) Use (a) to prove that $\displaystyle\int_a^b f(x)\, dx + \int_c^d g(y)dy = bd - ac$.

(c) Apply (b) and exercise 4(d) to $f(x) = e^x$ to prove that

$$\int_c^d \ln y \, dy = d \ln d - c \ln c - (d - c) \qquad \text{whenever } d > c > 0$$

9. Use the results of exercise 8(c) and subdivisions into intervals of length 1 to prove that if $n > 2$ is an integer, then

$$n \ln n - n + 1 = \int_1^n \ln x \, dx < \sum_{k=2}^n \ln k = \ln (n!) < \ln n + \int_2^n \ln x \, dx$$
$$= (n + 1) \ln n - \ln 4 - (n - 2)$$

and therefore

$$e\left(\frac{n}{e}\right)^n = n^n e^{-n+1} < n! < \frac{1}{4}n^{n+1}e^{-n+2} < 2n\left(\frac{n}{e}\right)^n$$

10. Sometimes one wishes to find a specific $\delta > 0$ (in terms of a given $\epsilon > 0$) that is small enough to assure the truth of the last sentence of ETI.

(a) Show that if f is monotonic (either nondecreasing or nonincreasing) on $[a,b]$, then $\delta = \epsilon/|f(b) - f(a)|$ is small enough. [Compare exercise 7.]

(b) Show that if f is differentiable on $[a,b]$ and $|f'(\xi)| \leq M < \infty$ for some constant M and every ξ in $[a,b]$, then $\delta = \epsilon/(Mb - Ma)$ is small enough. [*Hint:* Use MVT (page 151) to prove that this δ assures the truth of (6) in the proof of ETI.]

(c) Prove that

$$0 < \int_0^1 \frac{dx}{1 + x^2} - \sum_{k=1}^n \frac{n}{n^2 + k^2} < \frac{1}{2n}$$

for every positive integer n.

5   The Fundamental Theorem of Calculus

This theorem is so useful for evaluating definite integrals that most students come to regard it as defining the integral, while ignoring (or even forgetting) its definition in terms of approximating sums as given above. This practice is practical and harmless when an appropriate function F can be found (as it often can).

▷ *Fundamental Theorem of Calculus (FTC)*   Suppose that f is a function that is continuous on $[a,b]$ and that F is some function that is differentiable on $[a,b]$ with $F'(x) = f(x)$ for every x in $[a,b]$. Then

$$\int_a^b f(x)dx = F(b) - F(a)$$

Proof   Given any subdivision $P = \{a = x_0 < x_1 < \cdots < x_n = b\}$, it follows from MVT (page 151) that there exist numbers $\xi_1, \cdots, \xi_n$ such that $x_{k-1} < \xi_k < x_k$ and

$$F(x_k) - F(x_{k-1}) = F'(\xi_k)(x_k - x_{k-1}) = f(\xi_k)\Delta x_k$$

Thus, the sum S given by

$$S = \sum_{k=1}^n f(\xi_k)\Delta x_k = \sum_{k=1}^n [F(x_k) - F(x_{k-1})] = F(b) - F(a)$$

is a Riemann sum for f, and so ETI (page 294) shows that S can be made as near to $\int_a^b f$ as desired for an appropriate choice of P. But the value of our S is $F(b) - F(a)$ for every P and this proves the theorem:

$$\left|\left[F(b)-F(a)\right]-\int_a^b f\right| < \epsilon \qquad \text{for every } \epsilon > 0$$

and so this difference is 0. ∎

EXAMPLE Evaluate the following integrals.

(a) $\displaystyle\int_0^1 (2x - x^3)dx$ (b) $\displaystyle\int_0^\pi \sin x \, dx$ (c) $\displaystyle\int_0^1 \frac{dx}{1 + x^2}$

Solution (a) Since $\dfrac{d}{dx}\left(x^2 - \dfrac{1}{4}x^4\right) = 2x - x^3$, we have

$$\int_0^1 (2x - x^3)\,dx = \left(1^2 - \frac{1}{4}\cdot 1^4\right) - \left(0^2 - \frac{1}{4}\cdot 0^4\right) = \frac{3}{4}$$

(b) Since $\dfrac{d}{dx}(-\cos x) = \sin x$, we have

$$\int_0^\pi \sin x \, dx = (-\cos \pi) - (-\cos 0) = 1 - (-1) = 2$$

(c) Since $\dfrac{d}{dx}(\text{Tan}^{-1} x) = \dfrac{1}{1 + x^2}$,

$$\int_0^1 \frac{dx}{1 + x^2} = \text{Tan}^{-1} 1 - \text{Tan}^{-1} 0 = \frac{\pi}{4} - 0 = \frac{\pi}{4}$$

Any function F such that $F'(x) = f(x)$ for every x in some interval I is called an **antiderivative** of f on I. We also call F a **primitive** for f on I. Plainly, FTC by itself is useless for evaluating a definite integral unless we are successful in finding a primitive F for the integrand f on the given interval $[a,b]$. The process of finding a primitive F for a given f is called **integration** (or **antidifferentiation**). Chapter 7 is devoted to a study of methods that often work for carrying out this process. Unlike differentiation, though, it is *not* true that if a function f is such that $f(x)$ can be expressed in a simple "closed-form," then a primitive F can be calculated in a finite number of steps by repeated application of routine methods that we have learned (or could learn). Roughly speaking, the situation is this: If we can write a function down, then we can differentiate it, but we can write functions down that no one will ever integrate. Indeed, it has been proved in more advanced works that all attempts to find a primitive for any of the functions e^{-x^2}, $\sin x^2$, and $\dfrac{\sin x}{x}$ such that the primitive can be expressed as some finite combination of the functions which we have studied here are doomed to failure. The following theorem assures us that these functions *do* have primitives; it is just that we cannot write them down using customary "closed-form" expressions. The number $\int_0^1 \frac{\sin x}{x}\,dx$ cannot be expressed as a finite combination of well-known constants, but we shall learn later that

$$\int_0^1 \frac{\sin x}{x}\,dx = \lim_{n \to \infty} \sum_{k=0}^n \frac{(-1)^k}{(2k+1)!(2k+1)}$$

(an expression which gives very rapid approximations). The interested reader might enjoy philosophizing about what it means to know a number exactly. Do you *know* what π is (see section 8 below)?

▷ **Existence of Primitives Theorem (EPT)**   Suppose that f is a function that is defined and continuous on some interval I. Let c be in I and define F at each x in I by

$$F(x) = \int_c^x f$$

Then F is a primitive for f on I: $F'(x) = f(x)$ for every x in I.

Proof   Let x_0 in I be fixed and let $\epsilon > 0$ be given. Since f is continuous at x_0, there is a $\delta > 0$ such that

$$f(x_0) - \epsilon < f(x) < f(x_0) + \epsilon \tag{1}$$

whenever x is in I and $|x - x_0| < \delta$. We now consider numbers $h \neq 0$ for which $x_0 + h$ is in I. If $0 < h < \delta$, then (1) obtains for all x in $[x_0, x_0 + h]$ and so

$$[f(x_0) - \epsilon]h < L_{x_0}^{x_0+h}(f,\{x_0, x_0 + h\}) \leq \int_{x_0}^{x_0+h} f \leq U_{x_0}^{x_0+h}(f,\{x_0, x_0 + h\})$$
$$< [f(x_0) + \epsilon]h$$

and therefore

$$f(x_0) - \epsilon < \frac{1}{h}\int_{x_0}^{x_0+h} f < f(x_0) + \epsilon$$

If $-\delta < h < 0$, then (1) obtains for all x in $[x_0 + h, x_0]$ and so

$$[f(x_0) - \epsilon](-h) < L_{x_0+h}^{x_0}(f,\{x_0 + h, x_0\}) \leq \int_{x_0+h}^{x_0} f$$
$$\leq U_{x_0+h}^{x_0}(f,\{x_0 + h, x_0\}) < [f(x_0) + \epsilon](-h)$$

and therefore

$$f(x_0) - \epsilon < \frac{1}{-h}\int_{x_0+h}^{x_0} f = \frac{1}{h}\int_{x_0}^{x_0+h} f < f(x_0) + \epsilon$$

Combining these two cases, we have

$$\left| f(x_0) - \frac{1}{h}\int_{x_0}^{x_0+h} f \right| < \epsilon \qquad (2)$$

whenever $x_0 + h$ is in I and $0 < |h| < \delta$. But

$$\frac{1}{h}\int_{x_0}^{x_0+h} f = \frac{1}{h}\left\{ \int_{c}^{x_0+h} f - \int_{c}^{x_0} f \right\} = \frac{F(x_0 + h) - F(x_0)}{h} \qquad (3)$$

From (2), (3), and the definition of limit, we have proved that

$$\lim_{h \to 0} \frac{F(x_0 + h) - F(x_0)}{h} = f(x_0)$$

which is what it means to assert that $F'(x_0) = f(x_0)$. Since x_0 in I was arbitrary, our proof is complete. ∎

EXAMPLE Let f be the continuous function defined by $f(t) = (\sin t)/t$ if $t \neq 0$ and $f(0) = \lim_{t \to 0} f(t) = 1$. Show that the function F defined for all real x by $F(x) = \int_0^x f(t)\, dt$ is strictly increasing on $[-\pi,\pi]$ and find $F'(\pi/2)$.

Solution Since $F'(x) = f(x) > 0$ for $-\pi < x < \pi$, it is a corollary of MVT (page 154) that assures us that F is strictly increasing on $[-\pi,\pi]$. Also, $F'(\pi/2) = f(\pi/2) = 2/\pi$.

It is evident that if F_1 is a primitive for f on I and if $F_2(x) = F_1(x) + C$ for x in I (where C is any constant), then F_2 is also a primitive for f on I and $F_2'(x) = F_1'(x) = f(x)$. For instance, x^2, $x^2 + 7$, $x^2 - e$, and $x^2 + e^{-\pi}$ are all primitives for $2x$ on any interval. In the opposite direction, we have the following.

Theorem If F_1 and F_2 are both primitives for the same function f on an interval I, then there is a constant C such that $F_2(x) = F_1(x) + C$ for all x in I.

Proof The function g defined by $g(x) = F_2(x) - F_1(x)$ satisfies

$$g'(x) = F_2'(x) - F_1'(x) = f(x) - f(x) = 0$$

for every x in I and so a corollary of MVT provides C such that $g(x) = C$ for all x in I. ∎

As noted above, the process of finding a primitive is called integration. We now introduce a time honored and handy symbol called the **indefinite integral** to denote an arbitrary primitive of a given function that is displayed explicitly in that symbol. It is

$$\int f(x)\, dx$$

and it stands for *any* primitive of f. The adjective "indefinite" refers to the absence of limits of integration that specify a definite interval. A definite integral is a number while an indefinite integral is a function (actually a collection of functions any two of which differ by a constant on any given interval). Thus,

$$\int f(x)\, dx = F(x)$$

means that on some interval I the function F is a primitive of the function f. This usage of the equality mark is somewhat dangerous because the left-hand side stands for a whole collection of functions (on possibly different intervals) while any function that we put on the right-hand side is just one of them. To illustrate this minor difficulty, define functions f, F_1, F_2, and F_3 by

$$f(x) = \frac{x}{x^2 - 1} \qquad \text{if } x^2 \neq 1$$
$$F_1(x) = \ln \sqrt{1 - x^2} \qquad \text{if } x^2 < 1$$
$$F_2(x) = \ln [2\sqrt{x^2 - 1}\,] \qquad \text{if } x^2 > 1$$
$$F_3(x) = \ln [3\sqrt{x^2 - 1}\,] \qquad \text{if } x^2 > 1$$

Then $F_j{}'(x) = f(x)$ (provided that x is in the domain of F_j) for all three values of j (as one easily checks) and so we regard all three of the equalities

$$\int f(x)\, dx = F_1(x), \int f(x)\, dx = F_2(x), \int f(x)\, dx = F_3(x)$$

as being "correct" even though there is no interval on which two of the F's are equal: F_1 and F_2 have disjoint domains while

$$F_2(x) + \ln 3 = F_3(x) + \ln 2$$

whenever $|x| > 1$.

The danger just mentioned is truly minor once it is understood that it is possible to have more than one correct answer to a problem of evaluating an indefinite integral and, as the preceding theorem confirms, that on any given interval two correct answers can only differ by a constant. We have issued this warning only to forestall puzzlement over such matters as:

$$2 \sin^2 x = \int 4 \sin x \cos x \, dx = \int 2 \sin 2x \, dx = -\cos 2x$$

(which is surely correct) even though there is *no* x for which $2 \sin^2 x = -\cos 2x$. All puzzlement disappears as soon as it is realized that equalities involving indefinite integrals should not be interpreted in the strict sense but merely mean that the two sides differ by at most a constant on any *interval* where they are both defined. Of course, $2 \sin^2 x = 1 - \cos 2x$ for every x. Many authors try to account for this minor problem by insisting that $+C$ be written to the right of every answer to an integration problem. We regard this practice as a nuisance at best and we *do not* insist upon it (or forbid it). After all, it is false that $2 \sin^2 x = -\cos 2x + C$ unless $C = 1$ and it is true that $-2 \cos^2 x$ is another primitive for $4 \sin x \cos x$ and $-2 \cos^2 x = -\cos 2x - 1$ (not $+1$) for all x. We have undoubtedly flogged this dead horse far too much and so, now that all readers have become sufficiently sophisticated on this issue, we shall attempt not to mention it again.

In order to use FTC to evaluate definite integrals, it is necessary to be able to find primitives, that is, evaluate indefinite integrals. A large number of these can be found by simply reading derivative formulas from right to left. Thus, the reader should refresh his memorization of basic derivative formulas.

We describe now another handy piece of notation. If $F(x)$ is an expression involving x, then we write

$$F(x)\Big|_a^b = F(b) - F(a)$$

In case $F(x)$ involves letters other than x, we may write

$$F(x)\Big|_{x=a}^{x=b} = F(b) - F(a)$$

to make it clear which letter is to be replaced by b and a, respectively, namely, the variable of integration which appears just after the d in the differential following the integral sign [see (b), (d), and (e) below].

We now give five illustrations of the use of this notation. In each case, the reader can easily check, by differentiation with respect to the variable of integration, that the function to the right of the first equality is actually a primitive for the integrand on the left. In the next chapter we study methods for finding such primitives. Thus, FTC assures that:

(a) $\displaystyle\int_{\pi/6}^{\pi/3} \sec^2 x \, dx = \tan x \Big|_{\pi/6}^{\pi/3} = \tan\frac{\pi}{3} - \tan\frac{\pi}{6} = \sqrt{3} - \frac{1}{\sqrt{3}} = \frac{2\sqrt{3}}{3}$

(b) $\int_{-1}^{1} \cos tx \, dt = \dfrac{\sin tx}{x}\Big|_{t=-1}^{t=1} = \dfrac{1}{x} [\sin x - \sin (-x)] = \dfrac{2 \sin x}{x}$

if $x \neq 0$. Note that x is constant and t is the variable of integration.

(c) $\int_{0}^{1} 2ue^{-u^2} \, du = -e^{-u^2}\Big|_{0}^{1} = -e^{-1} - (-1) = \dfrac{e - 1}{e}$

(d) $\int_{0}^{2} \dfrac{2x \, dx}{1 + x^2y^2} = \dfrac{1}{y^2} \ln (1 + x^2y^2)\Big|_{x=0}^{x=2} = \dfrac{\ln (1 + 4y^2)}{y^2} \qquad$ if $y \neq 0$

(e) $\int_{0}^{2} \dfrac{2x \, dy}{1 + x^2y^2} = 2 \operatorname{Tan}^{-1} (xy)\Big|_{y=0}^{y=2} = 2 \operatorname{Tan}^{-1} 2x$

EXERCISES

In 1–20, use your knowledge of differentiation formulas to guess a primitive for the given integrand, check that your guess is correct by differentiating it, and then use FTC to evaluate the given integral.

1. $\int_{0}^{2} 2x \, dx$

2. $\int_{1}^{2} 3x^2 \, dx$

3. $\int_{1}^{4} (-2x^{-3}) \, dx$

4. $\int_{0}^{1} x^{\pi-1} \, dx$

5. $\int_{2}^{8} \dfrac{dx}{x}$

6. $\int_{0}^{2} (7x^6 - 9) \, dx$

7. $\int_{-3}^{3} 18x^{17} \, dx$

8. $\int_{0}^{1} (x^{99} - x^{100}) \, dx$

9. $\int_{1}^{2} e^x \, dx$

10. $\int_{0}^{1} \dfrac{dx}{x + 1}$

11. $\int_{-1}^{2} (3x^2 + 1) \, dx$

12. $\int_{0}^{2\pi} \cos \theta \, d\theta$

13. $\int_{1}^{\sqrt{3}} \dfrac{dx}{1 + x^2}$

14. $\int_{0}^{1/2} \dfrac{dx}{\sqrt{1 - x^2}}$

15. $\int_{0}^{\pi/4} \sec x \tan x \, dx$

16. $\int_{5}^{10} \sqrt{x - 1} \, dx$

17. $\int_{1}^{2} 2^x \, dx$

18. $\int_{\sqrt{2}}^{2} \dfrac{dx}{x \sqrt{x^2 - 1}}$

19. $\int_{0}^{1} (x^2 - 3xy^2) \, dy$

20. $\int_{0}^{2} (t + x) \, dt$

In 21–28, verify the truth of the formulas by differentiation.

21. $\int \tan x \, dx = \ln \sec x = -\ln \cos x$

22. $\int \cot x \, dx = \ln \sin x$

23. $\displaystyle\int \sec x \, dx = \ln\,(\sec x + \tan x)$

24. $\displaystyle\int \csc x \, dx = \ln\,(\csc x - \cot x)$

25. $\displaystyle\int \frac{dx}{a^2 + x^2} = \frac{1}{a}\,\mathrm{Tan}^{-1}\left(\frac{x}{a}\right) \qquad \text{if } a \neq 0$

26. $\displaystyle\int \frac{dx}{a^2 - x^2} = \frac{1}{2a}\,\ln \frac{a + x}{a - x} \qquad \text{if } x^2 < a^2$

27. $\displaystyle\int \ln x \, dx = x \ln x - x$

28. $\displaystyle\int \mathrm{Tan}^{-1} x \, dx = x\,\mathrm{Tan}^{-1} x - \ln \sqrt{1 + x^2}$

6 Basic Properties of Integrals

A definite integral $\displaystyle\int_a^b f$ is a number which is completely determined by two things: (i) the integrand f and (ii) the interval (or limits) of integration. For a fixed integrand, we saw at the end of section 4 that the integral depends additively on its interval of integration:

$$\int_a^b f = \int_a^c f + \int_c^b f$$

in the sense made precise there. The next theorem shows that if the interval of integration is fixed, then the integral depends additively on its integrand. It also shows that any constant can be factored out of the integral.

▷ **Theorem** Let f and g be two functions that are continuous on an interval I and let c be any real number.

(i) If F and G are primitives for f and g, respectively, on I, then the functions $F + G$ and cF are primitives for $f + g$ and cf, respectively, on I.

(ii) If a and b are in I, then

$$\int_a^b [f(x) + g(x)] \, dx = \int_a^b f(x) \, dx + \int_a^b g(x) \, dx$$

and

$$\int_a^b cf(x)\, dx = c \int_a^b f(x)\, dx$$

Proof Statement (i) follows from the corresponding properties of derivatives:

$$(F + G)'(x) = F'(x) + G'(x) = f(x) + g(x) = (f + g)(x)$$

and

$$(cF)'(x) = c \cdot F'(x) = cf(x) = (cf)(x)$$

for all x in I. Thus, $(F + G)' = f + g$ and $(cF)' = cf$ on I. To prove (ii), we first appeal to EPT (page 304) to see that primitives F and G as in (i) do exist and then we invoke (i) and FTC (page 302) to obtain

$$\int_a^b [f(x) + g(x)]\, dx = [F(x) + G(x)]\Big|_a^b = [F(b) + G(b)] - [F(a) + G(a)]$$

$$= [F(b) - F(a)] + [G(b) - G(a)] = \int_a^b f(x)\, dx + \int_a^b g(x)\, dx$$

and

$$\int_a^b cf(x)\, dx = [cF(x)]\Big|_a^b = cF(b) - cF(a) = c\,[F(b) - F(a)]$$

$$= c \int_a^b f(x)\, dx$$

which completes the proof. ■

We can use this theorem to obtain the analogous result for differences of two functions: $\int [f - g] = \int [f + (-1)g] = \int f + \int [(-1)g] = \int f + (-1) \int g = \int f - \int g$. The corresponding statements for products are false. Almost any example that we try will show that

$$\int_a^b f(x)g(x)\, dx \neq \left(\int_a^b f(x)\, dx \right)\left(\int_a^b g(x)\, dx \right)$$

For instance, take $f(x) = g(x) = x$ and $[a,b] = [0,1]$. Then

$$\int_a^b f(x)g(x)\, dx = \int_0^1 x^2\, dx = \frac{1}{3}x^3 \Big|_0^1 = \frac{1}{3}$$

but

$$\left(\int_a^b f(x)\, dx \right)\left(\int_a^b g(x)\, dx \right) = \left(\int_0^1 x\, dx \right)^2 = \left(\frac{1}{2}x^2 \Big|_0^1 \right)^2 = \frac{1}{4} \neq \frac{1}{3}$$

Assertion (i) of the theorem can be written symbolically as

$$\int [f(x) + g(x)]\, dx = \int f(x)\, dx + \int g(x)\, dx$$

and

$$\int cf(x)\, dx = c \int f(x)\, dx$$

Repeated application of this theorem justifies the statement that the integral of the sum of any finite number of continuous functions is equal to the sum of the integrals of those functions.

EXAMPLE (a) Find $\int [e^x + \cos x]\, dx$.

(b) Evaluate $\displaystyle\int_0^2 \frac{x\, dx}{x^2 + 1}$.

(c) Evaluate $\displaystyle\int_0^\pi \left[\sum_{k=1}^n k \sin kx\right] dx$.

Solution (a) Since $\int e^x\, dx = e^x$ and $\int \cos x\, dx = \sin x$, a solution is $e^x + \sin x$.

(b) The derivative with respect to x of $\ln (x^2 + 1)$ is $2x/(x^2 + 1)$ and so we have

$$\int_0^2 \frac{x\, dx}{x^2 + 1} = \frac{1}{2}\int_0^2 \frac{2x\, dx}{x^2 + 1} = \frac{1}{2}[\ln (2^2 + 1) - \ln (0^2 + 1)] = \frac{1}{2} \ln 5$$

(c) For any integer k, we have

$$\int_0^\pi k \sin kx\, dx = -\cos kx \Big|_0^\pi = -\cos k\pi + \cos 0 = -(-1)^k + 1$$

which is 0 or 2 according as k is even or odd. Thus, the required value is the sum of n integrals

$$\sum_{k=1}^n \int_0^\pi k \sin kx\, dx = p \cdot 2$$

where p is the number of odd integers k with $1 \le k \le n$ which is $n/2$ or $(n + 1)/2$ according as n is even or odd. Therefore

$$\int_0^\pi \left[\sum_{k=1}^n k \sin kx\right] dx = \begin{cases} n & \text{if } n \text{ is even} \\ n + 1 & \text{if } n \text{ is odd} \end{cases}$$

Incidentally, it can be proved that

$$\sum_{k=1}^n k \sin kx = \frac{n \sin (n + 1)x - (n + 1) \sin nx}{2[\cos x - 1]}$$

but we *do not* recommend trying to integrate the latter function to solve (c).

The next theorem gives some inequalities which are frequently useful in estimating the size of definite integrals.

▷ **Theorem** Suppose that f and g are continuous on $[a,b]$ and $f(x) \leqq g(x)$ for every x in $[a,b]$. Then

$$\int_a^b f(x)\,dx \leqq \int_a^b g(x)\,dx$$

and

$$\left| \int_a^b f(x)\,dx \right| \leqq \int_a^b |f(x)|\,dx$$

Proof Since $g(x) - f(x) \geqq 0$ for every x in $[a,b]$, all lower sums for $g - f$ over $[a,b]$ are nonnegative. By the definition of $\int_a^b (g - f)$ and the preceding theorem, we have

$$0 \leqq \int_a^b (g - f) = \int_a^b g - \int_a^b f$$

which proves the first claimed inequality. Now

$$f(x) \leqq |f(x)| \qquad \text{and} \qquad -f(x) \leqq |f(x)|$$

for any real number $f(x)$ (whether positive, negative, or 0), and so the inequality just proved yields

$$\int_a^b f \leqq \int_a^b |f| \qquad \text{and} \qquad -\int_a^b f = \int_a^b (-f) \leqq \int_a^b |f|$$

Since $\left| \int_a^b f \right|$ is one of the numbers $\int_a^b f$ or $-\int_a^b f$, our proof is complete. ∎

As an application, observe that since $x^{-1} \leqq x^{-\frac{1}{2}}$ for $x \geqq 1$, we have

$$\ln b = \ln b - \ln 1 = \int_1^b \frac{dx}{x} \leqq \int_1^b x^{-1/2}\,dx = 2x^{1/2} \Big|_1^b = 2(\sqrt{b} - 1)$$

for every $b \geqq 1$.

Because of ETI, definite integrals can be used to define functions as was done in EPT, and then EPT can be used to differentiate those functions. We give an example to illustrate this procedure.

EXAMPLE Define

$$F(x) = \int_x^{x^3} e^{-t^2}\, dt$$

for all real numbers x. Find $F'(x)$.

Solution Define a function G by

$$G(u) = \int_0^u e^{-t^2}\, dt$$

According to EPT, we have $G'(u) = e^{-u^2}$ for all u such that e^{-t^2} is continuous for $0 \le t \le u$ or $u \le t \le 0$ and so it is therefore true for all u. We have

$$F(x) = \int_x^0 e^{-t^2}\, dt + \int_0^{x^3} e^{-t^2}\, dt$$
$$= -\int_0^x e^{-t^2}\, dt + \int_0^{x^3} e^{-t^2}\, dt = -G(x) + G(x^3)$$

Using the Chain Rule, we have

$$F'(x) = -G'(x) + G'(x^3) \cdot 3x^2 = -e^{-x^2} + 3x^2 e^{-x^6}$$

EXERCISES

In 1–8, find $F'(x)$.

1. $F(x) = \displaystyle\int_0^{\sin x} 2t\, dt$

2. $F(x) = \displaystyle\int_{x^2}^{\ln x} 3t^2\, dt$

3. $F(x) = \displaystyle\int_x^{\sin x} 2t\, dt$

4. $F(x) = \displaystyle\int_{x^2}^{x^4} e^{-t^2}\, dt$

5. $F(x) = \displaystyle\int_{x^2}^1 e^{-t^2}\, dt$

6. $F(x) = \displaystyle\int_2^{x^2} \frac{\sin t}{t}\, dt$

7. $F(x) = \displaystyle\int_{\sin x}^x \frac{dt}{\sqrt[3]{t^2+1}}$

8. $F(x) = \displaystyle\int_{x^2}^{x^3-1} \frac{\sin t}{t}\, dt$

7 Application to Area Problems

It follows from our discussions in sections 3 and 4 that if f is a function that is continuous and nonnegative on a closed interval $[a,b]$, then the region R consisting of all points (x,y) such that $a \le x \le b$

and $0 \leq y \leq f(x)$ has an area A and this number A is given by the formula

$$A = \int_a^b f(x) \, dx$$

More generally, suppose that f_1 and f_2 are both continuous on $[a,b]$ with $f_1(x) \leq f_2(x)$ for every x in $[a,b]$. Let R be the plane region consisting of all points (x,y) for which $a \leq x \leq b$ and $f_1(x) \leq y \leq f_2(x)$

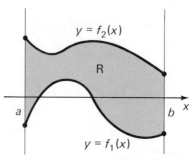

Figure 6–8

(see Fig. 6-8). We can assign a reasonable area to R as follows. Choose any constant c for which $f_1(x) + c \geq 0$ whenever $a \leq x \leq b$ and, for $j = 1$ and 2, let R_j be the region consisting of all (x,y) with $a \leq x \leq b$ and $0 \leq y \leq f_j(x) + c$ (see Fig. 6-9). The preceding paragraph shows that the area A_j of R_j is given by

$$A_j = \int_a^b [f_j(x) + c] \, dx = \int_a^b f_j(x) \, dx + c(b - a)$$

and so, if we are to have the five intuitively reasonable properties of "area" listed in section 3 (page 288), we are forced to have the area A of R to be the number

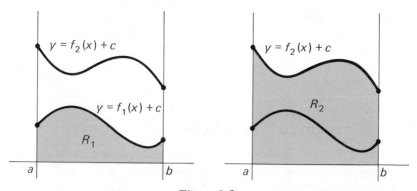

Figure 6–9

$$A = A_2 - A_1 = \int_a^b f_2(x)\, dx + c(b-a) - \left[\int_a^b f_1(x)\, dx + c(b-a) \right]$$

$$= \int_a^b f_2(x)\, dx - \int_a^b f_1(x)\, dx = \int_a^b [f_2(x) - f_1(x)]\, dx$$

We therefore choose to *define* the area A of R by

$$A = \int_a^b [f_2(x) - f_1(x)]\, dx$$

In the special case that $f_1(x) = 0$ everywhere on $[a,b]$, this definition reduces to the case treated in the preceding paragraph.

EXAMPLE   Find the area of the region bounded by the curves having equations $y = 4x - x^2$ and $y = x^2 - 2x$.

Solution   To see what the region R looks like, we sketch the two parabolas in the same coordinate plane (see Fig. 6-10), paying particular heed to their points of intersection, which are found as follows:

$$4x - x^2 = y = x^2 - 2x$$
$$2x^2 - 6x = 0$$
$$2x(x - 3) = 0$$
$$x = 0 \quad \text{or} \quad x = 3$$

and so $(0,0)$ and $(3,3)$ are the intersection points. Writing $f_2(x) - f_1(x) = (4x - x^2) - (x^2 - 2x) = 6x - 2x^2$, $a = 0$, and $b = 3$, the above definition gives

$$A = \int_0^3 [6x - 2x^2]\, dx$$

$$= \left[3x^2 - \frac{2}{3}x^3 \right]\Big|_0^3$$

$$= 27 - 18$$

$$= 9$$

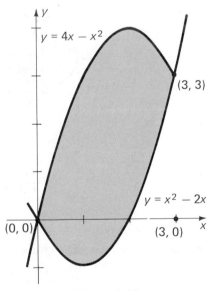

Figure 6-10

EXAMPLE   Find the area of the region bounded by the curves having equations $y^2 = x$ and $x + y = 2$.

First Solution   The described region R and the intersection points $(1,1)$ and $(4,-2)$ are shown in Fig. 6-11. In order to apply the above definition of area to this problem, we must take $a = 0$, $b = 4$, $f_1(x) = -\sqrt{x}$ for $0 \leq x \leq 4$, $f_2(x) = \sqrt{x}$ for $0 \leq x \leq 1$, and $f_2(x) = 2 - x$ for $1 \leq x \leq 4$. Because f_2 is defined by two different formulas, we split the interval of integration at $x = 1$ and obtain

$$A = \int_0^4 [f_2(x) - f_1(x)] \, dx = \int_0^1 [\sqrt{x} - (-\sqrt{x})] \, dx + \int_1^4 [2 - x - (-\sqrt{x})] \, dx$$

$$= \int_0^1 2x^{1/2} \, dx + \int_1^4 (2 - x + x^{1/2}) \, dx = \frac{4}{3}x^{3/2} \Big|_0^1 + \left(2x - \frac{1}{2}x^2 + \frac{2}{3}x^{3/2}\right)\Big|_1^4$$

$$= \frac{4}{3} + \left(8 - 8 + \frac{16}{3}\right) - \left(2 - \frac{1}{2} + \frac{2}{3}\right) = \frac{18}{3} - 2 + \frac{1}{2} = \frac{9}{2}$$

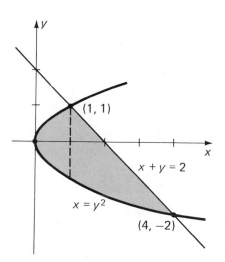

Figure 6-11

Second Solution   It is simpler to regard the two curves as the graphs of functions of y and to integrate over the interval $[-2,1]$ of the y-axis. Thus we take $g_1(y) = y^2$, $g_2(y) = 2 - y$, and obtain

$$A = \int_{-2}^1 [2 - y - y^2] \, dy = \left(2y - \frac{1}{2}y^2 - \frac{1}{3}y^3\right)\Big|_{-2}^1$$

$$= \left(2 - \frac{1}{2} - \frac{1}{3}\right) - \left(-4 - 2 + \frac{8}{3}\right) = 8 - \frac{1}{2} - \frac{9}{3} = \frac{9}{2}$$

In more advanced courses where the areas of plane regions are defined by approximating with sums of areas of rectangles having very small diagonals, it is proved that the method of finding an area by integrating over an interval of the y-axis (as we just did in our second solution) always gives the same answer as the method of integrating over an x-interval which is dictated by our definition of area. For this course we will accept the five properties of area listed in section 3 (page 288). These five properties can be proved as theorems in more advanced courses. It is no surprise that the two solutions of the previous example gave the same answer. After all, the region R there is congruent to the region bounded by $y = x^2$ and $y + x = 2$ which is obtained by reflecting R through the line $y = x$. We will not hesitate to use these five properties when convenient.

EXAMPLE Find the area of the region R enclosed by the ellipse having equation

$$\frac{x^2}{a^2} + \frac{y^2}{b^2} = 1$$

where $a > 0$ and $b > 0$.

Solution Since the part of R above the x-axis in Fig. 6-12 is congruent to the part below it and the part of the ellipse above (and on) the x-axis is the graph of the function given by

$$y = f(x) = b\sqrt{1 - \frac{x^2}{a^2}} = \frac{b}{a}\sqrt{a^2 - x^2} \qquad (-a \leq x \leq a)$$

we have

$$A = 2\int_{-a}^{a} \frac{b}{a}\sqrt{a^2 - x^2}\, dx = \frac{2b}{a}\int_{-a}^{a}\sqrt{a^2 - x^2}\, dx = \frac{2b}{a} \cdot \frac{A_0}{2}$$

where A_0 is the area of the region R_0 enclosed by the circle $x^2 + y^2 = a^2$. Using the well-known formula $A_0 = \pi a^2$ for the area of R_0, we have $A = \pi a b$.

In the next section, where we adopt (temporarily) a strictly analytical viewpoint, we actually *define* the number π to be the area of a circular disk of radius 1:

$$\pi = 2\int_{-1}^{1}\sqrt{1 - t^2}\, dt.$$

Then the formula

$$A_0 = 2\int_{-a}^{a}\sqrt{a^2 - x^2}\, dx = \pi a^2$$

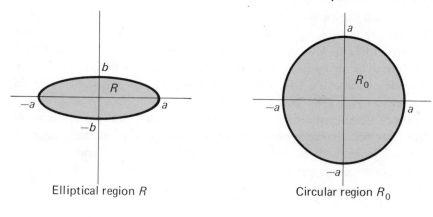

Elliptical region R Circular region R_0

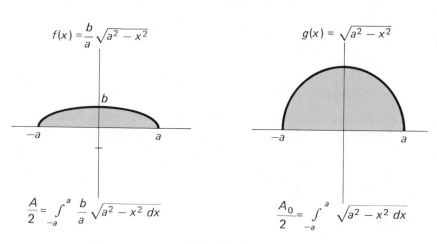

$f(x) = \dfrac{b}{a}\sqrt{a^2 - x^2}$ $g(x) = \sqrt{a^2 - x^2}$

$\dfrac{A}{2} = \displaystyle\int_{-a}^{a} \dfrac{b}{a}\sqrt{a^2 - x^2}\,dx$ $\dfrac{A_0}{2} = \displaystyle\int_{-a}^{a} \sqrt{a^2 - x^2}\,dx$

Figure 6-12

is obtained by the change of variable method ($x = at$) discussed in the next chapter.

E X E R C I S E S

In 1–16, find the area of the region bounded by the curves having the given equations and draw a sketch of that region with points of intersection labeled.

1. $y = x;\ y = x^2$
2. $y = x - x^2;\ y = -x$
3. $y^2 = 2x;\ y = x - 4$
4. $y^2 = 4x;\ x^2 = 4y$
5. $y = x^2 - x - 1;\ y = (x - 1)^3$

6. $x^2 = 5 - y$; $x^2 = 4y$
7. $2x + y = 2$; $x - y = 1$; $x + 2y = 7$
8. $x = 4$; $y = 0$; $y = -\sqrt{x}$
9. $y^2 = x^3$; $x + 2y + 1 = 0$; $y = x + 4$
10. $y = x^3 - x$; $y = 1 - x^2$
11. $y^2 = 8 - x$; $x - 4y = 12$; $y^2 = x$
12. $y = 10x - 9$; $y = 2x + 3$; $y = 2 - x^2$
13. $y = \sin x$; $y = \cos x$ between $x = \dfrac{\pi}{4}$ and $x = \dfrac{5\pi}{4}$
14. $xy = 1$; $y = 0$; $x = a$; $x = 2a$ $(a > 0)$
15. The loop of $y^2 = 4x^3(1 - x^2)^2$
16. $\sqrt{x} + \sqrt{y} = 7$; $x + y = 25$

17. Prove that the area of the region bounded by the parabola $y^2 = 4ax$ and its vertical chord along $x = b$ $(a > 0, b > 0)$ is exactly two-thirds the area of the circumscribed rectangle.
18. Prove that if $p > 0$ and $a > 0$, then the curve $y = x^p$ divides the rectangle having sides along $x = 0$, $x = a$, $y = 0$, and $y = a^p$ into two regions whose areas have the ratio $p:1$. Sketch pictures of this curve and rectangle for several values of p and a.
19. Use our definition of area in terms of integrals to confirm the formula $A = \dfrac{1}{2}bh$ for the area A of a triangle having base b and height h. Do this by choosing the coordinate system so that the vertices of the triangle are at $(0,0)$, $(b,0)$, and (a,h) where $b > 0$ and $h > 0$. Consider separately the five cases $a < 0$, $a = 0$, $0 < a < b$, $a = b$, and $b < a$. Draw sketches of each of these cases.

8 An Analytic Description of cos and sin*

In Chapter 5, we gave the traditional elementary description of the functions cos and sin that depends to a large extent on geometrical intuition. Now that we are armed with some integration theory, it is possible to give an uncompromisingly analytic construction of these functions (and proofs of their crucial properties) that depends in no way upon intuition. We do, however, point out how our analytic definitions are motivated by the traditional geometric ones. In this section, we adopt the attitude that we have never before heard of these two functions or of the number π.

*An optional section.

Since the function $\sqrt{1-t^2}$ is continuous for t in $[-1,1]$, it follows from ETI (page 294) that the formula

$$\theta(x) = x\sqrt{1-x^2} + 2\int_x^1 \sqrt{1-t^2}\,dt = x\sqrt{1-x^2} - 2\int_1^x \sqrt{1-t^2}\,dt \quad (1)$$

$(-1 \leq x \leq 1)$ defines a function θ on $[-1,1]$. Moreover, we use EPT (page 304) to see that θ is continuous on $[-1,1]$ and

$$\theta'(x) = \left[x \cdot \frac{1}{2}(1-x^2)^{-1/2} \cdot (-2x) + \sqrt{1-x^2} \right] - 2\sqrt{1-x^2}$$

$$= -\frac{x^2}{\sqrt{1-x^2}} - \sqrt{1-x^2} = \frac{-1}{\sqrt{1-x^2}} < 0 \quad (2)$$

for $-1 < x < 1$. Thus θ is a strictly decreasing continuous function on $[-1,1]$ and, from (1), $\theta(1) = 0$. We now *define* the number π by the formula

$$\pi = \theta(-1) = 2\int_{-1}^1 \sqrt{1-t^2}\,dt \quad (3)$$

Since $\sqrt{1-(-t)^2} = \sqrt{1-t^2}$, it is easy to see, by looking at upper and lower sums, that

$$\int_{-x}^1 \sqrt{1-t^2}\,dt = \int_{-1}^x \sqrt{1-t^2}\,dt$$

for every x in $[-1,1]$ and therefore (1) and (3) yield

$$\theta(-x) + \theta(x) = \pi \qquad (-1 \leq x \leq 1) \quad (4)$$

In particular, taking $x = 0$, we obtain $\theta(0) = \pi/2$. Since $1 - t^2 \leq \sqrt{1-t^2} \leq 1$ whenever $-1 \leq t \leq 1$, we have

$$\frac{4}{3} = \int_{-1}^1 (1-t^2)\,dt \leq \int_{-1}^1 \sqrt{1-t^2}\,dt \leq 2$$

which gives the rather crude estimates

$$\frac{8}{3} \leq \pi \leq 4$$

Though these bounds are sufficient for many purposes, we will, in Chapter 10, study methods for obtaining arbitrarily close rational approximations to this mysterious number π.

We now briefly interrupt our analytical exposition to examine just what is going on geometrically in the preceding paragraph. Fix any number a with $-1 \leq a \leq 1$ and write $b = \sqrt{1-a^2}$. It is easy to see from our definition of area given in sections 3 and 7 that the area A of the shaded circular sector POQ shown in Fig. 6-13a or Fig. 6-13b (for $a \geqq 0$ or $a \leqq 0$) is given by

$$A = \frac{1}{2}ab + \int_a^1 \sqrt{1 - t^2}\, dt = \frac{1}{2}\theta(a)$$

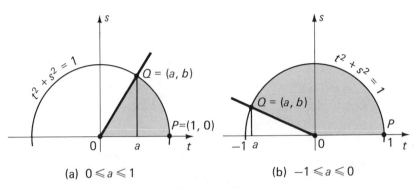

(a) $0 \leqslant a \leqslant 1$ (b) $-1 \leqslant a \leqslant 0$

Figure 6-13

Thus, $\theta(a) = 2A$ is the radian measure of the angle POQ, and so $a = \cos [\theta(a)]$ and $b = \sin [\theta(a)]$ according to the geometrical definitions given in Chapter 5. We also see that the number $\theta(-1)$, which we have decided to denote by the Greek letter π, is, according to our definition of area, just twice the area of the semicircular region lying above the t-axis and inside the unit circle whose equation is $t^2 + s^2 = 1$. Since $0 \leqq \theta(a) \leqq \pi$, we actually have $a = \mathrm{Cos}\,[\theta(a)]$ and hence $\theta(a) = \mathrm{Cos}^{-1}\, a$ as defined in Chapter 5. Therefore $\theta = \mathrm{Cos}^{-1}$.

Now, we return to our analytical presentation. The graph shown in Fig. 6-14 records the information that we have actually learned about the function θ as well as the equalities

$$\theta'(0) = -1, \lim_{x \to 1^-} \theta'(x) = \lim_{x \to -1^+} \theta'(x) = -\infty \tag{6}$$

which follow from (2). Even though this graph is *not* correct, further investigation is needed to discover that fact (for instance, one can compute θ'' to discover that θ is concave upward on $]-1,0[$ and concave downward on $]0,1[$). Since θ is continuous and strictly decreasing from the interval $[-1,1]$ onto the interval $[0,\pi]$, it has a continuous inverse function θ^{-1} which is strictly decreasing from $[0,\pi]$ onto $[-1,1]$ (using IVT, pages 111, 158, and 551). We *define* Cos to be θ^{-1}. That is,

$$\mathrm{Cos}\; x = y \; means \; 0 \leqq x \leqq \pi, -1 \leqq y \leqq 1 \; and \; \theta(y) = x \tag{7}$$

(for each such x, there is precisely one such y as IVT and the strict

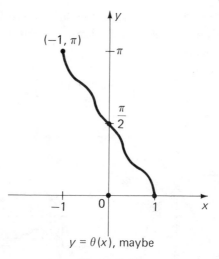

$y = \theta(x)$, maybe

Figure 6-14

monotonicity of θ show). By the theorem on differentiating inverse functions (pages 139 and 557–558), (2), and (7), we have

$$\text{Cos}'\, x = (\theta^{-1})'(x) = \frac{1}{\theta'(\theta^{-1}(x))} = -\sqrt{1 - [\theta^{-1}(x)]^2} = -\sqrt{1 - \text{Cos}^2\, x} \quad (8)$$

provided that $0 < x < \pi$ (so that $-1 < \theta(x) < 1$ and (2) applies). We now *define* cos and sin on $[-\pi, \pi]$ by

$$\cos x = \text{Cos}\,|x| = \begin{cases} \text{Cos}\, x & (0 \leq x \leq \pi) \\ \text{Cos}\,(-x) & (-\pi \leq x \leq 0) \end{cases} \quad (9)$$

$$\sin x = \begin{cases} \sqrt{1 - \cos^2 x} & (0 \leq x \leq \pi) \\ -\sqrt{1 - \cos^2 x} & (-\pi \leq x \leq 0) \end{cases} \quad (10)$$

and then extend these functions to all real x by requiring that

$$\cos(x + 2\pi) = \cos x \qquad \text{and} \qquad \sin(x + 2\pi) = \sin x \quad (11)$$

for all x. (Notice that $\cos \pi = -1 = \cos(-\pi)$ and $\sin \pi = 0 = \sin(-\pi)$ so that this is possible.) That is, given x, we choose the integer n such that $-\pi < x - 2n\pi \leq \pi$ and then *define* $\cos x = \cos(x - 2n\pi)$ and $\sin x = \sin(x - 2n\pi)$. It is easy to see that cos and sin are continuous. If x is *not* an integer multiple of π, then we use (8), (9), (10), and the Chain Rule (page 134) to see that

$$\cos' x = -\sin x \qquad \text{and} \qquad \sin' x = \cos x \quad (12)$$

For instance, for $-\pi < x < 0$

$$\cos'(x) = \text{Cos}'(-x) \cdot (-1) = \sqrt{1 - \text{Cos}^2(-x)} = \sqrt{1 - \cos^2 x} = -\sin x$$

and

$$\sin' x = -\frac{1}{2}(1 - \cos^2 x)^{-\frac{1}{2}}(-2 \cos x)(-\sin x) = -\frac{\sin x \cos x}{\sqrt{1 - \cos^2 x}} = \cos x$$

In case x is a multiple of π, formulas (12) remain valid, as can be seen by using MVT (page 151) and continuity. For instance,

$$\cos' (k\pi) = \lim_{x \to k\pi} \frac{\cos x - \cos (k\pi)}{x - k\pi} = \lim_{x \to k\pi} \cos' \xi_x = \lim_{x \to k\pi} (-\sin \xi_x)$$
$$= -\sin k\pi$$

(Here ξ_x is between x and $k\pi$.) Thus (12) holds good for all values of x. It is also obvious from our definitions that

$$\left. \begin{array}{l} \cos (-x) = \cos x \\ \sin (-x) = -\sin x \\ \cos^2 x + \sin^2 x = 1 \end{array} \right\} \tag{13}$$

for all values of x.

We next prove a theorem that enables us to give an analytic proof of the addition formulas for sin and cos which, together with (13), are the source of all trigonometric identities. The theorem is also of considerable independent interest. It is an important special case of a "uniqueness theorem" for differential equations.

$\Rightarrow$ **Theorem** Suppose that f is a function that is defined and twice differentiable on some interval I containing 0 and that

$$f''(x) + f(x) = 0$$

for all x in I. Write $\alpha = f(0)$ and $\beta = f'(0)$. Then it follows that

$$f(x) = \alpha \cos x + \beta \sin x$$

for every x in I.

Proof Define g on I by $g(x) = f(x) - \alpha \cos x - \beta \sin x$. Then (12) yields

$$g''(x) = f''(x) + \alpha \cos x + \beta \sin x$$

and so addition of equations gives

$$g''(x) + g(x) = f''(x) + f(x) = 0$$

for all x in I. The function h defined on I by

$$h(x) = [g(x)]^2 + [g'(x)]^2$$

satisfies

$$h'(x) = 2g(x)g'(x) + 2g'(x)g''(x) = 2g'(x)[g(x) + g''(x)] = 0$$

for all x in I and so a corollary of MVT shows that $h(x) = h(0)$ for every x in I. But $h(0) = [g(0)]^2 + [g'(0)]^2 = [f(0) - \alpha]^2 + [f'(0) - \beta]^2 = 0$. Thus $[g(x)]^2 + [g'(x)]^2 = h(x) = 0$ and therefore $g(x) = 0$ for every x in I. This completes the proof. ■

▷ **Addition Formulas**   For all real numbers x and y, we have

$$\sin (x + y) = \sin x \cos y + \cos x \sin y \qquad (14)$$

and

$$\cos (x + y) = \cos x \cos y - \sin x \sin y \qquad (15)$$

Proof   Fix any real number y. Apply the preceding theorem to the function $f(x) = \sin (x + y)$, where I is the entire real number line, $\alpha = f(0) = \sin y$, and $\beta = f'(0) = \cos y$. This gives (14). Keeping y fixed, differentiate both sides of (14) (with respect to x) to obtain (15). ■

EXERCISES

In 1–19, use only the material in this section to prove each of the following statements. The ones involving x are identities valid for all real numbers x. It may be helpful to prove them in order.

1. $\cos 0 = 1$ and $\cos \pi = -1$
2. $\cos (\pi/2) = \cos (-\pi/2) = 0$
3. $\sin 0 = \sin \pi = \sin (-\pi) = 0$
4. $\sin (\pi/2) = 1$ and $\sin (-\pi/2) = -1$
5. $\cos (x + \pi) = \cos (x - \pi) = -\cos x$
6. $\sin (x + \pi) = \sin (x - \pi) = -\sin x$

7. $\sin \left(x + \dfrac{\pi}{2} \right) = \cos x$ 9. $\cos \left(x + \dfrac{\pi}{2} \right) = -\sin x$

8. $\sin \left(x - \dfrac{\pi}{2} \right) = -\cos x$ 10. $\cos \left(x - \dfrac{\pi}{2} \right) = \sin x$

11. $\cos 2x = \cos^2 x - \sin^2 x = 2 \cos^2 x - 1 = 1 - 2 \sin^2 x$
12. $\sin 2x = 2 \sin x \cos x$
13. $\cos \dfrac{\pi}{4} = \dfrac{\sqrt{2}}{2} = \sin \dfrac{\pi}{4}$
14. $\cos 3x = 4 \cos^3 x - 3 \cos x$
15. $\sin 3x = 3 \sin x - 4 \sin^3 x$

16. $\cos \dfrac{\pi}{6} = \dfrac{\sqrt{3}}{2} = \sin \dfrac{\pi}{3}$

17. $\cos \dfrac{\pi}{3} = \dfrac{1}{2} = \sin \dfrac{\pi}{6}$

18. $\cos 5x = 16 \cos^5 x - 20 \cos^3 x + 5 \cos x$

19. $\cos \dfrac{\pi}{5} = \dfrac{1 + \sqrt{5}}{4}$

[*Hint*: $16u^5 - 20u^3 + 5u + 1 = (u + 1)(4u^2 - 2u - 1)^2$.]

20. Prove by induction on n that if n is a positive integer and x is a real number, then

$$\cos nx = \sum_j (-1)^j \binom{n}{2j} \cos^{n-2j} x \, \sin^{2j} x$$

$$\sin nx = \sum_j (-1)^j \binom{n}{2j+1} \cos^{n-2j-1} x \, \sin^{2j+1} x$$

where these sums are extended over all integers j such that $0 \leq 2j \leq n$ and $0 \leq 2j + 1 \leq n$, respectively. Here, $\dbinom{n}{k} = \dfrac{n!}{k!(n-k)!}$ if $1 \leq k \leq n$ and $\dbinom{n}{0} = 1$ are the usual binomial coefficients.

21. Verify each of the following by using only the information about sin and cos found in this section.

(a) $2\sqrt{1 - t^2} > \dfrac{\sqrt{1 - u^2}}{1 - u} (2 - 2t)$ if $-1 \leq u < t < 1$

(b) $2 \displaystyle\int_u^1 \sqrt{1 - t^2} \, dt > \sqrt{1 - u^2} \, (1 - u)$ if $-1 \leq u < 1$

(c) $\text{Cos}^{-1} (u) > \sqrt{1 - u^2}$ if $-1 \leq u < 1$

(d) $u < \cos \sqrt{1 - u^2}$ if $-1 \leq u < 1$

(e) $\sqrt{1 - x^2} < \cos x$ if $0 < x^2 \leq 1$

(f) $\dfrac{1 - \cos x}{x} < \dfrac{x}{1 + \cos x}$ if $0 < x < 1$

(g) $\displaystyle\lim_{x \to 0} \dfrac{1 - \cos x}{x} = 0$

(h) $\sin^2 x < x^2$ if $0 < x^2 \leq 1$

(i) $\sin x = \displaystyle\int_0^x \cos t \, dt > \displaystyle\int_0^x \sqrt{1 - t^2} \, dt > \displaystyle\int_0^x (1 - t^2) \, dt = x - \dfrac{x^3}{3}$

  if $0 < x \leq 1$

(j) $1 - \dfrac{x^2}{3} < \dfrac{\sin x}{x} < 1$ if $0 < |x| \leq 1$

(k) $\displaystyle\lim_{x \to 0} \dfrac{\sin x}{x} = 1$

Chapter 7

Techniques of Integration

THE MAIN PURPOSE of this chapter is to develop methods for finding specific primitives (antiderivatives or indefinite integrals) which can be written down in closed (finite) form. This cannot always be done. It is known, for example, that there is no closed-form function F for which

$$F'(x) = e^{-x^2} \tag{1}$$

for all x in some open interval. Of course, as explained in Chapter 6, the function F *defined* by

$$F(x) = \int_0^x e^{-t^2}\, dt \tag{2}$$

does satisfy equation (1) for every real number x. The point is that this function F cannot be expressed in closed form. If one wants to compute an approximation to the number $F(1)$, he or she is faced with approximating the integral on the right-hand side of equation (2), with x replaced by 1. (Methods of making such approximations to any desired accuracy are studied in Chapter 9.) There are, however, very many functions f for which it is possible to find a closed-form function F for which $F' = f$. In this chapter we study several useful techniques for doing this.

1 Integration by Inspection

Some primitives can be found by simply reading differentiation formulas from right to left. For instance, if b is a constant, then

$$\frac{d}{dx}x^b = bx^{b-1}$$

and so

$$\int bx^{b-1}\,dx = x^b$$

If $b \neq 0$, we may write $a = b - 1$ and then divide by $a + 1$ to obtain the important formula

$$\int x^a\,dx = \frac{x^{a+1}}{a+1} \qquad \text{if } a \neq -1$$

This and other important formulas obtained in this way are given in

Table 7-1

$$\int x^a\,dx = \frac{x^{a+1}}{a+1} \qquad (a \neq -1)$$

$$\int \frac{dx}{x} = \ln|x|$$

$$\int \sin x\,dx = -\cos x$$

$$\int \cos x\,dx = \sin x$$

$$\int \sec^2 x\,dx = \tan x$$

$$\int \csc^2 x\,dx = -\cot x$$

$$\int e^x\,dx = e^x$$

$$\int a^x\,dx = \frac{a^x}{\ln a} \qquad (a > 0,\, a \neq 1)$$

$$\int \frac{dx}{\sqrt{1-x^2}} = \operatorname{Sin}^{-1} x$$

$$\int \frac{dx}{1+x^2} = \operatorname{Tan}^{-1} x$$

Table 7-1. The student should have no trouble at all with these formulas, since they follow instantly from derivative formulas that he or she has already memorized. Of course, any formula of the form

$$\int f(x)\ dx = F(x)$$

can be checked by verifying that $F'(x) = f(x)$. The following two formulas (see exercises 51 and 52, page 341), which are needed surprisingly often in applications, can be so checked.

$$\int \sec x\ dx = \ln|\sec x + \tan x|$$

$$\int \csc x\ dx = \ln|\csc x - \cot x|$$

We wish to emphasize again that there can be more than one correct answer to an indefinite integration problem, although it is true that any two such answers must differ only by a constant on any open interval on which the integrand is continuous.

EXAMPLE   Consider the formulas

$$\int 4 \sin x \cos x\ dx = 2 \sin^2 x$$

and

$$\int 4 \sin x \cos x\ dx = -\cos 2x$$

Show (a) that both formulas are correct, and (b) that these answers are not equal.

Solution   (a) By using the Chain Rule and a trigonometric identity, we obtain

$$\frac{d}{dx} 2 \sin^2 x = 4 \sin x \cdot \frac{d}{dx} \sin x = 4 \sin x \cos x$$

and

$$\frac{d}{dx} (-\cos 2x) = 2 \sin 2x = 4 \sin x \cos x$$

(b) Since $2 \sin^2 \pi = 0$ but $-\cos 2\pi = -1$, the two answers are not equal for all x. However, for all x we do have

$$-\cos 2x = -(1 - 2\sin^2 x) = 2\sin^2 x - 1$$

Let us consider more examples.

EXAMPLE   Evaluate $\int \tan^2 x \, dx$.

Solution   This is an integral in which it is advisable to transform the integrand by a trigonometric identity before attempting integration. Since we know how to integrate $\sec^2 x$, we invoke the identity $\tan^2 x = \sec^2 x - 1$ to obtain

$$\int \tan^2 x \, dx = \int (\sec^2 x - 1) \, dx = \int \sec^2 x \, dx - \int 1 \, dx = \tan x - x$$

EXAMPLE   Integrate $\int (e^x + x^e) \, dx$.

Solution   We use two of the basic formulas of Table 7-1 to write

$$\int (e^x + x^e) \, dx = \int e^x \, dx + \int x^e \, dx = e^x + \frac{x^{e+1}}{e + 1}$$

EXAMPLE   Verify that

$$\int \sec^3 x \, dx = \frac{1}{2} \sec x \tan x + \frac{1}{2} \ln|\sec x + \tan x|$$

Solution   We have

$$\frac{d}{dx} (\sec x \tan x) = \sec x \cdot \sec^2 x + \tan x \cdot \sec x \tan x$$
$$= \sec^3 x + \sec x \tan^2 x$$

and

$$\frac{d}{dx} \ln|\sec x + \tan x| = \frac{\sec x \tan x + \sec^2 x}{\sec x + \tan x} = \sec x$$

Adding these two equations gives

$$\frac{d}{dx} (\sec x \tan x + \ln|\sec x + \tan x|) = \sec^3 x + \sec x(\tan^2 x + 1)$$
$$= 2\sec^3 x$$

Division by 2 completes the verification.

The formulas listed in the following set of exercises can, once verified, be used as a handy reference. We will see in the following sections how such formulas are derived. It is *not* necessary to memorize these.

E X E R C I S E S

In 1–16, use differentiation to verify the given formula. In each case
$a > 0$.

1. $\displaystyle \int \frac{dx}{ax + b} = \frac{1}{a} \ln|ax + b|$

2. $\displaystyle \int \frac{dx}{x^2 + a^2} = \frac{1}{a} \operatorname{Tan}^{-1} \frac{x}{a}$

3. $\displaystyle \int \frac{dx}{x^2 - a^2} = \frac{1}{2a} \ln\left|\frac{x - a}{x + a}\right|$

4. $\displaystyle \int \sqrt{x^2 + a}\; dx = \frac{1}{2}x\sqrt{x^2 + a} + \frac{1}{2}a \ln|x + \sqrt{x^2 + a}|$

5. $\displaystyle \int \frac{dx}{\sqrt{x^2 + a}} = \ln|x + \sqrt{x^2 + a}|$

6. $\displaystyle \int \frac{dx}{\sqrt{a^2 - x^2}} = \operatorname{Sin}^{-1} \frac{x}{a} \qquad (a > 0)$

7. $\displaystyle \int \sqrt{a^2 - x^2}\; dx = \frac{1}{2}x\sqrt{a^2 - x^2} + \frac{1}{2}a^2 \operatorname{Sin}^{-1} \frac{x}{a} \qquad (a > 0)$

8. $\displaystyle \int \sin^2 x\; dx = \frac{1}{2}x - \frac{1}{2}\sin x \cos x$

9. $\displaystyle \int \sin^3 x\; dx = -\cos x + \frac{1}{3}\cos^3 x$

10. $\displaystyle \int \cos^2 x\; dx = \frac{1}{2}x + \frac{1}{2}\sin x \cos x$

11. $\displaystyle \int \cos^3 x\; dx = \sin x - \frac{1}{3}\sin^3 x$

12. $\displaystyle \int \tan x\; dx = \ln|\sec x|$

13. $\displaystyle \int \cot x\; dx = \ln|\sin x|$

14. $\displaystyle \int \operatorname{Sin}^{-1} x\; dx = x \operatorname{Sin}^{-1} x + \sqrt{1 - x^2}$

15. $\displaystyle \int \operatorname{Tan}^{-1} x\; dx = x \operatorname{Tan}^{-1} x - \frac{1}{2}\ln(1 + x^2)$

16. $\displaystyle \int \ln x\; dx = x \ln x - x$

2 Integration by Direct Substitution

Suppose we wish to evaluate the indefinite integral $\int x\sqrt{x+2}\,dx$. Since it is not easy to think of a function whose derivative is $x\sqrt{x+2}$, we introduce a new method of integration. The idea of the method of **direct substitution** is that we choose a part of the integrand and replace it by a new variable, say u. Let's try $u = \sqrt{x+2}$. Then $x = u^2 - 2$ and, taking differentials, $dx = 2u\,du$. Making these replacements in the original integral, we get, by proceeding formally, that

$$\int x\sqrt{x+2}\,dx = \int (u^2 - 2)u \cdot 2u\,du = \int (2u^4 - 4u^2)\,du$$

$$= \frac{2}{5}u^5 - \frac{4}{3}u^3 = \frac{2}{5}(\sqrt{x+2})^5 - \frac{4}{3}(\sqrt{x+2})^3$$

$$= \frac{2}{5}(x+2)^{5/2} - \frac{4}{3}(x+2)^{3/2}$$

$$= (x+2)^{1/2}\left[\frac{2}{5}(x+2)^2 - \frac{4}{3}(x+2)\right]$$

$$= \frac{2}{15}\sqrt{x+2}\,[3x^2 + 2x - 8]$$

an answer which none but the most heroic could have guessed by inspecting the original integral. Upon differentiation (ignoring for the moment the constant 2/15), one finds that

$$\frac{d}{dx}\{\sqrt{x+2}\,[3x^2 + 2x - 8]\} = \sqrt{x+2}\,(6x+2) + \frac{3x^2 + 2x - 8}{2\sqrt{x+2}}$$

$$= \frac{2(x+2)(6x+2) + (3x^2 + 2x - 8)}{2\sqrt{x+2}}$$

$$= \frac{15x^2 + 30x}{2\sqrt{x+2}} = \frac{15x(x+2)}{2\sqrt{x+2}}$$

$$= \frac{15}{2}x\sqrt{x+2}$$

which, when multiplied by 2/15, proves that our answer is correct.

What general principle, if any, justifies the above purely formal manipulations? If we could justify such manipulations once and for all, that would relieve us of the necessity of justifying our answers so obtained by differentiating them. Well, we started with an integral $\int g(x)\,dx$, where $g(x) = x\sqrt{x+2}$, and then, by a judicious (or lucky) choice of a function ϕ ($u = \phi(x)$), which in our case was $\phi(x) = \sqrt{x+2}$, we were able to discover a function f which we could integrate such that $f(\phi(x))\phi'(x) = g(x)$. In our case we discovered $f(u) = 2u^4 - 4u^2$, whose indefinite integral $F(u) = \dfrac{2}{5}u^5 - \dfrac{4}{3}u^3$ was quite easy to find, and then we simply replaced u by $\phi(x)$ in this answer.

The justification is simply this: If a function g can be written in the form $g(x) = f(\phi(x))\phi'(x)$ for appropriate functions f and ϕ and if F is a primitive for f ($F' = f$), then the Chain Rule shows that

$$\frac{d}{dx}F(\phi(x)) = F'(\phi(x))\phi'(x) = f(\phi(x))\phi'(x) = g(x)$$

and so

$$\int g(x)\,dx = F(\phi(x))$$

That is, writing $u = \phi(x)$, we have

$$\int g(x)\,dx = \int f(\phi(x))\phi'(x)\,dx = \int f(\phi(x))\,d\phi(x) = \int f(u)\,du$$
$$= F(u) = F(\phi(x))$$

The success of this method depends on making a judicious choice of ϕ in the first place. It seems that the only way to acquire an ability to do this well is through much practice. This means that the student should work through a great many examples and exercises. There are no simple rules to follow (as in differentiation). The authors will try to give some useful tips as we work through several specific examples.

In some cases it is possible to change an integral to one of the standard ones of the preceding section by simply multiplying and dividing by the same constant.

EXAMPLE Integrate (a) $\displaystyle\int \cos 3x\,dx$, (b) $\displaystyle\int e^{-x}\,dx$, and (c) $\displaystyle\int \frac{dx}{3+x^2}$.

Solution (a) Since the integral of the cosine is the sine, the answer ought to be something like $\sin 3x$. If the dx were $d(3x)$, this would be correct. Multiplying and dividing by 3, we have

$$\int \cos 3x\,dx = \frac{1}{3}\int \cos 3x\,d(3x) = \frac{1}{3}\sin 3x$$

Here $u = 3x$ and $dx = \dfrac{1}{3}\,du$.

(b) Multiply and divide by -1 to get

$$\int e^{-x}\,dx = -\int e^{-x}\,d(-x) = -e^{-x}$$

Here $u = -x$ and $dx = -du = d(-u)$.

(c) If the 3 in this integrand were 1 instead, the answer would be $\text{Tan}^{-1} x$. We factor out the 3 in the bottom and get

$$\int \frac{dx}{3 + x^2} = \frac{1}{3}\int \frac{dx}{1 + (x/\sqrt{3})^2}$$

which indicates that the new variable ought to be $u = x/\sqrt{3}$. Then $x = \sqrt{3}\,u$, $dx = \sqrt{3}\,du$, and

$$\int \frac{dx}{3 + x^2} = \int \frac{\sqrt{3}\,du}{3 + 3u^2} = \frac{\sqrt{3}}{3}\int \frac{du}{1 + u^2} = \frac{\sqrt{3}}{3}\,\text{Tan}^{-1} u = \frac{\sqrt{3}}{3}\,\text{Tan}^{-1} \frac{x}{\sqrt{3}}$$

EXAMPLE Integrate (a) $\int xe^{x^2}\,dx$ and (b) $\int \sin x \sin (\cos x)\,dx$.

Solution (a) Since the $x\,dx$ is, except for the constant 2, the differential of x^2, try $u = x^2$. Then $du = 2x\,dx$, $x\,dx = \frac{1}{2}\,du$, and

$$\int xe^{x^2}\,dx = \int e^u \cdot \frac{1}{2}\,du = \frac{1}{2}\int e^u\,du = \frac{1}{2}e^u = \frac{1}{2}e^{x^2}$$

(b) Since the differential of $\cos x$ is (almost) $\sin x\,dx$ this integral resembles $\int \sin u\,du$. Let $u = \cos x$. Then $du = -\sin x\,dx$, $\sin x\,dx = -du$, and

$$\int \sin x \sin (\cos x)\,dx = -\int \sin u\,du = \cos u = \cos (\cos x)$$

EXAMPLE Evaluate (a) $\int \sec^4 x\,dx$ and (b) $\int \frac{\tan^3 x}{\sec^4 x}\,dx$.

Solution (a) We look for some part of the integrand which we recognize as the derivative of something. Since $\sec^2 x$ is the derivative of $\tan x$ and $\sec^2 x = 1 + \tan^2 x$, we obtain

$$\int \sec^4 x\,dx = \int \sec^2 x\,d(\tan x) = \int (\tan^2 x + 1)\,d(\tan x)$$

$$= \frac{1}{3}\tan^3 x + \tan x$$

That is, we substitute $u = \tan x$ and get $du = \sec^2 x\,dx$, and $\sec^2 x = u^2 + 1$ so that

$$\int \sec^4 x \, dx = \int \sec^2 x \cdot \sec^2 x \, dx = \int (u^2 + 1) \, du = \frac{1}{3} u^3 + u$$

$$= \frac{1}{3} \tan^3 x + \tan x$$

(b) We shall solve this problem in two different ways.

First solution. Since sec x tan x is the derivative of sec x and we can multiply top and bottom by sec x, we try the substitution $u = \sec x$. Then $du = \sec x \tan x \, dx$ and $\tan^2 x = u^2 - 1$, and so

$$\int \frac{\tan^3 x}{\sec^4 x} \, dx = \int \frac{\tan^2 x \sec x \tan x \, dx}{\sec^5 x} = \int \frac{u^2 - 1}{u^5} \, du$$

$$= \int u^{-3} \, du - \int u^{-5} \, du = -\frac{1}{2} u^{-2} + \frac{1}{4} u^{-4}$$

$$= -\frac{1}{2 \sec^2 x} + \frac{1}{4 \sec^4 x}$$

Second solution. First rewrite the integrand in terms of sines and cosines:

$$\frac{\tan^3 x}{\sec^4 x} = \frac{\sin^3 x}{\cos^3 x} \cdot \frac{\cos^4 x}{1} = \sin^3 x \cos x$$

Now cos x is the derivative of sin x, and so we let $u = \sin x$ and get

$$\int \frac{\tan^3 x}{\sec^4 x} \, dx = \int \sin^3 x \cos x \, dx = \int u^3 \, du = \frac{1}{4} u^4$$

$$= \frac{1}{4} \sin^4 x$$

Notice that these two solutions look very different, but the general theory says they can differ only by a constant. In fact,

$$-\frac{1}{2 \sec^2 x} + \frac{1}{4 \sec^4 x} = -\frac{1}{4} (\cos^2 x)(2 - \cos^2 x)$$

$$= \frac{1}{4} (\sin^2 x - 1)(\sin^2 x + 1)$$

$$= \frac{1}{4} \sin^4 x - \frac{1}{4}$$

EXAMPLE Find $\int \frac{x^2 \, dx}{\sqrt{x - 2}}$.

Solution As a general principle, *if the integrand is an algebraic function in which the only radical has a linear function* $ax + b$ *as* *radicand, then let the new variable equal that radical.* Here we let $u = \sqrt{x-2}$. Then $x = u^2 + 2$, $dx = 2u\,du$, and $x^2 = (u^2 + 2)^2 = u^4 + 4u^2 + 4$. Therefore,

$$\int \frac{x^2\,dx}{\sqrt{x-2}} = \int \frac{(u^4 + 4u^2 + 4)\cdot 2u\,du}{u} = 2\int (u^4 + 4u^2 + 4)\,du$$

$$= 2(\frac{u^5}{5} + \frac{4u^3}{3} + 4u) = \frac{2}{5}u^5 + \frac{8}{3}u^3 + 8u$$

$$= \frac{2}{5}(x-2)^{5/2} + \frac{8}{3}(x-2)^{3/2} + 8(x-2)^{1/2}$$

$$= (x-2)^{1/2}\left[\frac{2}{5}(x-2)^2 + \frac{8}{3}(x-2) + 8\right]$$

$$= \frac{\sqrt{x-2}}{15}[6x^2 + 16x + 64]$$

EXAMPLE   Evaluate:

(a) $\displaystyle\int \frac{2x+1}{4x^2 + 4x}\,dx$ (c) $\displaystyle\int \tan x\,dx$

(b) $\displaystyle\int \frac{\sec^2 x}{\tan x}\,dx$

Solution   When integrating a quotient, it is a good idea to check mentally whether or not the derivative of the bottom is (almost) the top.

(a) Since the derivative of the bottom is 4 times the top, let $u = x^2 + x$ so that $du = (2x + 1)\,dx$ and

$$\int \frac{2x+1}{4x^2 + 4x}\,dx = \frac{1}{4}\int \frac{du}{u} = \frac{1}{4}\ln|u| = \frac{1}{4}\ln|x^2 + x|$$

(b) Here the derivative of the bottom is the top and so we put $u = \tan x$ so that $du = \sec^2 x\,dx$ and

$$\int \frac{\sec^2 x}{\tan x}\,dx = \int \frac{du}{u} = \ln|u| = \ln|\tan x|$$

(c) Write $\tan x = (\sin x)/(\cos x)$, put $u = \cos x$, and get $du = -\sin x\,dx$ and

$$\int \tan x\,dx = -\int \frac{du}{u} = -\ln|u| = -\ln|\cos x|$$

EXAMPLE   Evaluate:

(a) $\displaystyle\int \frac{x}{x+2}\,dx$ (b) $\displaystyle\int \frac{x^3 - 2x^2 + 3}{x^2 + 4}\,dx$

Solution   When dealing with a quotient of two polynomials in which the degree of the top exceeds or equals that on the bottom, it is often advantageous to rewrite it as a polynomial plus a quotient in which the degree of the top is less than that of the bottom.

(a) Since $\dfrac{x}{x+2} = \dfrac{(x+2)-2}{x+2} = 1 - \dfrac{2}{x+2}$, we have

$$\int \frac{x}{x+2}\,dx = \int 1\,dx - 2\int \frac{dx}{x+2} = x - 2\ln|x+2|$$

(b) We use long division of polynomials,

$$
\begin{array}{r}
x - 2 \\
x^2 + 4\,\overline{\smash{)}\,x^3 - 2x^2 + 0x + 3} \\
\underline{x^3 \qquad\quad + 4x} \\
-2x^2 - 4x + 3 \\
\underline{-2x^2 \qquad\quad -8} \\
-4x + 11
\end{array}
$$

to obtain

$$\frac{x^3 - 2x^2 + 3}{x^2 + 4} = x - 2 + \frac{-4x + 11}{x^2 + 4}$$

Thus

$$\int \frac{x^3 - 2x^2 + 3}{x^2 + 4} = \int (x-2)\,dx + \int \frac{-4x+11}{x^2+4}\,dx$$

$$= \frac{1}{2}x^2 - 2x - 2\int \frac{2x\,dx}{x^2+4} + 11\int \frac{dx}{x^2+4}$$

$$= \frac{1}{2}x^2 - 2x - 2\ln(x^2+4) + 11\int \frac{dx}{x^2+4}$$

where we have taken advantage of the fact that the differential of $x^2 + 4$ is $2x\,dx$. With an eye on the formula

$$\frac{d}{du}\,\mathrm{Tan}^{-1}\,u = \frac{1}{1+u^2}$$

we factor a 4 from the bottom of the last integral and then make the substitution $u = x/2$ (so that $dx = 2\,du$) to obtain

$$\int \frac{dx}{x^2+4} = \frac{1}{4}\int \frac{dx}{(x/2)^2+1} = \frac{1}{2}\int \frac{du}{u^2+1}$$

$$= \frac{1}{2}\mathrm{Tan}^{-1}\,u = \frac{1}{2}\mathrm{Tan}^{-1}(x/2)$$

Collecting our results, we have

$$\int \frac{x^3 - 2x + 3}{x^2 + 4}\,dx = \frac{1}{2}x^2 - 2x - 2\,\ln\,(x^2 + 4) + \frac{11}{2}\mathrm{Tan}^{-1}\,(x/2)$$

EXAMPLE   Evaluate:

(a) $\displaystyle\int \frac{x^2\,dx}{x^6 + 1}$
(b) $\displaystyle\int \frac{dx}{\sqrt{x}(\sqrt[3]{x} + \sqrt[4]{x})}$

Solution   (a) To reduce the exponent 6, take $u = x^3$ so that $du = 3x^2\,dx$ and

$$\int \frac{x^2\,dx}{x^6 + 1} = \frac{1}{3}\int \frac{du}{u^2 + 1} = \frac{1}{3}\mathrm{Tan}^{-1}\,u = \frac{1}{3}\mathrm{Tan}^{-1}\,(x^3)$$

(b) To get rid of all radicals simultaneously, let $x = u^{12}$. Then $dx = 12u^{11}\,du$ and so

$$\int \frac{dx}{\sqrt{x}(\sqrt[3]{x} + \sqrt[4]{x})} = 12\int \frac{u^{11}\,du}{u^6(u^4 + u^3)}$$

$$= 12\int \frac{u^2\,du}{u + 1} = 12\int \left(u - 1 + \frac{1}{u + 1}\right)du$$

$$= 6u^2 - 12u + 12\,\ln\,|u + 1|$$
$$= 6x^{1/6} - 12x^{1/12} + 12\,\ln\,(x^{1/12} + 1)$$

One major reason for finding primitives (indefinite integrals) of functions is so that the Fundamental Theorem of Calculus (FTC) discussed in Chapter 6 can be invoked to evaluate *definite* integrals. Recall that FTC says that if g is *continuous* on $[a,b]$ and if G is a primitive for g on $[a,b]$ ($G'(x) = g(x)$ for all $x \in [a,b]$), then

$$\int_a^b g(x)\,dx = G(x)\,\Big|_a^b = G(b) - G(a)$$

Returning to our discussion just before the preceding list of examples, suppose that the given integrand g can be written as $g(x) = f(\phi(x))\phi'(x)$ and that F is a primitive for f. We saw that G, defined by $G(x) = F(\phi(x))$, is then a primitive for g. Thus

$$\int_a^b g(x)\,dx = G(x)\,\Big|_a^b = F(\phi(x))\,\Big|_a^b = F(\phi(b)) - F(\phi(a))$$

$$= F(u)\,\Big|_{\phi(a)}^{\phi(b)} = \int_{\phi(a)}^{\phi(b)} f(u)\,du$$

provided f is continuous on $[\phi(a),\phi(b)]$. In other words, when we successfully make a change of variable $u = \phi(x)$, we may simply change the limits of integration [setting $u = \phi(a)$ when $x = a$ and $u = \phi(b)$ when $x = b$] to convert the given definite integral to a new definite integral which we can evaluate.

EXAMPLE Evaluate $\displaystyle\int_0^2 x\sqrt{x^2 + 1}\,dx$.

Solution   If $u = x^2 + 1$, then $du = 2x\,dx$ and $u = 1$ when $x = 0$, and $u = 5$ when $x = 2$. Thus we write

$$\int_0^2 x\sqrt{x^2 + 1}\,dx = \int_1^5 \sqrt{u}\cdot\frac{1}{2}du = \frac{1}{3}u^{3/2}\Big|_1^5$$

$$= \frac{1}{3}(5^{3/2} - 1^{3/2}) = \frac{5}{3}\sqrt{5} - \frac{1}{3}$$

There is no need to go back to x again so long as the limits of integration have been properly changed. Of course we could return to x and not change the limits of integration if we wanted to, as follows:

$$\int x\sqrt{x^2 + 1}\,dx = \frac{1}{3}u^{3/2} = \frac{1}{3}(x^2 + 1)^{3/2}$$

so that

$$\int_0^2 x\sqrt{x^2 + 1}\,dx = \frac{1}{3}(x^2 + 1)^{3/2}\Big|_0^2 = \frac{1}{3}(5^{3/2} - 1^{3/2})$$

$$= \frac{5}{3}\sqrt{5} - \frac{1}{3}$$

If several successive changes of variable are needed in a single problem, it usually is more convenient to change the limits of integration at each variable change. Carefully note that

$$\int_0^2 x\sqrt{x^2 + 1}\,dx \neq \int_0^2 \frac{1}{2}\sqrt{u}\,du$$

because the limits of integration in the second integral have not been changed to accommodate the change of variable.

EXAMPLE Evaluate $\displaystyle\int_1^2 x^3\sqrt[3]{x^2 + 1}\,dx$.

Solution   To make the radicand linear, let $u = x^2$. Then $x^3\,dx = \frac{1}{2}x^2\cdot 2x\,dx = \frac{1}{2}u\,du$, so that

$$\int_1^2 x^3 \sqrt[3]{x^2+1}\ dx = \frac{1}{2}\int_1^4 u \sqrt[3]{u+1}\ du$$

(since $u=1$ when $x=1$ and $u=4$ when $x=2$). Next, let $t=\sqrt[3]{u+1}$. Then $u=t^3-1$ and $du=3t^2\ dt$, so that

$$\frac{1}{2}\int_1^4 u\sqrt[3]{u+1}\ du = \frac{3}{2}\int_{\sqrt[3]{2}}^{\sqrt[3]{5}} (t^3-1)\cdot t\cdot t^2\ dt$$

$$= \frac{3}{2}\int_{\sqrt[3]{2}}^{\sqrt[3]{5}} (t^6-t^3)\ dt = \frac{3}{2}\left(\frac{1}{7}t^7 - \frac{1}{4}t^4\right)\Bigg|_{\sqrt[3]{2}}^{\sqrt[3]{5}}$$

$$= \frac{3}{14}(5^{7/3}-2^{7/3}) - \frac{3}{8}(5^{4/3}-2^{4/3})$$

$$= \frac{75}{14}\sqrt[3]{5} - \frac{12}{14}\sqrt[3]{2} - \frac{15}{8}\sqrt[3]{5} + \frac{6}{8}\sqrt[3]{2} = \frac{195}{56}\sqrt[3]{5} - \frac{3}{28}\sqrt[3]{2}$$

which is the final answer. Notice that the single substitution $t=\sqrt[3]{x^2+1}$ would have worked here. However, our first goal was to make the radicand linear and this single substitution did not *seem* to be one that would work.

The hypothesis in **FTC** that the integrand be *continuous* on the *closed* interval of integration is very important. Consider the following careless computation in which $u=2x-1$ and $dx=\frac{1}{2}\ du$, so that $u=-1$ when $x=0$, and $u=1$ when $x=1$:

$$\int_0^1 \frac{dx}{(2x-1)^2} = \frac{1}{2}\int_{-1}^1 \frac{du}{u^2} = -\frac{1}{2u}\Bigg|_{-1}^1$$

$$= -\frac{1}{2\cdot 1} - \left(-\frac{1}{2(-1)}\right) = -1$$

This is a ridiculous answer, because if a function is always *positive* on $[a,b]$ (where $a<b$), then its integral over $[a,b]$ must at least be positive. The error above is the second equality because the integrand $\frac{1}{u^2}$ is not continuous on $[-1,1]$.

EXERCISES

In 1–48, evaluate the given integral.

1. $\int x \sin x^2\ dx$

2. $\int x^2\sqrt{x^3+2}\ dx$

3. $\int e^x \cos e^x\ dx$

4. $\int xe^{-x^2}\ dx$

5. $\int \frac{e^x + e^{2x}}{e^{3x}}\ dx$

6. $\int \frac{e^x\ dx}{1-2e^x+e^{2x}}$

7. $\int \dfrac{\ln x}{x}\, dx$

8. $\int \dfrac{\ln (\ln x)}{x \ln x}\, dx$

9. $\int \dfrac{\sin \sqrt{x}}{\sqrt{x}}\, dx$

10. $\int \ln (\sin x) \cot x\, dx$

11. $\int \dfrac{x\, dx}{\sqrt{2-x}}$

12. $\int \dfrac{x\, dx}{\sqrt{2-x^2}}$

13. $\int x^2 \sqrt{x+4}\, dx$

14. $\int \dfrac{dx}{x - \sqrt{x}}$

15. $\int \dfrac{dx}{\sqrt{x} + x\sqrt{x}}$

16. $\int \dfrac{dx}{1 + \sqrt{x+2}}$

17. $\int \dfrac{dx}{\sqrt[4]{x} + \sqrt{x}}$

18. $\int \dfrac{e^x\, dx}{e^x + 1}$

19. $\int \dfrac{e^x\, dx}{\sqrt{e^x + 1}}$

20. $\int \dfrac{\sin x - \cos x}{\sin x + \cos x}\, dx$

21. $\int \dfrac{x\, dx}{x^4 + 1}$

22. $\int \dfrac{x^3\, dx}{x^4 + 1}$

23. $\int \dfrac{x^2\, dx}{\sqrt{1 - x^6}}$

24. $\int \dfrac{x^5\, dx}{\sqrt{1 - x^6}}$

25. $\int \sec^3 x \tan x\, dx$

26. $\int \dfrac{\cos x\, dx}{3 \sin^2 x}$

27. $\int \dfrac{\cos x\, dx}{3 \sin^2 x + 1}$

28. $\int e^{\sin^2 x} \sin 2x\, dx$

29. $\int e^{3 \ln x + 1}\, dx$

30. $\int \tan^3 x \sec x\, dx$

31. $\int \tan \dfrac{x}{2}\, dx$

32. $\int \tan x \sec^2 x\, dx$

33. $\int \tan x \sec^4 x\, dx$

34. $\int \tan^2 x \csc x\, dx$

35. $\int \cos 2x \sin x\, dx$

36. $\int \dfrac{9^x - 1}{3^x - 1}\, dx$

37. $\int_0^3 \dfrac{dx}{9 + x^2}$

38. $\int_0^2 \dfrac{x\, dx}{(x^2 + 1)^2}$

39. $\int_0^{\pi/2} e^{\sin x} \cos x\, dx$

40. $\int_0^1 \dfrac{x\, dx}{1 + \sqrt{x^2 + 1}}$

41. $\int_0^1 x\sqrt{x + 3}\, dx$

42. $\int_1^4 \dfrac{e^{\sqrt{x}}}{\sqrt{x}}\, dx$

43. $\int_4^9 \dfrac{1 - \sqrt{x}}{1 + \sqrt{x}}\, dx$

44. $\int_0^7 \dfrac{x\, dx}{\sqrt[3]{x + 1}}$

45. $\int_1^{64} \dfrac{dx}{\sqrt[3]{x} + \sqrt{x}}$

46. $\int_0^{\sqrt{2}} \dfrac{x\, dx}{x^4 + 1}$

47. $\int_0^{\sqrt{2}} \dfrac{x\, dx}{\sqrt{16 - x^4}}$

48. $\int_0^{\pi/4} e^{\ln \sin x}\, dx$

49. Find the area of the region bounded by the curve

$$y = \dfrac{\ln x}{x} \text{ and the line } (e^2 - e)y = x - 1.$$

50. Find the area of the region bounded by the curves

$$y = \dfrac{x}{x^2 + 1} \text{ and } 2y = x^2.$$

51. Evaluate $\int \sec x \, dx$ by first writing

$$\sec x = \frac{(\sec x)(\tan x + \sec x)}{\sec x + \tan x}$$
$$= \frac{\sec x \tan x + \sec^2 x}{\sec x + \tan x}$$

52. Evaluate $\int \csc x \, dx$ by first writing

$$\csc x = \frac{(\csc x)(\csc x - \cot x)}{\csc x - \cot x}$$
$$= \frac{-\csc x \cot x + \csc^2 x}{\csc x - \cot x}$$

3 Some Trigonometric Integrals

In this section we consider integrals of the form

$$\int \sin^m x \cos^n x \, dx$$

where m and n are nonnegative numbers. If at least one of m and n is an *odd* positive integer, we simply split off one factor of that power to place with the dx and then use the identity $\sin^2 x + \cos^2 x = 1$ to change the rest of the integrand so as to involve only the other function. After that we substitute. A few examples should make this procedure clear.

EXAMPLE Evaluate $I = \int \sqrt{\sin x} \cos^3 x \, dx$.

Solution Split off one of the cosines to obtain

$$I = \int \sqrt{\sin x} \cos^3 x \, dx = \int \sqrt{\sin x} \cos^2 x \, (\cos x \, dx)$$
$$= \int \sqrt{\sin x} \, (1 - \sin^2 x)(\cos x \, dx)$$

Now substitute $u = \sin x$, $du = \cos x \, dx$ to obtain

$$I = \int \sqrt{u}(1 - u^2) \, du = \int (u^{1/2} - u^{5/2}) \, du$$
$$= \frac{2}{3} u^{3/2} - \frac{2}{7} u^{7/2} = \frac{2}{3}(\sin x)^{3/2} - \frac{2}{7}(\sin x)^{7/2}$$
$$= \sqrt{\sin x} \left(\frac{2}{3}\sin x - \frac{2}{7}\sin^3 x\right)$$

EXAMPLE   Evaluate $I = \displaystyle\int \sin^5 x \, dx$.

Solution   Split off one of the sines to get

$$I = \int \sin^4 x (\sin x \, dx) = \int (1 - \cos^2 x)^2 (\sin x \, dx)$$

Now substitute $u = \cos x$ and $du = -\sin x \, dx$ to obtain

$$I = -\int (1 - u^2)^2 \, du = -\int (1 - 2u^2 + u^4) \, du$$

$$= -\left(u - \frac{2}{3}u^3 + \frac{1}{5}u^5 \right)$$

$$= -\cos x + \frac{2}{3}\cos^3 x - \frac{1}{5}\cos^5 x$$

Thus, we see that the case in which m or n is an odd positive integer is very simple.

In case m and n are *both even* (nonnegative) integers, we make use of the identities

$$\sin^2 \alpha = \frac{1}{2}(1 - \cos 2\alpha) \qquad \text{and} \qquad \cos^2 \alpha = \frac{1}{2}(1 + \cos 2\alpha)$$

to reduce the size of the exponents.

EXAMPLE   Evaluate $I = \displaystyle\int \sin^4 x \cos^2 x \, dx$.

Solution   Writing $\sin^4 x = (\sin^2 x)^2$ and using the identities yields

$$I = \int \left(\frac{1 - \cos 2x}{2} \right)^2 \left(\frac{1 + \cos 2x}{2} \right) dx = \frac{1}{8} \int (1 - \cos^2 2x)(1 - \cos 2x) \, dx$$

$$= \frac{1}{8} \int (1 - \cos 2x - \cos^2 2x + \cos^3 2x) \, dx$$

$$= \frac{1}{8}x - \frac{1}{16} \sin 2x - \frac{1}{8} \int \cos^2 2x \, dx + \frac{1}{8} \int \cos^3 2x \, dx \qquad (1)$$

We have, by the above identity, that

$$\int \cos^2 2x \, dx = \frac{1}{2} \int (1 + \cos 4x) \, dx = \frac{1}{2}x + \frac{1}{8} \sin 4x \qquad (2)$$

Since 3 is odd, we use the preceding method to obtain

$$\int \cos^3 2x \, dx = \int (1 - \sin^2 2x) \cos 2x \, dx$$

$$= \int (1 - u^2) \cdot \frac{1}{2} \, du = \frac{1}{2}u - \frac{1}{6}u^3$$

$$= \frac{1}{2}\sin 2x - \frac{1}{6}\sin^3 2x \qquad (3)$$

Finally, we combine (1)–(3) to get

$$I = \frac{1}{8}x - \frac{1}{16}\sin 2x - \frac{1}{8}\left(\frac{1}{2}x + \frac{1}{8}\sin 4x\right) + \frac{1}{8}\left(\frac{1}{2}\sin 2x - \frac{1}{6}\sin^3 2x\right)$$

$$= \frac{1}{16}x - \frac{1}{64}\sin 4x - \frac{1}{48}\sin^3 2x$$

The case that one of m and n is not an integer and the other is not an odd integer can be handled by use of the Gamma Function (or Beta Function), which is beyond the scope of this book.

EXERCISES

In 1–16, evaluate the integrals.

1. $\displaystyle\int \sin^2 x \, dx$

2. $\displaystyle\int \cos^2 x \, dx$

3. $\displaystyle\int \cos^3 x \, dx$

4. $\displaystyle\int \sin^3 x \, dx$

5. $\displaystyle\int \sin^4 x \, dx$

6. $\displaystyle\int \cos^4 x \, dx$

7. $\displaystyle\int \sin^2 x \cos^2 x \, dx$

8. $\displaystyle\int \sin^3 x \cos^2 x \, dx$

9. $\displaystyle\int (\sin x)^{1/3} \cos^3 x \, dx$

10. $\displaystyle\int \sin 2x \cos^2 x \, dx$

11. $\displaystyle\int \sin^2 x \cos 2x \, dx$

12. $\displaystyle\int \sin^3 x \, (\cos x)^{1/4} \, dx$

13. $\displaystyle\int \sin 2x \cos^3 x \, dx$

14. $\displaystyle\int \sin^3 x \cos^9 x \, dx$

15. $\displaystyle\int \tan^2 x \cos^5 x \, dx$

16. $\displaystyle\int \sec^2 x \cos^6 x \, dx$

4 Integration by Parts

The formula for differentiating the product of two functions

$$\frac{d}{dx}(u(x)v(x)) = u(x)v'(x) + v(x)u'(x)$$

leads to the integration formula

$$u(x)v(x) = \int u(x)v'(x)\,dx + \int v(x)u'(x)\,dx$$

which, after rearranging, is

$$\int u(x)v'(x)\,dx = u(x)v(x) - \int v(x)u'(x)\,dx$$

This can be viewed as a formula for transforming one integration problem into another. This is known as the **integration by parts formula** and the process of applying it is called **integration by parts**. We write the formula more briefly as

$$\int u\,dv = uv - \int v\,du$$

A skillful use of it can often change a difficult problem into an easy one.

EXAMPLE   Evaluate $\int x \ln x\,dx$.

Solution   Since we can easily integrate $v'(x) = x$, we choose $dv = x\,dx$ and $u = \ln x$. Then $v = \frac{1}{2}x^2$ and $du = dx/x$, so that

$$\int x \ln x\,dx = \frac{1}{2}x^2 \ln x - \int \frac{1}{2}x\,dx = \frac{1}{2}x^2 \ln x - \frac{1}{4}x^2$$

$$= \frac{1}{4}x^2\,(2\ln x - 1)$$

Sometimes we simply let $dv = dx$ and successfully apply the formula.

EXAMPLE   Evaluate $\int \text{Tan}^{-1} x\,dx$.

Solution   Taking $dv = dx$ and $u = \text{Tan}^{-1} x$, we have $v = x$ and $du = (1 + x^2)^{-1}\,dx$, so that

$$\int \text{Tan}^{-1} x\,dx = x\,\text{Tan}^{-1} x - \int \frac{x\,dx}{1 + x^2} = x\,\text{Tan}^{-1}x - \frac{1}{2}\ln\,(1 + x^2)$$

EXAMPLE   Find $\int \ln x\,dx$.

Solution   Letting $dv = dx$ and $u = \ln x$, we get $v = x$ and $du = dx/x$, so that

$$\int \ln x\,dx = x \ln x - \int dx = x \ln x - x$$

Sometimes more than one application of integration by parts is needed to solve a problem.

EXAMPLE   Evaluate $I = \int x^2 \cos 2x \, dx$.

Solution   Our plan is to get rid of the x^2 by differentiating it twice. First take $u = x^2$ and $dv = \cos 2x \, dx$. Then $du = 2x \, dx$ and $v = \frac{1}{2}\sin 2x$, so that

$$I = \frac{1}{2}x^2 \sin 2x - \int x \sin 2x \, dx$$

To evaluate this last integral, take $u = x$, $dv = \sin 2x \, dx$, $du = dx$, and $v = -\frac{1}{2}\cos 2x$ to get

$$\int x \sin 2x \, dx = -\frac{1}{2}x \cos 2x + \frac{1}{2}\int \cos 2x \, dx$$

$$= -\frac{1}{2}x \cos 2x + \frac{1}{4}\sin 2x$$

Combining these results yields

$$I = \frac{1}{2}x^2 \sin 2x + \frac{1}{2}x \cos 2x - \frac{1}{4}\sin 2x$$

Sometimes one or two applications of our formula leads to an equation which can be solved for the desired integral.

EXAMPLE   Find $I = \int e^x \cos x \, dx$.

Solution   Choosing $u = e^x$ and $dv = \cos x \, dx$, we have $du = e^x \, dx$, $v = \sin x$, and

$$I = e^x \sin x - \int e^x \sin x \, dx$$

Next take $u = e^x$, $dv = \sin x \, dx$, $du = e^x \, dx$, and $v = -\cos x$ to get

$$\int e^x \sin x \, dx = -e^x \cos x + \int e^x \cos x \, dx = -e^x \cos x + I$$

Consequently,

$$I = e^x \sin x + e^x \cos x - I$$
$$2I = e^x(\sin x + \cos x)$$
$$I = \frac{1}{2}e^x(\sin x + \cos x)$$

EXAMPLE   Find $I = \int \sec^3 x \, dx$.

Solution   We want dv to be something we can integrate so we take $dv = \sec^2 x \, dx$ and $u = \sec x$. Then $v = \tan x$ and $du = \sec x \tan x \, dx$, so that

$$I = \sec x \tan x - \int \sec x \tan^2 x \, dx$$

$$= \sec x \tan x - \int (\sec x)(\sec^2 x - 1) \, dx$$

$$= \sec x \tan x - \int \sec^3 x \, dx + \int \sec x \, dx$$

$$= \sec x \tan x - I + \ln|\sec x + \tan x|$$

and therefore, solving for I,

$$I = \frac{1}{2}\sec x \tan x + \frac{1}{2}\ln|\sec x + \tan x|$$

For definite integrals, we have the formula

$$\int_a^b u(x)v'(x) \, dx = u(x)v(x)\Big|_a^b - \int_a^b v(x)u'(x) \, dx$$

which is valid if u, v, u', and v' are all continuous on $[a,b]$. More briefly,

$$\int_a^b u \, dv = uv\Big|_a^b - \int_a^b v \, du$$

EXAMPLE   Evaluate $I = \int_0^{1/2} \dfrac{x^3 \, dx}{\sqrt{1 - x^2}}$.

Solution   Taking $dv = \dfrac{x \, dx}{\sqrt{1 - x^2}}$ and $u = x^2$, we have $du = 2x \, dx$ and, substituting $t = 1 - x^2$,

$$v = \int \frac{x \, dx}{\sqrt{1 - x^2}} = -\frac{1}{2}\int t^{-1/2} \, dt = -t^{1/2} = -\sqrt{1 - x^2}$$

Thus

$$I = -x^2\sqrt{1 - x^2}\,\Big|_0^{1/2} + 2\int_0^{1/2} x\sqrt{1 - x^2} \, dx$$

$$= -\frac{\sqrt{3}}{8} - \int_1^{3/4} t^{1/2} \, dt = -\frac{\sqrt{3}}{8} + \frac{2}{3}t^{3/2}\,\Big|_{3/4}^{1}$$

$$= -\frac{\sqrt{3}}{8} + \frac{2}{3} - \frac{2}{3}\cdot\frac{3}{4}\cdot\frac{\sqrt{3}}{2} = \frac{2}{3} - \frac{3}{8}\sqrt{3}$$

Of course, this problem could also be done by the substitution $x = \sin \theta$, as follows:

$$I = \int_0^{\pi/6} \frac{\sin^3 \theta \cos \theta \, d\theta}{\sqrt{1 - \sin^2 \theta}}$$

$$= \int_0^{\pi/6} \sin^3 \theta \, d\theta$$

$$= \int_0^{\pi/6} (1 - \cos^2 \theta)\sin \theta \, d\theta$$

$$= \left(-\cos \theta + \frac{1}{3}\cos^3 \theta\right) \Big|_0^{\pi/6}$$

$$= \left(-\frac{\sqrt{3}}{2} + \frac{1}{3} \cdot \frac{3\sqrt{3}}{8}\right) - \left(-1 + \frac{1}{3}\right)$$

$$= -\frac{3}{8}\sqrt{3} + \frac{2}{3}$$

E X E R C I S E S

In 1–36, evaluate the given integral.

1. $\int x \sin x \, dx$

2. $\int xe^x \, dx$

3. $\int x^2 e^x \, dx$

4. $\int x^2 \sin x \, dx$

5. $\int x \cdot 2^x \, dx$

6. $\int xe^{-x} \, dx$

7. $\int \mathrm{Sin}^{-1} x \, dx$

8. $\int \mathrm{Cos}^{-1} x \, dx$

9. $\int \sec^5 x \, dx$

10. $\int \sin (\ln x) \, dx$

11. $\int \sin 3x \cos 2x \, dx$

12. $\int \csc^3 x \, dx$

13. $\int x \, \mathrm{Tan}^{-1} x \, dx$

14. $\int x^2 \ln x \, dx$

15. $\int (x^2 + 1) \ln x \, dx$

16. $\int x^2 \sqrt{x + 1} \, dx$

17. $\int \frac{\mathrm{Tan}^{-1} \sqrt{x}}{\sqrt{x}} \, dx$

18. $\int x \, \mathrm{Sec}^{-1} x \, dx$

19. $\int \mathrm{Sec}^{-1} x \, dx$
[let $t = \mathrm{Sec}^{-1} x$]

20. $\int \mathrm{Tan}^{-1} \sqrt{x} \, dx$

21. $\int e^{ax} \sin bx \, dx$

22. $\int x \tan^2 x \, dx$

23. $\int \frac{\mathrm{Sin}^{-1} x}{\sqrt{1 + x}} \, dx$

24. $\int (\ln x)^2 \, dx$

25. $\int \sqrt{x} \ln x \, dx$

26. $\int \ln \sqrt{x} \, dx$

27. $\int \ln (x^2 + 1) \, dx$

28. $\int \frac{\ln x}{x^2} \, dx$

29. $\int x^3 e^{x^2} \, dx$

30. $\int \frac{\ln (\ln x)}{x} \, dx$

31. $\int_0^1 \frac{\mathrm{Tan}^{-1} x}{1 + x^2} \, dx$

32. $\int_1^2 \ln \sqrt{x + 1} \, dx$

33. $\int_0^1 x^3 \sqrt{1 + x^2} \, dx$

34. $\displaystyle\int_0^{\pi} x \cos x\,dx$ **35.** $\displaystyle\int_0^{1} \text{Sin}^{-1} \sqrt{x}\,dx$ **36.** $\displaystyle\int_1^{2} x^2 \ln x\,dx$

37. Find the area of the region bounded by the curve $y = x^{-1} \ln x$ and the lines $y = 0$ and $x = e$.

38. Find the area of the region bounded by the curves $y = x \sin x$ and $y = x \cos x$ which is between the lines $x = 0$ and $x = \dfrac{\pi}{4}$.

39. Find the area of the region bounded by the curve $y = xe^{-x}$ and the line $x = ey$.

5   Reduction Formulas

Sometimes an integrand depends on an integer n as well as on the variable of integration. In such cases it often happens that one or two integrations by parts leads to the same (or a similar) integrand except that n is replaced by a smaller integer. Such a process is called **reduction**. For example, consider $\displaystyle\int \sin^n x\,dx$. Integrating by parts with $u = \sin^{n-1} x$, $dv = \sin x\,dx$, $v = -\cos x$, and $du = (n-1) \cdot \sin^{n-2} x \cos x\,dx$, and, using $\cos^2 x = 1 - \sin^2 x$, we obtain

$$\int \sin^n x\,dx = -\sin^{n-1} x \cos x + (n-1) \int \sin^{n-2} x \cos^2 x\,dx$$

$$= -\sin^{n-1} x \cos x + (n-1) \int \sin^{n-2} x\,dx - (n-1) \int \sin^n x\,dx$$

Transposing the last term and dividing by n yields the reduction formula

$$\int \sin^n x\,dx = -\frac{1}{n} \sin^{n-1} x \cos x + \frac{n-1}{n} \int \sin^{n-2} x\,dx$$

in which n gets replaced by $n - 2$ in the integrand. If $n > 1$ is an odd positive integer, then repeated application of this formula will eventually lead to $\displaystyle\int \sin x\,dx$, while if $n > 0$ is even, we will eventually get $\displaystyle\int 1\,dx$. Thus, the evaluation of $\displaystyle\int \sin^n x\,dx$ is accomplished by repeated application of our reduction formula. In particular we have

$$\int_0^{\pi/2} \sin^n x\,dx = \frac{n-1}{n} \int_0^{\pi/2} \sin^{n-2} x\,dx$$

EXAMPLE Use the above reduction formula to evaluate $\int \sin^6 x \, dx$.

Solution By the formula, we have

$$\int \sin^6 x \, dx = -\frac{1}{6} \sin^5 x \cos x + \frac{5}{6} \int \sin^4 x \, dx$$

$$\frac{5}{6} \int \sin^4 x \, dx = -\frac{5 \cdot 1}{6 \cdot 4} \sin^3 x \cos x + \frac{5 \cdot 3}{6 \cdot 4} \int \sin^2 x \, dx$$

and

$$\frac{5 \cdot 3}{6 \cdot 4} \int \sin^2 x \, dx = -\frac{5 \cdot 3 \cdot 1}{6 \cdot 4 \cdot 2} \sin x \cos x + \frac{5 \cdot 3 \cdot 1}{6 \cdot 4 \cdot 2} \int 1 \, dx$$

Combining these results yields

$$\int \sin^6 x \, dx = -\frac{1}{6} \sin^5 x \cos x - \frac{5 \cdot 1}{6 \cdot 4} \sin^3 x \cos x - \frac{5 \cdot 3 \cdot 1}{6 \cdot 4 \cdot 2}$$

$$\cdot \sin x \cos x + \frac{5 \cdot 3 \cdot 1}{6 \cdot 4 \cdot 2} x$$

$$= \left(-\frac{1}{6} \cos x \right) \left(\sin^5 x + \frac{5}{4} \sin^3 x + \frac{15}{8} \sin x \right) + \frac{5x}{16}$$

EXAMPLE Derive the reduction formula

$$\int x^n \sqrt{ax + b} \, dx = \frac{2x^n(ax + b)^{3/2}}{a(2n + 3)} - \frac{2bn}{a(2n + 3)} \int x^{n-1}\sqrt{ax + b} \, dx$$

Solution Choosing $u = x^n$, $dv = (ax + b)^{1/2} \, dx$, $v = \frac{2}{3a}(ax + b)^{3/2}$, $du = nx^{n-1} \, dx$, and writing

$$(ax + b)^{3/2} = ax\sqrt{ax + b} + b\sqrt{ax + b},$$

we obtain

$$\int x^n \sqrt{ax + b} \, dx = \frac{2x^n(ax + b)^{3/2}}{3a} - \frac{2n}{3a} \int x^{n-1}(ax + b)^{3/2} \, dx$$

$$= \frac{2x^n(ax + b)^{3/2}}{3a} - \frac{2n}{3} \int x^n \sqrt{ax + b} \, dx - \frac{2nb}{3a} \int x^{n-1}\sqrt{ax + b} \, dx$$

Transposing the middle term yields

$$\frac{2n + 3}{3} \int x^n \sqrt{ax + b} \, dx = \frac{2x^n(ax + b)^{3/2}}{3a} - \frac{2nb}{3a} \int x^{n-1}\sqrt{ax + b} \, dx$$

Now multiply through by $3/(2n + 3)$ to obtain the desired formula.

E X E R C I S E S

In 1–10, (a) derive the given reduction formula and (b) then use it to evaluate the given integral.

1. (a) $\displaystyle \int \frac{x^n dx}{\sqrt{ax+b}} = \frac{2x^n\sqrt{ax+b}}{a(2n+1)} - \frac{2bn}{a(2n+1)} \int \frac{x^{n-1}\, dx}{\sqrt{ax+b}}$

(b) $\displaystyle \int \frac{x^4\, dx}{\sqrt{x+2}}$ $\left[\textit{Hint: } \sqrt{ax+b} = \frac{ax}{\sqrt{ax+b}} + \frac{b}{\sqrt{ax+b}} \right]$

2. (a) $\displaystyle \int \frac{dx}{x^n\sqrt{ax+b}} = -\frac{\sqrt{ax+b}}{b(n-1)x^{n-1}} - \frac{a(2n-3)}{2b(n-1)} \int \frac{dx}{x^{n-1}\sqrt{ax+b}}$

for $n > 1$

(b) $\displaystyle \int \frac{dx}{x^3\sqrt{2x-1}}$

3. (a) $\displaystyle \int \frac{\sqrt{ax+b}}{x^n} dx = -\frac{(ax+b)^{3/2}}{b(n-1)x^{n-1}} - \frac{a(2n-5)}{2b(n-1)} \int \frac{\sqrt{ax+b}}{x^{n-1}} dx$

for $n > 1$

(b) $\displaystyle \int \frac{\sqrt{2x-1}}{x^3} dx$

4. (a) $\displaystyle \int \cos^n x\, dx = \frac{1}{n}\cos^{n-1} x \sin x + \frac{n-1}{n} \int \cos^{n-2} x\, dx$

(b) $\displaystyle \int \cos^5 x\, dx$

5. (a) $\displaystyle \int \tan^n x\, dx = \frac{\tan^{n-1} x}{n-1} - \int \tan^{n-2} x\, dx$ for $n > 1$

(b) $\displaystyle \int \tan^4 x\, dx$

6. (a) $\displaystyle \int \cot^n x\, dx = -\frac{\cot^{n-1} x}{n-1} - \int \cot^{n-2} x\, dx$ for $n > 1$

(b) $\displaystyle \int \cot^4 x\, dx$

7. (a) $\displaystyle \int \sec^n x\, dx = \frac{\sec^{n-2} x \tan x}{n-1} + \frac{n-2}{n-1} \int \sec^{n-2} x\, dx$ for $n > 1$

(b) $\displaystyle \int \sec^5 x\, dx$

8. (a) $\displaystyle\int \csc^n x\, dx = -\frac{\csc^{n-2} x \cot x}{n-1} + \frac{n-2}{n-1}\int \csc^{n-2} x\, dx$ for $n > 1$

(b) $\displaystyle\int \csc^6 x\, dx$

9. (a) $\displaystyle\int \sin^m x \cos^n x\, dx$

$$= \frac{\sin^{m+1} x \cos^{n-1} x}{m+n} + \frac{n-1}{m+n}\int \sin^m x \cos^{n-2} x\, dx$$

(b) $\displaystyle\int \sin^4 x \cos^4 x\, dx$

10. (a) $\displaystyle\int \sin^m x \cos^n x\, dx$

$$= -\frac{\sin^{m-1} x \cos^{n+1} x}{m+n} + \frac{m-1}{m+n}\int \sin^{m-2} x \cos^n x\, dx$$

(b) $\displaystyle\int \sin^6 x \cos^3 x\, dx$

6   The Wallis Formulas*

We saw in the preceding section that if we define I_n by

$$I_n = \int_0^{\pi/2} \sin^n x\, dx$$

then we have

$$I_n = \frac{n-1}{n} I_{n-2}$$

for all $n > 1$. Considering separately the case that $n = 2k$ is even and the case that $n = 2k + 1$ is odd we have

$$I_{2k} = \frac{2k-1}{2k} \cdot \frac{2k-3}{2k-2} \cdot \frac{2k-5}{2k-4} \cdot \ldots \cdot \frac{1}{2} \cdot I_0$$

and

$$I_{2k+1} = \frac{2k}{2k+1} \cdot \frac{2k-2}{2k-1} \cdot \frac{2k-4}{2k-3} \cdot \ldots \cdot \frac{2}{3} \cdot I_1$$

*An optional section.

This yields

$$\frac{2}{1} \cdot \frac{4}{3} \cdot \frac{6}{5} \cdot \cdots \cdot \frac{2k}{2k-1} = \frac{I_0}{I_{2k}} = \frac{\pi}{2} \cdot \frac{1}{I_{2k}}$$

and

$$\frac{2}{3} \cdot \frac{4}{5} \cdot \frac{6}{7} \cdot \cdots \cdot \frac{2k}{2k+1} = \frac{I_{2k+1}}{I_1} = I_{2k+1}$$

and so, multiplying these two equations,

$$\frac{2 \cdot 2}{1 \cdot 3} \cdot \frac{4 \cdot 4}{3 \cdot 5} \cdot \frac{6 \cdot 6}{5 \cdot 7} \cdot \cdots \cdot \frac{(2k) \cdot (2k)}{(2k-1) \cdot (2k+1)} = \frac{\pi}{2} \cdot \frac{I_{2k+1}}{I_{2k}}$$

For $0 < x < \dfrac{\pi}{2}$, we have $0 < \sin x < 1$

so that

$$0 < \sin^{2k+1} x < \sin^{2k} x < \sin^{2k-1} x$$

Integrating these inequalities over $[0, \pi/2]$, we obtain

$$0 < I_{2k+1} < I_{2k} < I_{2k-1}$$

Now divide by I_{2k+1} and use the formula $I_{2k+1} = \dfrac{2k}{2k+1} I_{2k-1}$ to deduce that

$$1 < \frac{I_{2k}}{I_{2k+1}} < \frac{I_{2k-1}}{I_{2k+1}} = \frac{2k+1}{2k} = 1 + \frac{1}{2k}$$

We conclude from this that

$$\lim_{k \to \infty} I_{2k}/I_{2k+1} = 1$$

Thus,

$$\lim_{k \to \infty} \frac{2 \cdot 2}{1 \cdot 3} \cdot \frac{4 \cdot 4}{3 \cdot 5} \cdot \frac{6 \cdot 6}{5 \cdot 7} \cdot \cdots \cdot \frac{(2k) \cdot (2k)}{(2k-1) \cdot (2k+1)} = \frac{\pi}{2} \qquad (1)$$

This formula is due to the English mathematician John Wallis (1616–1703). It seems to be the earliest formula known which expresses π explicitly as the limit of a sequence of rational numbers.

EXAMPLE Use $k = 5$ in formula (1) to estimate π.

Solution For $k = 5$, the left side of (1) becomes

$$\frac{2 \cdot 2 \cdot 4 \cdot 4 \cdot 6 \cdot 6 \cdot 8 \cdot 8 \cdot 10 \cdot 10}{1 \cdot 3 \cdot 3 \cdot 5 \cdot 5 \cdot 7 \cdot 7 \cdot 9 \cdot 9 \cdot 11} = \frac{14{,}745{,}600}{9{,}823{,}275} \approx 1.501$$

Setting $1.501 \approx \dfrac{\pi}{2}$ gives

$$\pi \approx 3.002$$

Of course, if we take much larger values of k, we will get much closer approximations to π.

We now use (1) to obtain another useful limit formula. Notice that the square root of the product on the left side of (1) is

$$\frac{2 \cdot 4 \cdot 6 \cdot \ldots \cdot 2k}{1 \cdot 3 \cdot 5 \cdot \ldots \cdot (2k-1)} \cdot \frac{1}{\sqrt{2k+1}}$$

$$= \frac{2^2 \cdot 4^2 \cdot 6^2 \cdot \ldots \cdot (2k)^2}{1 \cdot 2 \cdot 3 \cdot 4 \cdot 5 \cdot \ldots \cdot (2k-1)(2k)} \cdot \frac{1}{\sqrt{2k+1}}$$

$$= \frac{(2 \cdot 1)^2 (2 \cdot 2)^2 (2 \cdot 3)^2 \cdot \ldots \cdot (2 \cdot k)^2}{(2k)!} \cdot \frac{1}{\sqrt{2k+1}}$$

$$= \frac{2^{2k}(k!)^2}{(2k)!} \cdot \frac{1}{\sqrt{2k+1}}$$

Thus

$$\sqrt{\frac{\pi}{2}} = \lim_{k \to \infty} \frac{2^{2k}(k!)^2}{(2k)!} \cdot \frac{1}{\sqrt{2k+1}}$$

Since

$$\sqrt{2} = \lim_{k \to \infty} \frac{\sqrt{2k+1}}{\sqrt{k}}$$

it follows upon multiplication that

$$\sqrt{\pi} = \lim_{k \to \infty} \frac{2^{2k}(k!)^2}{(2k)!\sqrt{k}} \qquad (2)$$

This too is called a Wallis formula.

7 Trigonometric Substitutions

If an integrand contains an expression of one of the forms $\sqrt{a^2 + u^2}$, $\sqrt{a^2 - u^2}$, or $\sqrt{u^2 - a^2}$, where u is some function of the variable of integration, say x, and $a > 0$ is a constant, then it is possible to get rid of this radical by the respective substitutions $u = a \tan \theta$,

$u = a \sin \theta$, or $u = a \sec \theta$. This is because of the trigonometric identities $\tan^2 \theta + 1 = \sec^2 \theta$, $1 - \sin^2 \theta = \cos^2 \theta$, and $\sec^2 \theta - 1 = \tan^2 \theta$, which can be used to change a sum or difference of two squares into a single square. We now illustrate the method by giving two examples of each type.

EXAMPLE Evaluate $I = \int \sqrt{3 + x^2} \, dx$.

Solution Let $x = \sqrt{3} \tan \theta$, where $-\pi/2 < \theta < \pi/2$. Then $dx = \sqrt{3} \sec^2 \theta \, d\theta$ and, since $\sec \theta > 0$ for $-\pi/2 < \theta < \pi/2$,

$$\sqrt{3 + x^2} = \sqrt{3 + 3 \tan^2 \theta} = \sqrt{3 \sec^2 \theta} = \sqrt{3} \sec \theta$$

Thus

$$I = \int \sqrt{3} \sec \theta \cdot \sqrt{3} \sec^2 \theta \, d\theta = 3 \int \sec^3 \theta \, d\theta$$

We have already evaluated this last integral as an example in section 4 (see page 345). Using that example we have

$$I = \frac{3}{2} \sec \theta \tan \theta + \frac{3}{2} \ln |\sec \theta + \tan \theta|$$

As above, $\tan \theta = x/\sqrt{3}$ and $\sec \theta = \sqrt{3 + x^2}/\sqrt{3}$, and so we express our answer in terms of x by

$$I = \frac{1}{2} x \sqrt{3 + x^2} + \frac{3}{2} \ln \left| \frac{\sqrt{3 + x^2} + x}{\sqrt{3}} \right|$$

By adding the constant $\frac{3}{2} \ln \sqrt{3}$ to this answer, we obtain another correct answer

$$I = \frac{1}{2} x \sqrt{3 + x^2} + \frac{3}{2} \ln (\sqrt{3 + x^2} + x)$$

We have dropped the absolute value signs here because $\sqrt{3 + x^2} + x > 0$ for all x.

EXAMPLE Evaluate $I = \int \dfrac{x^2 \, dx}{(4x^2 + 4x + 2)^{3/2}}$.

Solution Since $4x^2 + 4x + 2 = (2x + 1)^2 + 1$, we use the substitution $2x + 1 = \tan \theta$, where $-\pi/2 < \theta < \pi/2$. Then $(4x^2 + 4x + 2)^{3/2} = (\tan^2 \theta + 1)^{3/2} = \sec^3 \theta$, $2 \, dx = \sec^2 \theta \, d\theta$, and $4x^2 = (\tan \theta - 1)^2 = \sec^2 \theta - 2 \tan \theta$. Thus

$$I = \frac{1}{8} \int \frac{(\sec^2 \theta - 2 \tan \theta) \sec^2 \theta \, d\theta}{\sec^3 \theta}$$

$$= \frac{1}{8} \int \sec \theta \, d\theta - \frac{1}{4} \int \sin \theta \, d\theta$$

$$= \frac{1}{8} \ln |\sec \theta + \tan \theta| + \frac{1}{4} \cos \theta$$

From above we see that $\sec \theta = \sqrt{4x^2 + 4x + 2} = 1/\cos \theta$ and $\tan \theta = 2x + 1$. Therefore ·

$$I = \frac{1}{8} \ln \left(\sqrt{4x^2 + 4x + 2} + 2x + 1 \right) + \frac{1}{4\sqrt{4x^2 + 4x + 2}}$$

EXAMPLE Evaluate $I = \int \dfrac{x^3 \, dx}{\sqrt{9 - x^2}}$.

Solution Let $x = 3 \sin \theta$, where $-\pi/2 < \theta < \pi/2$. Then $\cos \theta > 0$ and so $\sqrt{9 - x^2} = \sqrt{9 \cos^2 \theta} = 3 \cos \theta$. Also $x^3 = 27 \sin^3 \theta$ and $dx = 3 \cos \theta \, d\theta$. Therefore

$$I = \int 27 \sin^3 \theta \, d\theta = -27 \int (1 - \cos^2 \theta) \, d(\cos \theta) = -27 \cos \theta + 9 \cos^3 \theta$$

$$= (-\cos \theta)(27 - 9 \cos^2 \theta) = -\frac{1}{3}\sqrt{9 - x^2} \, (18 + x^2)$$

EXAMPLE Evaluate $I = \displaystyle\int_0^{\pi/4} \dfrac{\sec^2 x \, dx}{(4 - \tan^2 x)^{3/2}}$.

Solution Let $\tan x = 2 \sin \theta$, where $-\pi/2 < \theta < \pi/2$. Then $\theta = 0$ when $x = 0$ and $\theta = \pi/6$ when $x = \pi/4$. Also, $\sec^2 x \, dx = 2 \cos \theta \, d\theta$ and $(4 - \tan^2 x)^{3/2} = (4 \cos^2 \theta)^{3/2} = 8 \cos^3 \theta$. Thus

$$I = \int_0^{\pi/6} \frac{2 \cos \theta \, d\theta}{8 \cos^3 \theta} = \frac{1}{4} \int_0^{\pi/6} \sec^2 \theta \, d\theta = \frac{1}{4} \tan \theta \Big|_0^{\pi/6}$$

$$= \frac{1}{4}\left(\frac{1}{\sqrt{3}} - 0\right) = \frac{\sqrt{3}}{12}$$

EXAMPLE Evaluate $I = \int \dfrac{dx}{x^3 \sqrt{x^2 - 1}}$.

Solution Let $x = \sec \theta$, where $0 < \theta < \pi/2$ if $x > 1$ while $\pi < \theta < 3\pi/2$ if $x < -1$. In either case, we have $\tan \theta > 0$ so that $\sqrt{x^2 - 1} = \sqrt{\tan^2 \theta} = \tan \theta$ and so

$$I = \int \frac{\sec \theta \tan \theta \, d\theta}{\sec^3 \theta \tan \theta} = \int \cos^2 \theta \, d\theta = \frac{1}{2} \int (1 + \cos 2\theta) \, d\theta$$

$$= \frac{1}{2}\theta + \frac{1}{4} \sin 2\theta = \frac{1}{2}(\theta + \sin \theta \cos \theta)$$

since $\sin 2\theta = 2 \sin \theta \cos \theta$. Recall that in Chapter 5, section 4 (page 242) we defined Sec^{-1} as follows: For $x \geq 1$, $\text{Sec}^{-1} x = y$ means $0 \leq y < \pi/2$ and $\sec y = x$. For $x \leq -1$, $\text{Sec}^{-1} x = y$ means $\dfrac{\pi}{2} < y \leq \pi$ and $\sec y = x$. Thus, noting our ranges of θ above, we have $\theta = \text{Sec}^{-1} x$ if $x > 1$ while $\theta = 2\pi - \text{Sec}^{-1} x$ if $x < -1$. Consult Fig. 7-1 for the two intervals of values of θ. In either case we have

$$\sin \theta = \frac{\sqrt{x^2 - 1}}{x} \qquad \text{and} \qquad \cos \theta = \frac{1}{x}$$

Thus we have

$$I = \frac{1}{2} \text{Sec}^{-1} x + \frac{\sqrt{x^2 - 1}}{2x^2} \qquad \text{if } x > 1$$

and, using $\theta = 2\pi - \text{Sec}^{-1} x$ and subtracting the constant π from I,

$$I = -\frac{1}{2} \text{Sec}^{-1} x + \frac{\sqrt{x^2 - 1}}{2x^2} \qquad \text{if } x < -1$$

This is a case in which the indefinite integral I must be defined by two separate formulas.

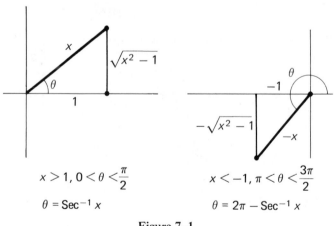

$$x > 1, 0 < \theta < \frac{\pi}{2} \qquad\qquad x < -1, \pi < \theta < \frac{3\pi}{2}$$

$$\theta = \text{Sec}^{-1} x \qquad\qquad\qquad \theta = 2\pi - \text{Sec}^{-1} x$$

Figure 7–1

EXAMPLE   Evaluate $I = \displaystyle\int \frac{\sqrt{x^2 + 2x - 3}\; dx}{x + 1}$.

Solution   Since $x^2 + 2x - 3 = (x + 1)^2 - 4$, we take $x + 1 = 2 \sec \theta$, where $0 \leq \theta < \pi/2$ if $x \geq 1$ and $\pi \leq \theta < 3\pi/2$ if $x \leq -3$. In either case

$\tan \theta > 0$ and so $\sqrt{x^2 + 2x - 3} = \sqrt{4 \tan^2 \theta} = 2 \tan \theta$. Also $dx = 2 \sec \theta$ $\tan \theta \, d\theta$ so that

$$I = \int \frac{2 \tan \theta \cdot 2 \sec \theta \tan \theta \, d\theta}{2 \sec \theta} = 2 \int (\sec^2 \theta - 1) \, d\theta = 2 \tan \theta - 2\theta$$

As in the preceding example, we have $\left(\text{using } \dfrac{x+1}{2} \text{ instead of } x\right)$

$$\theta = \text{Sec}^{-1} \frac{x+1}{2} \qquad \text{if } x \geq 1$$

and

$$\theta = 2\pi - \text{Sec}^{-1} \frac{x+1}{2} \qquad \text{if } x \leq -3$$

Thus

$$I = \sqrt{x^2 + 2x - 3} - 2 \, \text{Sec}^{-1} \frac{x+1}{2} \qquad \text{if } x \geq 1$$

and, adding the constant 4π,

$$I = \sqrt{x^2 + 2x - 3} + 2 \, \text{Sec}^{-1} \frac{x+1}{2} \qquad \text{if } x \leq -3$$

It is also possible to use the tangent substitution to evaluate integrals of the form

$$\int \frac{dx}{(ax^2 + bx + c)^n}$$

where n is a positive integer and the constant coefficients satisfy $b^2 - 4ac < 0$.

EXAMPLE   Evaluate $I = \displaystyle\int \frac{dx}{(2x^2 - 3x + 2)^3}$.

Solution   Upon completing the square, we obtain

$$(2x^2 - 3x + 2)^3 = 8\left[\left(x - \frac{3}{4}\right)^2 + \left(\frac{\sqrt{7}}{4}\right)^2\right]^3$$

and so we let $x - \dfrac{3}{4} = \dfrac{\sqrt{7}}{4} \tan \theta$ and get

$$I = \frac{\sqrt{7}}{32} \int \frac{\sec^2 \theta \, d\theta}{\left[\dfrac{7}{16} (\tan^2 \theta + 1)\right]^3} = \frac{2^7 \sqrt{7}}{7^3} \int \cos^4 \theta \, d\theta$$

We now use the reduction formula

$$\int \cos^n \theta \, d\theta = \frac{1}{n} \cos^{n-1} \theta \sin \theta + \frac{n-1}{n} \int \cos^{n-2} \theta \, d\theta$$

to obtain

$$\int \cos^4 \theta \, d\theta = \frac{1}{4} \cos^3 \theta \sin \theta + \frac{3}{4} \int \cos^2 \theta \, d\theta$$

$$= \frac{1}{4} \cos^3 \theta \sin \theta + \frac{3}{8} \cos \theta \sin \theta + \frac{3}{8} \theta$$

Consult Fig. 7-2 to see that, since $\tan \theta = (4x - 3)/\sqrt{7}$, we have

$$\cos \theta = \frac{\sqrt{7}}{2\sqrt{4x^2 - 6x + 4}} \qquad \text{and} \qquad \sin \theta = \frac{4x - 3}{2\sqrt{4x^2 - 6x + 4}}$$

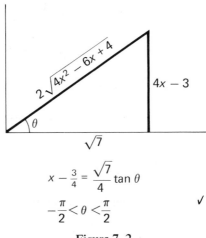

$$x - \frac{3}{4} = \frac{\sqrt{7}}{4} \tan \theta$$

$$-\frac{\pi}{2} < \theta < \frac{\pi}{2}$$

Figure 7-2

This yields

$$\int \cos^4 \theta \, d\theta = \frac{7\sqrt{7}(4x - 3)}{2^6(4x^2 - 6x + 4)^2} + \frac{3\sqrt{7}(4x - 3)}{2^5(4x^2 - 6x + 4)} + \frac{3}{8} \text{Tan}^{-1} \frac{4x - 3}{\sqrt{7}}$$

and therefore

$$I = \frac{2^7\sqrt{7}}{7^3} \int \cos^4 \theta \, d\theta$$

$$= \frac{4x - 3}{14(2x^2 - 3x + 2)^2} + \frac{6(4x - 3)}{49(2x^2 - 3x + 2)} + \frac{48\sqrt{7}}{343} \text{Tan}^{-1} \frac{4x - 3}{\sqrt{7}}$$

EXERCISES

In 1–30, evaluate the integrals.

1. $\displaystyle\int \frac{dx}{(4 + x^2)^{3/2}}$

11. $\displaystyle\int \frac{\sqrt{4 - t^2}\, dt}{t^4}$

21. $\displaystyle\int \frac{dx}{(x^2 + x + 1)^2}$

2. $\displaystyle\int \sqrt{x^2 + 9}\, dx$

12. $\displaystyle\int \frac{dx}{(9x^2 - 1)^{3/2}}$

22. $\displaystyle\int \frac{dx}{(x^2 - x + 1)^2}$

3. $\displaystyle\int \frac{dx}{(4 - x^2)^{3/2}}$

13. $\displaystyle\int \frac{dx}{x^2\sqrt{9 + 4x^2}}$

23. $\displaystyle\int \frac{(x + 1)\, dx}{(x^2 + x + 1)^2}$

4. $\displaystyle\int \frac{dx}{\sqrt{x^2 - 9}}$

14. $\displaystyle\int \sqrt{2x - x^2}\, dx$

24. $\displaystyle\int \frac{dx}{(2x^2 + 4x + 5)^2}$

5. $\displaystyle\int \sqrt{9 - x^2}\, dx$

15. $\displaystyle\int \frac{dx}{\sqrt{2x - x^2}}$

25. $\displaystyle\int_0^2 t^2\sqrt{4 - t^2}\, dt$

6. $\displaystyle\int \sqrt{x^2 - 9}\, dx$

16. $\displaystyle\int \frac{\sqrt{x}\, dx}{\sqrt{4 - x}}$

26. $\displaystyle\int_3^4 \frac{dx}{x^2\sqrt{x^2 - 4}}$

7. $\displaystyle\int \frac{dx}{x\sqrt{x^2 - 1}}$

17. $\displaystyle\int \frac{\sqrt{4 - x}}{\sqrt{x}}\, dx$

27. $\displaystyle\int_1^5 \frac{dx}{\sqrt{6x - x^2}}$

8. $\displaystyle\int \frac{dx}{x\sqrt{1 - x^2}}$

18. $\displaystyle\int \frac{dy}{\sqrt{12 - 4y - y^2}}$

28. $\displaystyle\int_0^a \sqrt{a^2 - x^2}\, dx$

9. $\displaystyle\int \frac{dx}{x^2\sqrt{16 - x^2}}$

19. $\displaystyle\int \frac{e^t\, dt}{\sqrt{9 - 4e^{2t}}}$

29. $\displaystyle\int_1^6 \frac{dx}{x\sqrt{x^2 + 10}}$

10. $\displaystyle\int \frac{\sqrt{4 - u^2}}{u^2}\, du$

20. $\displaystyle\int \frac{\cos x\, dx}{\sqrt{4 + \sin^2 x}}$

30. $\displaystyle\int_1^2 \frac{dx}{x^4\sqrt{x^2 + 2}}$

8 Integration of Rational Functions

A **rational function** is a function of the form

$$R(x) = \frac{a_m x^m + a_{m-1}x^{m-1} + \ldots + a_1 x + a_0}{b_n x^n + b_{n-1}x^{n-1} + \ldots + b_1 x + b_0}$$

where the a's and b's are constants with $a_m \neq 0$ and $b_n \neq 0$. That is, $R(x)$ is the quotient of two polynomials. If $m \geq n$, then the indicated quotient should be divided out by long division so as to express $R(x)$ as the sum of a polynomial and a proper rational function (in which the degree of the top is less than that of the bottom). For instance, if

$$R(x) = \frac{x^3 - 2x + 3}{x^2 - 2x - 3}$$

we apply long division to write

$$
\begin{array}{r}
x + 2 \\
x^2 - 2x - 3 \overline{\smash{\big)}\ x^3 \qquad\ - 2x + 3} \\
\underline{x^3 - 2x^2 - 3x} \\
2x^2 + \ x + 3 \\
\underline{2x^2 - 4x - 6} \\
5x + 9
\end{array}
$$

and so

$$R(x) = x + 2 + \frac{5x + 9}{x^2 - 2x - 3}$$

The next step is to factor the bottom of our proper rational function into a product of linear factors (of the form $ax + b$) and of irreducible quadratic factors (of the form $ax^2 + bx + c$, where $b^2 - 4ac < 0$). In principle this can always be done, but in practice it may be difficult if not impossible. For instance,

$$x^2 - 2x - 3 = (x + 1)(x - 3)$$

and

$$2x^5 - x^4 + 2x - 1 = x^4(2x - 1) + (2x - 1) = (2x - 1)(x^4 + 1)$$
$$= (2x - 1)(x^2 - \sqrt{2}x + 1)(x^2 + \sqrt{2}x + 1)$$

It is known that any proper rational function $P(x)$ can be decomposed as a finite sum of so-called **partial fractions**. The partial fractions have the form

$$\frac{A}{(ax + b)^k} \quad \text{or} \quad \frac{Bx + C}{(ax^2 + bx + c)^k}$$

where A, B, and C are constants and k is a positive integer. If the linear factor $ax + b$ occurs r times as a factor of the denominator of $P(x)$, then the above-mentioned decomposition has r summands of the first type:

$$\frac{A_1}{ax + b} + \frac{A_2}{(ax + b)^2} + \frac{A_3}{(ax + b)^3} + \ldots + \frac{A_r}{(ax + b)^r}$$

If an irreducible quadratic factor $ax^2 + bx + c$ of the denominator of $P(x)$ occurs s times, then the decomposition contains s summands of the second type:

$$\frac{B_1x + C_1}{ax^2 + bx + c} + \frac{B_2x + C_2}{(ax^2 + bx + c)^2} + \cdots + \frac{B_sx + C_s}{(ax^2 + bx + c)^s}$$

We now give three examples of such partial fraction decompositions.

EXAMPLE Decompose $P(x) = \dfrac{5x + 9}{x^2 - 2x - 3}$ into partial fractions.

Solution The denominator is $(x + 1)(x - 3)$, which has just two linear factors so that the decomposition has the form

$$P(x) = \frac{A}{x + 1} + \frac{B}{x - 3}$$

Multiply through by $(x + 1)(x - 3)$ to get

$$5x + 9 = A(x - 3) + B(x + 1) = (A + B)x + (-3A + B)$$

Equating coefficients of like powers of x yields

$$\begin{cases} A + B = 5 \\ -3A + B = 9 \end{cases}$$

Subtraction gives $4A = -4$, and so this system has the solution $A = -1$, and $B = 6$. Thus,

$$P(x) = \frac{-1}{x + 1} + \frac{6}{x - 3}$$

EXAMPLE Decompose $P(x) = \dfrac{8x^3 + 21x^2 + 18x + 5}{(2x + 3)^2(x^2 + x + 1)}$ into partial fractions.

Solution The linear factor $2x + 3$ occurs twice and so it contributes two summands while the irreducible quadratic factor contributes just one:

$$P(x) = \frac{A}{2x + 3} + \frac{B}{(2x + 3)^2} + \frac{Cx + D}{x^2 + x + 1}$$

Multiplying through by the denominator of $P(x)$, we get

$$8x^3 + 21x^2 + 18x + 5 = A(2x + 3)(x^2 + x + 1) + B(x^2 + x + 1)$$
$$+ (Cx + D)(2x + 3)^2$$
$$= (2A + 4C)x^3 + (5A + B + 12C + 4D)x^2$$
$$+ (5A + B + 9C + 12D)x + (3A + B + 9D)$$

Now we equate coefficients of like powers of x to get the system

$$\begin{cases} 2A & + 4C & = 8 \\ 5A + B + 12C + 4D = 21 \\ 5A + B + 9C + 12D = 18 \\ 3A + B & + 9D = 5 \end{cases}$$

To solve this system for the unknown constants A, B, C, and D, we first reduce it to a system of three equations in three unknowns as follows. Since B occurs in only three of the equations, we eliminate it by copying the first equation and then subtracting the second equation from each equation below it to obtain

$$\begin{cases} 2A + 4C & = 8 \\ - 3C + 8D = -3 \\ -2A - 12C + 5D = -16 \end{cases}$$

Next we eliminate A by adding the third equation to the first and we copy the second equation:

$$\begin{cases} -8C + 5D = -8 \\ -3C + 8D = -3 \end{cases}$$

Now we multiply the first of these by 3 and the second by -8 to get

$$\begin{cases} -24C + 15D = -24 \\ 24C - 64D = 24 \end{cases}$$

Adding gives $-49D = 0$ and so $D = 0$. Thus $C = 1$. Working backwards, we get $A = 2$ and then $B = -1$. Thus

$$P(x) = \frac{2}{2x + 3} - \frac{1}{(2x + 3)^2} + \frac{x}{x^2 + x + 1}$$

EXAMPLE Decompose $P(x) = \dfrac{3x^4 + 12x^3 + 43x^2 + 59x + 75}{x(x^2 + 2x + 5)^2}$ into partial fractions.

Solution This time we write

$$P(x) = \frac{A}{x} + \frac{Bx + C}{x^2 + 2x + 5} + \frac{Dx + E}{(x^2 + 2x + 5)^2}$$

which leads to

$3x^4 + 12x^3 + 43x^2 + 59x + 75$
$\quad = A(x^2 + 2x + 5)^2 + (Bx^2 + Cx)(x^2 + 2x + 5) + Dx^2 + Ex$
$\quad = (A + B)x^4 + (4A + 2B + C)x^3 + (14A + 5B + 2C + D)x^2$
$\quad\quad\quad\quad\quad\quad\quad\quad\quad\quad\quad\quad + (20A + 5C + E)x + 25A$

We obtain the system

$$\begin{cases} A + B & = 3 \\ 4A + 2B + C & = 12 \\ 14A + 5B + 2C + D & = 43 \\ 20A \quad\quad + 5C \quad\quad + E = 59 \\ 25A & = 75 \end{cases}$$

which has the solution $A = 3$, $B = 0$, $C = 0$, $D = 1$, and $E = -1$. Therefore,

$$P(x) = \frac{3}{x} + \frac{x - 1}{(x^2 + 2x + 5)^2}$$

In order to integrate proper rational functions which we can decompose into partial fractions, it is sufficient to know how to integrate the two types of partial fractions. We now set down how to do that and then give some examples.

The type arising from linear factors $ax + b$ is easy. We make the substitution $u = ax + b$ and obtain

$$\int \frac{A\, dx}{(ax + b)^k} = \frac{A}{a} \int u^{-k}\, du$$

For the type arising from an irreducible quadratic factor $ax^2 + bx + c$ with $a > 0$, we first rewrite the partial fraction as

$$\frac{Bx + C}{(ax^2 + bx + c)^k} = \frac{B'(2ax + b)}{(ax^2 + bx + c)^k} + \frac{C'}{(ax^2 + bx + c)^k}$$

where $B' = B/2a$ and $C' = C - B'b$. Then we integrate the two fractions on the right separately. We substitute $u = ax^2 + bx + c$ to get

$$\int \frac{B'(2ax + b)\, dx}{(ax^2 + bx + c)^k} = B' \int u^{-k}\, du$$

For the other one, we factor a^k from the denominator and then complete the square to get

$$(ax^2 + bx + c)^k = a^k[u^2 + p^2]^k$$

where $u = x + b/2a$ and $p^2 = (4ac - b^2)/4a^2 > 0$. Next we make the trigonometric substitution $u = p \tan \theta$ and obtain

$$\int \frac{C'\, dx}{(ax^2 + bx + c)^k} = \frac{C'}{a^k} \int \frac{du}{(u^2 + p^2)^k} = \frac{C'}{a^k p^{2k-1}} \int \cos^{2k-2} \theta\, d\theta$$

Finally, a reduction formula can be used to evaluate the last integral.

It is *not* necessary to remember the formulas in the preceding two paragraphs. Just remember the techniques outlined there. The following examples illustrate these techniques.

EXAMPLE   Evaluate $I = \int \dfrac{x^3 - 2x + 3}{x^2 - 2x - 3} \, dx$.

Solution   As shown above,

$$\frac{x^3 - 2x + 3}{x^2 - 2x - 3} = x + 2 + \frac{5x + 9}{x^2 - 2x - 3} = x + 2 - \frac{1}{x + 1} + \frac{6}{x - 3}$$

Thus, integrating term by term,

$$I = \frac{1}{2}x^2 + 2x - \ln|x + 1| + 6 \ln|x - 3|$$

EXAMPLE   Evaluate the integral

$$I = \int \frac{8x^3 + 21x^2 + 18x + 5}{(2x + 3)^2(x^2 + x + 1)} \, dx$$

Solution   As seen in the second example (page 361) of this section,

$$I = \int \frac{2 \, dx}{2x + 3} - \frac{1}{2} \int (2x + 3)^{-2} \cdot 2 \, dx + \int \frac{x \, dx}{x^2 + x + 1}$$

$$= \ln|2x + 3| + \frac{1}{2}(2x + 3)^{-1} + \int \frac{x \, dx}{x^2 + x + 1}$$

In the last integral, we write the integrand in the form

$$\frac{x}{x^2 + x + 1} = \frac{1}{2} \cdot \frac{2x + 1}{x^2 + x + 1} - \frac{1}{2} \cdot \frac{1}{x^2 + x + 1}$$

so that the first term on the right is a constant times a rational function whose numerator is the derivative of the quadratic in its denominator and the second term on the right is whatever it has to be to make the identity true. That is, we write the numerator in the form $x = B'(2x + 1) + C' = 2B'x + B' + C'$, as above, where the quantity in parentheses is the derivative of the irreducible quadratic in the denominator and the constants B' and C' are whatever they must be to make this identity correct. Thus $2B' = 1$ and $B' + C' = 0$, so that $B' = 1/2$ and $C' = -1/2$. Now

$$\int \frac{x \, dx}{x^2 + x + 1} = \frac{1}{2} \ln(x^2 + x + 1) - \frac{1}{2} \int \frac{dx}{x^2 + x + 1}$$

To evaluate the last integral, we first complete the square for the quadratic and then use the formula

$$\int \frac{du}{u^2 + a^2} = \frac{1}{a} \operatorname{Tan}^{-1} \frac{u}{a}$$

to obtain

$$\frac{1}{2} \int \frac{dx}{\left(x + \frac{1}{2}\right)^2 + \left(\frac{\sqrt{3}}{2}\right)^2} = \frac{1}{\sqrt{3}} \operatorname{Tan}^{-1} \frac{2x + 1}{\sqrt{3}}$$

Finally, we put the pieces together and get

$$I = \ln|2x + 3| + \frac{1}{4x + 6} + \frac{1}{2} \ln (x^2 + x + 1) - \frac{1}{\sqrt{3}} \operatorname{Tan}^{-1} \frac{2x + 1}{\sqrt{3}}$$

EXAMPLE   Evaluate the integral

$$I = \int \frac{3x^4 + 12x^3 + 43x^2 + 59x + 75}{x(x^2 + 2x + 5)^2} \, dx$$

Solution   Consult the third example (page 362) of this section to see that

$$I = 3 \int \frac{dx}{x} + \int \frac{(x - 1) \, dx}{(x^2 + 2x + 5)^2}$$

To evaluate the last integral, write the integrand as

$$\frac{x - 1}{(x^2 + 2x + 5)^2} = \frac{2x + 2}{2(x^2 + 2x + 5)^2} - \frac{2}{(x^2 + 2x + 5)^2}$$

so that the first term on the right has the derivative of the quadratic $u = x^2 + 2x + 5$ as its numerator. That is, $x - 1 = B'(2x + 2) + C' = 2B'x + 2B' + C'$ so that $2B' = 1$ and $2B' + C' = -1$, from which we obtain $B' = 1/2$ and $C' = -2$. Now

$$\int \frac{2x + 2}{2(x^2 + 2x + 5)^2} \, dx = \frac{1}{2} \int u^{-2} \, du = -\frac{1}{2} u^{-1} = \frac{-1}{2(x^2 + 2x + 5)}$$

As for the remaining integral, we complete the square of the quadratic and then make the substitution $x + 1 = 2 \tan \theta$ to get

$$\int \frac{2 \, dx}{(x^2 + 2x + 5)^2} = 2 \int \frac{dx}{[(x + 1)^2 + 4]^2} = 2 \int \frac{2 \sec^2 \theta \, d\theta}{4^2 \sec^4 \theta} = \frac{1}{4} \int \cos^2 \theta \, d\theta$$

$$= \frac{1}{8} \int (\cos 2\theta + 1) \, d\theta = \frac{1}{16} \sin 2\theta + \frac{\theta}{8}$$

$$= \frac{1}{8} \sin \theta \cos \theta + \frac{1}{8} \theta = \frac{1}{4} \cdot \frac{x + 1}{x^2 + 2x + 5} + \frac{1}{8} \operatorname{Tan}^{-1} \frac{x + 1}{2}$$

Summarizing, we have

$$I = 3 \ln|x| - \frac{1}{2} \cdot \frac{1}{x^2 + 2x + 5} - \frac{1}{4} \cdot \frac{x + 1}{x^2 + 2x + 5} - \frac{1}{8} \text{Tan}^{-1} \frac{x + 1}{2}$$

$$= 3 \ln|x| - \frac{x + 3}{4(x^2 + 2x + 5)} - \frac{1}{8} \text{Tan}^{-1} \frac{x + 1}{2}$$

EXERCISES

In 1–24, evaluate the integrals.

1. $\displaystyle\int \frac{dx}{x^2 + 4x}$

2. $\displaystyle\int \frac{dx}{x - x^3}$

3. $\displaystyle\int \frac{x^2 - x + 2}{x^2 - 1} \, dx$

4. $\displaystyle\int \frac{x \, dx}{(x + 2)^3}$

5. $\displaystyle\int \frac{1 - x + 3x^2}{x^2 - x^3} \, dx$

6. $\displaystyle\int \frac{dx}{x^4 - 1}$

7. $\displaystyle\int \frac{dx}{x^3 + 1}$

8. $\displaystyle\int \frac{dx}{x^3 - 8}$

9. $\displaystyle\int \frac{dx}{x^3 + x}$

10. $\displaystyle\int \frac{x^2 + 4x - 4}{(x + 2)(x^2 + 4)} \, dx$

11. $\displaystyle\int \frac{dx}{x^5 + 6x^3 + 9x}$

12. $\displaystyle\int \frac{4x^2 + x + 4}{x^3 + 4x} \, dx$

13. $\displaystyle\int \frac{2x^3 - 3x^2 + 3x + 1}{2x^2 - 3x + 2} \, dx$

14. $\displaystyle\int \left(\frac{x + 1}{x^2 - 2x + 2}\right)^2 \, dx$

15. $\displaystyle\int \frac{2x^2 - 1}{(2x^2 - x + 1)^2} \, dx$

16. $\displaystyle\int \frac{dx}{x^4 + 16}$

17. $\displaystyle\int \frac{3x^3 - 2x^2 + 3x - 1}{x^4 - x^3 + x^2} \, dx$

18. $\displaystyle\int \frac{2x^4 - 4x^3 + 7x^2 - 4x + 1}{(x - 1)(x^2 - x + 1)^2} \, dx$

19. $\displaystyle\int_0^1 \frac{dx}{x^3 + 1}$

20. $\displaystyle\int_0^{\pi/2} \frac{\cos \theta \, d\theta}{\sin^2 \theta + \sin \theta + 1}$

21. $\displaystyle\int_0^1 \frac{dx}{e^x + e^{3x}}$

22. $\displaystyle\int_0^1 \frac{dx}{2x^2 + 3x + 1}$

23. $\displaystyle\int_0^1 \frac{x^2 + 3x + 1}{x^4 + x^2 + 1} \, dx$

24. $\displaystyle\int_0^2 \frac{x^5 \, dx}{(x^2 + 9)^2}$

9 The Half-angle Substitution

In order to integrate a function of the form $R(\cos\theta, \sin\theta)$, where $R(x,y)$ is a rational function of the two variables x and y (that is, $R(x,y)$ is the quotient of two polynomials in the two variables x and y), the substitution $t = \tan\frac{1}{2}\theta$ reduces the problem to that of integrating a rational function of the single variable t.

In fact, letting $t = \tan\frac{1}{2}\theta$, we have

$$\cos\theta = 2\cos^2\frac{1}{2}\theta - 1 = \frac{2}{\sec^2\frac{1}{2}\theta} - 1 = \frac{2}{1+t^2} - 1 = \frac{1-t^2}{1+t^2}$$

$$\sin\theta = 2\sin\frac{1}{2}\theta\cos\frac{1}{2}\theta = 2\frac{\tan\frac{1}{2}\theta}{\sec^2\frac{1}{2}\theta} = \frac{2t}{1+t^2}$$

and

$$dt = \left(\frac{1}{2}\sec^2\frac{1}{2}\theta\right)d\theta = \frac{1}{2}(1+t^2)\,d\theta$$

so that

$$d\theta = \frac{2\,dt}{1+t^2}$$

Thus

$$\int R(\cos\theta,\sin\theta)\,d\theta = \int R\left(\frac{1-t^2}{1+t^2}, \frac{2t}{1+t^2}\right)\frac{2\,dt}{1+t^2}$$

which is the integral of a rational function of t.

EXAMPLE   Evaluate $I = \int \dfrac{d\theta}{1+\sin\theta}$.

Solution   The above substitution yields

$$I = \int \frac{\dfrac{2\,dt}{1+t^2}}{1+\dfrac{2t}{1+t^2}} = \int \frac{2\,dt}{(t+1)^2} = -\frac{2}{t+1} = -\frac{2}{1+\tan\frac{1}{2}\theta}$$

EXAMPLE Use the above substitution to evaluate:

(a) $\displaystyle\int \sec\theta\, d\theta$ (b) $\displaystyle\int \csc\theta\, d\theta$

Solution (a) We have

$$\int \sec\theta\, d\theta = \int \frac{d\theta}{\cos\theta} = \int \frac{1+t^2}{1-t^2}\cdot\frac{2\,dt}{1+t^2} = \int \frac{2\,dt}{1-t^2}$$

$$= \int \left(\frac{1}{1+t} - \frac{-1}{1-t}\right) dt = \ln\left|\frac{1+t}{1-t}\right| = \ln\left|\frac{1+\tan\frac{1}{2}\theta}{1-\tan\frac{1}{2}\theta}\right|$$

(b) $\displaystyle\int \csc\theta\, d\theta = \int \frac{1+t^2}{2t}\cdot\frac{2\,dt}{1+t^2} = \ln|t| = \ln\left|\tan\frac{1}{2}\theta\right|$

EXAMPLE Evaluate $\displaystyle I = \int \frac{16\,dx}{3\cos 4x + 1}$.

Solution First substitute $\theta = 4x$ and then use the half-angle substitution as above to get

$$I = \int \frac{4\,d\theta}{3\cos\theta + 1}$$

$$= \int \frac{\dfrac{8\,dt}{1+t^2}}{3\dfrac{1-t^2}{1+t^2}+1} = \int \frac{8\,dt}{4-2t^2} = \sqrt{2}\int \left(\frac{1}{\sqrt{2}+t} - \frac{-1}{\sqrt{2}-t}\right) dt$$

$$= \sqrt{2}\ln\left|\frac{\sqrt{2}+t}{\sqrt{2}-t}\right| = \sqrt{2}\ln\left|\frac{\sqrt{2}+\tan 2x}{\sqrt{2}-\tan 2x}\right|$$

EXERCISES

In 1–12, use the half-angle substitution to evaluate the integrals.

1. $\displaystyle\int \frac{d\theta}{4+5\sec\theta}$

2. $\displaystyle\int \frac{d\theta}{5+4\cos\theta}$

3. $\displaystyle\int \frac{d\theta}{\cos\theta + \sin\theta + 1}$

4. $\displaystyle\int \frac{d\theta}{6+4\sec\theta}$

5. $\displaystyle\int \frac{d\theta}{\tan\theta + \sin\theta}$

6. $\displaystyle\int \frac{d\theta}{\cos\theta - \sin\theta + 1}$

7. $\displaystyle\int \frac{dx}{1-\tan 2x}$

8. $\displaystyle\int \frac{d\theta}{2+\sin\theta}$

9. $\displaystyle\int_{\pi/3}^{\pi/2} \frac{d\theta}{\tan\theta - \sin\theta}$

10. $\displaystyle\int_{0}^{\pi/3} \frac{d\theta}{1+\tan\theta}$

11. $\displaystyle\int_{0}^{\pi} \frac{d\theta}{3+\cos\theta + 2\sin}$

12. $\displaystyle\int_{0}^{\pi/2} \frac{\sin 2\theta\, d\theta}{2+\cos\theta}$

10   Some Miscellaneous Techniques

Many integrals can be simplified by the **reciprocal substitution:**

$$x = \frac{1}{u} \quad \text{and} \quad dx = -\frac{du}{u^2}$$

EXAMPLE   Evaluate $I = \displaystyle\int \frac{\sqrt[3]{x^2 - x^3}}{x^3}\, dx.$

Solution   The reciprocal substitution yields

$$I = \int \frac{\sqrt[3]{u-1}}{u} \cdot u^3 \cdot \frac{du}{-u^2} = -\int (u-1)^{1/3}\, du$$

$$= -\frac{3}{4}(u-1)^{4/3} = -\frac{3}{4}\left(\frac{1-x}{x}\right)^{4/3}$$

EXAMPLE   Evaluate $I = \displaystyle\int_{1/2}^{1} \frac{dx}{x\sqrt{4x - x^2}}.$

Solution   The reciprocal substitution yields

$$I = \int_{2}^{1} u \cdot \frac{u}{\sqrt{4u-1}} \cdot \left(-\frac{du}{u^2}\right) = \int_{1}^{2} (4u-1)^{-1/2}\, du$$

$$= \frac{1}{2}(4u-1)^{1/2}\Big|_{1}^{2} = \frac{\sqrt{7}-\sqrt{3}}{2}$$

Warning. When making a substitution in a definite integral, it is important that the new variable vary continuously over its interval of integration as the old variable varies over its interval of integration. This is pointed up by the following example. It would seem that the reciprocal substitution gives

$$\int_{-1/2}^{1/2} \frac{dx}{(1+x^2)^{3/2}} = \int_{-2}^{2} \frac{|u|^3}{(u^2+1)^{3/2}} \cdot \left(-\frac{du}{u^2}\right)$$

$$= -\int_{-2}^{2} |u|\,(u^2+1)^{-3/2}\, du = -2\int_{0}^{2} u(u^2+1)^{-3/2}\, du$$

$$= 2(u^2+1)^{-1/2}\Big|_{0}^{2} = \frac{2}{\sqrt{5}} - 2 < -1$$

This is surely nonsense, since the integrand in the original integral is positive and continuous for all real values of x. That original integral does exist and its value is positive. The trouble is that $u = 1/x$ is not continuous for $-1/2 \leqq x \leqq 1/2$. The value of the original integral can be found by using the substitution $x = \tan \theta$ for $-\alpha \leq \theta \leq \alpha$, where $0 < \alpha < \pi/2$ and $\tan \alpha = 1/2$:

$$\int_{-1/2}^{1/2} \frac{dx}{(1 + x^2)^{3/2}} = \int_{-\alpha}^{\alpha} \frac{\sec^2 \theta \, d\theta}{\sec^3 \theta} = \int_{-\alpha}^{\alpha} \cos \theta \, d\theta$$

$$= \sin \theta \Big|_{-\alpha}^{\alpha} = 2 \sin \alpha = \frac{2}{\sqrt{5}}$$

An integral of the type $\displaystyle\int \frac{d\theta}{a \sin \theta + b \cos \theta}$ can be evaluated by the

method of section 9. However, here is an easier way. Choose α such that $\cos \alpha = a/c$ and $\sin \alpha = b/c$ where $c = \sqrt{a^2 + b^2} > 0$, and then notice that

$$a \sin \theta + b \cos \theta = c(\sin \theta \cos \alpha + \cos \theta \sin \alpha) = c \sin (\theta + \alpha)$$

Thus

$$\int \frac{d\theta}{a \sin \theta + b \cos \theta} = \frac{1}{c} \int \csc (\theta + \alpha) \, d\theta = \frac{1}{c} \ln |\cot (\theta + \alpha) - \csc (\theta + \alpha)|$$

$$= \frac{1}{c} \ln \left| \frac{\cos (\theta + \alpha) - 1}{\sin (\theta + \alpha)} \right|$$

Multiplication within the absolute value sign by $\dfrac{c}{c}$ and the addition formula for $\cos (\theta + \alpha)$ now gives us

$$\frac{1}{c} \ln \left| \frac{a \cos \theta - b \sin \theta - c}{a \sin \theta + b \cos \theta} \right|$$

As usual, this is valid on those intervals of θ's on which $\sin (\theta + \alpha) \neq 0$.

EXAMPLE Evaluate $I = \displaystyle\int \frac{d\theta}{2 \sin \theta - \cos \theta}$.

Solution We may apply the above technique with $a = 2$, $b = -1$, and $c = \sqrt{5}$. Thus,

$$I = \frac{1}{\sqrt{5}} \ln \left| \frac{2 \cos \theta + \sin \theta - \sqrt{5}}{2 \sin \theta - \cos \theta} \right|$$

In case an integrand contains a single linear factor $ax + b$ which appears raised to more than one rational power and n is the least common denominator of those rational exponents, then the substitution $u^n = ax + b$ may help.

EXAMPLE Evaluate the integral

$$I = \int \frac{dx}{\sqrt{x} \sqrt[3]{x} (1 + \sqrt[3]{x})}$$

Solution Let $x = u^6$ and $dx = 6u^5 \, du$, so that

$$I = \int \frac{6u^5 \, du}{u^3 \cdot u^2(1 + u^2)} = 6 \int \frac{du}{(1 + u^2)} = 6 \, \text{Tan}^{-1} \, u = 6 \, \text{Tan}^{-1} \, \sqrt[6]{x}$$

Sometimes we are faced with integrals which contain absolute values in the integrand. To evaluate such integrals, it is usually best to get rid of the absolute value first by using either $|u| = \sqrt{u^2}$ or the definition:

$$|u| = u \quad \text{if } u \geqq 0$$
$$|u| = -u \quad \text{if } u < 0$$

EXAMPLE Evaluate $\displaystyle\int_{-2}^{3} |x^2 - 1| \, dx$.

Solution Since $x^2 - 1 = (x - 1)(x + 1)$, we have $x^2 - 1 \geqq 0$ if $x \leqq -1$ or $x \geqq 1$, while $x^2 - 1 \leqq 0$ if $-1 \leqq x \leqq 1$. We break the interval of integration into three parts: $|x^2 - 1| = x^2 - 1$ on $[-2,-1]$, $|x^2 - 1| = 1 - x^2$ on $[-1,1]$, and $|x^2 - 1| = x^2 - 1$ on $[1,3]$. Thus

$$\int_{-2}^{3} |x^2 - 1| \, dx = \int_{-2}^{-1} (x^2 - 1) \, dx + \int_{-1}^{1} (1 - x^2) \, dx + \int_{1}^{3} (x^2 - 1) \, dx$$

$$= \left(\frac{1}{3}x^3 - x\right)\Big|_{-2}^{-1} + \left(x - \frac{1}{3}x^3\right)\Big|_{-1}^{1} + \left(\frac{1}{3}x^3 - x\right)\Big|_{1}^{3}$$

$$= \left(-\frac{1}{3} + 1\right) - \left(-\frac{8}{3} + 2\right) + \left(1 - \frac{1}{3}\right) - \left(-1 + \frac{1}{3}\right) + (9 - 3) - \left(\frac{1}{3} - 1\right)$$

$$= \frac{2}{3} + \frac{2}{3} + \frac{2}{3} + \frac{2}{3} + 6 + \frac{2}{3} = \frac{28}{3}$$

Notice that $\displaystyle\int_{-2}^{3} |x^2 - 1| \, dx \neq \left|\int_{-2}^{3} (x^2 - 1) \, dx\right| = \frac{20}{3}$.

The following exercises form a random mixture which may need any of the techniques of this chapter.

EXERCISES

In 1–38, evaluate the integrals.

1. $\displaystyle\int \frac{x \, dx}{5 + \sqrt{x}}$

2. $\displaystyle\int \frac{dx}{x^2\sqrt{4 + 9x^2}}$

3. $\displaystyle\int_{16}^{81} \frac{\sqrt{x} \, dx}{\sqrt{x} - \sqrt[4]{x}}$

4. $\displaystyle\int \frac{dx}{x\sqrt{4+9x^2}}$

5. $\displaystyle\int \frac{d\theta}{4\sin\theta - 5\cos\theta}$

6. $\displaystyle\int \frac{d\theta}{4+\cos\theta}$

7. $\displaystyle\int \frac{\ln x}{x}\,dx$

8. $\displaystyle\int e^x \cos x\,dx$

9. $\displaystyle\int x^2 \cos x\,dx$

10. $\displaystyle\int \frac{d\theta}{\sec\theta + \tan\theta}$

11. $\displaystyle\int_0^1 \frac{x^{5/2}\,dx}{x+4}$

12. $\displaystyle\int_3^8 \frac{dx}{\sqrt{x+1}(\sqrt{x+1}+9)}$

13. $\displaystyle\int \frac{\sin\sqrt{x}}{\sqrt{x}}\,dx$

14. $\displaystyle\int \frac{x\,dx}{\sqrt{x+2}}$

15. $\displaystyle\int \frac{dx}{x\sqrt{x^2+6x+1}}$

16. $\displaystyle\int x^2\sqrt{2x-1}\,dx$

17. $\displaystyle\int \tan^2 x \cos^3 x\,dx$

18. $\displaystyle\int \cos^5 x\,dx$

19. $\displaystyle\int \sin^2 \frac{1}{5}x\,dx$

20. $\displaystyle\int \cos 2x \cos x\,dx$

21. $\displaystyle\int_0^{\pi/2} \frac{\sin\theta\,d\theta}{1+\cos^2\theta}$

22. $\displaystyle\int \ln(x^2+4)\,dx$

23. $\displaystyle\int \frac{x^4+16}{x^4-16}\,dx$

24. $\displaystyle\int \tan^3 x\,dx$

25. $\displaystyle\int \frac{x^4-x^3+x^2+1}{x+x^3}\,dx$

26. $\displaystyle\int \frac{dx}{3\cos x - 2\sin x}$

27. $\displaystyle\int \frac{dx}{x^3-x^2+4x-4}\,dx$

28. $\displaystyle\int \sqrt{\tan\theta}\,d\theta$

29. $\displaystyle\int \frac{dx}{x\sqrt{25-x^2}}$

30. $\displaystyle\int \frac{dx}{\sqrt{x^2-x-1}}$

31. $\displaystyle\int \frac{1-\sqrt[3]{x}}{1-\sqrt{x}}\,dx$

32. $\displaystyle\int_0^{\pi/2} \frac{d\theta}{\sin\theta + \cos\theta}$

33. $\displaystyle\int_{-3}^3 |x+2|\,dx$

34. $\displaystyle\int_0^{2\pi} |\cos x|\,dx$

35. $\displaystyle\int_{-5}^{-1} \frac{|x+4|}{x}\,dx$

36. $\displaystyle\int_\pi^{2\pi} (\sin x)\cdot|\sin x|\,dx$

37. $\displaystyle\int_0^\pi (\cos x)\cdot|\cos x|\,dx$

38. $\displaystyle\int_{-3}^3 |(x^2-x-2)|\,dx$

11 Improper Integrals

To this point in the book all definite integrals that we have studied have been of the form $\int_a^b f(x)\,dx$, where (1) a and b are finite and (2) the function f is continuous on $[a,b]$.

We now define integrals with infinite limits of integration as follows. If a is finite and f is continuous on $[a,\infty[$, we define

$$\int_a^\infty f(x)\,dx = \lim_{b\to\infty} \int_a^b f(x)\,dx$$

if this limit exists. If the limit exists and is finite, we say that the **improper integral** $\int_a^\infty f(x)\,dx$ **converges**. Otherwise, we say that it **diverges**. Similarly, if b is finite and f is continuous on $]-\infty,b]$, we define

$$\int_{-\infty}^b f(x)\,dx = \lim_{a\to-\infty} \int_a^b f(x)\,dx$$

if this limit exists. If it exists and is finite, we say that this improper integral **converges**, and if not, we say it **diverges**. For functions f that are continuous everywhere on $]-\infty,\infty[$, we define

$$\int_{-\infty}^\infty f(x)\,dx = \int_{-\infty}^0 f(x)\,dx + \int_0^\infty f(x)\,dx$$

if both integrals on the right converge.

EXAMPLE Evaluate the improper integrals (a) $\int_1^\infty x^{-2}\,dx$,

(b) $\int_{-\infty}^{-2} x^{-3}\,dx$, (c) $\int_2^\infty (x\ln x)^{-1}\,dx$, and (d) $\int_{-\infty}^\infty (1+x^2)^{-1}\,dx$,

if they exist.

Solution (a) $\displaystyle\int_1^\infty x^{-2}\,dx = \lim_{b\to\infty} \int_1^b x^{-2}\,dx = \lim_{b\to\infty} (-1/x)\Big|_1^b$

$$= \lim_{b\to\infty} (1 - 1/b) = 1$$

(b) $\displaystyle\int_{-\infty}^{-2} x^{-3}\,dx = \lim_{a\to-\infty} (-x^{-2}/2)\Big|_a^{-2}$

$$= \lim_{a\to-\infty} (-1/8 + 1/2a^2) = -1/8$$

(c) $\displaystyle\int_2^\infty (x \ln x)^{-1}\, dx = \lim_{b\to\infty} \left[\ln (\ln x)\right] \Big|_2^b$

$\qquad\qquad = \lim_{b\to\infty} \left[\ln (\ln b) - \ln (\ln 2)\right] = \infty$

(d) $\displaystyle\int_{-\infty}^\infty (1+x^2)^{-1}\, dx = \int_{-\infty}^0 (1+x^2)^{-1}\, dx + \int_0^\infty (1+x^2)^{-1}\, dx$

$\qquad\qquad = \lim_{a\to-\infty} \mathrm{Tan}^{-1}\, x \Big|_a^0 + \lim_{b\to\infty} \mathrm{Tan}^{-1}x \Big|_0^b$

$\qquad\qquad = \lim_{a\to-\infty} (-\mathrm{Tan}^{-1}\, a) + \lim_{b\to\infty} \mathrm{Tan}^{-1}\, b$

$\qquad\qquad = -(-\pi/2) + \pi/2 = \pi$

Of these, (c) diverges and the other three converge.

Suppose that $-\infty < a < b < \infty$. If f is continuous on $[a,b]$ except at a, we define

$$\int_a^b f(x)\, dx = \lim_{s\to a^+} \int_s^b f(x)\, dx$$

if this limit exists. If f is continuous on $[a,b]$ except at b, we define

$$\int_a^b f(x)\, dx = \lim_{t\to b^-} \int_a^t f(x)\, dx$$

if this limit exists. In either of these cases, we say that the **improper integral** on the left side **converges** if the limit on the right side exists and is finite. Otherwise, we say that the integral **diverges**. If f is defined and continuous on $]a,b[$ but neither at a nor at b, we choose any c with $a < c < b$ and define

$$\int_a^b f(x)\, dx = \int_a^c f(x)\, dx + \int_c^b f(x)\, dx$$

provided that both integrals on the right side converge.

The most general integral that we will define is as follows. Suppose that $-\infty \le a < b \le \infty$, that $a = a_0 < a_1 < a_2 < \ldots < a_n = b$, and that f is continuous on $[a,b]$ (the corresponding bracket is reversed if a or b is infinite) except possibly at the finite number of points a_k ($0 \le k \le n$). Then we define

$$\int_a^b f(x)\, dx = \sum_{k=1}^n \int_{a_{k-1}}^{a_k} f(x)\, dx$$

provided that all n of the integrals on the right side exist and are finite.

EXAMPLE   Evaluate the improper integrals (if they exist):

(a) $\displaystyle\int_0^1 x^{-1/2}\, dx$ (b) $\displaystyle\int_{-1}^1 x^{-2}\, dx$

(c) $\displaystyle\int_{-1}^{1} x^{-3}\, dx$
(d) $\displaystyle\int_{0}^{\infty} \frac{dx}{x(1+|\ln x|)^2}$

Solution (a) The integrand is continuous on $]0,1]$, so that

$$\int_{0}^{1} x^{-1/2}\, dx = \lim_{s\to 0^+} 2x^{1/2}\Big|_{s}^{1} = \lim_{s\to 0^+} (2 - 2\sqrt{s}) = 2$$

(b) The integrand is continuous on $[-1,1]$ except at $x=0$, so that

$$\int_{-1}^{1} x^{-2}\, dx = \lim_{t\to 0^-} \int_{-1}^{t} x^{-2}\, dx + \lim_{s\to 0^+} \int_{s}^{1} x^{-2}\, dx$$

$$= \lim_{t\to 0^-} (-x^{-1})\Big|_{-1}^{t} + \lim_{s\to 0^+} (-x^{-1})\Big|_{s}^{1}$$

$$= \lim_{t\to 0^-} (-1/t - 1) + \lim_{s\to 0^+} (-1 + 1/s)$$

$$= \infty + \infty = \infty$$

Thus, this integral diverges to ∞.

(c) This integrand is continuous on $[-1,1]$ except at $x=0$. We have

$$\int_{0}^{1} x^{-3}\, dx = \lim_{s\to 0^+} (x^{-2}/(-2))\Big|_{s}^{1} = \lim_{s\to 0^+} (-1/2 + 1/(2s^2)) = \infty$$

and, similarly,

$$\int_{-1}^{0} x^{-3}\, dx = \lim_{t\to 0^-} (-1/(2t^2) + 1/2) = -\infty$$

Thus, the given integral does not exist.

(d) The integrand is continuous on $[0,\infty[$ except at $x=0$. We shall write the given integral as the sum of the integrals over $[1,\infty[$ and over $]0,1]$. We have

$$\int_{1}^{\infty} \frac{dx}{x(1+|\ln x|)^2} = \lim_{b\to\infty} \int_{1}^{b} \frac{dx}{x(1+\ln x)^2}$$

$$= \lim_{b\to\infty} \int_{1}^{1+\ln b} u^{-2}\, du = \lim_{b\to\infty} (-1/u)\Big|_{1}^{1+\ln b}$$

$$= \lim_{b\to\infty} (-1/(1+\ln b) + 1) = 1$$

where we made the substitution $u = 1 + \ln x$ to obtain the second equality. For the other part we have

$$\int_{0}^{1} \frac{dx}{x(1+|\ln x|)^2} = \lim_{a\to 0^+} \int_{a}^{1} \frac{dx}{x(1-\ln x)^2} = \lim_{b\to\infty} \int_{1}^{b} \frac{dz}{z(1+\ln z)^2} = 1$$

where we took $z = 1/x$ and $a = 1/b$ to get the second equality. The last equality follows from the first part. Adding these two results we see that

$$\int_0^\infty \frac{dx}{x(1 + |\ln x|)^2} = 1 + 1 = 2$$

E X E R C I S E S

In 1–25, evaluate each of the integrals if possible.

1. $\displaystyle\int_0^1 x^{-2/3}\, dx$

2. $\displaystyle\int_{-1}^0 x^{-2/3}\, dx$

3. $\displaystyle\int_{-1}^1 x^{-2/3}\, dx$

4. $\displaystyle\int_0^\infty e^{-x}\, dx$

5. $\displaystyle\int_1^\infty x e^{-x^2}\, dx$

6. $\displaystyle\int_{-\infty}^\infty e^{-|x|}\, dx$

7. $\displaystyle\int_0^\infty e^{-x} \sin x\, dx$

8. $\displaystyle\int_1^\infty \frac{dx}{x\sqrt{x^2 - 1}}$

9. $\displaystyle\int_{-\infty}^\infty \frac{\mathrm{Tan}^{-1} x\, dx}{1 + x^2}$

10. $\displaystyle\int_1^\infty \frac{dx}{\sqrt{x - 1}}$

11. $\displaystyle\int_0^2 \frac{dx}{(x - 1)^{4/5}}$

12. $\displaystyle\int_0^{\pi/2} \tan \theta\, d\theta$

13. $\displaystyle\int_0^{\pi/4} \frac{\sec^2 \theta\, d\theta}{\sqrt{1 - \tan \theta}}$

14. $\displaystyle\int_0^\infty \cos x\, dx$

15. $\displaystyle\int_{2/\pi}^\infty x^{-2} \cos (x^{-1})\, dx$

16. $\displaystyle\int_0^1 \frac{dx}{(1 - x)^{1/2}}$

17. $\displaystyle\int_{-\infty}^\infty \frac{dx}{(x^2 + 1)^2}$

18. $\displaystyle\int_0^\infty \frac{x\, dx}{(x^2 + 1)^2}$

19. $\displaystyle\int_0^1 \ln x\, dx$

20. $\displaystyle\int_0^1 \frac{\ln x\, dx}{\sqrt{x}}$

21. $\displaystyle\int_1^\infty \frac{\ln x\, dx}{x^2}$

22. $\displaystyle\int_{-1}^1 \frac{dx}{x}$

23. $\displaystyle\int_0^\infty \frac{dx}{(x - 1)(x - 2)}$

24. $\displaystyle\int_0^{\pi/2} \frac{d\theta}{1 - \sin \theta}$

25. $\displaystyle\int_0^\infty \frac{dx}{\sqrt{x}(x + 1)}$

Chapter 8

Applications of the Definite Integral

1 Areas

Recall that in Chapter 6 we saw that the definite integral may be used to find the area of a region bounded by the graphs of certain equations.

EXAMPLE Find the area bounded by the graphs of the equations $y = x^2$ and $y = x$.

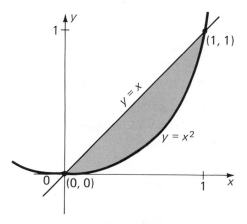

Figure 8–1

Solution The graphs obviously intersect in the points (0,0) and (1,1) (see Fig. 8-1). Thus, the desired area is given by

$$\int_0^1 (x - x^2)\, dx = \left[\frac{x^2}{2} - \frac{x^3}{3}\right]\Big|_0^1 = \frac{1}{6}$$

In Chapter 7 we learned how to integrate a wider class of functions, and we may now use this knowledge to find areas of more complicated regions.

EXAMPLE Find the area of the region bounded by the x-axis and one arch of the sine curve.

Solution Since all such regions are congruent, it suffices to compute the area of the region bounded by the x-axis ($y = 0$) and the portion of the sine curve $y = \sin x$ from $x = 0$ to $x = \pi$ (see Fig. 8-2).

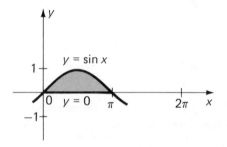

Figure 8–2

Thus, the area we want is given by

$$\int_0^\pi \sin x\, dx = -\cos x \Big|_0^\pi = -\cos \pi - (-\cos 0) = 1 + 1 = 2$$

EXAMPLE Find the area bounded by the graphs of the equations $x = y^2$ and $x = -2y^2 + 1$.

Solution To find the points of intersection of the two graphs, we solve the simultaneous system

$$\begin{cases} x = y^2 \\ x = -2y^2 + 1 \end{cases}$$

Subtraction of the equations yields $3y^2 = 1$ or $y = \pm\dfrac{\sqrt{3}}{3}$. Solving for x

now yields $x = \dfrac{1}{3}$. Thus, the points of intersection are $\left(\dfrac{1}{3}, \dfrac{\sqrt{3}}{3}\right)$ and $\left(\dfrac{1}{3}, \dfrac{-\sqrt{3}}{3}\right)$, as shown in Fig. 8-3.

We could integrate $y = \sqrt{x}$ from $x = 0$ to $x = \dfrac{1}{3}$ and then add to that the integral of $y = \sqrt{\dfrac{x-1}{-2}}$ from $\dfrac{1}{3}$ to 1. Finally, we could double the sum just obtained (because of the obvious symmetry) to find the desired area. However, it is simpler to integrate along the y-axis,

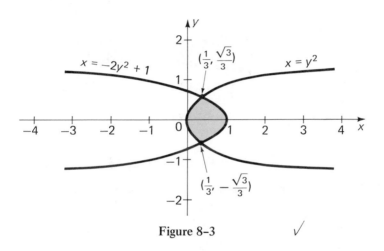

$$x = -2y^2 + 1 \qquad \left(\tfrac{1}{3}, \tfrac{\sqrt{3}}{3}\right) \qquad x = y^2$$

$$\left(\tfrac{1}{3}, -\tfrac{\sqrt{3}}{3}\right)$$

Figure 8–3 ✓

that is, to regard x as a function of y and integrate from $y = \dfrac{-\sqrt{3}}{3}$ to $y = \dfrac{\sqrt{3}}{3}$. The reader may find it helpful to turn the graph on its side, placing the y-axis in a horizontal position. We thus obtain

$$\int_{\frac{-\sqrt{3}}{3}}^{\frac{\sqrt{3}}{3}} ((-2y^2 + 1) - y^2)\, dy = \int_{\frac{-\sqrt{3}}{3}}^{\frac{\sqrt{3}}{3}} (-3y^2 + 1)\, dy = [-y^3 + y]\Big|_{\frac{-\sqrt{3}}{3}}^{\frac{\sqrt{3}}{3}}$$

$$= \frac{-\sqrt{3}}{9} + \frac{\sqrt{3}}{3} - \left(\frac{\sqrt{3}}{9} - \frac{\sqrt{3}}{3}\right) = \frac{-2\sqrt{3}}{9} + \frac{2\sqrt{3}}{3} = \frac{4\sqrt{3}}{9}$$

which is approximately .77.

EXAMPLE Find the area of the region bounded by the graphs of the equations $xy - 3y + 1 = 0$ and $x^2 y + y = 1$.

Solution Solving each equation for y, equating those solutions, and then solving that equation for x, we find that these curves intersect only at $(-2,1/5)$ and $(1,1/2)$, as shown in Fig. 8-4. Thus the required area A is

$$A = \int_{-2}^{1} \left[\frac{1}{1 + x^2} - \frac{1}{3 - x} \right] dx = \left[\text{Tan}^{-1} x + \ln (3 - x) \right] \Big|_{-2}^{1}$$
$$= \text{Tan}^{-1} 1 - \text{Tan}^{-1} (-2) + \ln 2 - \ln 5$$
$$= \pi/4 + \text{Tan}^{-1} 2 - \ln (5/2) \approx .98$$

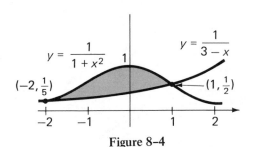

Figure 8–4

E X E R C I S E S

In 1–25, find the area of the region bounded by the given curves.

1. $y = x^2$, $x = y^2$
2. $y = x^2$, $x + y = 2$
3. $y = x^3$, $x + y = 2$, $y = 0$
4. $y = x^4$, $x = y^4$
5. $x - 2y + 3 = 0$, $x + 4y = 9$, $x + y = 6$
6. $y = x - 1$, $x + y = 1$, $2y = x^2 - 2x + 2$
7. $y = \cos x$, $y = \sin x$, $\pi/4 \leq x \leq 5\pi/4$
8. $y = e^{2x}$, $y = 6 - e^x$, $x = -\ln 3$
9. $x + 2 = y^2$, $x + y^2 = 6$
10. $x + y^2 = 4$, $x + 4y = 4$
11. $x^3 = 2y^2$, $x = 0$, $y = -2$
12. $y = 2x^3 - 3x^2 - 9x$, $y = x^3 - 2x^2 - 3x$, $x \geq 0$
13. $y = |x|$, $y = x^2 - x - 2$
14. $y = x^2 - x$, $y = x - x^2$
15. $y = |x - 1| + |x + 1|$, $y = 4 - x^2$
16. $y = x + |x|$, $y = x + 2$
17. $y = |x| - x$, $x + y = 4$
18. $y = |x| - x$, $y = x^2 - x - 2$
19. $2x^2 - 2y = 1$, $y(x^2 + 1) = 1$

20. $xy = 2,\ x + y = 3$

21. $xy = 5,\ x = y^2 - 7y + 11$

22. $y = \tan x,\ y = \cot x,\ y = \sqrt{3},\ 0 < x < \dfrac{\pi}{2}$

23. $y(x + 4) = 40,\ y = x^2 - 6x + 13,\ 1 \leq x \leq 4$

24. $y = \tan x,\ y = 0,\ \pi y = 2\pi - 4x,\ 0 \leq x \leq \pi/2$

25. $y = \sec x,\ y = \csc x,\ y = 1,\ 0 \leq x \leq \pi/2$

2 Solids of Revolution

Consider the problem of determining the "volume" of a solid object obtained by taking a given bounded region in a plane and revolving it completely about a given line in that plane that does not cut across the region. In this section we study two methods of finding the "volume" of such a solid. Both methods are based upon definite integration and the formula

$$V = \pi r^2 h$$

for the volume V of a right circular cylinder having a circular base of radius r and height h.

EXAMPLE   Suppose that $a > 0$ is given and that the region bounded by the x-axis and the semicircle $y = \sqrt{a^2 - x^2}$ is revolved about the x-axis to obtain a solid ball of radius a (see Fig. 8-5). Find the volume of this ball.

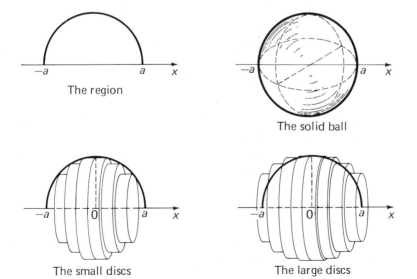

The region

The solid ball

The small discs

The large discs

Figure 8-5

Solution   Let us subdivide the x-axis from $-a$ to a into small subintervals of length Δx. Call this subdivision $P = \{-a = x_0 < x_1 < x_2 < \ldots < x_n = a\}$, where $x_k - x_{k-1} = \Delta x$ for $k = 1, 2, \ldots, n$. On each interval $[x_{k-1}, x_k]$ we erect two vertical cylindrical discs. The smaller has radius equal to the minimum, m_k, of the function $y = \sqrt{a^2 - x^2}$ on the interval $[x_{k-1}, x_k]$. The larger has radius equal to the maximum, M_k, of the function $y = \sqrt{a^2 - x^2}$ on the interval $[x_{k-1}, x_k]$. The volume of the smaller disc is $\pi m_k^2 \, \Delta x$ and the volume of the larger disc is $\pi M_k^2 \, \Delta x$. If we sum the volumes of all the smaller discs, we obtain a lower sum for the desired volume because the union of the small discs lies inside the ball. Also, if we sum the volumes of all the larger discs, we obtain an upper sum for the desired volume because the ball lies inside the union of these. By the methods of Chapter 6, these two sums approach the same limit as $\Delta x \to 0$, namely,

$$\int_{-a}^{a} \pi [f(x)]^2 \, dx$$

where $f(x) = y = \sqrt{a^2 - x^2}$.

Thus,

$$V = \int_{-a}^{a} \pi \Big[f(x) \Big]^2 \, dx = \int_{-a}^{a} \pi (a^2 - x^2) \, dx$$

$$= \pi \Big[a^2 x - \frac{x^3}{3} \Big] \Big|_{-a}^{a} = \pi \Big[\Big(a^3 - \frac{a^3}{3} \Big) - \Big(-a^3 + \frac{a^3}{3} \Big) \Big]$$

$$= \frac{4}{3} \pi a^3$$

This, at long last, is a rigorous justification for the well-known formula for the volume of a spherical solid of radius a,

$$V = \frac{4}{3} \pi a^3$$

In general, suppose R is the region bounded between two vertical lines $x = a$ and $x = b$ ($a < b$) and the graphs of two functions f and g which are defined and continuous on $[a, b]$ ($f(x) \leqq g(x)$ for $a \leqq x \leqq b$). Suppose l is the horizontal line having equation $y = c$ ($f(x) \geqq c$ for $a \leqq x \leqq b$). In order to find the volume V of the solid S swept out by revolving R completely about l, we proceed as follows (see Fig. 8-6). First, fix attention on any particular x between a and b and then consider a vertical slice across R of very small width dx that lies along the vertical line through our fixed x. When this slice is revolved about l, we obtain a washer (as on a bolt) of inner radius $f(x) - c$, outer

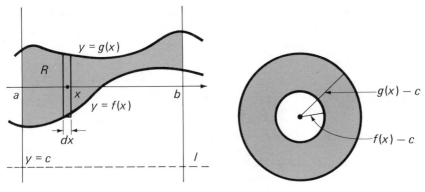

Figure 8–6

radius $g(x) - c$, and thickness dx. The volume dV of this washer is the difference of the volumes of two right circular cylinders of these radii and of height dx. Thus

$$dV = \pi[g(x) - c]^2 dx - \pi[f(x) - c]^2 dx$$
$$= \pi\{[g(x) - c]^2 - [f(x) - c]^2\} dx$$

The volume V of S is found by using a definite integral to "add up" these increments of volume dV as x varies from a to b. We have

$$V = \int_a^b dV = \pi \int_a^b \{[g(x) - c]^2 - [f(x) - c]^2\}\ dx$$

EXAMPLE Find the volume of the solid obtained by revolving the region bounded by $y = 2x - x^2$, $y = 2x$, and $x = 2$ about the line $y = -1$.

Solution First sketch a picture of the given region R and the line l (see Fig 8-7). Taking $f(x) = 2x - x^2$, $g(x) = 2x$, $a = 0$, $b = 2$, and $c = -1$, we have (factoring a difference of two squares)

$$dV = \pi\{[2x + 1]^2 - [2x - x^2 + 1]^2\}\ dx = \pi x^2(4x - x^2 + 2)\ dx$$
$$= \pi(4x^3 - x^4 + 2x^2)\ dx$$

and so

$$V = \pi \int_0^2 (4x^3 - x^4 + 2x^2)\ dx = \pi\left(x^4 - \frac{1}{5}x^5 + \frac{2}{3}x^3\right)\Big|_0^2$$
$$= \pi(16 - 32/5 + 16/3) = \frac{224\pi}{15}$$

In case the functions f or g are defined by more than one formula, it will be necessary to break the region R into several parts in order to evaluate the integral giving V.

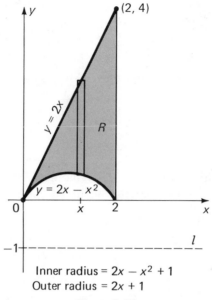

Inner radius = $2x - x^2 + 1$
Outer radius = $2x + 1$

Figure 8-7

EXAMPLE Find the volume of the solid swept out by revolving the region in the first quadrant bounded by $y = x^2$, $4y = x^2$, and $y = 1$ about the x-axis.

Solution The required region is shown in Fig. 8-8. Here we have $f(x) = x^2/4$ if $0 \le x \le 2$, $g(x) = x^2$ if $0 \le x \le 1$, and $g(x) = 1$ if $1 \le x \le 2$. Also, we have $a = 0$, $b = 2$, and $c = 0$. Let R_1 be the part of R to the left of $x = 1$ and let R_2 be the remaining part of R. If V_j, $j = 1, 2$, is the volume swept out by R_j, then we have

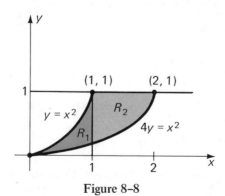

Figure 8-8

$$V_1 = \pi \int_0^1 \{[x^2]^2 - [x^2/4]^2\}\, dx = \frac{15\pi}{16} \int_0^1 x^4\, dx$$

$$= \frac{3\pi}{16} x^5 \Big|_0^1 = \frac{3\pi}{16}$$

and

$$V_2 = \pi \int_1^2 \{1^2 - [x^2/4]^2\}\, dx = \frac{\pi}{16} \int_1^2 (16 - x^4)\, dx$$

$$= \frac{\pi}{16}\left(16x - \frac{1}{5}x^5\right)\Big|_1^2 = \frac{49\pi}{80}$$

Thus the required volume is

$$V = V_1 + V_2 = \frac{15\pi + 49\pi}{80} = \frac{4\pi}{5}$$

If one wishes to revolve the given region R about a horizontal line that is above R, only slight modifications are needed in order to find the inner and outer radii of the incremental vertical washers. Here, as in all our applications, it is more useful to understand the technique involved than it is to memorize any particular formula.

EXAMPLE   Find the volume swept out by revolving the region shown in Fig. 8-7 about the line $y = 4$.

Solution   In this case, when we fix an x between 0 and 2, the corresponding washer has inner radius $4 - 2x$ and outer radius $4 - (2x - x^2)$. Thus

$$dV = \pi\{[4 - 2x + x^2]^2 - [4 - 2x]^2\}\, dx = \pi x^2(8 - 4x + x^2)dx$$
$$= \pi(8x^2 - 4x^3 + x^4)dx$$

and so

$$V = \pi \int_0^2 (8x^2 - 4x^3 + x^4)\, dx = \pi\left(\frac{8}{3}x^3 - x^4 + \frac{1}{5}x^5\right)\Big|_0^2$$

$$= \pi\left(\frac{64}{3} - 16 + \frac{32}{5}\right) = \frac{176\pi}{15}$$

If one wishes to find the volume swept out by revolving a region about a *vertical* line that does not cross the region, the same technique can be used except that we integrate along the y-axis.

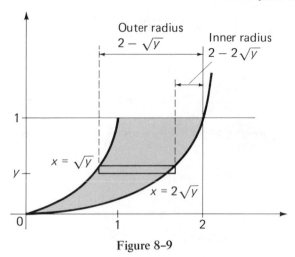

Figure 8–9

EXAMPLE Find the volume swept out by revolving the region shown in Fig. 8-8 about the line $x = 2$.

Solution Here we consider a horizontal slice across R determined by a fixed y between 0 and 1 (see Fig. 8-9). When this slice is revolved about $x = 2$, we obtain a horizontal washer having inner radius $2 - 2\sqrt{y}$, outer radius $2 - \sqrt{y}$, and thickness dy. Thus, the increment of volume contributed by this washer is

$$dV = \pi\{[2 - \sqrt{y}]^2 - [2 - 2\sqrt{y}]^2\}\, dy = \pi\sqrt{y}(4 - 3\sqrt{y})\, dy$$
$$= \pi(4y^{1/2} - 3y)\, dy$$

Therefore

$$V = \pi\int_0^1 (4y^{1/2} - 3y)\, dy = \pi\left(\frac{8}{3}y^{3/2} - \frac{3}{2}y^2\right)\Big|_0^1 = \frac{7\pi}{6}$$

The method we have just been discussing is the **washer method** for finding the volume of a solid of revolution. Our second method for solving the same problem is the **shell method,** which we now describe. Which, if either, of these two methods is preferable depends upon the region R in question.

Let R be the region bounded by two vertical lines $x = a$ and $x = b$ ($a < b$) and the graphs of two functions f and g which are continuous on $[a,b]$. Suppose $f(x) \leq g(x)$ for $a \leq x \leq b$. To find the volume of the solid S which is swept out when R is revolved about a vertical line $x = c$ ($c \leq a$ or $b \leq c$), we proceed as follows. For any fixed x between a and b, consider a slice across R along the vertical line through x that has a very small width dx (see Fig. 8-10). We revolve this slice

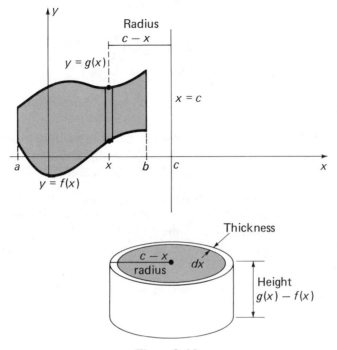

Figure 8–10

about the line $x = c$ and thereby obtain a cylindrical shell (curved part of an ordinary tin can) having height $g(x) - f(x)$ and thickness dx. The volume dV of this shell is approximated by its circumference $2\pi |c - x|$ times its height times its thickness:

$$dV = 2\pi |c - x| [g(x) - f(x)]dx$$

One finds V by using integration to "add up" these increments as x varies from a to b:

$$V = 2\pi \int_a^b dV = 2\pi \int_a^b |c - x| [g(x) - f(x)]\, dx$$

Of course $|c - x| = x - c$ if $c \leqq a$ while $|c - x| = c - x$ if $c \geqq b$.

EXAMPLE Find the volume of the solid swept out by revolving the region R of Fig. 8-7 about the line $x = 2$.

Solution For a fixed x between 0 and 2 the cylindrical shell obtained by revolving the slice shown in Fig. 8-7 about $x = 2$ has radius $2 - x$, height $2x - (2x - x^2) = x^2$, and thickness dx. Thus

$$dV = 2\pi (2 - x)x^2 \, dx = 2\pi (2x^2 - x^3) \, dx$$

and

$$V = 2\pi \int_0^2 (2x^2 - x^3)\, dx = 2\pi \left(\frac{2}{3}x^3 - \frac{1}{4}x^4 \right) \Big|_0^2$$
$$= 2\pi \left(\frac{16}{3} - 4 \right) = \frac{8\pi}{3}$$

EXAMPLE Use the shell method to find the volume of the solid swept out by revolving the region R shown in Fig. 8-9 about the x-axis. [Compare this with the fifth example of this section.]

Solution In this case we subdivide (integrate along) the y-axis. For a fixed y between 0 and 1, the cylindrical shell obtained by revolving the slice across R of width dy and along the horizontal line through y has radius y, height $2\sqrt{y} - \sqrt{y} = \sqrt{y}$, and thickness dy. Thus

$$dV = 2\pi y \cdot \sqrt{y}\, dy = 2\pi y^{3/2}\, dy$$

and

$$V = 2\pi \int_0^1 y^{3/2}\, dy = \frac{4\pi}{5} y^{5/2} \Big|_0^1 = \frac{4\pi}{5}$$

EXAMPLE Prove that the formula $V = \frac{1}{3}\pi a^2 h$ for the volume of a right circular cone having base radius a and height h is correct.

Solution Such a cone is obtained by revolving the triangular region R bounded by $x = h$, $hy = ax$, and the x-axis about the x-axis (see Fig. 8-11). If we fix x between 0 and h, then the corresponding

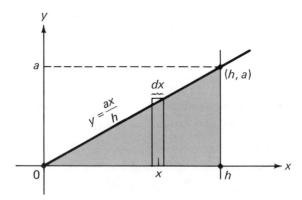

Figure 8–11

cross-sectional vertical disc has volume $dV = \pi(ax/h)^2 \, dx$ so that

$$V = \int_0^h dV = \frac{\pi a^2}{h^2} \int_0^h x^2 \, dx = \frac{1}{3}\pi a^2 h$$

Alternatively, if we fix y between 0 and a (see Fig. 8-12), then the corresponding cylindrical shell has radius y, height $h - (hy/a)$, and thickness dy so that its volume is

$$dV = 2\pi y[h - (hy/a)] \, dy = 2\pi h[y - y^2/a] \, dy$$

and so

$$V = 2\pi h \int_0^a [y - y^2/a] \, dy = 2\pi h[y^2/2 - y^3/3a]\Big|_0^a$$
$$= 2\pi h[a^2/2 - a^2/3] = \pi a^2 h/3$$

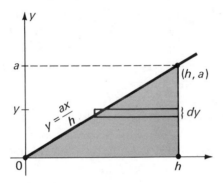

Figure 8–12

EXERCISES

In 1–10, use the washer method to find the volume of the solid obtained by revolving the region bounded by the given curves about the given line.

1. $y = x^2$, $y = x$; about x-axis
2. $y = x^2$, $y = x$; about y-axis
3. $y = 1 - x^2$, x-axis; about x-axis
4. $y = 1 - x^2$, x-axis; about $y = 1$
5. $6y^3 = x^2$, $y = \sqrt{1 - x^2}$; about x-axis
6. $y = x^2 - x^3$, x-axis; about x-axis
7. $y = \tan x$, $y = 0$, $x = \pi/4$; about $y = 1$
8. $y = e^x - 1$, $y = 0$, $x = 1$; about $y = -1$
9. $y = \ln x$, $y = 0$, $x = e$; about $x = 0$
10. $y = \sin x$, $y = 0$, $0 \le x \le \pi$; about $y = 0$

In 11–20, use the shell method to find the volume of the solid obtained by revolving the region bounded by the given curves about the given line.

11. $y=x^2$, $x=y^2$; about $x=1$
12. $y=x^2$, $x=y^2$; about $x=0$
13. $y=x$, $y=2x$, $x+y=6$; about $y=0$
14. $y=x$, $y=2x$, $x+y=6$; about $x=0$
15. $x+y=x^2$, $x^2+y=3$; about $x=2$
16. $x^2+y=4x$, $y=x$; about $x=3$
17. $y=\ln x$, $y=0$, $x=e$; about $x=0$
18. $y=\sin x$, $x=\pi/4$, $y=0$; about $x=0$
19. $\sqrt{x}+\sqrt{y}=1$, $x=0$, $y=0$; about $x=1$
20. $\sqrt{x}+\sqrt{y}=1$, $x=0$, $y=0$; about $x=0$

21. Find the volume of the torus (doughnut) obtained by revolving the circle $x^2+y^2=a^2$ about the line $x=b$, where $b \geq a > 0$.
22. Consider two constants $b \geq a > 0$. Find the volume generated by revolving the square region having vertices $(a,0)$, $(0,a)$, $(-a,0)$, and $(0,-a)$ about the line $x=b$.
23. Consider an ellipse $x^2/a^2 + y^2/b^2 = 1$, where $a > b > 0$.
    (a) Find the volume of the prolate spheroid (football) obtained by revolving this ellipse about its major axis.
    (b) Find the volume of the oblate spheroid (pill) obtained by revolving this ellipse about its minor axis.
24. Find the volume obtained by revolving the region inside the loop of $y^2 = x^2(1 - x)$ about (a) the x-axis, and (b) the y-axis.

In 25–34, find the volume of the solid obtained by revolving the region bounded by the given curves about the given line. Use either method.

25. $y = x^3 - 4x^2 + 5x - 2$, $y = 5x - 2$; about y-axis
26. $4x + y = 0$, $y = 2x - x^2$; about $x = -1$
27. $y = x^3$, $y = x^4$; about $y = 2$
28. $y(1 + x^2) = 1$, $2y = x$, $x = 2$; about y-axis
29. $y = x$, $y = 2x$, $x - 2y + 3 = 0$; about $y = 3$
30. $x + 3y = 1$, $x + 2y = 2$, $y = x + 1$; about $y = -1$
31. $y = 8x - 16$, $y = x^3 - 4x$; about $x = 2$
32. $y = \sqrt{4 - x^2}$, $xy = \sqrt{3}$; about $y = 0$
33. $y = \text{Cos}^{-1}(x/2)$, $y = \text{Sin}^{-1}(x/2)$, $y = 0$; about x-axis
34. $y = x$, $x + y = 2$, $y = 0$; about $y = 0$

3 Volumes of Solids of Known Cross-sectional Area

For certain solids S it is possible to choose a line l as x-axis and some interval $[a,b]$ on this axis in such a way that S meets the plane perpendicular to l at x in a region of known area $A(x)$ for each $x \in [a,b]$ and that no other plane perpendicular to l meets S. In such a case, it is very easy to find the volume V of S. In fact, we simply subdivide $[a,b]$ and obtain $dV = A(x) \, dx$ and

$$V = \int_a^b A(x) \, dx$$

If S is a solid of revolution, then the washer method is a good instance of the procedure just described for finding V. The numbers $A(x)$ are the areas of the washers obtained by taking cross-sections by planes perpendicular to the axis l of revolution.

We now give several other examples of this method.

EXAMPLE   Find the volume of the wedge-shaped solid S that is cut from a right circular cylinder of base radius 6 and height at least 6 by a plane that contains a fixed diameter of the base and makes a 45° angle with the base (see Fig. 8-13).

Solution   Let the base lie in the xy-plane with center at the origin so that the fixed diameter is along the x-axis and the positive y-axis passes under S. For $-6 \leq x \leq 6$, the cross-section at x is an isosceles right triangle. The triangle has legs of length $\sqrt{36 - x^2}$ because the

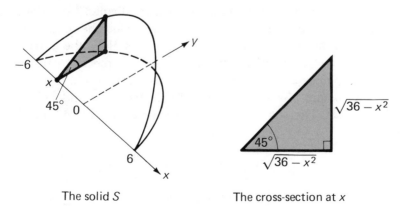

The solid S The cross-section at x

Figure 8–13

vertex of the right angle lies on the semicircle $x^2 + y^2 = 36$, $-6 \leq x \leq 6$, $y \geq 0$, and so its area is $A(x) = (36 - x^2)/2$. Thus

$$V = \frac{1}{2} \int_{-6}^{6} (36 - x^2)\, dx = \int_{0}^{6} (36 - x^2)\, dx = 144$$

EXAMPLE   The axes of two right circular cylinders of equal base radius a meet at right angles and extend through each other. Find the volume of the solid S that is common to the insides of both cylinders (see Fig. 8-14).

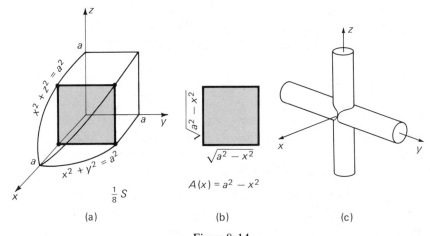

Figure 8-14

Solution   Consider three mutually perpendicular axes (labeled x, y, and z) for space that meet at a point (called the origin). As in Fig. 8-14, let the two cylinders have their axes along the y-axis and the z-axis. Now S is divided into eight congruent pieces by the three coordinate planes xz, yz, and xy. The cross-section at x ($0 \leq x \leq a$) of the first octant piece is a square of side $\sqrt{a^2 - x^2}$ and so its area $A(x)$ is $a^2 - x^2$. The volume V of S is eight times that of this one piece so that

$$V = 8 \int_{0}^{a} (a^2 - x^2)\, dx = \frac{16a^3}{3}$$

The present method can be used to find the volumes of a very general class of **cones** as our next example shows.

EXAMPLE Consider any region R in the yz-plane (horizontal) of known area A and fix any point P at vertical height h above the yz-plane (see Fig. 8-15). The **solid cone** S having **base** R and **vertex** P is defined to be the union of all line segments that join a point of R to P. Find the volume V of S.

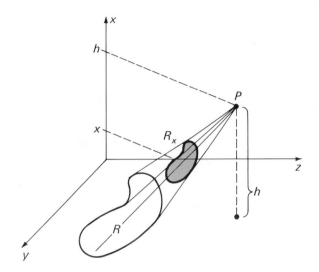

Figure 8–15

Solution For $0 \leqq x \leqq h$, the cross-section R_x of S at height x is shown in Fig. 8-15. The area of R_x is $A(x)$. The cone S_x having base R_x and vertex P has height $h - x$. Since S_x is similar to S, we have

$$\frac{A(x)}{A} = \frac{(h - x)^2}{h^2}$$

Thus

$$V = \int_0^h A(x)\, dx = \frac{A}{h^2} \int_0^h (h - x)^2\, dx = \frac{A}{h^2} \cdot \frac{-1}{3} (h - x)^3 \Big|_0^h$$
$$= \frac{1}{3} Ah$$

Notice that V does not depend on the particular shape of R or on the location of P in the horizontal plane h units above R.

EXAMPLE A solid S has an elliptical base having major axis of length 10 cm and minor axis of length 8 cm. Find the volume of S

if every section perpendicular to the major axis is an equilateral triangle.

Solution With the major axis along the x-axis and the minor axis along the y-axis, we have $2a = 10$ and $2b = 8$. Since $a^2 = 25$ and $b^2 = 16$, the ellipse has equation

$$x^2/25 + y^2/16 = 1$$

or

$$y = \pm\frac{4}{5}\sqrt{25 - x^2}.$$

For $-5 \leq x \leq 5$, the cross-section of S is an equilateral triangle of side $s = (8/5)\sqrt{25 - x^2}$ and so it has area

$$A(x) = (s/2)(s\sqrt{3}/2) = (16\sqrt{3}/25)(25 - x^2)$$

Figure 8-16 shows the first octant part of S. Thus,

$$V = \int_{-5}^{5} A(x)\, dx = 2\int_{0}^{5} A(x)\, dx = \frac{32\sqrt{3}}{25} \int_{0}^{5} (25 - x^2)\, dx$$
$$= \frac{320\sqrt{3}}{3} \text{ cm}^3$$

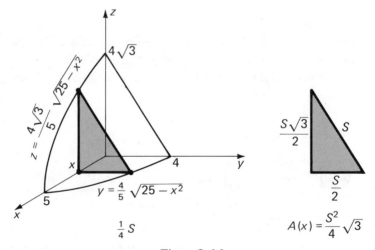

Figure 8-16

E X E R C I S E S

1. A solid S has a horizontal circular base of radius a. If every vertical cross-section perpendicular to a certain diameter of the base is a square, what is the volume of S?

2. A moving square of variable side length whose plane is perpendicular to the x-axis has one corner on the x-axis and the diagonally opposite corner on the parabola $y = 1 - x^2$. Find the volume generated as the square moves from $x = -1$ to $x = 1$.

3. Solve exercise 1 if the squares are replaced by isosceles triangles whose bases are chords of the circle and whose heights are always h.

4. Solve exercise 1 if the cross-sections are isosceles right triangles having hypotenuses as chords of the circular base.

5. Find the volume of a tetrahedron whose four faces are equilateral triangles of side s. [*Hint:* Consider a right triangle with one leg joining a vertex of the base to the center of the base and the other leg joining that center to the fourth vertex of the solid.]

6. Find the volume of an Egyptian pyramid whose base is a square of side s and which has four equilateral triangular faces. [See the hint for exercise 5.]

In 7–10, find the volume of the solid enclosed by the given surfaces. In each case first find $A(x)$ for fixed x.

7. $x^2 + y^2 + z^2 = a^2$, $x = a/2$, $x = a$

8. $4y^2 + 9z^2 = 36x$, $x = 4$

9. $y + z = x^2$, $x = 0$, $x = 2$, $y = 0$, $z = 0$

10. $\dfrac{x^2}{a^2} + \dfrac{y^2}{b^2} + \dfrac{z^2}{c^2} = 1$, where a, b, and c are positive constants

4 Arc Length

Consider a plane curve C defined by the parametric equations

$$\begin{aligned} x &= f(t) \\ y &= g(t) \end{aligned} \qquad (a \leq t \leq b)$$

where the functions f and g have continuous derivatives on the closed interval $[a,b]$. That is, C consists of the points $(x,y) = (f(t),g(t))$ as t varies from a to b. We call C a **smooth arc** joining the **initial point** $(f(a),g(a))$ to the **terminal point** $(f(b),g(b))$. Now consider any subdivision $a = t_0 < t_1 < t_2 < \cdots < t_n = b$ and the corresponding points

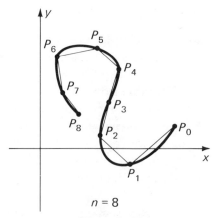

Figure 8–17

$P_k = (x_k, y_k) = (f(t_k), g(t_k))$. The **polygonal path inscribed in** C that is determined by this subdivision consists of the n line segments $\overline{P_{k-1}P_k}$ ($k = 1, 2, \ldots, n$) (as shown in Fig. 8-17). The sum of the lengths of these segments (the **perimeter** of the polygonal path) is (by the distance formula applied to each segment)

$$\sum_{k=1}^{n} [(\Delta x_k)^2 + (\Delta y_k)^2]^{1/2} \tag{1}$$

where $\Delta x_k = x_k - x_{k-1}$ and $\Delta y_k = y_k - y_{k-1}$. For each k, we invoke the Mean Value Theorem to obtain u_k and v_k in $]t_{k-1}, t_k[$ such that

$$\Delta x_k = f'(u_k)\Delta t_k \qquad \text{and} \qquad \Delta y_k = g'(v_k)\Delta t_k$$

where $\Delta t_k = t_k - t_{k-1}$. Substituting into (1) and using the fact that $\Delta t_k > 0$, we obtain

$$\sum_{k=1}^{n} [(f'(u_k))^2 + (g'(v_k))^2]^{1/2}\Delta t_k \tag{2}$$

as the perimeter of our polygonal path. It can be shown that the limit of (2) as $\max\{\Delta t_k: 1 \leq k \leq n\} \to 0$ is the number

$$\int_a^b [(f'(t))^2 + (g'(t))^2]^{1/2} \, dt$$

Therefore, we make the following definition:

▷ **Definition** If C is a smooth arc given by parametric equations $x = f(t)$, $y = g(t)$, $a \leq t \leq b$, we define the **length** of C to be the number

$$\boxed{l(C) = \int_a^b \left[\left(\frac{dx}{dt}\right)^2 + \left(\frac{dy}{dt}\right)^2\right]^{1/2} dt} \tag{3}$$

EXAMPLE   Find the length of the arc given by the parametric equations

$$x = t^3 \qquad y = t^2 \qquad 0 \le t \le 2$$

Solution   Here $a = 0$ and $b = 2$. Also, $\dfrac{dx}{dt} = 3t^2$ and $\dfrac{dy}{dt} = 2t$. Thus, the length is

$$l = \int_0^2 [(3t^2)^2 + (2t)^2]^{1/2} \, dt = \int_0^2 (9t^4 + 4t^2)^{1/2} \, dt$$

$$= \int_0^2 t(9t^2 + 4)^{1/2} \, dt = \frac{1}{18} \int_4^{40} u^{1/2} \, du$$

where $u = 9t^2 + 4$. Thus

$$l = \frac{1}{27} u^{3/2} \Big|_4^{40} = \frac{80\sqrt{10} - 8}{27}$$

EXAMPLE   Find the length of one arch of the cycloid

$$x = t - \sin t \qquad y = 1 - \cos t$$

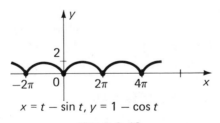

$x = t - \sin t, \; y = 1 - \cos t$

Figure 8–18

Solution   Each arch of this curve is determined by a parameter interval $2n\pi \le t \le 2(n + 1)\pi$ (see Fig. 8-18). We have

$$\frac{dx}{dt} = 1 - \cos t \qquad \frac{dy}{dt} = \sin t$$

and

$$\left[\left(\frac{dx}{dt} \right)^2 + \left(\frac{dy}{dt} \right)^2 \right]^{1/2} = [2 - 2 \cos t]^{1/2}$$

$$= \sqrt{2}(1 - \cos t)^{1/2}$$

and so the length l of the arch corresponding to $0 \le t \le 2\pi$ is

$$l = \sqrt{2} \int_0^{2\pi} \sqrt{1 - \cos t}\, dt = 2\sqrt{2} \int_0^{\pi} \sqrt{1 - \cos t}\, dt$$

$$= -4\sqrt{2}\, \sqrt{1 + \cos t}\, \Big|_0^{\pi} = 8$$

In case we wish to find the length of the graph of an equation $y = g(x)$ for $a \le x \le b$, where g is a function having its derivative g' continuous on $[a,b]$, we simply regard this graph as the smooth arc

$$x = t \qquad y = g(t) \qquad a \le t \le b$$

and apply formula (3) to obtain

$$l = \int_a^b [1 + (g'(t))^2]^{1/2}\, dt = \int_a^b [1 + (dy/dx)^2]^{1/2}\, dx \qquad (4)$$

Similarly, the length l of the graph of $x = f(y)$ for $a \le y \le b$ is

$$l = \int_a^b \left[\left(\frac{dx}{dy} \right)^2 + 1 \right]^{1/2} dy \qquad (5)$$

if f' is continuous on $[a,b]$.

EXAMPLE   Find the length of the loop in the curve $9y^2 = x(3 - x)^2$.

Solution   This curve is shown in Fig. 8-19. Since the graph is symmetric about the x-axis, we need only find the length of the upper half of the curve from $x = 0$ to $x = 3$ and multiply by 2. To do this we take positive square roots to solve for y and we get

$$y = \frac{1}{3} x^{1/2}(3 - x)$$

$$\frac{dy}{dx} = -\frac{x^{1/2}}{3} + \frac{3 - x}{6x^{1/2}} = \frac{1 - x}{2x^{1/2}}$$

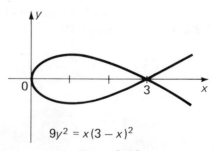

$$9y^2 = x(3 - x)^2$$

Figure 8-19

and

$$[(dy/dx)^2 + 1]^{1/2} = \left[\frac{1 - 2x + x^2}{4x} + 1\right]^{1/2} = \frac{1 + x}{2\sqrt{x}}$$

$$= \frac{1}{2}(x^{-1/2} + x^{1/2})$$

By (4), the length of our upper half-loop is

$$l = \frac{1}{2}\int_0^3 (x^{-1/2} + x^{1/2})\,dx = \frac{1}{2}\left(2x^{1/2} + \frac{2}{3}x^{3/2}\right)\Bigg|_0^3 = 2\sqrt{3}$$

The entire loop has length $4\sqrt{3}$.

If $r = h(\theta)$ is the equation of a curve in polar coordinates and we wish to find the length l of the arc of this curve corresponding to $\alpha \leq \theta \leq \beta$, where h has its derivative continuous on $[\alpha,\beta]$, then we proceed as follows. First, recall the transformation equations

$$x = r \cos \theta \qquad y = r \sin \theta$$

from polar to rectangular coordinates. Substituting $h(\theta)$ for r, we obtain the parametric representation

$$x = h(\theta) \cos \theta \qquad y = h(\theta) \sin \theta \qquad \alpha \leq \theta \leq \beta$$

for our arc. We then apply formula (3), with θ in place of t, α in place of a, and β in place of b. We have

$$\frac{dx}{d\theta} = -h(\theta) \sin \theta + h'(\theta) \cos \theta$$

$$\frac{dy}{d\theta} = h(\theta) \cos \theta + h'(\theta) \sin \theta$$

and

$$\left(\frac{dx}{d\theta}\right)^2 + \left(\frac{dy}{d\theta}\right)^2 = [h(\theta)]^2 + [h'(\theta)]^2$$

and so (3) gives

$$l = \int_\alpha^\beta \{[h(\theta)]^2 + [h'(\theta)]^2\}^{1/2}\,d\theta = \int_\alpha^\beta \left\{r^2 + \left(\frac{dr}{d\theta}\right)^2\right\}^{1/2}\,d\theta \qquad (6)$$

EXAMPLE   Find the length of the entire cardioid $r = a(1 + \cos \theta)$, where $a > 0$.

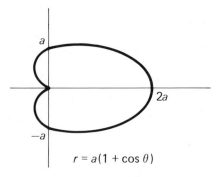

$$r = a(1 + \cos \theta)$$

Figure 8-20

Solution   The graph of this curve is shown in Fig. 8-20. Its upper half is traced out as θ varies from 0 to π and so, using symmetry with respect to the x-axis, its entire length l is

$$l = 2 \int_0^\pi \{[a(1 + \cos \theta)]^2 + [-a \sin \theta]^2\}^{1/2} \, d\theta$$

$$= 2a \int_0^\pi \{2 + 2 \cos \theta\}^{1/2} \, d\theta = 2a \int_0^\pi \left\{4 \cos^2 \frac{1}{2}\theta\right\}^{1/2} \, d\theta$$

$$= 4a \int_0^\pi \cos \frac{1}{2}\theta \, d\theta = 8a \sin \frac{1}{2}\theta \, \Big|_0^\pi = 8a$$

where we have used the fact that $\cos \frac{1}{2}\theta \geqq 0$ for $0 \leqq \theta \leqq \pi$.

E X E R C I S E S

In 1–16, find the length of the given arc.

1. $x = t^3 - 3t, \ y = 3t^2, \ 0 \leqq t \leqq 1$
2. $x = t^3 + 3/t, \ y = 6t, \ 1 \leqq t \leqq 3$
3. $x = \dfrac{t^2}{2}, \ y = t + 2, \ 0 \leqq t \leqq 1$
4. $x = \sin t - t \cos t, \ y = \cos t + t \sin t, \ 0 \leqq t \leqq \pi/4$
5. $x = t^3, \ y = 2t^2, \ 0 \leqq t \leqq 1$
6. $x = e^t \cos t, \ y = e^t \sin t, \ 0 \leqq t \leqq \pi$
7. The entire curve $x = \cos^3 t, \ y = \sin^3 t$
8. The entire circle $x = a \cos t, \ y = a \sin t$
9. $y = \ln \sec x, \ 0 \leqq x \leqq \pi/4$
10. $y = \ln x, \ 3/4 \leqq x \leqq 4/3$
11. The entire loop of the curve $9y^2 = x^2(3 - 2x)$
12. $r = \sec \theta \tan \theta, \ \pi/6 \leqq \theta \leqq \pi/3$

13. $r = \sec^2 \dfrac{1}{2}\theta,\ 0 \leq \theta \leq \pi/2$

14. The entire ellipse $r = 2a \cos \theta + 2b \sin \theta$

15. The entire circle $r = 2a \cos \theta$

16. The entire curve $r = \sin^3 \dfrac{1}{3}\theta$

5 Surfaces of Revolution

Let us consider the problem of determining the area S of the surface obtained by revolving a smooth arc C given by

$$x = f(t) \qquad y = g(t) \qquad a \leq t \leq b$$

about the x-axis. It can be shown that if C does not cross the x-axis, then

$$S = 2\pi \int_a^b |y|\ ds \tag{1}$$

where

$$ds = [(dx)^2 + (dy)^2]^{1/2} = [(dx/dt)^2 + (dy/dt)^2]^{1/2}\ dt$$

is the differential of arc length as in the preceding section. We do not prove formula (1), but it is reasonable because if we consider a very small increment ds of arc length and the corresponding distance $|y|$ from it to the x-axis (see Fig. 8-21), then the corresponding increment dS of surface area should be the circumference of the circle of revolution times ds:

$$dS = 2\pi |y|\ ds$$

Similarly, if C does not cross the y-axis and is revolved about the y-axis, then the area of the surface obtained is

$$S = 2\pi \int_a^b |x|\ ds \tag{2}$$

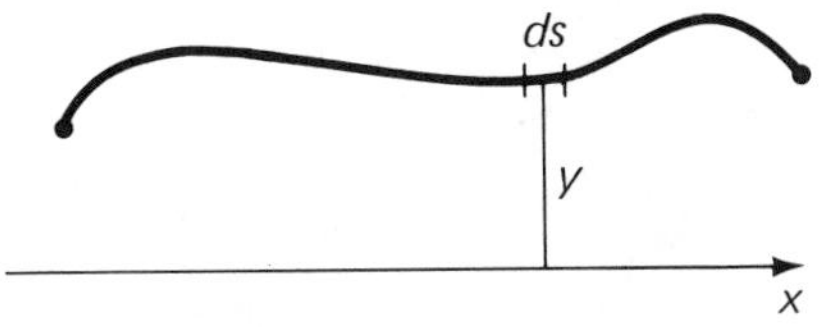

Figure 8–21

EXAMPLE Find the surface area of the sphere of radius a obtained by revolving the semicircle

$$x = a \cos t \qquad y = a \sin t \qquad 0 \leq t \leq \pi$$

about the x-axis.

Solution We have

$$dS = 2\pi(a \sin t)[(-a \sin t)^2 + (a \cos t)^2]^{1/2} \, dt$$
$$= 2\pi a^2 \sin t \, dt$$

and so (1) gives us

$$S = 2\pi a^2 \int_0^\pi \sin t \, dt = 4\pi a^2$$

EXAMPLE Find the surface area of the frustrum of a cone obtained by revolving the line segment joining the points $(0,r_1)$ and (h,r_2) about the x-axis. Here $0 \leq r_1 < r_2$ and $h > 0$ (see Fig. 8-22).

Solution This segment is given by

$$x = ht \qquad y = r_1 + (r_2 - r_1)t \qquad 0 \leq t \leq 1$$

Thus,

$$ds = [h^2 + (r_2 - r_1)^2]^{1/2} \, dt = l \, dt$$

where l is the length of the given segment. Therefore

$$S = 2\pi l \int_0^1 [r_1 + (r_2 - r_1)t] \, dt = 2\pi l \left[r_1 t + \frac{1}{2}(r_2 - r_1)t^2 \right]\Big|_0^1$$
$$= \pi l(r_1 + r_2)$$

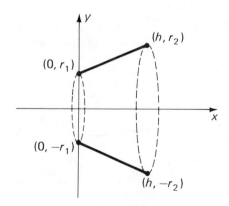

Figure 8-22

EXAMPLE   Revolve the arc $y = 2\sqrt{x}$ $(0 \leq x \leq b)$ about the x-axis. What is the area of the resulting surface?

Solution   Here we have

$$ds = [1 + (y')^2]^{1/2} \, dx = (\sqrt{1 + x}/\sqrt{x}) \, dx$$

so that

$$S = 2\pi \int_0^b y \, ds = 4\pi \int_0^b \sqrt{1 + x} \, dx = \frac{8\pi}{3} (1 + x)^{3/2} \Big|_0^b$$

$$= \frac{8\pi}{3} [(1 + b)^{3/2} - 1]$$

In case the arc to be revolved is given by a polar equation $r = h(\theta)$ for $\alpha \leq \theta \leq \beta$, we saw in section 3 that

$$ds = [r^2 + (r')^2]^{1/2} \, d\theta$$

so that (1) yields

$$\boxed{S = 2\pi \int_\alpha^\beta |r \sin \theta| \, [r^2 + (r')^2]^{1/2} \, d\theta} \qquad (3)$$

if C is to be revolved about the x-axis. If the axis of revolution is to be the y-axis, simply replace $\sin \theta$ by $\cos \theta$ in (3).

EXAMPLE   Find the area of the surface obtained by revolving the lemniscate $r^2 = 2a^2 \cos 2\theta$ about the x-axis. Here $a > 0$.

Solution   Fig. 8-23 shows this lemniscate. By symmetry we need only consider the first quadrant arc

$$r = \sqrt{2} \, a\sqrt{\cos 2\theta} \qquad 0 \leq \theta \leq \pi/4$$

and then multiply by 2. One checks that

$$r' = \sqrt{2} \, a(\cos 2\theta)^{-1/2}(-\sin 2\theta)$$
$$[r^2 + (r')^2]^{1/2} = \sqrt{2} \, a(\cos 2\theta)^{-1/2}$$
$$y \, ds = 2a^2 \sin \theta \, d\theta$$

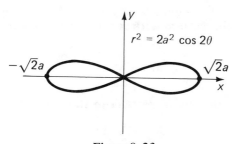

Figure 8–23

and so the total surface area is

$$S = 4\pi \int_0^{\pi/4} 2a^2 \sin\theta \; d\theta = 8\pi a^2 \left(-\cos\theta\right) \Big|_0^{\pi/4}$$
$$= 4\pi a^2 (2 - \sqrt{2})$$

E X E R C I S E S

In 1–11, find the area of the surface obtained by revolving the given arc about the given axis.

1. $y = \sin x$, $0 \le x \le \pi$; about x-axis

2. $y = x^3$, $0 \le x \le 2$; about x-axis

3. $y = x^2$, $0 \le x \le 1$; about y-axis

4. $x = 3t^2 - 6t$, $y = 8t^{3/2}$, $0 \le t \le 1$; about y-axis

5. $x = \sqrt{t}$, $y = \ln(t-1)$, $4 \le t \le 9$; about y-axis

6. $x = \cos^3 t$, $y = \sin^3 t$, $0 \le t \le \pi$; about x-axis

7. $r^2 = 2a^2 \cos 2\theta$, $(a > 0)$; about y-axis

8. $r = a(1 + \cos\theta)$, $(a > 0)$; about x-axis

9. The loop of $9y^2 = x(3 - x)^2$; about x-axis

10. The ellipse $x = a \cos t$, $y = b \sin t$, $0 \le t \le 2\pi$ $(a > 0, b > 0)$; about x-axis

11. The circle $x = b + a \cos t$, $y = a \sin t$, $0 \le t \le 2\pi$ $(b \ge a > 0)$; about y-axis

12. Consider the unbounded surface obtained by revolving the curve $xy = 1$, $1 \le x < \infty$, about the x-axis. Show that the area of this surface is $S = \infty$ and that the volume contained inside it is $V = \pi/3$. Conclude that if the surface is transparent and one wishes to color it, then it is cheaper to fill it with paint than it is to paint the surface.

6   Centroids

Suppose that n particles of masses m_1, m_2, . . ., m_n are located at the points (x_1, y_1), (x_2, y_2), . . ., (x_n, y_n) in the plane. The **first moment** of this system **with respect to the x-axis** is the number M_x defined by

$$M_x = \sum_{k=1}^n y_k m_k$$

while its **first moment with respect to the y-axis** is

$$M_y = \sum_{k=1}^n x_k m_k$$

and the **total mass** of the system is

$$M = \sum_{k=1}^{n} m_k$$

The **center of mass** of this system is the point $(\bar{x}, \bar{y})$ such that if a single particle of mass M were located there, then its first moments would be the same as those of the whole system. That is,

$$\bar{x}M = M_y \quad \text{and} \quad \bar{y}M = M_x$$

With the above as motivation, we define the **center of mass** of a continuous planar mass M as $(\bar{x}, \bar{y})$, where

$$\bar{x}M = \int x_c \, dm = M_y$$

and

$$\bar{y}M = \int y_c \, dm = M_x$$

where (x_c, y_c) is the center of the element of mass dm and the limits of integration are determined by the shape of the whole mass.

In case a continuous mass has a uniform density, its center of mass is called the **centroid** or **geometrical center**. The centroid is always on any line of symmetry of the object.

EXAMPLE   Find the centroid of a semicircular region of radius a.

Solution   We consider the region above the x-axis and inside $x^2 + y^2 = a^2$. Plainly the centroid is on the y-axis, so that $\bar{x} = 0$. Let us consider vertical increments of area as shown in Fig. 8-24. For the increment of area located at x of width dx we have

$$y_c = \frac{1}{2}y = \frac{1}{2}\sqrt{a^2 - x^2}$$

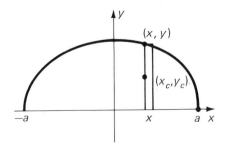

Figure 8–24

and $dA = y\,dx = \sqrt{a^2 - x^2}\,dx$ so that

$$M_x = \int_{-a}^{a} y_c\,dA = \frac{1}{2}\int_{-a}^{a} (a^2 - x^2)\,dx$$

$$= \frac{1}{2}\left(a^2 x - \frac{1}{3}x^3\right)\Bigg|_{-a}^{a} = \frac{2}{3}a^3$$

where we have supposed $dm = dA$. Also, $M = A = \pi a^2/2$ and so $\bar{y} = M_x/M = 4a/3\pi$. The centroid is $(0, 4a/3\pi)$.

EXAMPLE   Find the centroid of the hemispherical solid obtained by revolving the first quadrant region bounded by $x^2 + y^2 = a^2$ about the y-axis.

Solution   As for any solid of revolution, the centroid is on the axis of revolution. If we subdivide $[0,a]$ on the y-axis (see Fig. 8-25), we have $y_c = y$ and $dV = \pi x^2 dy = \pi(a^2 - y^2)dy$, so that

$$M_x = \int_0^a y_c\,dV = \pi \int_0^a (a^2 y - y^3)\,dy = \pi\left(\frac{1}{2}a^2 y^2 - \frac{1}{4}y^4\right)\Bigg|_0^a$$

$$= \frac{\pi a^4}{4}$$

and

$$V = 2\pi a^3/3$$

so that

$$\bar{y} = M_x/V = 3a/8$$

The centroid is $(0, 3a/8)$.

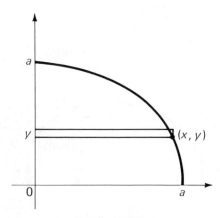

Figure 8–25

EXAMPLE   Find the centroid of the semicircular arc

$$y = \sqrt{a^2 - x^2} \qquad -a \leq x \leq a$$

Solution   By symmetry, the centroid is on the y-axis. We have

$$ds = [1 + (y')^2]^{1/2} \, dx = \frac{a \, dx}{\sqrt{a^2 - x^2}}$$

and

$$y_c = y = \sqrt{a^2 - x^2}$$

so that

$$M_x = \int_{-a}^{a} y \, ds = \int_{-a}^{a} a \, dx = 2a^2$$

Also, the length s is πa so that $\bar{y} = M_x/s = 2a/\pi$. The centroid is $(0, 2a/\pi)$.

EXAMPLE   Find the centroid of the hemispherical surface obtained by revolving the arc $y = \sqrt{a^2 - x^2}$, $0 \leq x \leq a$, about the y-axis.

Solution   Plainly the centroid is on the y-axis. Taking ds as in the preceding example, we have

$$dS = 2\pi y \, ds = 2\pi a \, dx$$

so that

$$S = \int_{0}^{a} 2\pi a \, dx = 2\pi a^2$$

and, since $y_c = y = \sqrt{a^2 - x^2}$,

$$M_x = \int_{0}^{a} y_c \, dS = 2\pi a \int_{0}^{a} \sqrt{a^2 - x^2} \, dx = (2\pi a)\left(\frac{\pi a^2}{4}\right) = \frac{\pi^2 a^3}{2}$$

Thus $\bar{y} = M_x/S = \pi a/4$. The centroid is $(0, \pi a/4)$.

EXAMPLE   Find how far the centroid is above the base of a solid right circular cone having height h and base radius a.

Solution   We obtain the cone by revolving the right triangular region bounded by the coordinate axes and the line $x/a + y/h = 1$ about the y-axis. Subdividing the interval $[0,h]$ on the y-axis (see Fig. 8-26), we have $y_c = y$ and

$$dV = \pi x^2 \, dy = \pi(a - ay/h)^2 dy = \pi a^2(1 - 2y/h + y^2/h^2) \, dy$$

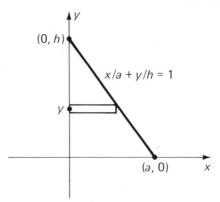

Figure 8–26

Thus

$$M_x = \int_0^h y_c \, dV = \pi a^2 \int_0^h (y - 2y^2/h + y^3/h^2) \, dy$$

$$= \pi a^2 \left(\frac{1}{2} y^2 - \frac{2y^3}{3h} + \frac{y^4}{4h^2}\right)\Big|_0^h = \frac{\pi a^2 h^2}{12}$$

Since $V = \pi a^2 h/3$, we see that $\bar{y} = M_x/V = h/4$ is the desired answer.

Since the centroids of many planar arcs and planar regions are obvious (particularly if they have two lines of symmetry), the following two theorems of Pappus are often useful in finding surface areas or volumes of revolution.

▷ **First Theorem of Pappus** If a planar arc of length s is revolved about a coplanar line that does not cross the arc and if the distance from the centroid of the arc to the axis of revolution is r, then the area S of the surface swept out is

$$S = 2\pi r s$$

Proof Choose the coordinate system so that the axis of revolution is the x-axis and the arc is above the x-axis. Then $r = \bar{y}$ and

$$S = 2\pi \int y \, ds = 2\pi M_x = 2\pi \bar{y} s = 2\pi r s \quad ∎$$

▷ **Second Theorem of Pappus** If a plane region of area A is revolved about a coplanar line that does not cross the region and if the distance from the centroid of the region to the axis of revolution is r, then the volume V of the solid of revolution swept out is

$$V = 2\pi r A$$

Proof   Choose the coordinate system as in the previous proof. Then $r = \bar{y}$ and

$$V = 2\pi \int y \, dA = 2\pi M_x = 2\pi \bar{y} A = 2\pi r A \quad \blacksquare$$

EXAMPLE   Given $b \geqq a > 0$, find the volume and the surface area of the torus (doughnut) that is obtained when the circle centered at $(0,b)$ of radius a is revolved around the x-axis.

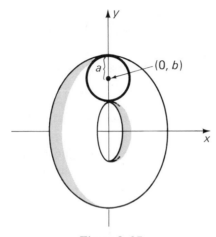

Figure 8–27

Solution   As can be seen from Fig. 8-27, in both cases we have $r = b$. Also, $s = 2\pi a$ and $A = \pi a^2$ so that Pappus' Theorems show that

$$S = (2\pi b)(2\pi a) = 4\pi^2 ab$$

and

$$V = (2\pi b)(\pi a^2) = 2\pi^2 a^2 b$$

E X E R C I S E S

In 1–10, find the centroid of the region bounded by the given curves.

1. $y = x^2$, $x = y^2$
2. $y = \sin x$, $y = \cos x$, $0 \leqq x \leqq \pi/4$
3. $y = x^2$, $y = 4$
4. $y = x^3$, $y = x(2 - x)$, $0 \leqq x \leqq 1$
5. $y = 4x + 1$, $2x + y = 7$, $x = 4$
6. $y^2 = x$, $y = x - 2$
7. $y = 2 + 2x$, $y = 2 - 2x$, $y = 1 - x^2$

8. $\sqrt{x} + \sqrt{y} = 1$, $x = 0$, $y = 0$
9. $y = \ln x$, $x = e$, $y = 0$
10. $y = \sin x$, $y = 0$, $0 \leq x \leq \pi$

11. The region inside $x^2/a^2 + y^2/b^2 = 1$ is revolved about the line $y = c$ ($c \geq b > 0$, $a > 0$). What is the volume of the solid of revolution?
12. The square region whose corners are at $(0, b - a)$, (a,b), $(0, b + a)$, $(-a,b)$, where $b \geq a > 0$, is revolved about the x-axis. Find the volume and the surface area of the resulting solid.
13. A regular hexagonal region inscribed in a circle of radius a is revolved about one of its sides. Find the volume and the surface area of the resulting solid.
14. A triangular region has its vertices at $(0,0)$, $(b,0)$, and (a,h), where $b > 0$ and $h > 0$. Show that the centroid of this region is $\left(\dfrac{a+b}{3}, \dfrac{h}{3}\right)$.
    Find the volume obtained when this region is revolved about the x-axis.
15. The region bounded by $y = x(2 - x)$ and $y = x(x - 2)$ is revolved about the y-axis. Find the resulting volume.

In 16–25, find the centroid of the solid obtained by revolving the given region about the given line.

16. Region of exercise 1 about $y = 0$
17. Region of exercise 2 about $y = 0$
18. Region of exercise 3 about $x = 0$
19. Region of exercise 4 about $y = 0$
20. Region of exercise 5 about $x = 4$
21. Region of exercise 6 about $x = 0$
22. Region of exercise 7 about $x = 0$
23. Region of exercise 8 about $x = 0$
24. Region of exercise 9 about $y = 0$
25. Region of exercise 10 about $y = 0$

26. Find the centroid of the portion (arc) of the circle $x^2 + y^2 = a^2$ in the first quadrant.
27. Find the centroid of the arc $x = 6t^2$, $y = t^3 - 12t$, $0 \leq t \leq 2$.
28. Find the centroid of the arc of $x^6 - 8x^2y + 2 = 0$ from $(1, 3/8)$ to $(\sqrt{2}, 5/8)$.
29. Find the centroid of the surface obtained by revolving the arc of exercise 27 about the x-axis.
30. Find the centroid of the surface obtained by revolving the arc in exercise 28 about the x-axis.

7 Areas in Polar Coordinates

Let $r = h(\theta)$ be an equation in polar coordinates, where h is a nonnegative continuous function on $[\alpha,\beta]$ and where $\beta \leqq \alpha + 2\pi$. Consider the problem of finding the area A of the region R bounded by the two rays $\theta = \alpha$ and $\theta = \beta$ and the graph of $r = h(\theta)$ (see Fig. 8-28). Divide $[\alpha,\beta]$ into n equal subintervals of size $\Delta\theta = (\beta - \alpha)/n$ by the points $\alpha = \theta_0 < \theta_1 < \ldots < \theta_n = \beta$. The rays $\theta = \theta_k$, $k = 0, 1, \ldots, n$, divide R into n subregions R_k, $k = 1, 2, \ldots, n$. The region R_k is shown in Fig. 8-29. It is geometrically evident that there is a value $\theta = \theta_k' \in [\theta_{k-1},\theta_k]$ such that the area of R_k equals the area of the circular sector of radius $r_k = h(\theta_k')$ between the same rays. The area of this sector is $\frac{1}{2}r_k{}^2\Delta\theta$ [see equation (7), page 217]. Thus

$$A = \sum_{k=1}^{n} (\text{area of } R_k) = \sum_{k=1}^{n} \frac{1}{2}r_k{}^2\Delta\theta = \frac{1}{2}\sum_{k=1}^{n} [h(\theta_k')]^2\Delta\theta$$

As seen in Chapter 6, the limit of this last sum as $\Delta\theta \to 0$ $(n \to \infty)$ is

$$\frac{1}{2}\int_{\alpha}^{\beta} [h(\theta)]^2 \, d\theta$$

Therefore

$$A = \frac{1}{2}\int_{\alpha}^{\beta} [h(\theta)]^2 \, d\theta = \frac{1}{2}\int_{\alpha}^{\beta} r^2 \, d\theta$$

and the differential of area in polar coordinates is

$$dA = \frac{1}{2}r^2 \, d\theta$$

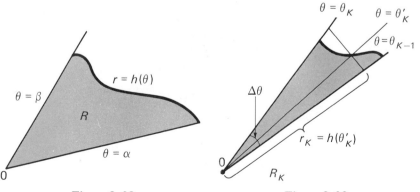

Figure 8–28   Figure 8–29

EXAMPLE   Find the area of the region enclosed by the cardioid $r = a(1 + \cos \theta)$, where $a > 0$.

Solution   This curve is shown in Fig. 8-20 (on page 400). It is traced out exactly once as θ varies from 0 to 2π. We have

$$dA = \frac{1}{2}r^2 \, d\theta = \frac{1}{2}a^2(1 + 2 \cos \theta + \cos^2 \theta) \, d\theta$$

$$= \frac{1}{2}a^2\left(1 + 2 \cos \theta + \frac{1}{2}(1 + \cos 2\theta)\right) d\theta$$

so that

$$A = \frac{1}{2}a^2 \int_0^{2\pi} (1 + 2 \cos \theta) \, d\theta + \frac{1}{4}a^2 \int_0^{2\pi} (1 + \cos 2\theta) \, d\theta$$

$$= \frac{1}{2}a^2[\theta + 2 \sin \theta]\Big|_0^{2\pi} + \frac{1}{4}a^2\left[\theta + \frac{1}{2} \sin 2\theta\right]\Big|_0^{2\pi}$$

$$= \pi a^2 + \frac{1}{2}\pi a^2 = \frac{3\pi a^2}{2}$$

EXAMPLE   Find the total area enclosed by the four-leafed rose $r = \sin 2\theta$.

Solution   This curve, which is traced out exactly once as θ varies from 0 to 2π, is shown in Fig. 8-30. Proceeding directly, we obtain

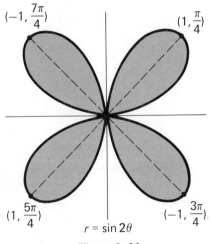

$r = \sin 2\theta$

Figure 8–30

$$A = \frac{1}{2} \int_0^{2\pi} \sin^2 2\theta \; d\theta = \frac{1}{4} \int_0^{2\pi} (1 - \cos 4\theta) \; d\theta$$

$$= \frac{1}{4} \left[\theta - \frac{1}{4} \sin 4\theta \right] \Big|_0^{2\pi} = \frac{\pi}{2}$$

EXAMPLE   Find the area of the region that is inside the circle $r = \cos \theta$ and outside the rose $r = \sin 2\theta$.

Solution   The region is shown in Fig. 8-31. Solving simultaneously to find the points at which these curves intersect, we write

$$\cos \theta = r = \sin 2\theta = 2 \sin \theta \cos \theta$$
$$(\cos \theta)(1 - 2 \sin \theta) = 0$$
$$\cos \theta = 0 \qquad \sin \theta = 1/2$$

Since the circle is traced out just once as θ varies from 0 to π, we need solutions only for this interval. They are $\theta = \pi/6$, $\pi/2$, and $5\pi/6$. By symmetry we need only double the area of our region that is above the x-axis. This is the difference of two areas. We have

$$A = 2 \left[\frac{1}{2} \int_0^{\pi/6} \cos^2 \theta \; d\theta - \frac{1}{2} \int_0^{\pi/6} \sin^2 2\theta \; d\theta \right]$$

$$= \frac{1}{2} \int_0^{\pi/6} (1 + \cos 2\theta) \; d\theta - \frac{1}{2} \int_0^{\pi/6} (1 - \cos 4\theta) \; d\theta$$

$$= \frac{1}{2} \left[\left(\theta + \frac{1}{2} \sin 2\theta \right) - \left(\theta - \frac{1}{4} \sin 4\theta \right) \right] \Big|_0^{\pi/6}$$

$$= \frac{1}{2} \left[\left(\frac{\pi}{6} + \frac{\sqrt{3}}{4} \right) - \left(\frac{\pi}{6} - \frac{\sqrt{3}}{8} \right) \right] = \frac{3\sqrt{3}}{16}$$

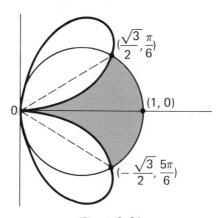

Figure 8-31

EXERCISES

In 1–10, (a) draw a sketch of the given curve and (b) find the area
that it encloses.

1. $r = 2 - \cos \theta$
2. $r = 6 \sin \theta$
3. $r^2 = \sin 2\theta$
4. $r = 4 \sin^2 \frac{1}{2}\theta$
5. $r = 3 \cos 3\theta$
6. $r = 5 - 2 \sin \theta$
7. $r = 8 \cos^2 \theta \sin \theta$
8. $r \cos \theta = \cos 2\theta$
9. $r^2 = 3 \cos 3\theta$
10. $r = 4(2 - \cos \theta)^{-1}$

11. Find the area of the smaller loop of $r = 1 - 2 \cos \theta$.
12. Find the area between the inner loops and the outer loop of
    $r^2 = 1 + \sin \theta$.
13. Find the area inside the loop of $r = \sec \theta - \tan \theta$.
14. Find the area that is inside $r = 5 \sin \theta$ and outside $r = 2 + \sin \theta$.
15. Find the area that is inside $r = 2 \sin \theta$ and outside $r = \cos \theta + \sin \theta$.
16. Find the area that is inside both $r = 1 + \cos \theta$ and $r = 3 \cos \theta$.
17. Find the area that is inside both $r^2 = 6 \cos 2\theta$ and $r = 2 \cos \theta$.
18. Use polar coordinates to find the area inside $(x^2 + y^2)^3 = 4x^2y^2$.

8 Work

If a constant force F directed along a straight line causes
an object to move a distance s along that line, then the **work** W that
has been done is defined by

$$W = Fs$$

For instance, the work done in lifting a 75-pound object a distance
of 7 feet is 525 foot-pounds (ft-lb). On the other hand, if the force
applied is variable, then the definition of work is somewhat more
complicated.

Suppose that an object is moved along a number line from position
a to position b by a variable force directed along that line whose magnitude at position x is $F(x)$. Suppose also that the function F is continuous on $[a,b]$. In order to make a definition of the amount of work

done, we proceed as follows. Divide the interval $[a,b]$ into some large number n of intervals of equal length $(b - a)/n = \Delta x$ by means of points $a = x_0 < x_1 < \ldots < x_n = b$. Since the force varies but little over $[x_{k-1},x_k]$, the increment of work done over this interval is taken to be $\Delta W_k = F(x_k)\Delta x$. Summing over $k = 1, 2, \ldots, n$, we obtain

$$\sum_{k=1}^{n} F(x_k)\Delta x$$

The limit of this sum as $n \to \infty$ is the integral of F over $[a,b]$, and so we *define* the **work** W done in the present situation to be

$$W = \int_a^b F(x)\ dx$$

EXAMPLE   A cable of length 100 feet hangs straight down from a windlass. If the cable weighs 4 pounds per foot, what amount of work is required to wind it completely onto the windlass?

Solution   We direct the x-axis straight down along the cable with position 0 at the windlass (see Fig. 8-32). The increment dW of work required to lift the part of the cable from x to $x + dx$ up to 0 is its weight ($4\ dx$ pounds) times the distance it is to be lifted (x feet) so that

$$dW = 4x\ dx$$

Integrating these increments for $0 \leq x \leq 100$, we have

$$W = \int_0^{100} 4x\ dx = 2x^2 \Big|_0^{100} = 20{,}000 \text{ ft-lb}$$

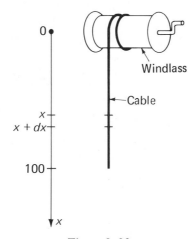

Figure 8–32

EXAMPLE   A hemispherical tank of radius 9 feet is full of oil. If the oil has density 60 lb/ft³, find the work required to pump the oil to a position 7 feet above the top of the tank.

Solution   Look at Fig. 8-33, which shows a cross-section of the tank. Consider a thin horizontal sheet of oil at level x having thickness dx. The volume of this sheet is $\pi y^2 dx = \pi(81 - x^2)\, dx$ ft³ so that its

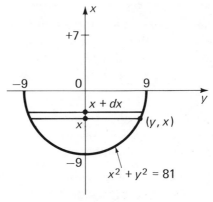

Figure 8–33

weight is $60\pi(81 - x^2)\, dx$ lb. It must be lifted $-x + 7$ ft. Thus, the work required to pump this sheet is

$$dW = 60\pi(-x + 7)(81 - x^2)\, dx = 60\pi(567 - 81x - 7x^2 + x^3)\, dx \text{ ft-lb}$$

and so

$$W = \int_{-9}^{0} dW = 60\pi(567x - 81x^2/2 - 7x^3/3 + x^4/4)\Big|_{-9}^{0}$$

$$= 302{,}535\pi \text{ ft-lb}$$

EXAMPLE   What is the minimum velocity that a rocket traveling straight up from Earth's surface must travel in order for it to escape the gravitational attraction of Earth?

Solution   According to Newton's universal law of gravitation, the force $F(x)$ of attraction between two particles of masses m and m_0 at a distance x apart is given by

$$F(x) = kmm_0/x^2 \tag{1}$$

where k is some "universal" constant. Let m_0 be the mass of Earth, let m be the mass of the rocket, and let R be the radius of Earth. We, of course, regard m_0 as being concentrated at Earth's center. To evaluate k, we let g denote the acceleration due to gravity at Earth's surface and invoke (1) to write $mg = F(R) = kmm_0/R^2$ so that $k = R^2g/m_0$ and (1) becomes

$$F(x) = R^2gm/x^2 \tag{2}$$

Therefore, the work $W(r)$ required for the rocket to travel to a distance r from Earth's center $(r \geqq R)$ is

$$W(r) = \int_R^r F(x) \, dx = R^2gm(1/R - 1/r) \tag{3}$$

In order for the rocket to "escape," the work required is

$$W = \lim_{r \to \infty} W(r) = Rgm$$

For this work to be accomplished, the kinetic energy $E = mv^2/2$ that the rocket develops must satisfy

$$mv^2/2 = E \geqq W > W(r)$$

for all r. Thus the velocity v of the rocket must satisfy

$$mv^2/2 \geqq Rgm \qquad v \geqq \sqrt{2Rg}$$

The minimum v that will allow the escape (the so-called **escape velocity** from Earth's surface) is

$$v_0 = \sqrt{2Rg} \approx 37{,}000 \text{ ft/sec}$$
$$\approx 25{,}000 \text{ mi/hr}$$
$$\approx 11.3 \text{ km/sec}$$

EXAMPLE   It is found that a certain hanging spring of normal length 10 inches is stretched to a length of 11 inches when a weight of 12 pounds is hung on it. Find the work done in stretching this spring from a length of 12 inches to a length of 16 inches.

Solution   We use Hooke's law, which states that (within the limits of elasticity) the force $F(x)$ required to cause a displacement of x units in an object is directly proportional to x. That is,

$$F(x) = kx$$

for some constant k (called the **modulus** of the object). In our case the displaced object is the lower end of the spring. The spring stretches $x = 1$ in. due to a force of 12 lb so that $12 = F(1) = k \cdot 1$ and so the modulus (also called the **spring constant**) is $k = 12$ lb/in. Thus,

$$F(x) = 12x$$

We wish to displace the spring from $x = 2$ in. to $x = 6$ in. The work required to do this is

$$W = \int_2^6 12x\ dx = 6x^2 \Big|_2^6 = 192 \text{ in-lb} = 16 \text{ ft-lb}$$

EXERCISES

1. A tank in the shape of a right circular cone with vertex at the bottom has height 10 ft and the radius at the top is 3 ft. If the tank is full of water (density: 62.4 lb/ft³), find the work required to pump this water to the top of the tank.

2. The tank of exercise 1 contains oil (density: 60 lb/ft³) to a depth of 6 ft. What work is required to pump this oil to the top of the tank?

3. Solve exercise 1 if the vertex of the tank is at its top.

4. Solve exercise 2 if the vertex of the tank is at its top.

5. A tank in the shape of a paraboloid of revolution with vertical axis is full of water. The radius at the top is 9 ft and the depth is 27 ft. How much work is required to pump the water to a height of 18 ft above the top of the tank?

6. Solve exercise 5 if the tank is filled with water only to a depth of 18 ft.

7. A piano weighing 800 lb is to be raised by a cable weighing 3 pounds per foot to the balcony of a penthouse 300 feet above the piano. Find the work needed to do this.

8. Two charged particles attract each other with a force of $30/x^2$ dynes, where x is the number of centimeters (cm) between them. What work is required to move them from 2 cm apart to 6 cm apart?

9. Find the work required to compress a spring of modulus (spring constant) 18 tons/ft a distance of 2 inches.

10. What work is necessary to compress the spring of exercise 9 an additional 2 inches?

11. What is the modulus (spring constant) of a spring if 600 in-lb of work are needed to stretch it a distance of 4 inches?

12. A bucket weighing 5 pounds and containing 50 pounds of water hangs in a deep well by a chain 40 feet long which weighs 3 pounds per foot. What is the work required to lift the bucket to the top of the well?

13. Solve exercise 12 if, in addition, the water is leaking out of the bucket at a constant rate in such a way that the bucket has only 30 pounds of water left in it when it reaches the top.

14. A hemispherical tank of radius 10 ft is full of oil having a density of 60 lb/ft³ which leaks out of the bottom of the tank at a rate of 1 ft³/min. If oil is pumped to the top of the tank at the rate of 3 ft³/min, how much work must the pump do in order to empty the tank?

15. Some boys are pushing a spherical snowball at a constant speed up a hill having inclination 30° to the horizontal. At the base of the hill the ball has radius 3 in. and its radius increases at the rate of 1 in/min as it goes up the hill. It is 200 ft along the hill from its bottom to its top. They reach the top in 15 min. If the density of the snow is 15 lb/ft³, how much work did the boys do?

9 Fluid Pressure

The pressure p (force per unit area) that a fluid exerts at a level x units below its surface is $p = xw$, where w is the density (weight per unit volume) of the fluid. For instance, for water, $w = 62.4$ lb/ft³ so that the pressure exerted by water at a level 10 feet below its surface is

$$p = (10 \text{ ft})(62.4 \text{ lb/ft}^3) = 624 \text{ lb/ft}^2$$

The force F that is exerted on one side of a surface having area S that is located at a uniform depth x in a fluid of density w is given by

$$F = xwS = pS$$

In view of this, we compute the total force exerted on one side of any surface that is submerged in a fluid of density w as follows. Direct the x-axis vertically downward with origin at the top surface of the fluid. For vertical depths x and $x + dx$ let dS be the area of that portion of our surface that lies between these two depths and then let dF be the increment of the force that is contributed by the increment $[x, x + dx]$ of depth. Thus

$$dF = wx \, dS$$

Add these increments by integration to get

$$F = \int_a^b wx \, dS \tag{1}$$

where our surface lies between depths a and b ($a < b$).

EXAMPLE   A plate of glass in the shape of a right triangle is submerged in water with a leg of length 4 feet being horizontal at a depth of 3 feet and the other leg being vertical of length 6 feet and extending to a depth of 9 feet. What is the total force on one side of this plate?

Solution   We place the x-axis vertically with the origin at the water's surface (see Fig. 8-34). The equation of the hypotenuse is $y = (-2/3)(x - 9)$. The area dS of the horizontal increment between x and $x + dx$ is $dS = y\,dx$ so that

$$dF = (62.4)\,xy\,dx = (62.4)\left(-\frac{2}{3}\right)x(x - 9)\,dx$$
$$= (41.6)(9x - x^2)\,dx$$

Thus

$$F = \int_3^9 dF = (41.6)(9x^2/2 - x^3/3)\Big|_3^9 = (41.6)(90)$$
$$= 3744\ \text{lb}$$

EXAMPLE   An open hemispherical bowl of radius 3 ft rests with its circular rim on the bottom of a flat-bottomed pool of water of depth 10 feet. What is the total force on the bottom side of this bowl?

Solution   Fig. 8-35 shows a cross-section of the bowl where the x-axis passes through the center of the sphere at $(10,0)$. This semicircular cross-section has parametric equations

$$x = 10 + 3\cos t \qquad y = 3\sin t \qquad \pi/2 \leqq t \leqq 3\pi/2$$

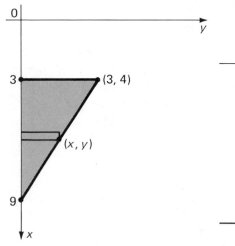

Figure 8–34

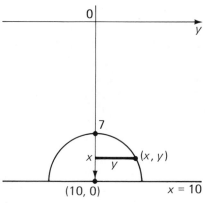

Figure 8–35

The ribbon of surface between depths x and $x + dx$ has area

$$dS = 2\pi y \ ds = 2\pi(3 \sin t)\left[\left(\frac{dx}{dt}\right)^2 + \left(\frac{dy}{dt}\right)^2\right]^{1/2} dt$$

$$= 2\pi(3 \sin t)(3) \ dt = 18\pi \sin t \ dt \qquad (\pi/2 \leq t \leq \pi)$$

Therefore,

$$dF = (62.4) \ x \ dS = (1123.2)\pi(\sin t)(10 + 3 \cos t) \ dt \qquad (\pi/2 \leq t \leq \pi)$$

Thus

$$F = (1123.2)\pi \int_{\pi/2}^{\pi} (10 + 3 \cos t) \sin t \ dt$$

$$= -(1123.2)\pi[10 \cos t + (3/2)\cos^2 t]\Big|_{\pi/2}^{\pi}$$

$$= (1123.2)\pi[17/2] \approx 29{,}993.41 \ \text{lb}$$

EXAMPLE A trough with vertical ends has a cross-section which is a parabolic segment of width 8 feet and depth 4 feet. If the trough is full of a liquid of density 50 lb/ft³, then find the total force on one end of the trough.

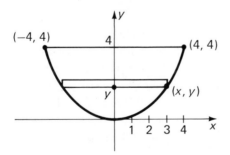

Figure 8–36

Solution We choose the coordinate system as shown in Fig. 8-36, where one end of the trough is pictured. The equation of the parabola is $4y = x^2$. We have $dF = w(4 - y) \ dS$ (where $dS = 2x \ dy$ is the area and $4 - y$ is the depth of the horizontal slice), so that

$$dF = 50(4 - y) \cdot 2x \ dy = 200(4y^{1/2} - y^{3/2}) \ dy$$

Therefore,

$$F = 200 \int_{0}^{4} (4y^{1/2} - y^{3/2}) \ dy = 200\left(\frac{8}{3}y^{3/2} - \frac{2}{5}y^{5/2}\right)\Big|_{0}^{4}$$

$$= 25{,}600/15 \ \text{lb} \approx 1706.67 \ \text{lb}$$

E X E R C I S E S

In 1–10, a glass plate of the given shape is submerged vertically in a fluid of density w. In each case find the total force on one side of the plate.

1. A rectangle of width a and depth b with its upper edge in the surface.
2. An equilateral triangle with side a and one edge in the surface.
3. An isosceles right triangle with legs of length a and hypotenuse in the surface.
4. A semicircle of radius a with its straight edge in the surface.
5. An isosceles trapezoid with bases a and b and height h and the base of length a in the surface.
6. Solve exercise 1 if the upper edge is c units below the surface.
7. Solve exercise 2 if the upper edge is c units below the surface.
8. Solve exercise 3 if the upper edge is c units below the surface.
9. Solve exercise 4 if the upper edge is c units below the surface.
10. Solve exercise 5 if the upper edge is c units below the surface.
11. A tank in the shape of a right circular cylinder of radius 12 feet and height 20 feet is full of water and stands on its circular base. What is the total force on the curved vertical surface of the tank?
12. A tank in the shape of a right circular cone of base radius 12 feet and height 20 feet stands with its vertex directly below the center of its circular base. If the tank is full of water, what is the total force on its curved surface?
13. Solve exercise 12 if "below" is replaced by "above."
14. A sphere of radius 5 feet rests on the bottom of a fresh water lake 50 feet deep. Find the total force on the outside of the sphere.

10 Moments of Inertia

Let n particles of masses $m_1, m_2, \ldots, m_n$ be located at distances $r_1, r_2, \ldots, r_n$, respectively, from a fixed line (axis). Suppose this system of particles rotates rigidly about the axis at a rate of ω radians per unit time. Then the kinetic energy of the kth particle is $m_k(\omega r_k)^2/2$ because ωr_k is the distance traveled by the kth particle in unit time. Thus the kinetic energy of the system is

$$E = \sum_{k=1}^{n} m_k(\omega r_k)^2/2 = \left(\sum_{k=1}^{n} m_k r_k^2\right)\omega^2/2 = I\omega^2/2$$

The number

$$I = \sum_{k=1}^{n} m_k r_k^2$$

which does not depend on the angular velocity ω, is called the **moment of inertia** (or the **second moment**) of the system about the given axis. Letting $M = m_1 + m_2 + \ldots + m_n$ be the mass of the entire system, we define the **radius of gyration** R of the system to be the distance R from the given axis at which a single particle of mass M can be placed so that

$$I = MR^2$$

Guided by the above, we define the **moment of inertia** I of a continuous mass about a given axis by

$$I = \int r^2 \, dm$$

where the increment of mass dm is at a constant distance r from the axis and the integration is over the entire mass. In this section, we shall restrict our attention to plane regions whose mass distributions equal one unit per unit of area ($dm = dA$).

EXAMPLE   A rectangle in the plane has vertices (x_1,y_1), (x_2,y_1), (x_2,y_2), and (x_1,y_2), where $x_1 < x_2$ and $y_1 < y_2$. Find the moment of inertia I_x of this rectangle about the x-axis (see Fig. 8-37). Also, find the radius of gyration R_x about the x-axis.

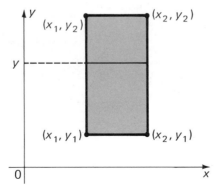

Figure 8-37

424   **Techniques of Calculus**

Solution For $y_1 \leq y \leq y_2$, the horizontal increment of area at y is $dA = (x_2 - x_1)\, dy$ and the distance to the axis is $r = |y|$. Thus, since $dA = (x_2 - x_1)\, dy$,

$$I_x = \int_{y_1}^{y_2} r^2\, dA = (x_2 - x_1) \int_{y_1}^{y_2} y^2\, dy = (x_2 - x_1)(y_2{}^3 - y_1{}^3)/3$$

$$= (x_2 - x_1)(y_2 - y_1)(y_2{}^2 + y_1 y_2 + y_1{}^2)/3$$

Since the area A of the rectangle is $(x_2 - x_1)(y_2 - y_1)$ and $I_x = AR_x{}^2$, we have

$$R_x = [(y_2{}^2 + y_1 y_2 + y_1{}^2)/3]^{1/2}$$

In case we wish to compute the moment of inertia I_x of a plane region about the x-axis by taking vertical increments (see Fig. 8-38), we proceed as follows. The increment at x is a rectangle, as in the above example, where $y_1 = f(x)$, $y_2 = g(x)$, and $x_2 - x_1 = dx$. By the example, the corresponding increment of I_x is

$$dI_x = \frac{1}{3}[(g(x))^3 - (f(x))^3]\, dx$$

so that

$$\boxed{I_x = \frac{1}{3}\int_a^b [(g(x))^3 - (f(x))^3]\, dx} \tag{1}$$

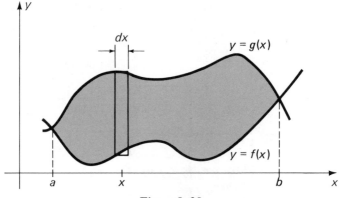

Figure 8–38

A similar formula holds for moments of inertia about the y-axis (see Fig. 8-39):

$$\boxed{I_y = \frac{1}{3}\int_c^d [(\psi(y))^3 - (\phi(y))^3]\, dy} \tag{2}$$

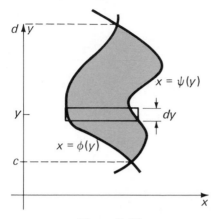

Figure 8–39

EXAMPLE   Find the moment of inertia of the region in the first quadrant bounded by $y = x^2$, $x + y = 2$, and $x = 0$ about the x-axis. Also find the radius of gyration.

First Solution   The region is shown in Fig. 8-40. Using formula (1) with $f(x) = x^2$, $g(x) = 2 - x$, $a = 0$, and $b = 1$, we have

$$I_x = \frac{1}{3} \int_0^1 [(2 - x)^3 - x^6]\, dx$$

$$= \frac{1}{3} \left[-\frac{1}{4}(2 - x)^4 - \frac{1}{7}x^7 \right] \Big|_0^1$$

$$= \frac{1}{3} \left[\left(-\frac{1}{4} - \frac{1}{7} \right) - (-4 - 0) \right] = \frac{101}{84}$$

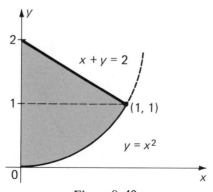

Figure 8–40

The area of the region is

$$A = \int_0^1 [(2 - x) - x^2]\, dx = \left[-\frac{1}{2}(2 - x)^2 - \frac{1}{3}x^3 \right]\Big|_0^1$$

$$= \left[\left(-\frac{1}{2} - \frac{1}{3} \right) - (-2 - 0) \right] = \frac{7}{6}$$

so that the radius of gyration is

$$R_x = \sqrt{I_x/A} = \sqrt{\frac{101}{98}} \approx 1.02$$

Second Solution   Now let us find I_x by using horizontal slices. For $0 \leq y \leq 1$, the slice at y contributes $dA = \sqrt{y}\, dy$ and so $dI_x = y^2\, dA = y^{5/2}\, dy$. For $1 \leq y \leq 2$, the slice at y gives $dA = (2 - y)\, dy$ and so $dI_x = y^2\, dA = (2y^2 - y^3)\, dy$. Thus

$$I_x = \int_0^1 y^{5/2}\, dy + \int_1^2 (2y^2 - y^3)\, dy$$

$$= \frac{2}{7} y^{7/2}\Big|_0^1 + \left(\frac{2}{3}y^3 - \frac{1}{4}y^4 \right)\Big|_1^2$$

$$= \frac{2}{7} + \left(\frac{16}{3} - \frac{16}{4} \right) - \left(\frac{2}{3} - \frac{1}{4} \right) = \frac{101}{84}$$

EXAMPLE   Find the moment of inertia of a circular disc of radius a about a diameter. Also find the radius of gyration.

Solution   We take the disc to be the region bounded by $x^2 + y^2 = a^2$ and the axis to be the x-axis. Considering horizontal slices (see Fig. 8-41), we see that $dA = 2x\, dy = 2\sqrt{a^2 - y^2}\, dy$ and the distance of

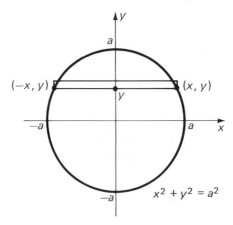

Figure 8–41

the slice to the axis is $|y|$. Thus

$$dI_x = 2y^2\sqrt{a^2 - y^2}\ dy$$

and

$$I_x = \int_{-a}^{a} 2y^2\sqrt{a^2 - y^2}\ dy$$

Making the trigonometric substitution $y = a \sin \theta$, we have $\sqrt{a^2 - y^2} = |a \cos \theta|$ and $dy = a \cos \theta\ d\theta$. Thus

$$I_x = 2\int_{-\pi/2}^{\pi/2} (a^2 \sin^2 \theta)(a \cos \theta)(a \cos \theta\ d\theta)$$

$$= 2a^4 \int_{-\pi/2}^{\pi/2} \sin^2 \theta \cos^2 \theta\ d\theta$$

$$= 2a^4 \int_{-\pi/2}^{\pi/2} \frac{1 - \cos 2\theta}{2} \cdot \frac{1 + \cos 2\theta}{2}\ d\theta$$

$$= \frac{a^4}{2} \int_{-\pi/2}^{\pi/2} (1 - \cos^2 2\theta)\ d\theta$$

$$= \frac{\pi a^4}{2} - \frac{a^4}{2} \int_{-\pi/2}^{\pi/2} \frac{1 + \cos 4\theta}{2}\ d\theta$$

$$= \frac{\pi a^4}{2} - \frac{\pi a^4}{4} - \frac{a^4}{16} \sin 4\theta\ \Big|_{-\pi/2}^{\pi/2} = \frac{\pi a^4}{4}$$

Since $A = \pi a^2$, we have

$$R_x = \sqrt{I_x/A} = a/2$$

EXERCISES

In 1–15, find (a) the moment of inertia and (b) the radius of gyration of the region bounded by the given curves about the given axis.

1. $y = x^2$, $x = 1$, $y = 0$; about y-axis
2. $y = x^2$, $x = 1$, $y = 0$; about x-axis
3. $y^2 = x$, $x + y = 2$, $x = 0$; about x-axis
4. $y^2 = x$, $x + y = 2$, $x = 0$; about y-axis
5. $y^2 = x + 9$, $x = 0$; about y-axis
6. $y^2 = x + 9$, $x = 0$; about x-axis
7. $x + y = 2$, $x = 0$, $y = 0$; about $x = 2$
8. $y = 4x - x^2$, $y = x$; about x-axis
9. $y = x^3$, $x = 0$, $y = 8$; about $x = 3$

10. $y = x^3$, $x = 0$, $y = 8$; about $y = 8$
11. $y = x^2 - 2x + 1$, $y = 1 + 4x - x^2$; about x-axis
12. $x^3 = y^2$, $x + y^2 = 2$; about x-axis
13. $y = \sin x$, $y = 0$, $0 \le x \le \pi$; about x-axis
14. $y = e^{2x}$, $y = 5e^x - 4$; about y-axis
15. $y = e^{2x}$, $y = 5e^x - 4$; about x-axis

In 16–21, find (a) the moment of inertia and (b) the radius of gyration of the given plane region about the given axis.

16. An equilateral triangle of side a about a side.
17. A circular disc of radius a about a tangent line.
18. A square of side a about a diagonal.
19. An isosceles triangle of base b and two sides of length a about the perpendicular bisector of the base.
20. The triangle of exercise 19 about its base.
21. A rectangle of sides a and b about a diagonal.

11   Some Applications of the Integral to Business

Before we begin we recommend that the reader review section 5 of Chapter 4.

If $R(x)$ is a differentiable revenue function (in dollars), then $R'(x)$ is the corresponding marginal revenue function. For $0 \le a \le b$ we clearly have

$$R(b) - R(a) = \int_a^b R'(x)\, dx \tag{1}$$

EXAMPLE   If $R'(x) = \dfrac{x^2}{4} + x + 10$, (a) find $R(100)$, and (b) find the change in revenue when the production level, x, changes from 40 to 50.

Solution   (a) Clearly $R(0) = 0$. Thus, by (1),

$$R(100) = R(100) - R(0) = \int_0^{100} \left(\frac{x^2}{4} + x + 10 \right) dx$$

$$= \left[\frac{x^3}{12} + \frac{x^2}{2} + 10x \right] \Big|_0^{100} = \$89{,}333.33$$

(b) $R(50) - R(40) = \int_{40}^{50} R'(x)\, dx = \left[\frac{x^3}{12} + \frac{x^2}{2} + 10x \right] \Big|_{40}^{50}$

$$= \$5{,}633.33$$

Note. Similar considerations also apply to $P'(x)$, the marginal profit function and $C'(x)$, the marginal cost function.

The next example concerns the **present value of an income stream.** Suppose that, over a period of time t, $0 \leq a \leq t \leq b$, measured in years, income is being continuously produced by, for example, a machine. Let $f(t)$ be a continuous function representing the annual rate of income (in dollars) at time t. We would like to find the present value at an annual interest rate r compounded continuously, of the "income stream" produced from $t = a$ to $t = b$. Recall that the present value of A dollars in t years at an annual rate of r compounded continuously is the principal, P dollars, which must be invested now at an annual rate r compounded continuously in order to amount to A dollars in t years. We have $P = Ae^{-rt}$.

Let us divide the time interval $[a,b]$ into consecutive intervals of length $\dfrac{b - a}{n} = \Delta t$, whose endpoints are $a = t_0 < t_1 < \ldots < t_n = b$. Then if n is large, the income earned during the time interval $t_k \leq t \leq t_{k+1}$, $0 \leq k \leq n - 1$, is approximately $f(t_k)\Delta t$. Thus, the present value of this amount is approximately

$$(f(t_k)\Delta t)e^{-rt_k}$$

where we regard the total income earned during $[t_k, t_{k+1}]$ as earned at time t_k.

We now sum over $0 \leq k \leq n - 1$ to obtain

$$f(t_0)\Delta t e^{-rt_0} + f(t_1)\Delta t e^{-rt_1} + \ldots + f(t_{n-1})\Delta t e^{-rt_{n-1}} \qquad (2)$$

as an approximation for the present value of the income stream.

Finally, we factor out Δt and let $n \to \infty$ to obtain

$$\boxed{\int_a^b f(t)e^{-rt}\, dt} \qquad (3)$$

for the present value of the income stream.

EXAMPLE   A machine produces a continuous stream of income. The rate of income at time t years, $0 \leq t \leq 10$, is $1000 - \dfrac{t^2}{2}$ dollars per year.

(a) Find, to the nearest dollar, the present value of the income stream if interest is compounded continuously at a rate of 5% annually.

(b) Find, to the nearest dollar, the value of the income stream.

Solution   (a) Here $a = 0$, $b = 10$, $r = .05$, and $f(t) = 1000 - \dfrac{t^2}{2}$. The number we seek is

$$\int_0^{10} \left(1000 - \frac{t^2}{2}\right) e^{-.05t} \, dt$$

We integrate by parts with $u(t) = 1000 - t^2/2$ and

$$v(t) = \frac{e^{-.05t}}{-.05} = -20 e^{-.05t}$$

Thus,

$$\int_0^{10} (1000 - t^2/2) e^{-.05t} \, dt = (1000 - t^2/2)(-20 e^{-.05t}) \Big|_0^{10} - \int_0^{10} -20 e^{-.05t}(-t) \, dt$$

$$= 8475.91 - 20\left(t\frac{e^{-.05t}}{-.05}\Big|_0^{10} - \int_0^{10} \frac{e^{-.05t}}{-.05}(+1) \, dt\right) \qquad \text{(integrating by parts again)}$$

$$= 8475.91 - 20\left(-121.31 + 20\int_0^{10} e^{-.05t} \, dt\right)$$

$$= 8475.91 - 20\left(-121.31 + 20\left(-20 e^{-.05t}\Big|_0^{20}\right)\right)$$

$$= 8475.91 - 20(-121.31 + 157.39) = 7754.31 = \$7754$$

to the nearest dollar.

(b) Since the rate of income produced at time t is $1000 - \dfrac{t^2}{2}$ dollars per year, the value of the income stream, which is the total income produced, is

$$\int_0^{10} \left(1000 - \frac{t^2}{2}\right) dt = \left(1000t - \frac{t^3}{6}\right)\Big|_0^{10} = \$9833$$

to the nearest dollar.

We close with another application of the integral.

EXAMPLE   A large company estimates that, in a period of increasing demand, it will produce its product at a rate of $1000 + 2t^{1.2}$ units per unit time. Find the total number of units which will be produced between $t = 2$ and $t = 5$.

Solution   Since $1000 + 2t^{1.2}$ is the rate of production, then the amount produced from time $t = 2$ to $t = 5$ is the integral

$$\int_2^5 (1000 + 2t^{1.2}) \, dt = \left(1000t + \frac{2t^{2.2}}{2.2} \right) \Big|_2^5 \approx 5031 - 2004 = 3027$$

EXERCISES

1. Suppose a marginal cost function is given by $C'(x) = 2000 + 2.5\sqrt{x}$ (in dollars).
   (a) Find, to the nearest dollar, the cost of producing the first 100 units if the fixed cost, $C(0)$, is \$3500.
   (b) Find, to the nearest dollar, the cost of producing the second hundred units.

2. A continuous income stream produces income at an annual rate of $150 - 3t/2$ dollars per year from $t = 2$ years to $t = 8$ years.
   (a) Find, to the nearest dollar, the present value of this income stream if interest is compounded continuously at a rate of 8% annually.
   (b) Find, to the nearest dollar, the value of the income stream.

3. From time $t = 4$ to $t = 10$, a company produces its product at a rate of $5000 - 20t^2$ units per unit time. Find the number of units produced during this time period.

4. A manufacturer wishes to produce 200 units of his product. One production method has marginal profit function $P'_1(x) = 2 + \dfrac{\sqrt{x}}{100}$ in hundreds of dollars. A second method of production has marginal profit function $P'_2(x) = .8 + \dfrac{\ln (x + 1)}{3}$. Which production method will yield the greatest profit? By how much?

Chapter 9

Approximations

1 Newton's Method and Linear Approximations

In this chapter, we will study several methods for obtaining numerical values which are close to specific numbers in which we may be interested. The first of these is called **Newton's Method**, in honor of the English mathematician, Sir Isaac Newton (1642–1727), one of the founders of the calculus.

Suppose we wish to find an approximation to $\sqrt{31}$. Since $\sqrt{31}$ is an irrational number, we cannot express $\sqrt{31}$ as a terminating or repeating decimal. However, our aim is to find some terminating decimal which is close to $\sqrt{31}$. Before we proceed, it is appropriate here to discuss the role of the pocket calculator. Most calculators will approximate $\sqrt{31}$ for you to eight or more decimal places by the push of a button. Why then do we need to be able to calculate $\sqrt{31}$ by some other method? The answer is threefold. First of all, it is helpful to see how the calculus may be used to solve practical problems, many of which *cannot* be done on a calculator. Second, Newton's Method (and other methods we will learn) will enable us to achieve virtually any degree of accuracy which we desire, whereas a calculator's accuracy is limited to eight or ten decimal places. Third, it is desirable to be able to do mathematics without the aid of a crutch. Of course calculators are a wonderful tool. They can save us much time and effort and the authors freely use them, especially in this chapter. However, whenever possible, it is nice to know how to do something on your own.

432

Recall that $f'(a) = \lim\limits_{x \to a} \dfrac{f(x) - f(a)}{x - a}$, assuming that the limit exists.

Thus, if x is "close enough" to a, $x \neq a$, then $\dfrac{f(x) - f(a)}{x - a}$ is "close" to $f'(a)$. We use the symbol $\approx$ to mean "close to." We have

$$f'(a) \approx \frac{f(x) - f(a)}{x - a} \qquad \text{if } x \approx a,\, x \neq a \qquad (1)$$

Equivalently, we may write

$$\boxed{f(x) \approx f(a) + (x - a)f'(a) \qquad \text{if } x \approx a} \qquad (2)$$

We make a small digression here and observe that this relationship by itself will allow us to approximate linearly both the value of a function at a point and also the change in the value of a function between two points. However, at present, we don't have any estimate of the size of our error in approximation. We must have faith that our approximations are indeed "close." In the next section, we will be able to estimate our error.

EXAMPLE Use expression (2) to approximate $\sqrt[3]{35}$.

Solution Let $f(x) = \sqrt[3]{x}$. Since we are interested in $\sqrt[3]{35}$, let's choose $a = 27$, since $\sqrt[3]{27}$ is a number we know and 27 is reasonably close to 35. Then by (2), with $x = 35$, $\sqrt[3]{35} \approx \sqrt[3]{27} + (35 - 27)f'(27)$. Since $f'(x) = (1/3)x^{-2/3}$, we see that $f'(27) = (1/3)(27)^{-2/3} = 1/27$. Thus,

$$\sqrt[3]{35} \approx 3 + (35 - 27)(1/27) \approx 3.296$$

Note. $\sqrt[3]{35}$ is actually between 3.271 and 3.272.

EXAMPLE Use expression (2) to approximate $\ln 10$. Use $e \approx 2.718$.

Solution Let $f(x) = \ln x$. Since e^2 is not far from 10, let $a = e^2$. Then (2) becomes $\ln 10 \approx \ln e^2 + (10 - e^2)f'(e^2)$. Now $f'(x) = 1/x$, so that

$$\ln 10 \approx 2 + (10 - e^2) \cdot 1/e^2 \approx 2.354$$

Note. $\ln 10$ is actually a little less than 2.303.

EXAMPLE Let $f(x) = x^4 + 2x^3 - x^2 + 5$. Estimate the change in f as x varies from 10 to 10.5.

Solution To make the notation less confusing, write (2) as

$$f(b) \approx f(a) + (b - a)f'(a)$$

Subtract $f(a)$ from both sides of this approximation to obtain

$$f(b) - f(a) \approx (b - a)f'(a)$$

Let $b = 10.5$ and $a = 10$. Since $f'(x) = 4x^3 + 6x^2 - 2x$, we see that $f'(10) = 4580$. Thus,

$$f(10.5) - f(10) \approx (10.5 - 10) \cdot 4580 = 2290$$

Note. Actually, $f(10.5) - f(10) = 14365.0625 - 11905 = 2460.0625$.

EXAMPLE   Approximate $\ln 20 - \ln 18$.

Solution   Let $f(x) = \ln x$. Then $f'(x) = 1/x$. If $b = 20$ and $a = 18$,
then $f(b) - f(a) \approx (b - a)f'(a)$ becomes

$$\ln 20 - \ln 18 \approx 2 \cdot \frac{1}{18} = \frac{1}{9} \approx .111$$

Note. Actually, $\ln 20 - \ln 18$ is between .105 and .106.

We now return to our basic relationship:

$$f(x) \approx f(a) + (x - a)f'(a) \tag{2}$$

Instead of trying to approximate $\sqrt{31}$ by the method we have been using, we turn the tables a bit. We will think of $\sqrt{31}$ as the positive solution to the equation $x^2 - 31 = 0$. What we then wish to do is approximate the positive solution of $x^2 - 31 = 0$.

Newton's method uses the relationship (2) over and over in order to generate a sequence $a_0, a_1, a_2, a_3, \ldots$ of approximations to a solution $x = x_0$ of an equation of the form $f(x) = 0$ where f is differentiable. The procedure is to begin by choosing any approximation a_0 that is "near" x_0. Once we have arrived at a_n for some $n \geq 0$ (for example, $n = 0$), we calculate the next approximation a_{n+1} as follows. Substitute $x = x_0$ and $a = a_n$ into (2) to obtain $0 \approx f(a_n) + (x_0 - a_n)f'(a_n)$ and then "solve" for x_0 as if this were an equation to get

$$\boxed{x_0 \approx a_n - \frac{f(a_n)}{f'(a_n)} = a_{n+1}}$$

where this equality defines a_{n+1}.

We apply this method with $f(x) = x^2 - 31$ and $x_0 = \sqrt{31}$. Choosing $a_0 = 6$, we obtain

$$a_1 = a_0 - \frac{f(a_0)}{f'(a_0)} = 6 - \frac{5}{12} \approx 5.6$$

$$a_2 = a_1 - \frac{f(a_1)}{f'(a_1)} \approx 5.6 - \frac{f(5.6)}{f'(5.6)}$$

$$= 5.6 - \frac{.36}{11.2} \approx 5.568$$

This is quite an accurate approximation to $\sqrt{31}$. In fact, it can be shown that in Newton's Method,

$$|x_0 - a_n| \le \frac{U}{2L}(a_n - a_{n-1})^2 \tag{3}$$

if U and L are any numbers which satisfy $|f'(x)| \ge L > 0$ and $|f''(x)| \le U$ for all x between a_{n-1} and a_n. Since $|x_0 - a_n|$ represents the error in the approximation a_n, we see that the size of this error can be estimated if we can estimate the sizes of $f'(x)$ and $f''(x)$ for x between a_{n-1} and a_n. In our case we have $f'(x) = 2x \ge 11 = L$ and $f''(x) = 2 = U$ for $x \ge 5.5$, so (3) tells us that $|\sqrt{31} - a_2| \le \frac{(a_2 - a_1)^2}{11} < .0001$.

We will not go into details here, but for most cases, just a few iterations of Newton's Method will approximate our desired value x_0 to a high degree of accuracy (small error).

Note. It is possible to "cook up" functions and values x_0 such that if a_0 is not chosen very close to x_0 to start with, then Newton's Method does not "zero in" on x_0. However, in many applications, just an integer close to x_0 is quite good enough for our choice for a_0.

EXAMPLE Use Newton's Method to find a first and a second approximation to the solution of the equation $x^3 + x - 1 = 0$.

Solution Let $f(x) = x^3 + x - 1$. Then $f(0) = -1 < 0$ and $f(1) = 1 > 0$. Since $f'(x) = 3x^2 + 1 > 0$ for all x, f is increasing everywhere. Thus, the solution x_0 is somewhere between 0 and 1. Take $a_0 = 1$; then, since $f'(1) = 4$, expression (2) becomes

$$0 \approx 1 + (x_0 - 1) \cdot 4$$

So, $x_0 \approx 3/4 = a_1$, which is a first approximation. Taking $a = a_1 = 3/4$, we have

$$0 \approx 11/64 + (x_0 - 3/4) \cdot 43/16$$

So, $x_0 \approx 59/86 = a_2$, which is a second approximation. One checks that $f\left(\dfrac{59}{86}\right) = 0.009$ to three decimal places.

Note. Of course, the accuracy of our successive approximations depends on our initial choice of a_0. If, in the previous example, we had chosen $a_0 = 0$ instead of $a_0 = 1$, we would have found $a_1 = 1$ and $a_2 = 3/4$, which is not quite as accurate as $a_1 = 3/4$ and $a_2 = 59/86$. Therefore, to get the best results, we should try to choose a_0 as accurately as possible. Even so, as long as we make some viable choice for a_0, enough iterations of Newton's Method will bring us as close as we wish to our goal.

EXAMPLE Use Newton's Method to find a first and a second approximation to the largest solution of the equation $\ln x = x - 2$.

Solution From the graphs of $y = \ln x$ and $y = x - 2$ shown in Fig. 9-1, we see that the value x_0 which we are seeking is a little greater than 3. We rewrite the equation as $f(x) = \ln x - x + 2 = 0$ and take $a = 3$. Then (2) becomes

$$0 \approx \ln 3 - 1 + (x_0 - 3) \cdot \left(\frac{1}{3} - 1\right)$$

Thus, we have $x_0 \approx 3.1 = a_1$. (We use either a log table or a calculator to approximate $\ln 3$.)

Next, setting $a = 3.1$, we obtain

$$0 \approx \ln (3.1) - 1.1 + (x_0 - 3.1)\left(\frac{1}{3.1} - 1\right)$$

and so $x_0 \approx 3.15 = a_2$, which is our second approximation.

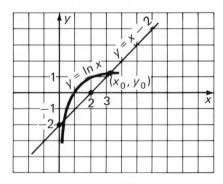

Figure 9-1

Note. Whenever we apply Newton's Method to solve an equation, we should always first put the equation in the form $f(x) = 0$ and then proceed.

EXAMPLE For $900 Mrs. Bucks bought a bond which had a face value of $1000. The bond paid $50 interest per year. The bond was to mature in 1.5 years. That is, 1.5 years after she bought the bond she could cash it in for $1000.

(a) The **percent of annual return** on her investment is the fraction of her original cost (expressed as a percent) which she earns each year. Write a formula for the percent of annual return and compute her percent of annual return.

(b) Suppose that, due to rising interest rates immediately after Mrs. Bucks bought the bond, the percent of annual return on similar bonds began to rise at an annual rate of 40% annually compounded continuously until the maturity date of the bond. Thus, the value of Mrs. Bucks' bond dropped immediately after she bought it because the percent of annual return rose considerably and this increased annual return must result from a lower value for the bond. On the other hand, the value of the bond eventually increased because in 1.5 years it was worth $1000. If $v(t)$ is the value of the bond t years after her purchase, $0 \le t \le 1.5$, use Newton's Method to approximate the value of $t > 0$ for which $v(t) = 900$. In other words, estimate how long it takes until her bond is again worth $900.

Solution (a) Mrs. Bucks' percent of annual return is

$$\frac{\text{annual interest} + \dfrac{(\text{maturity value} - \text{cost})}{\text{time till maturity}}}{\text{cost}} \cdot 100\% = \frac{50 + \dfrac{100}{1.5}}{900} \cdot 100\%$$
$$= 12.96\%$$

(b) At time t, the percent of annual return, due to the continuous compounding at 40% annually, is $.1296e^{.4t}$. Therefore, at time t we must have

$$.1296e^{.4t}v(t)(1.5 - t) = 1000 - v(t) + 50(1.5 - t) \tag{1}$$

because $1000 - v(t)$ is the amount of increase in value of the bond from time t till maturity and $50(1.5 - t)$ is the total interest earned from time t till maturity.

In (1), we set $v(t) = 900$ and obtain

$$.1296e^{.4t} \cdot 900 \cdot (1.5 - t) = 100 + 50(1.5 - t) \tag{2}$$

or

$$116.64e^{.4t}(1.5 - t) = 100 + 50(1.5 - t) \tag{3}$$

or

$$f(t) = 116.64e^{.4t}(1.5 - t) - 100 - 50(1.5 - t) = 0 \tag{4}$$

Notice that

$$f'(t) = .4(116.64)e^{.4t}(1.5 - t) - 116.64e^{.4t} + 50 \tag{5}$$

We want to find $t_0 > 0$ for which $f(t_0) = 0$. If we try $a = .5$ as a first approximation, then $f(a) \approx -7.54$. Also, $f'(a) \approx -35.48$. Thus, the approximation

$$0 \approx f(a) + (t_0 - a)f'(a)$$

becomes

$$0 \approx -7.54 + (t_0 - .5)(-35.48)$$

so that $t_0 \approx .29 = t_1$.

Since $f(t_1) \approx -2.01$ and $f'(t_1) \approx -17.72$, a second approximation is given by

$$0 \approx -2.01 + (t_0 - .29)(-17.72)$$

so that $t_0 \approx .18 = t_2$

Since $f(t_2) \approx -.54$ and $f'(t_2) \approx -9.16$, a third approximation yields

$$0 \approx -.54 + (t_0 - .18)(-9.16)$$

so that $t_0 \approx .12 = t_3$.

Finally, since $f(t_3) \approx -.12$ and $f'(t_3) \approx -4.82$, a fourth approximation yields

$$0 \approx -.12 + (t_0 - .12)(-4.82)$$

This gives $t_0 \approx .095$ years, or approximately 35 days.

If we substitute $t = .095$ into (1) and solve for $v(t)$ we find that $v(.095) \approx 900.02$.

Of course, if we had chosen a better first approximation, then we would not need so many iterations to get near our final result, but sometimes it is difficult to choose a very precise first approximation and sometimes our successive approximations may not rapidly approach the approximation with the desired degree of accuracy which we seek.

E X E R C I S E S

In 1–6, use the relationship $f(x) \approx f(a) + (x-a)f'(a)$ to obtain a two-decimal-place approximation of the number. Use $e \approx 2.718$ and $\pi \approx 3.142$.

1. $\sqrt{5}$; $f(x) = \sqrt{x}$, $x = 5$, $a = 4$
2. $\ln 8$; $f(x) = \ln x$, $x = 8$, $a = e^2$
3. $e^{.5}$; $f(x) = e^x$, $x = .5$, $a = 0$
4. $\sqrt[5]{33}$; $f(x) = \sqrt[5]{x}$, $x = 33$, $a = 32$
5. $(1.02)^{10}$; $f(x) = x^{10}$, $x = 1.02$, $a = 1$
6. $\sin 3.5$; $f(x) = \sin x$, $x = 3.5$, $a = \pi$

In 7–12, use the relationship $f(b) - f(a) \approx (b-a)f'(a)$ to obtain a two-decimal-place approximation of the change in $f(x)$ as x goes from a to b. Use $\pi \approx 3.142$.

7. $f(x) = x^2$; $a = 4$, $b = 4.2$
8. $f(x) = \ln 2x$; $a = 1$, $b = 2$
9. $f(x) = e^x$; $a = 0$, $b = -.3$
10. $f(x) = x^3 - x^2$; $a = 5$, $b = 5.1$
11. $f(x) = \sin x$; $a = \pi$, $b = 4$
12. $f(x) = \cos x$; $a = 0$, $b = -.1$

In 13–22, use Newton's Method to give a first and a second approximation to the indicated value. In each case give the first approximation to one decimal place and the second approximation to two decimal places.

13. $\sqrt{3}$ 14. $\sqrt[3]{11}$ 15. $\sqrt{77}$ 16. $\sqrt[3]{1.2}$ 17. $\sqrt[3]{9}$ 18. $\sqrt{96}$

19. The solution to $x^3 + 2x - 4 = 0$.
20. The solution to $-x^3 + x - 1 = 0$.
21. (a) The positive solution of $x^4 + x - 1 = 0$.
    (b) The negative solution of $x^4 + x - 1 = 0$.
22. The solution to $e^x = x^2$.
23. (a) Graph $f(x) = \ln (x + 2)$ and $g(x) = x - 1$ on the same coordinate plane.
    (b) Use the result of part (a) to approximate the negative solution to $\ln (x + 2) = x - 1$ and then apply Newton's Method to improve your estimate.
    (c) Use the result of part (a) to approximate the positive solution to $\ln (x + 2) = x - 1$ and then apply Newton's Method to improve your estimate.

24. Without the use of trig tables, use the solution to exercise 13 above to approximate the positive solution to $\sin x = .8x$. [*Hint:* Search among the "common" angles, 0, $\pi/6$, $\pi/4$, $\pi/3$, $\pi/2$, etc., whose trig functions are well known to find a suitable value for a_0 in Newton's Method.]

2 Taylor's Formula

Suppose we begin with the polynomial function

$$f(x) = a_4 x^4 + a_3 x^3 + a_2 x^2 + a_1 x + a_0 \qquad a_4 \neq 0$$

Then,

$$\begin{aligned}
f'(x) &= 4a_4 x^3 + 3a_3 x^2 + 2a_2 x + a_1 \\
f''(x) &= 4 \cdot 3a_4 x^2 + 3 \cdot 2a_3 x + 2a_2 \\
f'''(x) &= 4 \cdot 3 \cdot 2a_4 x + 3 \cdot 2a_3 \\
f''''(x) &= 4 \cdot 3 \cdot 2a_4
\end{aligned}$$

Thus,

$$\begin{aligned}
f(0) &= a_0 \\
f'(0) &= a_1 \\
f''(0) &= 2a_2 \\
f'''(0) &= 3 \cdot 2a_3 \\
f''''(0) &= 4 \cdot 3 \cdot 2a_4
\end{aligned}$$

If we define $0! = 1$, $1! = 1$, $2! = 2 \cdot 1$, and, in general, $n! = n((n-1)!) = n \cdot (n-1) \cdot (n-2) \cdot \ldots \cdot 3 \cdot 2 \cdot 1$, for $n > 1$, we may write

$$a_0 = \frac{f(0)}{0!}$$

$$a_1 = \frac{f'(0)}{1!}$$

$$a_2 = \frac{f''(0)}{2!}$$

$$a_3 = \frac{f'''(0)}{3!}$$

$$a_4 = \frac{f''''(0)}{4!}$$

The same line of reasoning allows us to generalize as follows: If $f(x) = a_n x^n + a_{n-1} x^{n-1} + \ldots + a_1 x + a_0$, $a_n \neq 0$, is any polynomial function of degree n, then (recalling that $f^{(n)}(x)$ means the nth derivative of f at x)

$$a_0 = \frac{f(0)}{0!} = f(0)$$

$$a_1 = \frac{f'(0)}{1!} = f'(0)$$

$$a_2 = \frac{f''(0)}{2!}$$

$$a_3 = \frac{f'''(0)}{3!}$$

$$\cdot$$
$$\cdot$$
$$\cdot$$

$$a_{n-1} = \frac{f^{(n-1)}(0)}{(n-1)!}$$

$$a_n = \frac{f^{(n)}(0)}{n!}$$

We have just seen that the coefficients of a polynomial function f may be expressed in terms of the derivatives of f at 0. Specifically,

$$f(x) = a_n x^n + a_{n-1}x^{n-1} + \ldots + a_1 x + a_0$$

$$= \frac{f^{(n)}(0)}{n!}x^n + \frac{f^{(n-1)}(0)}{(n-1)!}x^{n-1} + \ldots + \frac{f'''(0)}{3!}x^3 + \frac{f''(0)}{2!}x^2 + f'(0)x + f(0) \qquad (1)$$

A very important theorem named for the English mathematician Brook Taylor (1685–1731) tells us that many nonpolynomial functions behave somewhat like polynomials in this respect. We have the following theorem:

> **Theorem (Taylor's Formula)** Suppose f is $n + 1$ times differentiable on some closed interval having endpoints a and b ($a \neq b$). Then, there is some number c strictly between a and b such that

$$f(b) = f(a) + \frac{f'(a)}{1!}(b - a) + \frac{f''(a)}{2!}(b - a)^2$$

$$+ \ldots + \frac{f^{(n)}(a)}{n!}(b - a)^n + \frac{f^{(n+1)}(c)}{(n + 1)!}(b - a)^{n+1} \qquad (2)$$

That is,

$$f(b) = \sum_{k=0}^{n} \frac{f^{(k)}(a)}{k!}(b - a)^k + \frac{f^{(n+1)}(c)}{(n + 1)!}(b - a)^{n+1} \qquad (2')$$

Note. By convention, $f^{(0)} = f$; that is, the 0th derivative is the function itself. In case f is a polynomial function of degree n, then, for $b = x$ and $a = 0$, (2) reduces to (1) for *any* c between 0 and x, because $f^{(n+1)}(c) = 0$, for all c. If we let $n = 0$ in (2), then we get

$$f(b) = f(a) + \frac{f'(c)}{1!}(b - a)$$

for some c between a and b. That is, $f'(c) = \dfrac{f(b) - f(a)}{b - a}$. This is, of course MVT (Mean Value Theorem). Thus, Taylor's Formula is a generalization of MVT. In fact, we will use MVT (whose proof is in the Appendix) to prove Taylor's Formula.

Proof   For $n \geq 0$, we define the number A_{n+1} by

$$A_{n+1} = \frac{f(b) - f(a) - f'(a)(b - a) - \dfrac{f''(a)}{2!}(b - a)^2 - \ldots - \dfrac{f^{(n)}(a)}{n!}(b - a)^n}{(b - a)^{n+1}} \tag{3}$$

Also, we define a function F on our closed interval by

$$F(x) = -f(b) + f(x) + f'(x)(b - x) + \frac{f''(x)}{2!}(b - x)^2$$

$$+ \ldots + \frac{f^{(n)}(x)}{n!}(b - x)^n + A_{n+1}(b - x)^{n+1} \tag{4}$$

Since each term on the right side of equation (4) is differentiable on our interval, it follows that F too is differentiable there. Now, differentiating in (4) gives

$$F'(x) = 0 + f'(x) + [-f'(x) + f''(x)(b - x)]$$

$$+ \left[-\frac{f''(x)}{2!}2(b - x) + \frac{f'''(x)}{2!}(b - x)^2 \right]$$

$$+ \left[-\frac{f'''(x)}{3!}3(b - x)^2 + \frac{f''''(x)}{3!}(b - x)^3 \right] + \ldots$$

$$+ \left[-\frac{f^{(n)}(x)}{n!}n(b - x)^{n-1} + \frac{f^{(n+1)}(x)}{n!}(b - x)^n \right]$$

$$- (n + 1)A_{n+1}(b - x)^n \tag{5}$$

Now shift the brackets to obtain

$$F'(x) = [f'(x) - f'(x)] + \left[f''(x)(b - x) - \frac{f''(x)}{2!}2(b - x) \right]$$

$$+ \left[\frac{f'''(x)}{2!}(b - x)^2 - \frac{f'''(x)}{3!}3(b - x)^2 \right] + \ldots$$

$$+ \left[\frac{f^{(n)}(x)}{(n - 1)!}(b - x)^{n-1} - \frac{f^{(n)}(x)}{n!}n(b - x)^{n-1} \right]$$

$$+ \frac{f^{(n+1)}(x)}{n!}(b - x)^n - (n + 1)A_{n+1}(b - x)^n \tag{6}$$

Since each bracket is obviously 0, we have

$$F'(x) = \frac{f^{(n+1)}(x)}{n!}(b - x)^n - (n + 1)A_{n+1}(b - x)^n \tag{7}$$

Now, for $x = a$, (4) becomes

$$F(a) = -f(b) + f(a) + f'(a)(b-a) + \frac{f''(a)}{2!}(b-a)^2 + \dots$$
$$+ \frac{f^{(n)}(a)}{n!}(b-a)^n + A_{n+1}(b-a)^{n+1}$$

which is 0 by (3).

It is also clear that if we substitute $x = b$ in (4), we obtain $F(b) = 0$. Thus, since $F(a) = F(b) = 0$ and F is differentiable on our closed interval, MVT tells us that there is some c between a and b such that

$$F'(c) = \frac{F(b) - F(a)}{b - a} = 0$$

From (7) it now follows that

$$0 = F'(c) = \frac{f^{(n+1)}(c)}{n!}(b-c)^n - (n+1)A_{n+1}(b-c)^n \qquad (8)$$

We solve (8) for A_{n+1} to obtain

$$A_{n+1} = \frac{f^{(n+1)}(c)}{(n+1)!} \qquad (9)$$

Finally, substitute (9) into (3) and multiply through by $(b-a)^{n+1}$ to arrive at (2). This completes the proof. ∎

If x is in the closed interval between a and b, then clearly we may substitute x for b in (2) to obtain

$$f(x) = f(a) + \frac{f'(a)}{1!}(x-a) + \frac{f''(a)}{2!}(x-a)^2 + \dots + \frac{f^{(n)}(a)}{n!}(x-a)^n$$
$$+ \frac{f^{(n+1)}(c)}{(n+1)!}(x-a)^{n+1} \qquad n \geq 0 \qquad (10)$$

The right side of equation (10) is called a **Taylor expansion of f centered at a.**

In (10), we write

$$P_n(x) = f(a) + \frac{f'(a)}{1!}(x-a) + \frac{f''(a)}{2!}(x-a)^2 + \dots + \frac{f^{(n)}(a)}{n!}(x-a)^n$$
$$= \sum_{k=0}^{n} \frac{f^{(k)}(a)}{k!}(x-a)^k \qquad (11)$$

and

$$R_n(x) = \frac{f^{(n+1)}(c)}{(n+1)!}(x-a)^{n+1} \qquad n \geq 0$$

The polynomial $P_n(x)$ is called the **nth degree Taylor polynomial of f at a,** while $R_n(x)$ is called the **remainder.** When $a = 0$, the Taylor polynomials are called **Maclaurin polynomials.** Note carefully that the number c which appears in formula (11) for $R_n(x)$ depends upon the number x and all that we know for sure about c is that it is somewhere in the open interval between a and x.

Recall that in the last section we made use of the linear approximation

$$f(x) \approx f(a) + (x - a)f'(a)$$

The difficulty was that we couldn't estimate the error in our approximation. Now, provided that f is twice differentiable on the closed interval from a to x, we may use Taylor's Formula to estimate the error. We have

$$f(x) = f(a) + (x - a)f'(a) + \frac{f''(c)}{2}(x - a)^2 \tag{12}$$

for some c between a and x.

EXAMPLE Approximate $\sqrt[3]{35}$ by using (12) with $a = 27$, $x = 35$, and $f(x) = \sqrt[3]{x}$. Estimate the error.

Solution When we did this problem in the last section, we found that $\sqrt[3]{35} \approx \sqrt[3]{27} + (35 - 27) \cdot \dfrac{1}{27} \approx 3.296$. Here, we have (since $f''(x) = -\dfrac{2}{9}x^{-5/3}$)

$$\sqrt[3]{35} = \sqrt[3]{27} + (35 - 27) \cdot \frac{1}{27} + \frac{-2}{18}c^{-5/3}(35 - 27)^2$$

Thus, our error is $\dfrac{-2}{18}c^{-5/3}(35 - 27)^2$. Since $27 < c < 35$, the absolute value of the error is less than

$$\frac{2}{18}27^{-5/3}(35 - 27)^2 = \frac{1}{9} \cdot \frac{1}{243} \cdot 64 = \frac{64}{2187} \approx .0293$$

Thus, we see that

$$3.296 - .0293 < \sqrt[3]{35} < 3.296$$

That is,

$$3.2667 < \sqrt[3]{35} < 3.296$$

Taylor's Formula allows us, in suitable intervals, to express many nonpolynomial functions f in the form $P_n(x) + R_n(x)$. If, in the suitable interval, $R_n(x)$ is relatively small, then $P_n(x)$ is a good approximation to f.

E X E R C I S E S

In exercises 1–12 on page 439, estimate the error in the approximation. That is. find how big its absolute value can be.

WE ARE OFTEN ASKED to approximate (or estimate) some specific number to a certain number of decimal places of accuracy. When we say that a number d approximates a number w to k **decimal place accuracy,** we mean that d has a decimal representation with just k digits to the right of the decimal point and that

$$d - \frac{5}{10^{k+1}} \leq w < d + \frac{5}{10^{k+1}}$$

For instance, it is known that $\pi = 3.14159265358979 . . .$, so 3.142 is the three-decimal-place estimate of π ($3.1415 \leq \pi < 3.1425$), 3.1416 approximates π to four decimal places ($3.14155 \leq \pi < 3.14165$), 3.14 is the two-decimal-place approximation of π ($3.135 \leq \pi < 3.145$), and 3.141592653590 approximates π to 12 decimal places. In order to approximate a number $f(x)$ to k decimal places by the use of Taylor's Formula, we choose a convenient center a near to x and then choose n as small as possible so that $|R_n(x)| < 5/10^{k+1}$. Next, taking account of the location of c, compute numbers α, β, γ, and δ such that $\alpha \leq R_n(x) \leq \beta$ and $\gamma \leq P_n(x) \leq \delta$ (making $\beta - \alpha$ and $\delta - \gamma$ as small as possible). Then $\alpha + \gamma \leq f(x) \leq \beta + \delta$. If $\alpha + \gamma$ and $\beta + \delta$ are the same to k decimal place accuracy, then the problem is solved. Otherwise, we repeat this procedure with a larger n. A few examples should make this technique clear.

EXAMPLE Use a Taylor polynomial centered at 0 (Maclaurin polynomial) to estimate $\sqrt[3]{e}$ to three-decimal-place accuracy.

Solution   Let $f(x) = e^x$. Then, $f'(x) = f''(x) = . . . = e^x$ and so $f^{(n)}(0) = e^0 = 1$ for all $n \geq 0$. So, (11) becomes

$$P_n(x) = 1 + x + \frac{x^2}{2!} + \frac{x^3}{3!} + . . . + \frac{x^n}{n!}$$

and

$$R_n(x) = \frac{e^c x^{n+1}}{(n+1)!}$$

for some c between 0 and x.

Since we want accuracy to three decimal places, we want $|R_n(x)| < .0005$. Since we want to estimate $\sqrt[3]{e}$, we take $x = 1/3$ and we have (since $0 < e^c < e^{1/3} < 2$)

$$0 < R_n(1/3) < \frac{2}{3^{n+1}(n+1)!}$$

which is less than .0005 if $n = 4$. In fact,

$$0 < R_4(1/3) < \frac{2}{3^5(5!)} = \frac{2}{243 \cdot 120} < .00007$$

Thus, we will use the 4th degree Taylor polynomial centered at 0 evaluated at $x = \frac{1}{3}$ to get

$$\sqrt[3]{e} \approx P_4\left(\frac{1}{3}\right) = 1 + \frac{1}{3} + \frac{1}{18} + \frac{1}{162} + \frac{1}{1944} = 1.39557 \ldots$$

Thus, we get the three-decimal-place approximation

$$\sqrt[3]{e} \approx 1.396$$

In fact, we have proven that $1.39557 < \sqrt[3]{e} < 1.39564$.

EXAMPLE   Use a Taylor expansion centered at 1 of $f(x) = \ln x$ to estimate $\ln 1.3$ to two-decimal-place accuracy.

Solution   Here, we take $f(x) = \ln x$, $a = 1$, and $x = 1.3$. Since $f'(x) = x^{-1}$, $f''(x) = -x^{-2}$, $f'''(x) = 2x^{-3}$, and, in general, $f^{(n)}(x) = (-1)^{n-1}(n-1)!x^{-n}$, we have $f^{(n)}(1)/n! = (-1)^{n-1}/n$ for $n \geq 1$. Therefore (11) becomes

$$P_n(x) = 0 + (x-1) - \frac{1}{2}(x-1)^2 + \frac{1}{3}(x-1)^3 - \ldots + \frac{(-1)^{n-1}}{n}(x-1)^n$$

and

$$R_n(x) = \frac{(-1)^n c^{-n-1}}{n+1}(x-1)^{n+1}$$

Taking $x = 1.3$ and using the fact that $1 < c < 1.3$, we obtain

$$|R_n(1.3)| = \left| \frac{(-1)^n c^{-n-1}}{n+1} (.3)^{n+1} \right|$$

$$= \frac{(.3)^{n+1}}{(n+1)c^{n+1}} < \frac{(.3)^{n+1}}{n+1}$$

Thus, in order to obtain the desired two-decimal-place accuracy, we first choose n such that $(.3)^{n+1}/(n+1) < .005$. For $n = 3$ we have

$$\frac{(.3)^{n+1}}{n+1} = \frac{(.3)^4}{4} = \frac{.0081}{4} < .005$$

In fact, $R_3(1.3) = -(.0081)/(4c^4)$ and $1 < c < 1.3$, so

$$-.0021 < -\frac{.0081}{4} < R_3(1.3) < -\frac{.0081}{4(1.3)^4} < -\frac{.0081}{11.5} < -.0007$$

Also,

$$P_3(1.3) = .3 - \frac{(.3)^2}{2} + \frac{(.3)^3}{3} = .264$$

Thus,

$$.2619 = .264 - .0021 < \ln(1.3) = P_3(1.3) + R_3(1.3) < .264 - .0007 = .2633$$

Note. In general, when we use Taylor expansions for approximation purposes, we must find a suitable n so that $|R_n(x)|$ is suitably small. There is no way, in general, to tell for which value of n a particular remainder is small enough. We must simply, by trial and error, try $n = 1$, $n = 2$, $n = 3$, etc., until we find an n which works. Of course it is crucial that f, x, and a are such that $|R_n(x)|$ does eventually get small enough. There are no guarantees that this will happen in general, but in many situations, it does. Also, in general, the closer x is to a, the smaller $|R_n(x)|$ is. Therefore, we should always use the closest convenient value of a to the given x.

EXAMPLE Use a Taylor expansion of $f(x) = \sin x$ centered at $a = \pi/6$ to approximate $\sin 28°$ to four decimal places.

Solution We have $f'(x) = \cos x$, $f''(x) = -\sin x$, $f'''(x) = -\cos x$, $f''''(x) = \sin x = f(x)$, and the pattern keeps repeating. Next, in order to apply the calculus, we must convert $28°$ to radians: $28° = 28 \cdot \pi/180 =$

$7\pi/45$ radians. Now, recall that formula (2) holds even if $b < a$, so that we may use the Taylor Formula with $x = 7\pi/45 \approx .488692 < a = \pi/6 \approx .523600$.

The remainder terms are of the form

$$R_0(x) = \frac{\cos c}{1!}(x - a)$$

$$R_1(x) = \frac{-\sin c}{2!}(x - a)^2$$

$$R_2(x) = \frac{-\cos c}{3!}(x - a)^3$$

$$R_3(x) = \frac{\sin c}{4!}(x - a)^4$$

etc.

Since $|\sin c| \leq 1$ and $|\cos c| \leq 1$ for all c, we see that $|R_n(x)| \leq \left|\frac{(x - a)^{n+1}}{(n + 1)!}\right|$. Hence, since we desire accuracy to four decimal places, we want $|R_n(x)| < .00005$. We take $n = 2$, because

$$|R_2(x)| \leq \left|\frac{(x - a)^3}{3!}\right| \approx \left|\frac{(-.034908)^3}{6}\right| < .0000071$$

Thus, using $\sqrt{3} \approx 1.732051$,

$$\sin 28° = f(x) \approx P_2(.488692)$$

$$\approx \sin \pi/6 + \frac{\cos \pi/6}{1!}(-.034908) + \frac{-\sin \pi/6}{2!}(-.034908)^2$$

$$= \frac{1}{2} + \frac{\sqrt{3}}{2}(-.034908) - \frac{1}{4}(-.034908)^2 \approx .4695$$

Note. In the previous example, we used $\pi \approx 3.1415927$. This approximation to π will be precise enough for all applications in this book.

EXAMPLE   Write the nth Taylor polynomial for $f(x) = (1 + x)^{1/2}$ centered at $a = 0$.

Solution   We have $f'(x) = \frac{1}{2}(1 + x)^{-1/2}, f''(x) = \frac{-1}{4}(1 + x)^{-3/2}, f'''(x) = \frac{3}{8}(1 + x)^{-5/2}, f''''(x) = \frac{-15}{16}(1 + x)^{-7/2}$, and, in general,

$$f^{(n)}(x) = \frac{(-1)^{n+1}(2n - 3)(2n - 5) \ldots (3)(1)}{2^n}(1 + x)^{\frac{-(2n-1)}{2}}$$

Thus, $f^{(n)}(0) = \dfrac{(-1)^{n+1}(2n-3)(2n-5)\ldots(3)(1)}{2^n}$, and therefore

$$P_n(x) = 1 + \frac{x}{1! \cdot 2} - \frac{x^2}{2! \cdot 4} + \frac{3x^3}{3! \cdot 8} - \frac{15x^4}{4! \cdot 16} + \ldots$$
$$+ \frac{(-1)^{n+1}(2n-3)(2n-5)\ldots(3)(1)x^n}{n! \cdot 2^n}$$

Note. The coefficients of $P_n(x)$ in the previous example are called the **binomial coefficients for exponent 1/2.** There are binomial coefficients for *any* exponent and we will say more about them in Chapter 10 (page 498).

Our next example shows how Taylor's Formula may be used to approximate a definite integral. The idea is a simple one. If we wish to approximate $\displaystyle\int_a^b f(x)\,dx$, we write $f(x) = P_n(x) + R_n(x)$. Then

$$\int_a^b f(x)\,dx = \int_a^b P_n(x)\,dx + \int_a^b R_n(x)\,dx$$

and so

$$\left| \int_a^b f(x)\,dx - \int_a^b P_n(x)\,dx \right| \le \left| \int_a^b R_n(x)\,dx \right| \le (b-a)M$$

where M is the maximum value of $|R_n(x)|$ on $[a,b]$.

Thus, provided $R_n(x)$ is small enough on $[a,b]$, we can approximate $\displaystyle\int_a^b f(x)\,dx$ by evaluating the integral $\displaystyle\int_a^b P_n(x)\,dx$, which is the integral of a polynomial and, therefore, easy to evaluate.

EXAMPLE Approximate the number $\displaystyle\int_0^1 e^{-x^2}\,dx$ to four-decimal-place accuracy.

Solution The first example in this section shows that

$$e^t = P_n(t) + R_n(t)$$

where

$$P_n(t) = \sum_{k=0}^{n} \frac{t^k}{k!}$$

and

$$R_n(t) = \frac{e^c t^{n+1}}{(n+1)!}$$

for some number c between 0 and t. Letting $t = -x^2$ we have $e^{-x^2} = P_n(-x^2) + R_n(-x^2)$. Since $-x^2 < c < 0$, we have

$$|R_n(-x^2)| = \left| \frac{e^c(-x^2)^{n+1}}{(n+1)!} \right| < \frac{x^{2n+2}}{(n+1)!}$$

Thus, we obtain

$$\left| \int_0^1 e^{-x^2}\,dx - \sum_{k=0}^n \frac{(-1)^k}{k!(2k+1)} \right| = \left| \int_0^1 e^{-x^2}\,dx - \sum_{k=0}^n \int_0^1 \frac{(-x^2)^k}{k!}\,dx \right|$$

$$= \left| \int_0^1 [e^{-x^2} - P_n(-x^2)]\,dx \right| = \left| \int_0^1 R_n(-x^2)\,dx \right|$$

$$\leq \int_0^1 |R_n(-x^2)|\,dx < \int_0^1 \frac{x^{2n+2}}{(n+1)!}\,dx = \frac{1}{(n+1)! \cdot (2n+3)}$$

Therefore, in order to obtain

$$\int_0^1 e^{-x^2}\,dx \approx \sum_{k=0}^n \frac{(-1)^k}{k!(2k+1)}$$

to four decimal places, we first seek n so large that

$$\frac{1}{(n+1)! \cdot (2n+3)} \leq .00005 = \frac{1}{20,000}$$

That is,

$$(n+1)! \cdot (2n+3) \geq 20,000$$

Let us find the smallest n for which this inequality is true. By trial and error we find that if $n = 5$, then

$$(n+1)! \cdot (2n+3) = 6! \cdot 13 = 720 \cdot 13 < 20,000$$

while if $n = 6$, we have

$$\frac{1}{(n+1)! \cdot (2n+3)} = \frac{1}{7! \cdot 15} = \frac{1}{75,600} < .000014$$

and

$$\sum_{k=0}^6 \frac{(-1)^k}{k! \cdot (2k+1)} = 1 - \frac{1}{3} + \frac{1}{10} - \frac{1}{42} + \frac{1}{216} - \frac{1}{1320} + \frac{1}{9360} = .74683 \ldots$$

so

$$\int_0^1 e^{-x^2}\,dx \approx .7468$$

to four-decimal-place accuracy.

We now mention another form of the Taylor expansion of a function centered at the point a. In the expansion which we have been discussing, the remainder is given by $R_n(x) = \dfrac{f^{(n+1)}(c)}{(n+1)!}(x-a)^{n+1}$ for some c between x and a. This form is sometimes called the **Lagrange form** of the remainder after the French mathematician Joseph Lagrange (1736–1813). It can be shown that

$$R_n(x) = \frac{1}{n!}\int_a^x f^{(n+1)}(t)(x-t)^n \, dt$$

(see exercise 33 on page 452). This is called the **integral form** or the **Cauchy form** of the remainder for the French mathematician Augustin Cauchy (1789–1857). When one is interested in showing that $R_n(x)$ is small, indeed that $R_n(x) \to 0$, it is helpful to have both forms of the remainder at one's disposal.

EXERCISES

In 1–11, find the Taylor polynomial $P_n(x)$ of f, of given degree n, centered at the point a. Also find $R_n(x)$.

1. $f(x) = e^x$, $n = 4$, $a = 0$
2. (a) $f(x) = \ln(1+x)$, $n = 4$, $a = 1$
   (b) $f(x) = \ln x$, $n = 4$, $a = 1$
3. (a) $f(x) = \sin x$, $n = 4$, $a = 0$
   (b) $f(x) = \sin x$, $n = 4$, $a = 2\pi/3$
4. (a) $f(x) = \cos x$, $n = 4$, $a = 0$
   (b) $f(x) = \cos x$, $n = 4$, $a = \pi/4$
5. $f(x) = \sqrt{x}$, $n = 3$, $a = 1$
6. $f(x) = \tan x$, $n = 3$, $a = 0$
7. $f(x) = e^{x^2}$, $n = 4$, $a = 0$ [*Hint:* First let $x^2 = t$ and expand e^t.]
8. $f(x) = (1+x)^{3/2}$, $n = 4$, $a = 0$
9. $f(x) = \sqrt[3]{x}$, $n = 4$, $a = -1$
10. $f(x) = xe^x$, $n = 4$, $a = 0$ [*Hint:* First expand e^x.]
11. $f(x) = x^2 \sin x$, $n = 4$, $a = 0$

In 12–28, use Taylor's Formula to approximate the given number with the given accuracy.

12. e, 4 decimal places
13. $\sin 32°$, 4 decimal places
14. $\cos 97°$, 4 decimal places
15. $\ln 1.1$, 3 decimal places
16. $e^{1/5}$, 3 decimal places
17. $(1.1)^{3/2}$, 3 decimal places
18. $\sin 145°$, 4 decimal places
19. $\cos(-47°)$, 4 decimal places

20. $\tan 2°$, 4 decimal places

21. $\sqrt{3}$, 4 decimal places

22. $e^{-.2}$, 4 decimal places

23. $\sqrt[3]{2}$, 3 decimal places

24. $\displaystyle\int_0^{1/2} e^{-x^2}\,dx$, 5 decimal places

25. $\displaystyle\int_0^1 e^{x^3}\,dx$, 3 decimal places

26. $\displaystyle\int_0^{3/4} \sin x^2\,dx$, 5 decimal places

27. $\displaystyle\int_0^{1/3} x^{-1}e^{-x}\,dx$, 3 decimal places [*Hint:* First apply Taylor's Formula to $f(x) = e^{-x}$, with $a = 0$.]

28. $\displaystyle\int_0^{1/4} \cos x^2\,dx$, 5 decimal places

29. Express the polynomial $f(x) = x^4 - x^3 + x^2 + x - 2$ as a polynomial in powers of $(x + 1)$. [*Hint:* Take a Taylor expansion of f centered at $a = -1$.]

30. Use the fact that $\sqrt{e} < \sqrt{3} < 1.75$ to show that $|e^x - (1 + x)| < .22$ if $|x| \le 1/2$. [*Hint:* Expand e^x in a Taylor expansion centered at $a = 0$.]

31. Show that $|\ln(1 + x) - x| < 1/8$ if $-1/2 < x < 1/2$.

32. Show that $\left|\cos x - \left(1 - \dfrac{x^2}{2}\right)\right| < .0004$ if $-.15 < x < .15$.

33. Prove the Cauchy form of the remainder for Taylor's Formula, i.e., prove

$$R_n(x) = \frac{1}{n!}\int_a^x f^{(n+1)}(t)(x - t)^n\,dt$$

[*Hint:* Clearly, $f(x) = f(a) + \displaystyle\int_a^x f'(t)\,dt$. Now integrate $\displaystyle\int_a^x f'(t)\,dt$ by parts with $u = f'(t)$ and $dv = dt$. Keep repeating the process.]

3 The Trapezoidal Rule

In many applications of the definite integral, it is sufficient to obtain an approximate value instead of an exact value for a given definite integral. Indeed, as we mentioned in Chapter 6, functions like e^{-x^2}, $\sin x^2$, and $\dfrac{\sin x}{x}$ have no primitives which can be expressed as finite combinations of the trigonometric, exponential, logarithmic, or polynomial functions. In other words, we will be unable to evaluate

$$\int_0^1 e^{-x^2}\, dx,$$ for example, by simply evaluating some primitive at 0

and at 1.

The **Trapezoidal Rule** is a method for approximating definite integrals. We already have seen that a definite integral may be expressed as a limit of Riemann sums. Specifically, if f is integrable on $[a,b]$, then

$$\int_a^b f(x)\, dx = \lim_{|P| \to 0} \sum_{k=1}^n f(\xi_k)\Delta x_k \tag{1}$$

where each $P = \{a = x_0 < x_1 < \cdots < x_{n-1} < x_n = b\}$ is a subdivision of $[a,b]$, $\Delta x_k = x_k - x_{k-1}$, and $x_{k-1} \le \xi_k \le x_k$.

The terms in the sum in (1) represent the areas of rectangles with height $f(\xi_k)$ and base Δx_k (for our purposes, the area is negative if the rectangle is below the x-axis). The idea behind the Trapezoidal Rule is to replace the rectangles by trapezoids and to use evenly spaced subdivisions of $[a,b]$ (see Fig. 9-2).

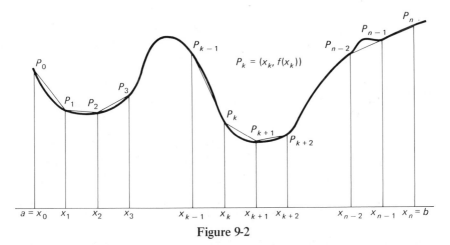

Figure 9-2

If an evenly spaced subdivision has $n + 1$ points, then each of the n intervals $[x_{k-1}, x_k]$ has length $\dfrac{b - a}{n}$. Thus, $\Delta x_k = \dfrac{b - a}{n}$ for all k, $1 \le k \le n$. We will designate this common value of Δx_k by Δx. Also, the area of the trapezoid which "sits on" the interval $[x_{k-1}, x_k]$ is (see Fig. 9-3)

$$(f(x_{k-1}) + f(x_k))\frac{\Delta x}{2} \tag{2}$$

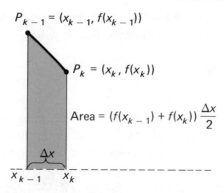

Figure 9–3

because the area of a trapezoid is the product of the sum of the bases and half the height.

Thus, we have the approximation

$$\int_{x_{k-1}}^{x_k} f(x)\, dx \approx (f(x_{k-1}) + f(x_k))\frac{\Delta x}{2} \tag{3}$$

Since

$$\int_a^b f(x)\, dx = \int_{x_0}^{x_1} f(x)\, dx + \int_{x_1}^{x_2} f(x)\, dx + \ldots + \int_{x_{k-1}}^{x_k} f(x)\, dx$$

$$+ \ldots + \int_{x_{n-1}}^{x_n} f(x)\, dx \tag{4}$$

we may write

$$\boxed{\int_a^b f(x)\, dx \approx (f(x_0) + 2f(x_1) + 2f(x_2) + \ldots + 2f(x_{n-1}) + f(x_n))\frac{\Delta x}{2}} \tag{5}$$

Expression (5) is called the Trapezoidal Rule. Since the right-hand side of (5) is between $U_a^b(f,P)$ and $L_a^b(f,P)$, it is clear that as $n \to \infty$, the right hand side of (5) approaches $\int_a^b f(x)\, dx$. Thus, the Trapezoidal Rule gives us arbitrarily close approximations to the definite integral.

EXAMPLE   Use the Trapezoidal Rule with $n = 5$ to approximate $\int_1^2 \sqrt{x}\, dx.$

Solution   The integral is easy enough to evaluate exactly:

$$\int_1^2 \sqrt{x}\, dx = \frac{2x^{3/2}}{3}\Big|_1^2 = \frac{4\sqrt{2}}{3} - \frac{2}{3}$$

However, our purpose is to show how the Trapezoidal Rule works and how close an approximation it gives.

We have $n = 5$, so that $\Delta x = \dfrac{b-a}{5} = \dfrac{2-1}{5} = .2$. Thus, $x_0 = 1$, $x_1 = 1.2$, $x_2 = 1.4$, $x_3 = 1.6$, $x_4 = 1.8$, $x_5 = 2$, and we have

$$\int_1^2 x^{1/2}\,dx \approx (1^{1/2} + 2(1.2)^{1/2} + 2(1.4)^{1/2} + 2(1.6)^{1/2} + 2(1.8)^{1/2} + 2^{1/2})\dfrac{.2}{2}$$

$$\approx 1.2185$$

Notice that the exact value, $\dfrac{4\sqrt{2}}{3} - \dfrac{2}{3}$, is, to four decimal places, 1.2190.

EXAMPLE Use the Trapezoidal Rule to approximate $\displaystyle\int_0^1 e^{-x^2}\,dx$ by taking $n = 10$.

Solution Here $\Delta x = \dfrac{1-0}{10} = .1$ and we have $x_0 = 0$, $x_1 = .1$, $x_2 = .2$, $x_3 = .3$, $x_4 = .4$, $x_5 = .5$, $x_6 = .6$, $x_7 = .7$, $x_8 = .8$, $x_9 = .9$, $x_{10} = 1$. Thus,

$$\int_0^1 e^{-x^2}\,dx \approx (1 + 2e^{-.01} + 2e^{-.04} + 2e^{-.09} + 2e^{-.16}$$

$$+ \ldots + 2e^{-.81} + e^{-1})\dfrac{1}{2} \approx .746$$

E X E R C I S E S

In 1–10, use the Trapezoidal Rule with the given value of n to estimate the integral.

1. $\displaystyle\int_0^1 x^2\,dx$, $n = 5$

2. $\displaystyle\int_0^2 x^3\,dx$, $n = 5$

3. $\displaystyle\int_2^3 \dfrac{dx}{x}$, $n = 4$

4. $\displaystyle\int_{-\pi/2}^{\pi/2} \cos x\,dx$, $n = 6$

5. $\displaystyle\int_0^{1/2} e^{-x^2}\,dx$, $n = 5$

6. $\displaystyle\int_0^{\pi} \sin x^2\,dx$, $n = 4$

7. $\displaystyle\int_0^{\pi/2} \dfrac{\sin x}{x}\,dx$, $n = 3$ [Assume that at 0, $\dfrac{\sin x}{x} = 1$.]

8. $\displaystyle\int_0^{\pi} x\sin^2 x\,dx$, $n = 6$

9. $\displaystyle\int_1^2 \sqrt{1 + 2x^2}\,dx$, $n = 5$

10. $\displaystyle\int_1^2 \ln\,(1 + x^3)\,dx,\; n = 10$

11. (a) Show that $2\displaystyle\int_{-1}^1 \sqrt{1 - x^2}\,dx = \pi$.

(b) Use the result of (a) and the Trapezoidal Rule with $n = 10$ to approximate π.

4 Simpson's Rule

We now investigate another method for approximating definite integrals, called **Simpson's Rule**, in honor of the English mathematician Thomas Simpson (1710-1761). This method is similar to the Trapezoidal Rule, except that we use segments of parabolas to connect points on a graph rather than straight-line segments. For this reason Simpson's Rule is sometimes called the **Parabolic Rule**. Simpson's Rule is often more accurate than the Trapezoidal Rule.

We take an evenly spaced subdivision, P, with an *odd* number of points, say

$$P = \{a = x_0 < x_1 < x_2 < \cdots < x_{2n-1} < x_{2n} = b\}$$

with $\Delta x = \dfrac{b-a}{2n}$. We start with P_0, P_1, and P_2 and look at the parabolic

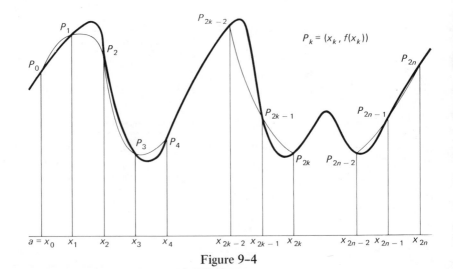

Figure 9-4

arc joining these three points (see Fig. 9-4). We do the same for P_2, P_3, and P_4, and, in general, P_{2k-2}, P_{2k-1}, P_{2k}, where $1 \leq k \leq n$. What we want to do is to compute the area shown in Fig. 9-5 and use this to approximate

$$\int_{x_{2k-2}}^{x_{2k}} f(x)\, dx$$

in much the same way that we previously used the area of a trapezoidal region to approximate the integral.

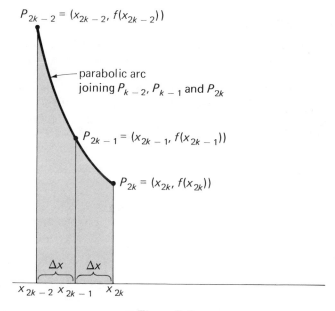

$P_{2k-2} = (x_{2k-2}, f(x_{2k-2}))$

parabolic arc
joining P_{k-2}, P_{k-1} and P_{2k}

$P_{2k-1} = (x_{2k-1}, f(x_{2k-1}))$

$P_{2k} = (x_{2k}, f(x_{2k}))$

$\Delta x \qquad \Delta x$

$x_{2k-2} \quad x_{2k-1} \qquad x_{2k}$

Figure 9–5

We now proceed to compute the area of the region in Fig. 9-5. First, we'll assume that $y = ax^2 + bx + c$ is the equation of the parabola joining P_{2k-2}, P_{2k-1}, and P_{2k}. In case these three points are collinear, then $a = 0$ and our parabola degenerates into a straight line. This does not affect our calculations. It is easy to see that any three given points satisfy an equation of the form $y = ax^2 + bx + c$; simply substitute the three given ordered pairs and obtain three linear equations in the three unknowns a, b, and c.

Thus, we now have:

$$\begin{aligned}
y_{2k-2} &= ax_{2k-2}^2 + bx_{2k-2} + c \\
y_{2k-1} &= ax_{2k-1}^2 + bx_{2k-1} + c \\
y_{2k} &= ax_{2k}^2 + bx_{2k} + c
\end{aligned} \tag{1}$$

Since $x_{2k-1} - x_{2k-2} = \Delta x = x_{2k} - x_{2k-1}$, (1) becomes

$$
\begin{aligned}
y_{2k-2} &= ax_{2k-2}^2 & + bx_{2k-2} & + c \\
y_{2k-1} &= a(x_{2k-2} + \Delta x)^2 & + b(x_{2k-2} + \Delta x) & + c \\
y_{2k} &= a(x_{2k-2} + 2\Delta x)^2 & + b(x_{2k-2} + 2\Delta x) & + c
\end{aligned}
\tag{2}
$$

Thus, after some algebra,

$$
\begin{aligned}
y_{2k-2} &= ax_{2k-2}^2 & + bx_{2k-2} & + c \\
y_{2k-1} &= a(x_{2k-2}^2 + 2\Delta x \cdot x_{2k-2} + (\Delta x)^2) & + b(x_{2k-2} + \Delta x) & + c \\
y_{2k} &= a(x_{2k-2}^2 + 4\Delta x \cdot x_{2k-2} + 4(\Delta x)^2) & + b(x_{2k-2} + 2\Delta x) & + c
\end{aligned}
\tag{3}
$$

We may now write

$$
\begin{aligned}
y_{2k-2} + 4y_{2k-1} + y_{2k} = {}& a(6x_{2k-2}^2 + 12\Delta x \cdot x_{2k-2} + 8(\Delta x)^2) \\
& + b(6x_{2k-2} + 6\Delta x) + 6c
\end{aligned}
\tag{4}
$$

Equation (4), although true, may indeed seem a strange step to take. Why should we wish to consider such an unnatural combination of y_{2k-2}, y_{2k-1}, and y_{2k}? The answer will be clear in a moment.

The area, A, of the region in Fig. 9-5 is

$$
\begin{aligned}
\int_{x_{2k-2}}^{x_{2k}} (ax^2 + bx + c)\, dx &= \int_{x_{2k-2}}^{x_{2k-2}+2\Delta x} (ax^2 + bx + c)\, dx \\
&= \left(\frac{1}{3}ax^3 + \frac{1}{2}bx^2 + cx \right) \Big|_{x_{2k-2}}^{x_{2k-2}+2\Delta x} \\
&= \frac{1}{3}a(x_{2k-2} + 2\Delta x)^3 + \frac{1}{2}b(x_{2k-2} + 2\Delta x)^2 + \\
&\quad c(x_{2k-2} + 2\Delta x) - \left(\frac{1}{3}ax_{2k-2}^3 + \frac{1}{2}bx_{2k-2}^2 + cx_{2k-2} \right) \\
&= [a(6x_{2k-2}^2 + 12\Delta x \cdot x_{2k-2} + 8(\Delta x)^2) + \\
&\qquad b(6x_{2k-2} + 6\Delta x) + 6c]\frac{\Delta x}{3}
\end{aligned}
$$

Thus, from (4), it follows that

$$
A = (y_{2k-2} + 4y_{2k-1} + y_{2k})\frac{\Delta x}{3}
\tag{5}
$$

Since

$$
\int_a^b f(x)\, dx = \int_{x_0}^{x_2} f(x)\, dx + \int_{x_2}^{x_4} f(x)\, dx + \ldots + \int_{x_{2k-2}}^{x_{2k}} f(x)\, dx
$$
$$
+ \ldots + \int_{x_{2n-2}}^{x_{2n}} f(x)\, dx
$$

it follows from (5) that

$$\int_a^b f(x)\,dx \approx (f(x_0) + 4f(x_1) + f(x_2))\frac{\Delta x}{3}$$

$$+ (f(x_2) + 4f(x_3) + f(x_4))\frac{\Delta x}{3}$$

$$+ (f(x_4) + 4f(x_5) + f(x_6))\frac{\Delta x}{3} + \ldots$$

$$+ (f(x_{2k-2}) + 4f(x_{2k-1}) + f(x_{2k}))\frac{\Delta x}{3} + \ldots$$

$$+ (f(x_{2n-2}) + 4f(x_{2n-1}) + f(x_{2n}))\frac{\Delta x}{3} \qquad (6)$$

Thus, for $\Delta x = \dfrac{b-a}{2n}$,

$$\int_a^b f(x)\,dx \approx (f(x_0) + 4f(x_1) + 2f(x_2) + 4f(x_3)$$

$$+ 2f(x_4) + \ldots + 2f(x_{2k-2}) + 4f(x_{2k-1}) + 2f(x_{2k}) + \ldots$$

$$+ 2f(x_{2n-2}) + 4f(x_{2n-1}) + f(x_{2n}))\frac{\Delta x}{3}$$

(7)

Expression (7) is called Simpson's Rule. Although the right-hand side of (7) is not necessarily between $U_a^b(f,P)$ and $L_a^b(f,P)$, it still can be shown, although we do not do so here, that as $n \to \infty$, the right-hand side of (7) approaches $\int_a^b f(x)\,dx$. Thus, Simpson's Rule gives us arbitrarily close approximations to the definite integral.

EXAMPLE   Use Simpson's Rule with $2n = 10$ to approximate

$$\int_0^1 \frac{\sin x}{x}\,dx$$

Solution   Since $f(x) = \dfrac{\sin x}{x}$ is not defined at 0, it may appear that, since $f(x_0)$ does not exist, we cannot apply Simpson's Rule. However, $\int_a^b \dfrac{\sin x}{x}\,dx$ certainly exists. Furthermore, $\lim\limits_{x \to 0} \dfrac{\sin x}{x} = 1$ and so we take $f(0) = 1$ for purposes of estimating the integral. Actually, if you look at the right side of (7), you can see that if $n \to \infty$ (i.e., if $\Delta x \to 0$), it really doesn't matter which value is assigned to $f(x_0)$, since $f(x_0)\dfrac{\Delta x}{3} \to 0$.

However, for small values of $2n$, it obviously makes a great difference. This is why we choose the "correct" value $f(0) = \lim_{x \to 0} f(x) = 1$.

Now, $\Delta x = \dfrac{b-a}{2n} = \dfrac{1-0}{10} = .1$. Thus, $x_0 = 0$, $x_1 = .1$, $x_2 = .2$, $x_3 = .3$, $\ldots$, $x_9 = .9$, $x_{10} = 1$. From (7), we have

$$\int_0^1 \frac{\sin x}{x}\, dx \approx [1 + (4 \cdot .9983) + (2 \cdot .9933) + (4 \cdot .9851)$$

$$+ (2 \cdot .9735) + (4 \cdot .9589) + (2 \cdot .9411) + (4 \cdot .9203)$$

$$+ (2 \cdot .8967) + (4 \cdot .8704) + .8415]\, \frac{.1}{3} \approx .9461$$

E X E R C I S E S

In 1–10, use Simpson's Rule with the indicated value of $2n$ to estimate the definite integral.

1. $\displaystyle\int_0^\pi \sin x\, dx$, $2n = 8$

2. $\displaystyle\int_2^4 \frac{dx}{\sqrt{2+x^2}}$, $2n = 4$

3. $\displaystyle\int_1^2 \frac{dx}{x}$, $2n = 6$

4. $\displaystyle\int_0^1 e^{-x^2}\, dx$, $2n = 6$

5. $\displaystyle\int_0^\pi \sin x^2\, dx$, $2n = 8$

6. $\displaystyle\int_1^2 \ln(x+1)\, dx$, $2n = 4$

7. $\displaystyle\int_{-\pi/2}^0 \sqrt{\cos x}\, dx$, $2n = 6$

8. $\displaystyle\int_0^1 \sqrt{1+x^3}\, dx$, $2n = 4$

9. $\displaystyle\int_0^{\pi/9} \tan\sqrt{x}\, dx$, $2n = 4$

10. $\displaystyle\int_0^{\pi/4} \ln\cos x\, dx$, $2n = 6$

11. If f is a polynomial function of degree three or less, then for $2n = 2$ it can be proven that Simpson's Rule yields an exact value for

$$\int_a^b f(x)\, dx.$$

(a) Show that this value is $\displaystyle\int_a^b f(x)\, dx = \frac{b-a}{6}\left[f(a) + 4f\!\left(\frac{a+b}{2}\right) + f(b)\right]$. This is called the **Prismoidal Formula**.

(b) Use the result of part (a) to evaluate $\displaystyle\int_0^1 (x^3 - 2x^2 + 3x - 1)\, dx$.

Chapter 10

Infinite Series

1 Introduction

Notice that if n is a positive integer, then the finite sum

$$S_n = \sum_{j=0}^{n} \frac{1}{2^j} = 1 + \frac{1}{2} + \frac{1}{4} + \frac{1}{8} + \frac{1}{16} + \ldots + \frac{1}{2^n}$$

satisfies $S_n = 2 - 1/2^n < 2$. Also, $\lim_{n \to \infty} S_n = 2$. For this reason it seems reasonable to write

$$\sum_{n=0}^{\infty} \frac{1}{2^n} = 2$$

and call 2 the **sum** of this infinite series of terms. Motivated by this simple example, and because sums of an infinite number of terms have not yet been defined, we feel free to make the following definitions.

Definition An **infinite series** is an indicated sum

$$\sum_{n=k}^{\infty} a_n = a_k + a_{k+1} + a_{k+2} + \ldots$$

where the a_n's ($n = k, k+1, \ldots$) are given numbers. The number a_n is called the nth **term** of the series. The sum of all the terms up to a_n is the number

$$S_n = \sum_{j=k}^{n} a_j = a_k + a_{k+1} + \ldots + a_n$$

and we call S_n the **nth partial sum** of the series. In case

$$\lim_{n\to\infty} S_n = S$$

exists (possibly infinite), we call S the **sum** of the series and write

$$\sum_{n=k}^{\infty} a_n = S$$

where we use "=," not "→." If the sum S exists *and* is finite, we say that the series **converges**. All series that do not converge are said to **diverge**.

EXAMPLE   Which of the following series converge?

(a) $\sum_{n=1}^{\infty} \dfrac{1}{n}$ (b) $\sum_{n=1}^{\infty} \dfrac{1}{n(n+1)}$ (c) $\sum_{n=1}^{\infty} \dfrac{1}{n^2}$

Solution   (a) Since

$$1 + \frac{1}{2} > \frac{1}{2} = \frac{1}{2}$$

$$\frac{1}{3} + \frac{1}{4} > \frac{2}{4} = \frac{1}{2}$$

$$\frac{1}{5} + \frac{1}{6} + \frac{1}{7} + \frac{1}{8} > \frac{4}{8} = \frac{1}{2}$$

$$\cdot$$
$$\cdot$$
$$\cdot$$

$$\frac{1}{2^{n-1}+1} + \ldots + \frac{1}{2^n} > \frac{2^{n-1}}{2^n} = \frac{1}{2}$$

We can add these n inequalities and obtain

$$S_{2^n} = \sum_{j=1}^{2^n} \frac{1}{j} > \frac{n}{2}$$

Also, $S_1 < S_2 < S_3 < S_4 < S_5 < \ldots$ It follows that

$$S = \lim_{r\to\infty} S_r = \lim_{n\to\infty} S_{2^n} = \infty$$

This is because if β is any given positive number and if N is so large that $N > 2\beta$, then for all $r \geq 2^N$ we have

$$S_r \geq S_{2^N} > \frac{N}{2} > \beta$$

The series (a) therefore diverges to the sum ∞ and we write

$$\sum_{n=1}^{\infty} \frac{1}{n} = \infty$$

This is called the **harmonic series.**

(b) We have

$$S_n = \frac{1}{1 \cdot 2} + \frac{1}{2 \cdot 3} + \frac{1}{3 \cdot 4} + \ldots + \frac{1}{(n-1)n} + \frac{1}{n(n+1)}$$

$$= \left(1 - \frac{1}{2}\right) + \left(\frac{1}{2} - \frac{1}{3}\right) + \left(\frac{1}{3} - \frac{1}{4}\right) + \ldots + \left(\frac{1}{n-1} - \frac{1}{n}\right) + \left(\frac{1}{n} - \frac{1}{n+1}\right)$$

Notice that the second term in each parenthesis eliminates the first term in the next one. After this simplification all that remains is

$$S_n = 1 - \frac{1}{n+1}$$

Therefore

$$\sum_{n=1}^{\infty} \frac{1}{n(n+1)} = S = \lim_{n \to \infty} S_n = 1$$

and so the series converges to the sum $S = 1$.

(c) Let S_n be as in part (b) and let T_n be the nth partial sum of (c). Then, for all $n > 1$, we have

$$T_n = \frac{1}{1^2} + \frac{1}{2^2} + \frac{1}{3^2} + \frac{1}{4^2} + \ldots + \frac{1}{n^2}$$

$$< 1 + \frac{1}{1 \cdot 2} + \frac{1}{2 \cdot 3} + \frac{1}{3 \cdot 4} + \ldots + \frac{1}{(n-1)n}$$

$$= 1 + S_{n-1} < 1 + 1 = 2$$

This proves that $T_n < 2$ for every $n \geq 1$. Also, the T_n's march upward: $T_1 < T_2 < T_3 < T_4 \ldots$, but they can never pass 2. We conclude that

$$\sum_{n=1}^{\infty} \frac{1}{n^2} = \lim_{n \to \infty} T_n = T \leq 2$$

and so we can conclude that series (c) converges. However, it is not so easy to find the exact value of its sum T.

There are two main problems with which we are concerned when we deal with infinite series. First, does the given series converge? Second, if it does, then what is its sum? We will often be able to answer the first question, but we will seldom be able to answer the second exactly. We will usually have to settle for close approximations. Our success with the above three examples depended on tricks. Tricks are useful if we can think of any to use, but we will now try to set forth some systematic procedures for testing series for convergence. The simplest test is as follows.

▷ **nth Term Test**   If $\sum\limits_{n=k}^{\infty} a_n$ is a convergent series, then

$$\lim_{n \to \infty} a_n = 0 \tag{1}$$

In other words, the failure of (1) assures that the series diverges.

Proof   If $\sum\limits_{n=k}^{\infty} a_n = S$, where S is finite and if

$$S_n = a_k + a_{k+1} + \ldots + a_n$$

then $S_n - S_{n-1} = a_n$ and so we have

$$\lim_{n \to \infty} a_n = \lim_{n \to \infty} S_n - \lim_{n \to \infty} S_{n-1} = S - S = 0 \ \blacksquare$$

Of course the converse of this theorem is *false*. That is, a series $\sum a_n$ can satisfy (1) *and* also diverge. This is seen by a glance at part (a) in the example above:

$$\lim_{n \to \infty} 1/n = 0 \qquad \text{and} \qquad \sum_{n=1}^{\infty} 1/n = \infty$$

EXAMPLE   Test for convergence the series

$$\sum_{n=1}^{\infty} \frac{2n-1}{100n+40} = \frac{1}{140} + \frac{3}{240} + \frac{5}{340} + \ldots$$

Solution   Since

$$\lim_{n \to \infty} \frac{2n-1}{100n+40} = \lim_{n \to \infty} \frac{1 - 1/2n}{50 + 20/n} = \frac{1}{50} \neq 0$$

the series diverges.

The simplest of all series to test is one of the following type. We even know the sum when it converges.

▷ **Geometric Series Test**   Let a and r be given numbers.
   (i) If $|r| < 1$, then

$$\sum_{n=0}^{\infty} ar^n = a + ar + ar^2 + \ldots = \frac{a}{1-r}$$

(ii) If $a \neq 0$ and $|r| \geq 1$, then $\sum_{n=0}^{\infty} ar^n$ diverges.

Proof (i) Suppose $|r| < 1$. Writing

$$S_n = a + ar + ar^2 + \ldots + ar^n$$

we also have

$$rS_n = ar + ar^2 + \ldots + ar^n + ar^{n+1}$$

Now subtract the second equation from the first to get

$$(1-r)S_n = a - ar^{n+1}$$

$$S_n = \frac{a}{1-r} - \frac{ar^{n+1}}{1-r}$$

Since $\lim_{n \to \infty} r^{n+1} = 0$, we obtain

$$\sum_{n=0}^{\infty} ar^n = \lim_{n \to \infty} S_n = \frac{a}{1-r}$$

(ii) Suppose that $a \neq 0$ and $|r| \geq 1$. Then

$$0 < |a| \leq |ar| \leq |ar^2| \leq \ldots$$

and so it is impossible that $\lim_{n \to \infty} ar^n = 0$. By the preceding theorem the series cannot converge. ∎

The series treated in this theorem are called **geometric series**. Such a series begins with a term a and each successive term is obtained from the preceding one by multiplying by the same constant r. Notice that the series whose nth term is $a_n = 1/n$ is **not** a geometric series because $a_{n+1}/a_n = n/(n+1)$ is not a constant – it depends on n.

EXAMPLE   Find the sum of the series

$$\sum_{n=-2}^{\infty} (-1)^n 3^{n+1}/4^n = \frac{16}{3} - \frac{4}{1} + \frac{3}{1} - \frac{9}{4} + \frac{27}{16} - \ldots$$

Solution   This is a geometric series that begins with the term $a = 16/3$ and the **common ratio** of successive terms is $r = -3/4$. Since $|r| < 1$, the sum S of this series is

$$S = \frac{a}{1-r} = \frac{16/3}{1+3/4} = \frac{64}{21}$$

We next show that the alteration of any finite number of terms of a series cannot affect its convergence behavior.

▷ **Theorem**   Let $\sum\limits_{j=k}^{\infty} a_j$ and $\sum\limits_{j=k}^{\infty} b_j$ be two series such that there is an $m \geq k$ with the property that $b_j = a_j$ for all $j > m$. If $\sum\limits_{j=k}^{\infty} a_j$ converges, then so does $\sum\limits_{j=k}^{\infty} b_j$.

Proof   Let $\sum\limits_{j=k}^{\infty} a_j = S$. For $n > m$, we have

$$\sum_{j=k}^{n} b_j = \sum_{j=k}^{m} b_j + \sum_{j=m+1}^{n} a_j$$
$$= \sum_{j=k}^{m} (b_j - a_j) + \sum_{j=k}^{n} a_j$$

and so

$$\sum_{j=k}^{\infty} b_j = \lim_{n \to \infty} \sum_{j=k}^{n} b_j = \sum_{j=k}^{m} (b_j - a_j) + S$$

This completes the proof. ∎

Here is another useful fact about series.

▷ **Theorem**   Let $\sum\limits_{j=k}^{\infty} a_j = S$ and $\sum\limits_{j=k}^{\infty} b_j = T$ be two convergent series and let c be a number. Then

$$\sum_{j=k}^{\infty} ca_j = cS \qquad \text{and} \qquad \sum_{j=k}^{\infty} (a_j + b_j) = S + T$$

are both convergent.

Proof   Writing $S_n = a_k + a_{k+1} + \ldots + a_n$ and $T_n = b_k + b_{k+1} + \ldots + b_n$, we have

$$\sum_{j=k}^{n} ca_j = cS_n \qquad \text{and} \qquad \sum_{j=k}^{n} (a_j + b_j) = S_n + T_n$$

and so the proof is completed by letting $n \to \infty$. ∎

A series with both positive and negative terms need not have a sum. For instance, the partial sums of $\sum\limits_{n=0}^{\infty} (-1)^n$ are $S_0 = 1$, $S_1 = 1 - 1 = 0$, $S_2 = 1 - 1 + 1 = 1, \ldots$, and $S_n = 1$ or 0 according as n is even or odd; hence $\lim\limits_{n \to \infty} S_n$ does not exist. However, a series $\sum\limits_{j=k}^{\infty} a_j$ with $a_j \geq 0$ for all j must have a sum S. This is because the partial sums satisfy

$$S_k \leq S_{k+1} \leq S_{k+2} \leq \ldots \leq S_n \leq \ldots$$

so that there are only two possibilities: either (1) there is a constant $C < \infty$ such that $S_n \leq C$ for all $n \geq k$ (in which case $S = \lim\limits_{n \to \infty} S_n \leq C$ and the series converges), or (2) no such C exists (in which case $S = \lim\limits_{n \to \infty} S_n = \infty$ and the series diverges). Therefore, for series of *non-negative* terms we write

$$\sum_{j=k}^{\infty} a_j < \infty$$

to mean the series converges and

$$\sum_{j=k}^{\infty} a_j = \infty$$

to mean it diverges. The final theorem of this section is often useful in testing series for convergence.

> **Theorem (Comparison Test)**   Let $\sum\limits_{j=k}^{\infty} a_j = S$ and $\sum\limits_{j=k}^{\infty} b_j = T$ be series such that $0 \leq a_j \leq b_j$ for all $j \geq k$. Then $S \leq T$. Thus

$$T < \infty \quad \text{implies} \quad S < \infty$$

while

$$S = \infty \quad \text{implies} \quad T = \infty$$

Proof   Adding the inequalities $0 \leq a_j \leq b_j$ for $j = k, k+1, \ldots, n$ yields $0 \leq S_n \leq T_n \leq T$ and so $S = \lim\limits_{n \to \infty} S_n \leq T$. ∎

EXAMPLE   Test for convergence the series

(a) $\sum\limits_{n=2}^{\infty} 1/(n - \sqrt{n})$ and   (b) $\sum\limits_{n=1}^{\infty} 1/(n^2 + \sqrt{n})$

Solution (a) For $n \geq 2$, we have $1/n < 1/(n - \sqrt{n})$ and we already know that $\sum\limits_{n=2}^{\infty} 1/n = \infty$. Thus, series (a) diverges to the sum ∞.

(b) For $n \geq 1$, we have $1/(n^2 + \sqrt{n}) < 1/n^2$ and we already know that $\sum\limits_{n=1}^{\infty} 1/n^2 < \infty$. Thus, series (b) converges to a finite sum.

E X E R C I S E S

In 1–14, test each of the series for convergence.

1. $\sum\limits_{n=1}^{\infty} \dfrac{n}{n + 1}$

2. $\sum\limits_{n=3}^{\infty} \dfrac{n - 2}{3n - 8}$

3. $\sum\limits_{n=1}^{\infty} \dfrac{n^2}{n + 1}$

4. $\sum\limits_{n=0}^{\infty} (-1)^n/7^n$

5. $\sum\limits_{n=2}^{\infty} 2^{n-1}/5^{n+1}$

6. $\sum\limits_{n=0}^{\infty} (3/2)^n$

7. $\sum\limits_{n=1}^{\infty} (1/n)^n$

8. $\sum\limits_{n=1}^{\infty} 1/\sqrt{n}$

9. $\sum\limits_{n=1}^{\infty} \dfrac{2^n}{3^n + n}$

10. $\sum\limits_{n=1}^{\infty} \dfrac{2^n - n^2}{n^2 \cdot 2^n}$

11. $\sum\limits_{n=1}^{\infty} \left(\dfrac{1}{n} - \dfrac{1}{n + 2} \right)$

12. $\sum\limits_{n=1}^{\infty} 2^n/n^2$

13. $\sum\limits_{n=1}^{\infty} \dfrac{2^n - n^2}{2^n + n^2}$

14. $\sum\limits_{n=1}^{\infty} \left(\dfrac{1}{n^2} - \dfrac{1}{(n + 1)^2} \right)$

2 The Integral Test

We are often able to use integrals to estimate certain sums as well as to test series for convergence.

▷ **Theorem (Integral Test)** Suppose that f is a function which is (a) positive, (b) continuous, and (c) decreasing on $[k, \infty[$ for some integer $k > 0$. Then, for every integer $m \geq k$ we have

$$\int_k^{m+1} f(x) \, dx < \sum_{n=k}^{m} f(n) \leq f(k) + \int_k^m f(x) \, dx \qquad (1)$$

Thus,

$$\int_k^{\infty} f(x) \, dx \leq \sum_{n=k}^{\infty} f(n) \leq f(k) + \int_k^{\infty} f(x) \, dx \qquad (2)$$

In particular, the series $\sum\limits_{n=k}^{\infty} f(n)$ and the improper integral $\int_{k}^{\infty} f(x)\,dx$

either both converge or both diverge.

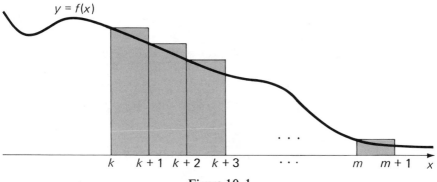

Figure 10–1

Proof   The sum of the areas of the rectangles shown in Fig. 10-1 is $\sum\limits_{n=k}^{m} f(n)$ and it is plain that this total area exceeds the area under $y = f(x)$ from $x = k$ to $x = m + 1$. The sum of the areas of the rectangles shown in Fig. 10-2 is $\sum\limits_{n=k+1}^{m} f(n)$ and this is evidently less than the area under $y = f(x)$ from $x = k$ to $x = m$. These observations prove (1). Now (2) follows from (1) by letting $m \to \infty$. The last sentence of the theorem follows immediately from (2). ■

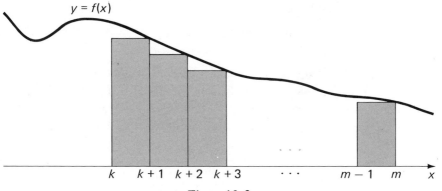

Figure 10–2

▷ *Corollary* Let p be a positive real number. Then

$$p > 1 \quad \text{implies} \quad \frac{1}{p-1} < \sum_{n=1}^{\infty} \frac{1}{n^p} < \frac{p}{p-1} < \infty \qquad (3)$$

and

$$p \leq 1 \quad \text{implies} \quad \sum_{n=1}^{\infty} \frac{1}{n^p} = \infty \qquad (4)$$

These series are called **p-series**. They will be found to be very useful in the next section.

Proof Let $k = 1$ and $f(x) = x^{-p}$. If $p > 1$, then $1 - p < 0$ so that

$$\int_1^\infty f(x)\,dx = \lim_{m \to \infty} \frac{x^{1-p}}{1-p} \Big|_1^m = \frac{1}{p-1}$$

and so, according to (2) of the preceding theorem,

$$\frac{1}{p-1} < \sum_{n=1}^{\infty} \frac{1}{n^p} < \frac{1}{1^p} + \frac{1}{p-1} = \frac{p}{p-1}$$

which proves (3). If $p \leq 1$, then $1/x \leq 1/x^p$ for all $x > 0$ so that

$$\infty = \lim_{m \to \infty} \ln m = \lim_{m \to \infty} \int_1^m \frac{dx}{x} \leq \lim_{m \to \infty} \int_1^m \frac{dx}{x^p} = \int_1^\infty \frac{dx}{x^p}$$

and so (4) also follows from (2). ∎

EXAMPLE Does the series

$$\sum_{n=1}^{\infty} \frac{1}{4n^2 - 16n + 7} = -\frac{1}{5} - \frac{1}{9} - \frac{1}{5} + \frac{1}{7} + \cdots$$

converge? If so, estimate its sum.

Solution We want to use the Integral Test with $f(x) = 1/(4x^2 - 16x + 7)$. For this, we must find some integer $k > 0$ so that the hypotheses (a)–(c) are satisfied on $[k, \infty[$. Since $4x^2 - 16x + 7 = (2x - 1)(2x - 7)$, it is clear that (a) and (b) obtain if we take $k = 4$. Since

$$f'(x) = \frac{-8(x-2)}{(4x^2 - 16x + 7)^2} < 0$$

if $x \geq 4$, the choice $k = 4$ also satisfies (c). Therefore (1) and (2) hold if $k = 4$. We have, using partial fractions,

$$\int_4^\infty f(x)\,dx = \lim_{m\to\infty} \frac{1}{12} \int_4^m \left[\frac{2}{2x-7} - \frac{2}{2x-1} \right] dx$$

$$= \lim_{m\to\infty} \frac{1}{12} \left[\ln \frac{2m-7}{2m-1} - \ln \frac{1}{7} \right] = (\ln 7)/12$$

Thus, the given series converges. It also follows from (2) of the Theorem that

$$\frac{\ln 7}{12} < \sum_{n=4}^\infty \frac{1}{4n^2 - 16n + 7} < \frac{1}{7} + \frac{\ln 7}{12}$$

so that

$$-\frac{23}{45} + \frac{\ln 7}{12} < \sum_{n=1}^\infty \frac{1}{4n^2 - 16n + 7} < -\frac{116}{315} + \frac{\ln 7}{12}$$

EXAMPLE Does the series $\sum_{n=2}^\infty \frac{\ln n}{n^2}$ converge? If so, estimate its sum.

First Solution We shall use the Integral Test with $f(x) = x^{-2} \ln x$, which is positive and continuous for $x > 1$. Since

$$f'(x) = \frac{1 - 2 \ln x}{x^3} < 0$$

if $x > \sqrt{e}$ and $\sqrt{e} < 2$, we see that f is decreasing on $[2, \infty[$ and so we can take $k = 2$. We integrate by parts to obtain

$$\int_2^m x^{-2} \ln x\,dx = -x^{-1} \ln x \Big|_2^m + \int_2^m x^{-2}\,dx$$

$$= \frac{\ln 2}{2} - \frac{\ln m}{m} + \frac{1}{2} - \frac{1}{m}$$

Thus,

$$\int_2^\infty x^{-2} \ln x\,dx = \frac{1 + \ln 2}{2}$$

and so

$$\frac{1 + \ln 2}{2} < \sum_{n=2}^\infty \frac{\ln n}{n^2} < \frac{\ln 2}{4} + \frac{1 + \ln 2}{2} = \frac{2 + 3 \ln 2}{4}$$

Second Solution We prove first that $\ln x < \sqrt{x}$ if $x \geqq 4$. Indeed, writing $g(x) = \sqrt{x} - \ln x$, we have $g(4) = 2(1 - \ln 2) > 0$ and $g'(x) =$

$x^{-1/2}/2 - 1/x = (\sqrt{x} - 2)/(2x) > 0$ if $x > 4$ and so g is increasing on $[4,\infty[$. Thus $g(x) > 0$ if $x \geq 4$ and so $\ln n < \sqrt{n}$ if $n \geq 4$. It follows from this and the Corollary (with $p = 3/2$) that

$$\sum_{n=4}^{\infty} \frac{\ln n}{n^2} < \sum_{n=4}^{\infty} \frac{\sqrt{n}}{n^2} = \sum_{n=2}^{\infty} \frac{1}{n^{3/2}} < 3$$

This is not nearly as good an estimate as the first solution gives.

EXAMPLE   Find upper and lower estimates of the sums

(a) $\displaystyle\sum_{n=1}^{100} \frac{1}{\sqrt{n}}$ and   (b) $\displaystyle\sum_{n=k}^{2k} \frac{1}{n}$

where m is a given positive integer.

Solution   (a) Taking $k = 1$, $m = 100$, and $f(x) = x^{-1/2}$ in the above theorem, we have

$$\int_{k}^{m+1} f(x)\, dx = 2x^{1/2}\Big|_{1}^{101} = 2\sqrt{101} - 2$$

and

$$\int_{k}^{m} f(x)\, dx = 2x^{1/2}\Big|_{1}^{100} = 20 - 2 = 18$$

and so

$$2\sqrt{101} - 2 < \sum_{n=1}^{100} \frac{1}{\sqrt{n}} < f(1) + 18 = 19$$

(b) Take $m = 2k$ and $f(x) = x^{-1}$ to obtain

$$\int_{k}^{m+1} f(x)\, dx = \ln x\Big|_{k}^{2k+1} = \ln(2k+1) - \ln k = \ln\left(2 + \frac{1}{k}\right)$$

and

$$\int_{k}^{m} f(x)\, dx = \ln x\Big|_{k}^{2k} = \ln 2k - \ln k = \ln 2$$

so that

$$\ln\left(2 + \frac{1}{k}\right) < \sum_{n=k}^{2k} \frac{1}{n} < \frac{1}{k} + \ln 2$$

EXERCISES

In 1–25, use the results of sections 1 and 2 to decide which of the series converge. For those which converge, either compute the sum or, if that is not possible, make reasonable upper and lower estimates of the sum.

1. $\displaystyle\sum_{n=0}^{\infty} (2/3)^n$

2. $\displaystyle\sum_{n=1}^{\infty} (-1)^{n-1}(7/8)^n$

3. $\displaystyle\sum_{n=0}^{\infty} (-1)^n 2^n / 5^{n+2}$

4. $\displaystyle\sum_{n=3}^{\infty} (2/5)^n$

5. $\displaystyle\sum_{n=-1}^{\infty} 3^{-n}$

6. $\displaystyle\sum_{n=-2}^{\infty} (4/\pi^2)^n$

7. $\displaystyle\sum_{n=-2}^{\infty} \left(-\frac{2}{e}\right)^n$

8. $\displaystyle\sum_{n=0}^{\infty} (-1)^n 2^{n+1} / 3^n$

9. $\displaystyle\sum_{n=1}^{\infty} \frac{n^2 + 1}{9n^2 - 2}$

10. $\displaystyle\sum_{n=0}^{\infty} \frac{n}{23n + 100}$

11. $\displaystyle\sum_{n=0}^{\infty} \frac{2^n}{2^{n+1} + 20}$

12. $\displaystyle\sum_{n=1}^{\infty} \frac{n^2}{\sqrt{n^3 + 1}}$

13. $\displaystyle\sum_{n=1}^{\infty} \frac{n - 2}{\sqrt{n^2 + 2n}}$

14. $\displaystyle\sum_{n=1}^{\infty} \frac{\sin n\pi}{n}$

15. $\displaystyle\sum_{n=1}^{\infty} \frac{1}{n^2 + 1}$

16. $\displaystyle\sum_{n=1}^{\infty} ne^{-n}$

17. $\displaystyle\sum_{n=1}^{\infty} \frac{2n}{9n^2 - 4}$

18. $\displaystyle\sum_{n=3}^{\infty} \frac{n + 1}{n^3 - 8}$

19. $\displaystyle\sum_{n=2}^{\infty} \frac{1}{n \ln n}$

20. $\displaystyle\sum_{n=2}^{\infty} \frac{1}{(\ln n)^n}$

21. $\displaystyle\sum_{n=2}^{\infty} \frac{1}{n(\ln n)^p}$ $(p > 1)$

22. $\displaystyle\sum_{n=1}^{\infty} \frac{\sin (\pi/2^n)}{2^n}$

23. $\displaystyle\sum_{n=1}^{\infty} \sin (\pi/2^n)$

24. $\displaystyle\sum_{n=1}^{\infty} \frac{n + 3}{n(n + 1)(n + 2)}$

25. $\displaystyle\sum_{n=1}^{\infty} \frac{\pi}{n} \sin \frac{\pi}{n}$

In 26–29 use the theorem of this section to find upper and lower estimates for the following finite sums.

26. $\displaystyle\sum_{n=1}^{100} \frac{n}{n^2 + 1}$

27. $\displaystyle\sum_{n=1}^{100} \frac{\sqrt{n}}{2\sqrt{n} - 1}$

28. $\displaystyle\sum_{n=2}^{1000} \frac{1}{n^2 - 1}$

29. $\displaystyle\sum_{n=1}^{1000} \frac{1}{n^2}$

30. Give an argument similar to that used for the proof of the theorem of this section to prove the following: If $k < m$ are integers and f is a function that is nonnegative, continuous, and *increasing* on $[k, m + 1]$, then

$$f(k) + \int_k^m f(x)\, dx < \sum_{n=k}^{m} f(n) < \int_k^{m+1} f(x)\, dx$$

31. In exercise 30, take $k = 1$ and $f(x) = \ln x$ to prove that

$$m \ln m - m + 1 < \ln (m!) < (m + 1) \ln (m + 1) - m$$

and so

$$m^m e^{1-m} < m! < (m + 1)^{m+1} e^{-m}$$

for each integer $m > 1$.

3 Limit Comparison Tests

If $a_n = n/(n^3 - 2)$ and $c_n = 1/n^2$, then we know that

$$\sum_{n=1}^{\infty} c_n < \infty \qquad \text{and} \qquad a_n > c_n \qquad \text{for } n > 1$$

Since this last inequality goes the wrong way, we cannot conclude from the Comparison Test that $\sum a_n < \infty$. However, it is clear that a_n is "about the same as" c_n for large n, and so we suspect that $\sum a_n < \infty$. In fact, we have

$$\frac{a_n}{c_n} = \frac{n^3}{n^3 - 2} = \frac{1}{1 - 2/n^3} \to 1 \qquad \text{as } n \to \infty$$

and so there is some N such that $a_n/c_n < 2$ if $n \geqq N$. Thus,

$$\sum_{n=N}^{\infty} a_n < \sum_{n=N}^{\infty} 2c_n = 2 \cdot \sum_{n=N}^{\infty} \frac{1}{n^2} < \infty$$

and so $\sum a_n < \infty$. This is just a special case of the following very useful theorem.

▷ ***Limit Comparison Test for Convergence*** Suppose that $\sum_{n=k}^{\infty} a_n$ and $\sum_{n=k}^{\infty} c_n$ are two series which satisfy

(i) $a_n \geqq 0$ and $c_n > 0$ for all n greater than or equal to some $m \geqq k$

(ii) $\sum_{n=k}^{\infty} c_n < \infty$

(iii) $\lim_{n \to \infty} a_n/c_n = L < \infty$

Then $\sum_{n=k}^{\infty} a_n < \infty$.

Proof Choose any b with $L < b < \infty$ (say, $b = L + 1$). Because of (iii), there is some $N > m$ such that

$$a_n/c_n < b \qquad \text{for all } n \geq N$$

and therefore

$$a_n < bc_n \qquad \text{for } n \geq N$$

Thus

$$\sum_{n=N}^{\infty} a_n \leq \sum_{n=N}^{\infty} bc_n = b \cdot \sum_{n=N}^{\infty} c_n < \infty$$

This completes the proof. ■

Next we have an equally useful theorem on divergence.

> **Limit Comparison Test for Divergence** Suppose that $\sum_{n=k}^{\infty} a_n$ and $\sum_{n=k}^{\infty} d_n$ are two series which satisfy

  (i) $a_n \geq 0$ and $d_n > 0$ for all n greater than or equal to some $m \geq k$

  (ii) $\sum_{n=k}^{\infty} d_n = \infty$

  (iii) $\lim_{n \to \infty} a_n/d_n = L > 0$

Then $\sum_{n=k}^{\infty} a_n = \infty$.

Proof Choose any b with $L > b > 0$ (say, $b = L/2$). Because of (iii), there is some $N \geq m$ such that

$$a_n/d_n > b \qquad \text{for all } n \geq N$$

and therefore

$$a_n > bd_n \qquad \text{for all } n \geq N$$

Thus

$$\sum_{n=N}^{\infty} a_n \geq \sum_{n=N}^{\infty} bd_n = \infty$$

The proof is complete. ■

In order to use these tests to determine the convergence behavior of a given series $\sum_{n=k}^{\infty} a_n$, we must first take a good look at a_n and try to see that it is "about the same" as the nth term b_n of some series whose behavior we already know. We then compute $\lim a_n/b_n$ and apply the appropriate one of the two tests. Of course, these tests apply only to series whose terms (except for a finite number) are *nonnegative*. The p-series are often useful for comparison.

EXAMPLE   Test each of the following series for convergence.

(a) $\displaystyle\sum_{n=1}^{\infty} \frac{3n+7}{2n^2-4n+5}$

(c) $\displaystyle\sum_{n=1}^{\infty} \frac{n^{10}}{2^n-n}$

(b) $\displaystyle\sum_{n=1}^{\infty} \frac{\ln n}{\sqrt{2n^3-1}}$

(d) $\displaystyle\sum_{n=1}^{\infty} \sin(1/n)$

Solution   (a) The nth term a_n is a linear function of n divided by a quadratic function of n. The degree of the bottom is just 1 more than that of the top and so we guess that the series diverges and test this guess by choosing $d_n = 1/n$. We have

$$\frac{a_n}{d_n} = \frac{3n^2+7n}{2n^2-4n+5} \to \frac{3}{2} > 0$$

and so, since $\sum d_n = \infty$, we conclude that the given series diverges.

(b) The nth term a_n is "about like" $(\ln n)/n^{3/2}$ and since $\ln n$ "grows more slowly" than $n^{1/4}$, we take $c_n = n^{1/4}/n^{3/2} = 1/n^{5/4}$ and hope for convergence. More precisely, we have

$$\sum_{n=1}^{\infty} c_n < \infty$$

because $5/4 > 1$, and

$$\frac{a_n}{c_n} = \frac{n^{3/2}}{\sqrt{2n^3-1}} \cdot \frac{\ln n}{n^{1/4}} = \frac{1}{\sqrt{2-1/n^3}} \cdot \frac{\ln n}{n^{1/4}} \to \frac{1}{\sqrt{2}} \cdot 0 = 0 < \infty$$

Thus, the given series converges.

(c) The $-n$ doesn't change 2^n much for "large" n, so that a_n is "about like" $n^{10}/2^n$. Now $n^{10}/2^n$ is "much larger" than $1/2^n$, but we guess that $n^{10}/2^n$ is "much smaller" than $(3/4)^n = c_n$. Now let's stop guessing. Since $0 < 3/4 < 1$, the geometric series $\sum c_n$ converges. Also,

$$\frac{a_n}{c_n} = \frac{n^{10}}{2^n-n} \cdot \frac{4^n}{3^n} = \frac{1}{1-n/2^n} \cdot \frac{n^{10}}{(3/2)^n}$$

Now ten applications of l'Hôpital's Rule show that

$$\lim_{x\to\infty} \frac{x^{10}}{(3/2)^x} = \lim_{x\to\infty} \frac{(10)!}{(3/2)^x(\ln(3/2))^{10}} = 0$$

Thus,

$$\lim_{n\to\infty}\frac{a_n}{c_n}=1\cdot 0=0<\infty$$

We conclude that the given series converges.

(d) We guess that $\sin(1/n)$ is "about like" $1/n=d_n$. We have $\sum d_n=\infty$ and

$$\lim_{n\to\infty}\frac{a_n}{d_n}=\lim_{n\to\infty}\frac{\sin(1/n)}{1/n}=\lim_{x\to 0^+}\frac{\sin x}{x}=1>0$$

We conclude that the given series diverges.

EXERCISES

In 1–20, test the series for convergence.

1. $\displaystyle\sum_{n=1}^{\infty}\frac{1}{2n^2-1}$

2. $\displaystyle\sum_{n=1}^{\infty}\frac{4n+5}{3n^3-2}$

3. $\displaystyle\sum_{n=1}^{\infty}\frac{1}{n\sqrt{2n-1}}$

4. $\displaystyle\sum_{n=1}^{\infty}\frac{1}{(2n-1)^{3/2}}$

5. $\displaystyle\sum_{n=1}^{\infty}\frac{\sqrt{4n+3}}{(2n-1)^2}$

6. $\displaystyle\sum_{n=1}^{\infty}\frac{8n+9}{\sqrt{n^4+1}}$

7. $\displaystyle\sum_{n=1}^{\infty}\frac{n!}{(n+1)!}$

8. $\displaystyle\sum_{n=1}^{\infty}\frac{n!}{(n+2)!}$

9. $\displaystyle\sum_{n=2}^{\infty}\frac{\ln n}{n^2-1}$

10. $\displaystyle\sum_{n=1}^{\infty}\frac{(\ln n)^2}{n^3+1}$

11. $\displaystyle\sum_{n=2}^{\infty}\frac{1}{(n-1)\ln n}$

12. $\displaystyle\sum_{n=2}^{\infty}\frac{1}{(n-1)(\ln n)^2}$

13. $\displaystyle\sum_{n=0}^{\infty}\frac{1}{2^n-\sin n}$

14. $\displaystyle\sum_{n=0}^{\infty}\frac{1}{2^n+\cos n}$

15. $\displaystyle\sum_{n=1}^{\infty}\sin(1/n^2)$

16. $\displaystyle\sum_{n=1}^{\infty}\cos(1/n^2)$

17. $\displaystyle\sum_{n=1}^{\infty}\frac{\sin(1/n)}{n}$

18. $\displaystyle\sum_{n=1}^{\infty}\frac{\sin(1/n)}{\sqrt{n}}$

19. $\displaystyle\sum_{n=1}^{\infty}(\sqrt{n+1}-\sqrt{n})^2$

20. $\displaystyle\sum_{n=1}^{\infty}(\sqrt{n+1}-\sqrt{n})^3$

21. Prove the following **Log Test:** If $a_n>0$ for all $n\geq 1$ and

$$\lim_{n\to\infty}\frac{\ln(1/a_n)}{\ln n}>1$$

then $\displaystyle\sum_{n=1}^{\infty}a_n<\infty$. [*Hint:* Choose p between 1 and the limit.]

22. Prove the following **Log Test:** If $a_n > 0$ for all $n \geq 1$ and

$$\lim_{n \to \infty} \frac{\ln (1/a_n)}{\ln n} < 1$$

then $\sum_{n=1}^{\infty} a_n = \infty$.

4 Alternating Series

In this section we study a type of series which, though very special, frequently occurs in applications.

▷ **Definition** A series is said to be **alternating** if every other term is nonnegative and the other terms are nonpositive. Thus, every alternating series is of one of the forms

$$\sum_{n=1}^{\infty} (-1)^{n-1} a_n \qquad \text{or} \qquad \sum_{n=1}^{\infty} (-1)^n a_n$$

where $a_n \geq 0$ for all $n \geq 1$.

Which form the series takes depends only on whether the first term is positive or negative. Also, since the two forms are just the negatives of each other, information about the series on the left immediately translates to corresponding information about the series on the right.

Examples of alternating series are the series $1 - 1/2 + 1/3 - 1/4 + 1/5 - 1/6 + \ldots$ which can be written $\sum_{n=1}^{\infty} \frac{(-1)^{n-1}}{n}$ and the series

$-1 + 2 - 3 + 4 - 5 + 6 - \ldots$ which can be written $\sum_{n=1}^{\infty} (-1)^n n$.

There is a very useful convergence test for alternating series which we now present. It also gives estimates for the sum of such a series.

▷ **Alternating Series Test (AST)** Suppose that

(i) $a_n \geq 0$ for $n = 1, 2, 3, \ldots$
(ii) $a_n \geq a_{n+1}$ for all $n \geq 1$
(iii) $\lim_{n \to \infty} a_n = 0$

Then $\sum_{n=1}^{\infty} (-1)^{n-1} a_n$ converges. Moreover, if

$$S_n = a_1 - a_2 + a_3 - a_4 + \ldots + (-1)^{n-1} a_n$$

is the nth partial sum of this series and S is the sum of the series, then we have

(iv) $S_1 \geq S_3 \geq S_5 \geq S_7 \geq \ldots$
(v) $S_2 \leq S_4 \leq S_6 \leq S_8 \leq \ldots$
(vi) $S_m \leq S \leq S_n$ if m is even and n is odd
(vii) $|S - S_n| \leq a_{n+1}$ for all $n \geq 1$

Proof Let k be any positive integer. Then

$$S_{2k+1} - S_{2k-1} = (-1)^{2k-1}a_{2k} + (-1)^{2k}a_{2k+1}$$
$$= -a_{2k} + a_{2k+1} \leq 0$$

by (ii) and therefore (iv) obtains. Also,

$$S_{2k+2} - S_{2k} = (-1)^{2k}a_{2k+1} + (-1)^{2k+1}a_{2k+2}$$
$$= a_{2k+1} - a_{2k+2} \geq 0$$

by (ii) and so we have (v).

Now let m be even and let n be odd. If $m < n$, then (v) yields $S_m \leq S_{n-1}$ and so we use (i) to get

$$S_n - S_m \geq S_n - S_{n-1} = (-1)^{n-1}a_n = a_n \geq 0$$

and so $S_m \leq S_n$. If $m > n$, then (iv) shows that $S_{m-1} \leq S_n$ so that, using (i), we have

$$S_m - S_n \leq S_m - S_{m-1} = (-1)^{m-1}a_m = -a_m \leq 0$$

and hence $S_m \leq S_n$. In either case $S_m \leq S_n$.

Now the sequence S_{2j} ($j = 1, 2, \ldots$) marches upward and is bounded above by S_{2k-1} (for any odd subscript $2k-1$) and so it has a limit

$$\underline{S} = \lim_{j \to \infty} S_{2j} \leq S_{2k-1}$$

(see Fig. 10-3). Next, notice that the sequence S_{2k-1} ($k = 1, 2, 3, \ldots$) marches downward and is bounded below by $\underline{S}$ (see Fig. 10-4) and so it has a limit

$$\overline{S} = \lim_{k \to \infty} S_{2k-1} \geq \underline{S}$$

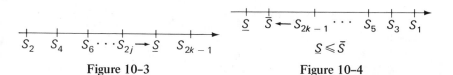

Figure 10-3   Figure 10-4

Now we use (iii) to see that

$$0 \leq \bar{S} - \underline{S} = \lim_{n \to \infty} S_{2n+1} - \lim_{n \to \infty} S_{2n}$$

$$= \lim_{n \to \infty} (S_{2n+1} - S_{2n}) = \lim_{n \to \infty} a_{2n+1} = 0$$

Therefore, $\underline{S} = \bar{S}$. We conclude that the sequence S_n $(n = 1, 2, 3, \ldots)$ has a limit

$$S = \underline{S} = \bar{S} = \lim_{n \to \infty} S_n$$

This proves that the series converges and that (vi) obtains.

Finally, for m even, we have

$$0 \leq S - S_m \leq S_{m+1} - S_m = a_{m+1}$$

and, for n odd, we have

$$0 \leq |S - S_n| = S_n - S \leq S_n - S_{n+1} = a_{n+1}$$

This proves (vii) and completes the proof. ∎

EXAMPLE Show that the series $\sum_{n=1}^{\infty} (-1)^{n-1}/n$ converges and that its sum S is between 7/12 and 5/6.

Solution The sequence $a_n = 1/n$ satisfies (i)–(iii) of the above theorem and so the series converges. Also, (vi) yields

$$\frac{7}{12} = 1 - \frac{1}{2} + \frac{1}{3} - \frac{1}{4} = S_4 \leq S \leq S_3 = 1 - \frac{1}{2} + \frac{1}{3} = \frac{5}{6}$$

EXAMPLE Test $\sum_{n=1}^{\infty} (-1)^{n-1} \dfrac{n+2}{2n}$ for convergence.

Solution Since $\lim_{n \to \infty} (n+2)/(2n) = 1/2$, the terms of this series fail to converge to 0. Thus the series diverges. Notice that, with $a_n = (n+2)/(2n)$, both (i) and (ii) of AST obtain, but (iii) fails.

EXAMPLE If n is odd, let $a_n = 1/n$, and if n is even, let $a_n = 1/2^n$. Test $\sum_{n=1}^{\infty} (-1)^{n-1} a_n$ for convergence.

Solution We have

$$S_{2n} = 1 - \frac{1}{4} + \frac{1}{3} - \frac{1}{16} + \frac{1}{5} - \frac{1}{64} + \frac{1}{7} - \frac{1}{256} + \ldots + \frac{1}{2n-1} - \frac{1}{2^{2n}}$$

$$> \sum_{k=1}^{n} \frac{1}{2k-1} - \sum_{k=1}^{\infty} \frac{1}{4^k} = \sum_{k=1}^{n} \frac{1}{2k-1} - \frac{1}{3}$$

Since $\displaystyle\sum_{k=1}^{\infty} \frac{1}{2k-1} = \infty$, it follows that $\displaystyle\lim_{n\to\infty} S_{2n} = \infty$. Thus, the series diverges. Notice that (i) and (iii) of AST both obtain, but (ii) fails.

These last two examples are included to emphasize that all the hypotheses of a theorem must be satisfied before we can safely infer that the conclusions hold. Actually, (i) of AST is unnecessary because it follows from (ii) and (iii) in conjunction.

EXAMPLE   Use AST to write the first six decimal places of the sum S of the series

$$\sum_{n=0}^{\infty} \frac{(-1)^n}{(2n)!} = 1 - \frac{1}{2} + \frac{1}{24} - \frac{1}{720} + \cdots$$

Solution   We have $|S - S_n| \le a_{n+1}$ and so we begin by finding n such that $1/(2n + 2)! < 5/10^7$. We do this by trial and error. We have $6! = 720$, $8! = 40{,}320$ and $10! = 3{,}628{,}800$ and so, taking $n = 4$,

$$a_{n+1} = a_5 = \frac{1}{10!} < \frac{1}{2 \cdot (10)^6} = \frac{5}{(10)^7}$$

We have

$$S_3 = \frac{1}{0!} - \frac{1}{2!} + \frac{1}{4!} - \frac{1}{6!} = 1 - \frac{1}{2} + \frac{1}{24} - \frac{1}{720}$$

$$= \frac{389}{720} = .5402777777 \ldots$$

and

$$S_4 = S_3 + \frac{1}{8!} = .540302579 \ldots$$

Since the last term of S_4 is positive, we have $S_3 < S < S_4$. Finally $0 < S_4 - S < a_5 = \dfrac{1}{(10)!} < \dfrac{5}{10^7}$ and so

$$.540302079 \ldots < S_4 - a_5 < S < S_4 = .540302579 \ldots$$

Thus $S = .540302 \ldots$.

E X E R C I S E S

In 1–10, test the given series for convergence.

1. $\displaystyle\sum_{n=1}^{\infty} (-1)^{n-1} \cdot \frac{n}{n^2 + 1}$

6. $\displaystyle\sum_{n=1}^{\infty} (-1)^{n-1} \cdot \frac{1}{\sqrt{n+1}}$

2. $\displaystyle\sum_{n=1}^{\infty} (-1)^{n-1} \frac{n+1}{2n^2 - 1}$

7. $\displaystyle\sum_{n=1}^{\infty} (-1)^{n-1}[1 - \cos (1/n)]$

3. $\displaystyle\sum_{n=1}^{\infty} (-1)^{n-1} \frac{n+1}{4n - 3}$

8. $\displaystyle\sum_{n=1}^{\infty} (-1)^{n-1} \sin (1/n)$

4. $\displaystyle\sum_{n=1}^{\infty} (-1)^{n-1} \frac{\sqrt{n^4 + 1}}{2n^2 - 1}$

9. $\displaystyle\sum_{n=2}^{\infty} (-1)^{n} \frac{(\ln n)^{10}}{n}$

5. $\displaystyle\sum_{n=1}^{\infty} (-1)^{n-1} \operatorname{Tan}^{-1} n$

10. $\displaystyle\sum_{n=0}^{\infty} (-1)^{n} n^{43} e^{-n}$

11. Approximate the sum of $\displaystyle\sum_{n=1}^{\infty} \frac{(-1)^{n-1}}{n^3}$ to two-decimal-place accuracy.

12. How many terms of the series $\displaystyle\sum_{n=1}^{\infty} (-1)^{n-1}/n$ are needed to obtain an approximation that is accurate to two decimal places?

5 Absolute Convergence

Aside from the preceding section and the nth Term Test, all of our tests apply only to series of nonnegative terms. These tests, when combined with the following theorem, can often be used to test series of arbitrary terms.

▷ **Theorem** Let $a_k, a_{k+1}, a_{k+2}, \ldots$, be any sequence of real numbers for which $\displaystyle\sum_{n=k}^{\infty} |a_n| < \infty$. Then $\displaystyle\sum_{n=k}^{\infty} a_n$ converges.

Proof For each $n \geq k$, define a_n^+ and a_n^- by

$$a_n^+ = \begin{cases} a_n & \text{if } a_n \geq 0 \\ 0 & \text{if } a_n < 0 \end{cases}$$

$$a_n^- = \begin{cases} 0 & \text{if } a_n \geq 0 \\ -a_n & \text{if } a_n < 0 \end{cases}$$

Now it is evident that

$$0 \le a_n^+ \le |a_n| \qquad 0 \le a_n^- \le |a_n|$$
$$a_n = a_n^+ - a_n^- \qquad |a_n| = a_n^+ + a_n^-$$

By the Comparison Test, we see that

$$\sum_{n=k}^{\infty} a_n^+ < \infty \qquad \text{and} \qquad \sum_{n=k}^{\infty} a_n^- < \infty$$

Therefore

$$\sum_{n=k}^{\infty} a_n = \sum_{n=k}^{\infty} (a_n^+ - a_n^-) = \sum_{n=k}^{\infty} a_n^+ - \sum_{n=k}^{\infty} a_n^-$$

This completes the proof. ■

Inspired by this theorem, we make the following definition.

▷ **Definition**   A series $\sum_{n=k}^{\infty} a_n$ is said to be **absolutely convergent** if $\sum_{n=k}^{\infty} |a_n| < \infty$. All other convergent series are called **conditionally convergent.**

The above theorem simply says that every absolutely convergent series is convergent.

EXAMPLE   Decide whether each of the following series is absolutely convergent, conditionally convergent, or divergent:

(a) $\displaystyle\sum_{n=1}^{\infty} \frac{(-1)^{n-1}}{n}$ (b) $\displaystyle\sum_{n=1}^{\infty} \frac{(-1)^{n-1}}{n^2}$ (c) $\displaystyle\sum_{n=1}^{\infty} \frac{n(-1)^n}{2n+1}$

Solution   (a) This series converges by AST, but

$$\sum_{n=1}^{\infty} \left| \frac{(-1)^{n-1}}{n} \right| = \sum_{n=1}^{\infty} 1/n = \infty$$

Thus, the given series is conditionally convergent.

(b) Since

$$\sum_{n=1}^{\infty} \left| \frac{(-1)^{n-1}}{n^2} \right| = \sum_{n=1}^{\infty} 1/n^2 < \infty$$

the given series is absolutely convergent.

(c) Since $\lim\limits_{n \to \infty} \dfrac{n}{2n+1} = \dfrac{1}{2} \ne 0$, it is impossible that the terms of the given series converge to 0, and so it diverges.

The next two theorems are quite useful in testing for absolute convergence. They will be found invaluable in our study of power series later in this chapter.

Ratio Test   Let $\sum\limits_{n=k}^{\infty} a_n$ be a series of nonzero numbers. Suppose that

$$\lim_{n \to \infty} \left| \frac{a_{n+1}}{a_n} \right| = L$$

Then

(i) $L < 1$ implies $\sum\limits_{n=k}^{\infty} a_n$ converges absolutely

and

(ii) $L > 1$ implies $\sum\limits_{n=k}^{\infty} a_n$ diverges

Proof   (i) Suppose $L < 1$. Choose any number r such that $L < r < 1$ (say, $r = (L + 1)/2$). Then there exists some $N \geq k$ such that

$$\left| \frac{a_{n+1}}{a_n} \right| < r \qquad \text{whenever } n \geq N$$

Thus $n > N$ implies that

$$|a_n| = \left| \frac{a_n}{a_{n-1}} \cdot \frac{a_{n-1}}{a_{n-2}} \cdot \ldots \cdot \frac{a_{N+1}}{a_N} \cdot a_N \right|$$
$$< r^{n-N} \cdot |a_N| = (|a_N|/r^N)r^n$$

Since the geometric series $\sum\limits_{n=N+1}^{\infty} (|a_N|/r^N)r^n$ converges ($|r| < 1$), it follows from the Comparison Test that

$$\sum_{n=N+1}^{\infty} |a_n| < \infty$$

and so

$$\sum_{n=k}^{\infty} |a_n| < \infty$$

(ii) Suppose $L > 1$. Then there is some $N \geq k$ such that

$$\left| \frac{a_{n+1}}{a_n} \right| > 1 \qquad \text{whenever } n \geq N$$

Thus, $n > N$ implies that

$$|a_n| = \left| \frac{a_n}{a_{n-1}} \cdot \frac{a_{n-1}}{a_{n-2}} \cdot \ldots \cdot \frac{a_{N+1}}{a_N} \cdot a_N \right|$$

$$> 1^{n-N}|a_N| = |a_N| > 0$$

and so it is false that $a_n \to 0$. We deduce from the nth Term Test that $\sum\limits_{n=k}^{\infty} a_n$ diverges. ∎

Notice that this theorem says nothing about the case that $L = 1$. There is good reason for this because in that case the series could have either property. In fact, if $a_n = 1/n$ for all n, then

$$\lim_{n \to \infty} \left| \frac{a_{n+1}}{a_n} \right| = \lim_{n \to \infty} \frac{n}{n+1} = 1 \quad \text{and} \quad \sum_{n=1}^{\infty} a_n = \infty$$

while, if $a_n = 1/n^2$ for all n, then

$$\lim_{n \to \infty} \left| \frac{a_{n+1}}{a_n} \right| = \lim_{n \to \infty} \left(\frac{n}{n+1} \right)^2 = 1^2 = 1 \quad \text{and} \quad \sum_{n=1}^{\infty} a_n < \infty$$

▷ **Root Test** Let $\sum\limits_{n=k}^{\infty} a_n$ be any series of numbers. Suppose that

$$\lim_{n \to \infty} |a_n|^{1/n} = L$$

Then

(i) $L < 1$ implies $\sum\limits_{n=k}^{\infty} a_n$ is absolutely convergent

and

(ii) $L > 1$ implies $\sum\limits_{n=k}^{\infty} a_n$ diverges

Proof (i) Suppose $L < 1$. Choose any r with $L < r < 1$. Then there is some $N \geq k$ such that

$$|a_n|^{1/n} < r \quad \text{whenever } n \geq N$$

Therefore

$$\sum_{n=N}^{\infty} |a_n| < \sum_{n=N}^{\infty} r^n = \frac{r^N}{1-r} < \infty$$

(ii) Suppose $L > 1$. Then an $N \geq k$ exists such that

$$|a_n|^{1/n} > 1 \qquad \text{whenever } n \geq N$$

But then $|a_n| > 1$ for $n \geq N$ and so we cannot have $a_n \to 0$. This implies that $\sum\limits_{n=k}^{\infty} a_n$ diverges. ∎

EXAMPLE   Test for convergence the series:

(a) $\sum\limits_{n=1}^{\infty} \dfrac{n}{2^n}$ (b) $\sum\limits_{n=1}^{\infty} \dfrac{1}{n!}$ (c) $\sum\limits_{n=1}^{\infty} (-1)^{n-1} \left(\dfrac{n}{2n+1}\right)^n$

Solution   (a) With $a_n = n/2^n$, we have

$$\left|\frac{a_{n+1}}{a_n}\right| = \frac{n+1}{2^{n+1}} \cdot \frac{2^n}{n} = \frac{1}{2}\left(1+\frac{1}{n}\right) \to \frac{1}{2} < 1$$

and so the Ratio Test shows that this series is (absolutely) convergent.

(b) With $a_n = 1/n!$, we have

$$\left|\frac{a_{n+1}}{a_n}\right| = \frac{n!}{(n+1)!} = \frac{1}{n+1} \to 0 < 1$$

and so the Ratio Test shows that this series is (absolutely) convergent.

(c) With $a_n = (-1)^{n-1} \cdot [n/(2n+1)]^n$, we have

$$|a_n|^{1/n} = n/(2n+1) \to \frac{1}{2} < 1$$

and so the Root Test shows that this is an absolutely convergent series.

E X E R C I S E S

In 1–17, tell whether (and show why) the given series is absolutely convergent, conditionally convergent, or divergent.

1. $\sum\limits_{n=1}^{\infty} \dfrac{(-1)^n}{\ln(n+1)}$

2. $\sum\limits_{n=1}^{\infty} (-1)^{n-1} \dfrac{\ln n}{n}$

3. $\sum\limits_{n=1}^{\infty} \dfrac{3^n}{n!}$

4. $\sum\limits_{n=1}^{\infty} \dfrac{\cos n\pi}{n}$

5. $\sum\limits_{n=1}^{\infty} \dfrac{\sin n\pi}{n}$

6. $\sum\limits_{n=1}^{\infty} \dfrac{\sin n}{n^2}$

7. $\sum\limits_{n=1}^{\infty} (-1)^n \dfrac{\text{Tan}^{-1} n}{n^2}$

8. $\sum\limits_{n=1}^{\infty} \dfrac{2^n + (-2)^n}{5^n}$

9. $\displaystyle\sum_{n=1}^{\infty} (-1)^{n-1} \frac{(n!)^2}{(2n)!}$

10. $\displaystyle\sum_{n=1}^{\infty} \frac{(-1)^{n+1} \cdot n!}{1 \cdot 3 \cdot 5 \cdot \ldots \cdot (2n-1)}$

11. $\displaystyle\sum_{n=1}^{\infty} (-1)^{n-1} \operatorname{Sin}^{-1} (1/n)$

12. $\displaystyle\sum_{n=1}^{\infty} (-1)^{n-1} \operatorname{Tan}^{-1} (1/n)$

13. $\displaystyle\sum_{n=1}^{\infty} \frac{(-1)^{x_n}}{n^2}$ where x_n is the nth digit in the decimal expansion of π: $x_1 = 3,\ x_2 = 1,\ x_3 = 4,\ x_4 = 1, \ldots$

14. $\displaystyle\sum_{n=1}^{\infty} \left(1 - \frac{1}{n}\right)^{n^2}$
16. $\displaystyle\sum_{n=1}^{\infty} \left(\frac{n}{2n-1}\right)^n$

15. $\displaystyle\sum_{n=1}^{\infty} (-1)^{n-1} \ln\left(1 + \frac{1}{n}\right)$
17. $\displaystyle\sum_{n=1}^{\infty} \frac{(-1)^n}{1 + 2^{1/n}}$

6 Power Series

A **power series** is a series of the form

$$\sum_{n=0}^{\infty} c_n(x-a)^n = c_0 + c_1(x-a) + c_2(x-a)^2 + \ldots \qquad (1)$$

where a and $c_0, c_1, c_2, \ldots$ are given numbers and x is a variable. It is clear that this series converges to the sum c_0 when $x = a$. It can happen that there is no other value of x for which the series converges.

EXAMPLE Show that $\displaystyle\sum_{n=1}^{\infty} n^n x^n$ converges for no $x \neq 0$.

Solution Fix any number $x \neq 0$. We apply the Root Test and obtain

$$\lim_{n\to\infty} |n^n x^n|^{1/n} = \lim_{n\to\infty} n|x| = \infty > 1$$

and so the series diverges.

It is also possible that a power series converges at some x's and diverges at others.

EXAMPLE Find all values of x at which $\displaystyle\sum_{n=0}^{\infty} \frac{nx^n}{3^n}$ converges.

Solution Write $a_n = nx^n/3^n$. We apply the Ratio Test for an arbitrary $x \neq 0$ to get

$$\lim_{n\to\infty}\left|\frac{a_{n+1}}{a_n}\right| = \lim_{n\to\infty}\left|\frac{(n+1)x^{n+1}}{3^{n+1}} \cdot \frac{3^n}{nx^n}\right|$$
$$= \frac{|x|}{3} \cdot \lim_{n\to\infty}\frac{n+1}{n} = \frac{|x|}{3}$$

Thus, the series is absolutely convergent if $|x|/3 < 1$ and is divergent if $|x|/3 > 1$. That is, it converges absolutely if $-3 < x < 3$ and diverges if $x < -3$ or $x > 3$. At $x = -3$ and at $x = 3$ the series become

$$\sum_{n=1}^{\infty} (-1)^n n \qquad \text{and} \qquad \sum_{n=1}^{\infty} n$$

respectively. Both of these diverge (nth Term Test). Therefore, for $-3 < x < 3$ the series converges, and for all other x it diverges.

Our next example shows that a power series can converge at every x.

EXAMPLE Show that $\displaystyle\sum_{n=1}^{\infty} x^n/n^n$ converges for every x.

Solution We apply the Root Test to see that

$$\lim_{n\to\infty} |x^n/n^n|^{1/n} = \lim_{n\to\infty} |x|/n = 0 < 1$$

for all x. Thus the series converges absolutely for all x.

▷ **Theorem** Corresponding to each given power series (1), there is some R, $0 \leq R \leq \infty$, such that the series converges absolutely for all x with $|x - a| < R$ and it diverges for all x with $|x - a| > R$.

Note. This number R is called the **radius of convergence** of the given series. In the above three examples, the values for R are 0, 3, and ∞, respectively.

Proof If the series diverges at each $x \neq a$, we take $R = 0$. If it converges absolutely for all x, we take $R = \infty$. Suppose the series converges at some $x_0 \neq a$. Then

$$\lim_{n\to\infty} c_n(x_0 - a)^n = 0$$

so that there is some N such that

$$|c_n(x_0 - a)^n| < 1 \qquad \text{if } n \geqq N$$

Now consider any x with $|x - a| < |x_0 - a|$. Then

$$|c_n(x - a)^n| = |c_n(x_0 - a)^n| \cdot \left|\frac{x - a}{x_0 - a}\right|^n \leqq \left|\frac{x - a}{x_0 - a}\right|^n$$

Since the geometric series

$$\sum_{n=0}^{\infty} \left|\frac{x - a}{x_0 - a}\right|^n$$

converges, it follows from the Comparison Test that (1) converges absolutely at x. Thus, we see that if (1) converges at an x_0 (perhaps only conditionally), then it converges *absolutely* at every x that is nearer to a than x_0 is. It follows from this that if the series converges at x_0 and diverges at x_1, then $|x_1 - a| \geqq |x_0 - a|$. In this case we see there is an R with $0 < R < \infty$ such that (1) converges absolutely for $a - R < x < a + R$ and diverges for $x < a - R$ and $x > a + R$. ∎

For our purposes, we will be able to determine R by applying either the Ratio Test or the Root Test to the given series.

EXAMPLE Find the radius of convergence of $\displaystyle\sum_{n=1}^{\infty} \frac{(x - 2)^n}{n}$ and find all x for which this series converges.

Solution For $x \neq 2$, we have

$$\lim_{n \to \infty} \left|\frac{(x - 2)^{n+1}}{n + 1} \cdot \frac{n}{(x - 2)^n}\right| = |x - 2|$$

and so the Ratio Test shows that our series converges absolutely if $|x - 2| < 1$ and that it diverges if $|x - 2| > 1$. That is, we have absolute convergence for $1 < x < 3$ and divergence for $x < 1$ and $x > 3$. Thus $R = 1$. At $x = 1$, our series is

$$\sum_{n=1}^{\infty} \frac{(-1)^n}{n}$$

which is convergent by AST. At $x = 3$, we get the harmonic series which diverges. We conclude that our series converges if and only if $1 \leqq x < 3$. The interval $[1,3[$ is called the **interval of convergence**.

For an arbitrary power series the **interval of convergence** is just the set of all x for which the series converges. On its interval of convergence, a power series defines a function by

$$f(x) = \sum_{n=0}^{\infty} c_n (x - a)^n$$

The simplest example of this is the geometric series

$$\sum_{n=0}^{\infty} x^n = \frac{1}{1 - x} \qquad (-1 < x < 1)$$

For functions defined by power series, we can legitimately perform operations of calculus and algebra just as if the series in question were polynomials (finite sums). We list without proof the relevant theorems about this matter. The proofs of these theorems are given in more advanced courses. We shall concentrate here only on understanding what these theorems say and how to use them.

▷ **Theorem**   Suppose that

$$f(x) = \sum_{n=0}^{\infty} c_n (x - a)^n \tag{2}$$

where the radius of convergence of this series is $R > 0$. Then we have the following:

(i) The function f has finite derivatives of all orders at each point of the open interval $]a - R, a + R[$, and for all x in this interval and all integers $k \geq 0$ we have

$$f^{(k)}(x) = \sum_{n=k}^{\infty} \frac{n! c_n}{(n - k)!} (x - a)^{n-k}$$

$$= k! c_k + \frac{(k + 1)! c_{k+1}}{1!} (x - a) + \frac{(k + 2)! c_{k+2}}{2!} (x - a)^2 + \dots$$

and this power series also has radius of convergence R.

(ii) For each integer $k \geq 0$, we have

$$c_k = \frac{f^{(k)}(a)}{k!}$$

(iii) If series (2) converges at $x = t$, then

$$\int_a^t f(x)\, dx = \sum_{n=0}^{\infty} c_n \int_a^t (x - a)^n\, dx = \sum_{n=0}^{\infty} \frac{c_n}{n + 1} (t - a)^{n+1}$$

EXAMPLE   Discuss the preceding theorem for the case

$$f(x) = \sum_{n=0}^{\infty} x^n$$

Solution   In this case $a = 0$, $R = 1$, and $f(x) = (1 - x)^{-1}$ for $|x| < 1$. Part (i) says that if $-1 < x < 1$ and $k \geqq 0$, then

$$k!(1 - x)^{-k-1} = f^{(k)}(x) = \sum_{n=k}^{\infty} \frac{n!}{(n - k)!} x^{n-k}$$

$$= \sum_{j=0}^{\infty} \frac{(j + k)!}{j!} x^j$$

(where we have replaced n by $j + k$) and this series has radius of convergence 1. Thus

$$\frac{1}{(1 - x)^{k+1}} = \sum_{j=0}^{\infty} \binom{j + k}{j} x^j$$

for $-1 < x < 1$ and $k \geqq 0$. Part (ii) simply says that $f^{(k)}(0)/k! = 1$ for all $k \geqq 0$ and part (iii) says that, for $|t| < 1$,

$$-\ln (1 - t) = \int_0^t \frac{dx}{1 - x} = \sum_{n=0}^{\infty} \frac{t^{n+1}}{n + 1}$$

Replacing n by $j - 1$ and t by x, we have

$$-\ln (1 - x) = \sum_{j=1}^{\infty} \frac{x^j}{j} \qquad (-1 < x < 1)$$

EXAMPLE   Use the preceding theorem to find a power series expansion for $\mathrm{Tan}^{-1} x$.

Solution   The formula for the sum of a geometric series shows that

$$\frac{1}{1 + t^2} = \sum_{n=0}^{\infty} (-t^2)^n = \sum_{n=0}^{\infty} (-1)^n t^{2n}$$

if $|-t^2| < 1$, that is, if $-1 < t < 1$. Part (iii) of the theorem assures us that if $-1 < x < 1$, then

$$\mathrm{Tan}^{-1} x = \int_0^x \frac{dt}{1 + t^2} = \sum_{n=0}^{\infty} (-1)^n \int_0^x t^{2n}\, dt$$

$$= \sum_{n=0}^{\infty} \frac{(-1)^n x^{2n+1}}{2n + 1}$$

The next theorem describes permissible algebraic operations with power series.

⇨ **Theorem**   Suppose we have two functions f and g defined by power series:

$$f(x) = \sum_{n=0}^{\infty} a_n(x-a)^n \qquad (|x-a| < R_1)$$

and

$$g(x) = \sum_{n=0}^{\infty} b_n(x-a)^n \qquad (|x-a| < R_2)$$

where R_1 and R_2 are the respective radii of convergence of these series. Let R be the smaller of R_1 and R_2. Then we have the following:

(i) If c is any real number, then $|x-a| < R_1$ implies that

$$cf(x) = \sum_{n=0}^{\infty} ca_n(x-a)^n$$

(ii) For $|x-a| < R$, we have

$$f(x) + g(x) = \sum_{n=0}^{\infty} (a_n + b_n)(x-a)^n$$

(iii) If $|x-a| < R$, then

$$f(x)g(x) = \sum_{n=0}^{\infty} c_n(x-a)^n$$

where

$$c_n = \sum_{k=0}^{n} a_k b_{n-k} = a_0 b_n + a_1 b_{n-1} + a_2 b_{n-2} + \ldots + a_n b_0$$

EXAMPLE   Use power series expansions found above to find a power series expansion for $-[\ln(1-x)]/(1-x)$ that is valid for $-1 < x < 1$.

Solution   The expansions

$$-\ln(1-x) = f(x) = \sum_{n=1}^{\infty} x^n/n$$

and

$$1/(1-x) = g(x) = \sum_{n=0}^{\infty} x^n$$

are both valid for $-1 < x < 1$ and so, taking $a_0 = 0$, $b_0 = 1$, $a_n = 1/n$, and $b_n = 1$ for $n \geq 1$, we see from (iii) of the preceding theorem that if $-1 < x < 1$, then

$$-\frac{\ln (1-x)}{1-x} = f(x)g(x) = \sum_{n=0}^{\infty} c_n x^n$$

where $c_0 = a_0 b_0 = 0$ and, for $n \geq 1$,

$$c_n = \sum_{k=0}^{n} a_k b_{n-k} = \sum_{k=1}^{n} \frac{1}{k}$$

E X E R C I S E S

In 1–16, find the radius of convergence and the interval of convergence of the given power series.

1. $\displaystyle\sum_{n=0}^{\infty} n! x^n$

2. $\displaystyle\sum_{n=1}^{\infty} n x^n$

3. $\displaystyle\sum_{n=0}^{\infty} 2^n (x-3)^n$

4. $\displaystyle\sum_{n=0}^{\infty} \frac{(x-3)^n}{2^n}$

5. $\displaystyle\sum_{n=1}^{\infty} (-1)^n x^n / n$

6. $\displaystyle\sum_{n=1}^{\infty} \frac{(-1)^{n-1}(x-1)^n}{n}$

7. $\displaystyle\sum_{n=2}^{\infty} \frac{x^n}{\ln n}$

8. $\displaystyle\sum_{n=1}^{\infty} \frac{(x+4)^n}{n(n+1)}$

9. $\displaystyle\sum_{n=0}^{\infty} \frac{(x-1)^n}{\sqrt{n+1}}$

10. $\displaystyle\sum_{n=1}^{\infty} \frac{x^n}{n^2 \cdot 2^n}$

11. $\displaystyle\sum_{n=0}^{\infty} \left(\frac{x+2}{3}\right)^n$

12. $\displaystyle\sum_{n=1}^{\infty} \frac{1}{n}\left(\frac{x+2}{3}\right)^{n-1}$

13. $\displaystyle\sum_{n=1}^{\infty} \frac{n! x^n}{n^n}$

14. $\displaystyle\sum_{n=0}^{\infty} (-1)^n \frac{x^{2n}}{(2n)!}$

15. $\displaystyle\sum_{n=1}^{\infty} \tau(n) x^n$, where $\tau(n)$ is the number of positive integers k for which n/k is an integer. [*Hint:* $1 \leq \tau(n) \leq n$.]

16. $\displaystyle\sum_{n=1}^{\infty} \sigma(n) x^n$, where $\sigma(n)$ is the sum of those positive integers k for which n/k is an integer. [*Hint:* $n \leq \sigma(n) \leq n^2$.]

17. Show that:

(a) $\ln (1+x) = \displaystyle\sum_{n=1}^{\infty} (-1)^{n-1} x^n / n \qquad$ if $-1 < x < 1$

(b) $\ln \left(\dfrac{1+x}{1-x}\right) = 2 \cdot \displaystyle\sum_{k=0}^{\infty} \frac{x^{2k+1}}{2k+1} \qquad$ if $-1 < x < 1$

(c) $\ln t = 2 \cdot \displaystyle\sum_{k=0}^{\infty} \frac{1}{2k+1}\left(\frac{t-1}{t+1}\right)^{2k+1} \qquad$ for all $t > 0$

(d) $0 < \ln t - \displaystyle\sum_{k=0}^{m} \frac{1}{2k+1}\left(\frac{t-1}{t+1}\right)^{2k+1} < \frac{(t-1)^2}{(8m+12)t}\left(\frac{t-1}{t+1}\right)^{2m+1}$

if $t > 1$ and $m \geqq 0$. [*Hint:* To obtain the last inequality, estimate the sum over $k > m$ in series (c) by replacing $1/(2k + 1)$ by $1/(2m + 3)$ and then summing a geometric series.]

18. Use the result of exercise 17(d) to find a decimal expansion for ln 2 that is accurate to at least four decimal places.

19. Show that:

(a) $\text{Tan}^{-1} (1/2) + \text{Tan}^{-1} (1/3) = \pi/4$. [*Hint:* Express $\tan (\alpha + \beta)$ in terms of $\tan \alpha$ and $\tan \beta$.]

(b) $\pi = \sum\limits_{n=0}^{\infty} 4 \cdot \dfrac{(-1)^n}{2n + 1} \left[\dfrac{1}{2^{2n+1}} + \dfrac{1}{3^{2n+1}} \right]$

(c) If S_k is the sum of the terms from $n = 0$ to $n = k$ of the series in (b), then

$$S_{2j-1} < S_{2j+1} < \pi < S_{2j} < S_{2j-2}$$

for every integer $j \geqq 1$.

(d) Use (c) to prove that

$$3.1408 \ldots = S_3 < \pi < S_2 = 3.1455 \ldots$$

and so $\pi = 3.14 \ldots$.

20. Use multiplication of series to show that

$$\frac{1}{(1 - x)^2} = \sum_{n=0}^{\infty} (n + 1)x^n \qquad \text{if} -1 < x < 1$$

21. Use multiplication of series and the Binomial Theorem to show that if

$$f(x) = \sum_{n=0}^{\infty} x^n/n!$$

then $f(a + b) = f(a)f(b)$ for all a and b.

7 Taylor Series

In the preceding section we saw that if a function f is expressible as the sum of a power series at each x in some open interval containing a number a:

$$f(x) = \sum_{n=0}^{\infty} c_n(x - a)^n \qquad \text{for } |x - a| < R$$

then the coefficients c_n *must* be given by

$$c_n = \frac{f^{(n)}(a)}{n!} \qquad \text{for all } n \geq 0$$

For this reason, we make the following definition.

⇨ *Definition* If f is a function that is defined in a neighborhood of some point a and if f has finite derivatives of all orders at a, then the power series

$$\sum_{n=0}^{\infty} \frac{f^{(n)}(a)}{n!} (x - a)^n$$

is called the **Taylor series** of f about the **center** a. In the special case that $a = 0$, this series is called the **Maclaurin series** of f.

We have seen that the Taylor series of a given function f about a given point a is the only power series about a that has a chance of converging to $f(x)$ at each x in some neighborhood of a. But does it in fact converge to $f(x)$ in some such neighborhood? The answer depends on the function f. An affirmative answer may often be proved by use of Taylor's Formula (see Chapter 9). Recall that Taylor's Formula says that if f is $n + 1$ times differentiable at each point in some open interval I containing a and if x is in I, then

$$f(x) - P_n(x) = R_n(x)$$

where

$$P_n(x) = \sum_{k=0}^{n} \frac{f^{(k)}(a)}{k!} (x - a)^k$$

is the nth partial sum of the Taylor series and the remainder $R_n(x)$ has the form

$$R_n(x) = \frac{f^{(n+1)}(c)}{(n + 1)!} (x - a)^{n+1}$$

for some c between a and x. Thus, to show that $\lim_{n \to \infty} P_n(x) = f(x)$ (that is, f is the sum of its Taylor series at x), it is enough to show that $\lim_{n \to \infty} R_n(x) = 0$.

EXAMPLE Find the Maclaurin series for e^x and prove that it converges to e^x at each real number x.

Solution   If $f(x) = e^x$, then $f^{(n)}(x) = e^x$, and so

$$f^{(n)}(0)/n! = e^0/n! = 1/n! \qquad \text{for all } n \geq 0$$

Thus, the required series is

$$\sum_{n=0}^{\infty} \frac{x^n}{n!}$$

Now fix any x. The remainder is

$$R_n(x) = \frac{e^c}{(n+1)!} x^{n+1}$$

for some c between 0 and x. If $x \leq 0$, then $c \leq 0$ and so $e^c \leq 1$. If $x > 0$, then $e^c < e^x$. In either case $e^c \leq M$, where M is the larger of 1 and e^x. Therefore,

$$|R_n(x)| \leq M \cdot \frac{|x|^{n+1}}{(n+1)!}$$

The right side of this inequality has limit 0 as $n \to \infty$ because

$$\sum_{n=0}^{\infty} M \cdot \frac{|x|^{n+1}}{(n+1)!} < \infty$$

by the Ratio Test. We conclude that

$$\lim_{n \to \infty} R_n(x) = 0$$

and hence

$$\boxed{e^x = \sum_{n=0}^{\infty} \frac{x^n}{n!}}$$

EXAMPLE   Find the Maclaurin series for $\sin x$ and for $\cos x$ and prove that these series converge to the functions from which they were obtained at every real number x.

Solution   Let $f(x) = \sin x$ and $g(x) = \cos x$. Then

$$\begin{aligned}
f^{(4k)}(x) &= \sin x & g^{(4k)}(x) &= \cos x \\
f^{(4k+1)}(x) &= \cos x & g^{(4k+1)}(x) &= -\sin x \\
f^{(4k+2)}(x) &= -\sin x & g^{(4k+2)}(x) &= -\cos x \\
f^{(4k+3)}(x) &= -\cos x & g^{(4k+3)}(x) &= \sin x
\end{aligned}$$

for each integer $k \geq 0$ and every x. Therefore

$$\begin{aligned}
f^{(2n)}(0) &= 0 & g^{(2n)}(0) &= (-1)^n \\
f^{(2n+1)}(0) &= (-1)^n & g^{(2n+1)}(0) &= 0
\end{aligned}$$

for all integers $n \geq 0$. Thus, the required series for $\sin x$ and $\cos x$ are

$$\sum_{n=0}^{\infty} \frac{(-1)^n}{(2n+1)!} \cdot x^{2n+1} \quad \text{and} \quad \sum_{n=0}^{\infty} \frac{(-1)^n}{(2n)!} \cdot x^{2n}$$

respectively. Fix any x. In either case, we have

$$R_n(x) = \frac{u}{(n+1)!} x^{n+1}$$

where u is $\pm \sin c$ or $\pm \cos c$, so that $|u| \leq 1$. It follows that

$$|R_n(x)| \leq |x|^{n+1}/(n+1)! \to 0 \quad \text{as } n \to \infty$$

as in the preceding example. Therefore

$$\sin x = \sum_{n=0}^{\infty} (-1)^n \frac{x^{2n+1}}{(2n+1)!} = x - \frac{x^3}{6} + \frac{x^5}{120} - \frac{x^7}{5040} + \cdots$$

and

$$\cos x = \sum_{n=0}^{\infty} (-1)^n \frac{x^{2n}}{(2n)!} = 1 - \frac{x^2}{2} + \frac{x^4}{24} - \frac{x^6}{720} + \cdots$$

Sometimes it is possible to find a Taylor series for a function and prove that it converges to the function without computing any derivatives or estimating any remainders. Because of the somewhat uncertain location of the number c (which changes with n) in the remainder, it is often difficult or impossible to *prove* that the remainder has limit 0 even when it does.

EXAMPLE Let $a > 0$ be a given number. Find the Taylor series for $\ln x$ centered at a and prove that it converges to $\ln x$ for all x such that $0 < x < 2a$.

First Solution In section 6 we saw that

$$\ln(1-u) = -\sum_{n=1}^{\infty} u^n/n \quad \text{if } -1 < u < 1$$

For $0 < x < 2a$, we have $-1 < (x-a)/(-a) < 1$ and so

$$\ln x = \ln a + \ln \left(1 - \frac{x-a}{-a}\right)$$

$$= \ln a - \sum_{n=1}^{\infty} \frac{1}{n}\left(\frac{x-a}{-a}\right)^n$$

$$= \ln a + \sum_{n=1}^{\infty} \frac{(-1)^{n+1}(x-a)^n}{na^n}$$

As pointed out above, we know that this last series *must* be the Taylor series of ln x. Of course, one could compute the coefficients $(\ln^{(n)}a)/n!$ directly, but that would not tell us the sum of the resulting series.

Second Solution   For $0 < x < 2a$, we have

$$\ln x = \ln a + \int_a^x \frac{dt}{t}$$

$$= \ln a + \frac{1}{a}\int_a^x \frac{dt}{1 - \dfrac{t-a}{-a}}$$

$$= \ln a + \frac{1}{a}\int_a^x \sum_{n=1}^{\infty} \left(\frac{t-a}{-a}\right)^{n-1} dt$$

$$= \ln a + \sum_{n=1}^{\infty} \frac{(-1)^{n-1}}{a^n}\int_a^x (t-a)^{n-1}\, dt$$

$$= \ln a + \sum_{n=1}^{\infty} \frac{(-1)^{n-1}}{a^n}\cdot\frac{(x-a)^n}{n}$$

where the third equality follows from the formula for the sum of a geometric series and the fact that $|(t-a)/(-a)| < 1$ for t between a and x, while the fourth equality follows from the theorem on term-by-term integration of convergent power series given in section 6.

Our next example concerns the very useful **Binomial Series**. It also illustrates another way of proving that a function is the sum of its Taylor series.

EXAMPLE   Let α be any given real number that is not a nonnegative integer. For integers $n \geqq 1$, define

$$\binom{\alpha}{n} = \frac{\alpha(\alpha-1)(\alpha-2)\cdot\ldots\cdot(\alpha-n+1)}{n!}$$

Also define

$$\binom{\alpha}{0} = 1$$

Prove that

$$\boxed{(1+x)^\alpha = \sum_{n=0}^{\infty}\binom{\alpha}{n}x^n \qquad \text{if } -1 < x < 1}$$

Solution Given any x with $0 < |x| < 1$, the Ratio Test shows that the given series converges absolutely because

$$\left| \binom{\alpha}{n+1} x^{n+1} \Big/ \binom{\alpha}{n} x^n \right| = \left| \frac{\alpha(\alpha-1) \ldots (\alpha-n+1)(\alpha-n)}{(n+1)!} \right.$$

$$\left. \frac{n!x}{\alpha(\alpha-1) \ldots (\alpha-n+1)} \right| = \frac{|\alpha-n|}{n+1} \cdot |x|$$

$$= \frac{|1-\alpha/n|}{1+1/n} \cdot |x| \to |x| < 1 \text{ as } n \to \infty$$

Thus the formula

$$f(x) = \sum_{n=0}^{\infty} \binom{\alpha}{n} x^n = 1 + \sum_{n=1}^{\infty} \binom{\alpha}{n} x^n \tag{1}$$

defines a function f on $]-1,1[$. It is our job to show that $f(x) = (1+x)^\alpha$ whenever $|x| < 1$. By the theorem in section 6 on term-by-term differentiation of convergent power series, we have

$$(1+x)f'(x) = f'(x) + xf'(x) = \sum_{n=1}^{\infty} n\binom{\alpha}{n} x^{n-1} + \sum_{n=1}^{\infty} n\binom{\alpha}{n} x^n$$

$$= \alpha + \sum_{k=1}^{\infty} (k+1)\binom{\alpha}{k+1} x^k + \sum_{k=1}^{\infty} k\binom{\alpha}{k} x^k$$

if $|x| < 1$. (We replaced $n-1$ by k in the first series and n by k in the second.) Noticing that, for $k \geq 1$, we have

$$(k+1)\binom{\alpha}{k+1} + k\binom{\alpha}{k} = \alpha(\alpha-1) \cdot \ldots \cdot (\alpha-k+1)\left[\frac{(k+1)(\alpha-k)}{(k+1)!} + \frac{k}{k!} \right]$$

$$= \binom{\alpha}{k} \cdot \alpha$$

it follows that

$$(1+x)f'(x) = \alpha f(x) \qquad \text{if } -1 < x < 1$$

Therefore

$$\frac{d}{dx}[f(x)(1+x)^{-\alpha}] = f(x)(-\alpha)(1+x)^{-\alpha-1} + f'(x)(1+x)^{-\alpha}$$

$$= (1+x)^{-\alpha-1}[-\alpha f(x) + (1+x)f'(x)] = 0$$

for all x in $]-1,1[$, and so there is a constant C such that

$$f(x)(1+x)^{-\alpha} = C \qquad f(x) = C(1+x)^\alpha$$

whenever $-1 < x < 1$. Substituting $x = 0$ into (1) shows that

$$1 = f(0) = C(1 + 0)^\alpha = C$$

and hence $f(x) = (1 + x)^\alpha$ for $-1 < x < 1$.

Our final example concerns the Taylor expansion of a polynomial.

EXAMPLE   Let $f(x) = x^3 - 4x^2 + 7x - 2$. Find the Taylor series for f about $a = 2$ and prove that its sum is $f(x)$ at each real number x.

Solution   We have

$$f'(x) = 3x^2 - 8x + 7$$
$$f''(x) = 6x - 8$$
$$f'''(x) = 6$$
$$f^{(n)}(x) = 0 \qquad n > 3$$

for all x. Thus $R_n(x) = 0$ for all x and all $n \geq 3$ and so $f(x) = P_3(x)$ for all x. We have

$$\frac{f(2)}{0!} = 4 \qquad \frac{f'(2)}{1!} = 3 \qquad \frac{f''(2)}{2!} = 2 \qquad \frac{f'''(2)}{3!} = 1$$

and so

$$f(x) = P_3(x) = 4 + 3(x - 2) + 2(x - 2)^2 + (x - 2)^3$$

for all x and this finite sum is the required Taylor series.

EXERCISES

In 1–12, find the Maclaurin series of the given function, find its radius of convergence R, and show that it converges to the given function at each x with $|x| < R$. It is not necessary to compute derivatives.

1. $f(x) = 1/(1 + x^3)$
2. $f(x) = 1/(2 - 3x)$
3. $f(x) = (e^x + e^{-x})/2 = \cosh x$
4. $f(x) = (e^x - e^{-x})/2 = \sinh x$
5. $f(x) = \ln (2 + x)$
6. $f(x) = \sin x^3$
7. $f(x) = e^{-x^2}$
8. $f(x) = \cos 2x$
9. $f(x) = \sin^2 x$
10. $f(x) = \text{Tan}^{-1} (3x^2)$
11. $f(x) = e^x/(1 - x)$
12. $f(x) = \cos^3 x$ [*Hint:* $4 \cos^3 x = \cos 3x + 3 \cos x$.]

In 13-20, find the first three nonzero terms of the Taylor series for the given function about the given center a.

13. $f(x) = \tan x$, $a = 0$

14. $f(x) = e^{\sin x}$, $a = \pi/2$

15. $f(x) = \sec x$, $a = 0$

16. $f(x) = \csc x$, $a = \pi/2$

17. $f(x) = \cot x$, $a = \pi/2$

18. $f(x) = \sec^2 x$, $a = 0$

19. $f(x) = \ln \cos x$, $a = 0$

20. $f(x) = \sin x$, $a = \pi/6$

In 21-26, express the given polynomial in x as a polynomial in $x - a$ for the given a.

21. $f(x) = x^4$, $a = 1$

22. $f(x) = x^3 + x^2 + x + 1$, $a = -1$

23. $f(x) = x^3 + 4x^2 + 6x + 4$, $a = -1$

24. $f(x) = x^3 - 6x^2 + 13x - 10$, $a = 2$

25. $f(x) = x^4 + 12x^3 + 53x^2 + 102x + 72$, $a = -3$

26. $f(x) = x^3$, $a = 1/2$

27. Use the Binomial series to show that

$$(1 - t^2)^{-1/2} = \sum_{n=0}^{\infty} \frac{(2n)!}{2^{2n}(n!)^2} t^{2n}$$

if $-1 < t < 1$ and then find the Maclaurin series for $\mathrm{Sin}^{-1} x$ and prove that it converges to $\mathrm{Sin}^{-1} x$ for $-1 < x < 1$.

28. Use power series to evaluate $\lim_{x \to 0} \dfrac{x - \sin x}{x^3}$.

29. Use power series to evaluate $\lim_{x \to 0} \dfrac{\tan^2 x - x^2}{x^4}$.

30. Define $f(x) = e^{-1/x^2}$ for $x \neq 0$ and $f(0) = 0$. Define a sequence of polynomials by $Q_0(t) = 1$, $Q_1(t) = 2t^3$, $Q_2(t) = 4t^6 - 6t^4, \ldots, Q_{n+1}(t) = 2t^3 Q_n(t) - t^2 Q_n'(t)$. Prove that:

(a) If $x \neq 0$ and $n \geq 0$, then $f^{(n)}(x) = Q_n(1/x)e^{-1/x^2}$

(b) For $n \geq 0$, we have

$$f^{(n+1)}(0) = \lim_{x \to 0} \frac{f^{(n)}(x) - f^{(n)}(0)}{x - 0} = \lim_{t \to \infty} tQ_n(t)/e^{t^2} = 0$$

(c) The Maclaurin series for f converges to 0 at every x and $0 \neq f(x)$ unless $x = 0$.

Chapter 11
Differential Equations

1 Separable Differential Equations

In applications of the calculus we are sometimes presented with an equation involving the derivative of a function and asked to solve for the function. An equation involving the derivative of a function is called a **differential equation.** In this chapter we require that each solution to a differential equation be a function whose domain is an interval. (See exercise 20 on page 507.) However, for the sake of convenience, we sometimes write two or more solutions together as a single solution. You will see an illustration of this in the second example when we solve $xe^y y' = 1$. Examples of differential equations are (assuming that y is a differentiable function of x):

$y' = 4x$; $y'x + y = xy$; $3y'' + y' = 2x + y$; and $2y'' = \dfrac{y'}{2} - y$. Let's look

at a specific example.

EXAMPLE   Solve the differential equation $y' = 4x$.

Solution   We are being asked to find all functions $y = f(x)$ such that $y' = f'(x) = 4x$. In other words we are being asked to find all primitives for the function $4x$. We do this, of course, by evaluating $\displaystyle\int 4x\,dx$ and obtaining the function $y = f(x) = 2x^2$. All the primitives of $4x$ are given by $2x^2 + C$ for any constant C. Thus, the solutions to the differential equation $y' = 4x$ are $y = 2x^2 + C$. This is called the **general solution** to the differential equation.

Suppose, in the previous example, we are told, in addition, that when $x = 0$, $y = -1$ (we write $y(0) = -1$). We know that all solutions to the differential equation are of the form $y = 2x^2 + C$. However, since $y = -1$ when $x = 0$, we may substitute these values to see that $C = -1$. Thus, the solution to our problem is now the unique function $y = 2x^2 - 1$. A condition which tells us specific values of the solution function(s) or one of its derivatives is called an **initial condition** (or **boundary condition**). Initial conditions often enable us to find unique solutions to differential equations. Such a unique solution is called a **particular solution**.

Some differential equations can be written in the form

$$y' P(y) = Q(x) \tag{1}$$

where $P(y)$ is a function of y alone and $Q(x)$ is a function of x alone. (In the previous case, $P(y) = 1$ and $Q(x) = 4x$.) Such a differential equation is called **separable**.

There is a general technique of solution for such a differential equation which is as follows:

We write $y' = \dfrac{dy}{dx}$ and (1) becomes

$$P(y) \frac{dy}{dx} = Q(x) \tag{2}$$

We now integrate both sides with respect to x to obtain

$$\int \left(P(y) \frac{dy}{dx} \right) dx = \int Q(x) \, dx \tag{3}$$

This is (with the substitution $y = f(x)$, $dy = f'(x) \, dx$) the same as

$$\int P(y) \, dy = \int Q(x) \, dx \tag{4}$$

Now take indefinite integrals of both sides (if possible) and (if possible) solve for y.

EXAMPLE   Solve the differential equation $xe^y y' = 1$, with initial condition $y(1) = 0$.

Solution   Write $e^y y' = \dfrac{1}{x}$ ($x \neq 0$). We have $P(y) = e^y$ and $Q(x) = \dfrac{1}{x}$.

Then integrate to obtain

$$\int e^y \, dy = \int \frac{1}{x} \, dx$$

Thus, $e^y = \ln|x| + C$ and the general solution is $y = \ln(\ln|x| + C)$, where it is understood that $\ln|x| + C > 0$. Since $y(1) = 0$, we see that $0 = \ln(\ln 1 + C)$. Thus, $C = 1$ and the particular solution is

$$y = \ln(\ln|x| + 1)$$

Note. We have actually found two general solutions to the differential equation $xe^y y' = 1$. Since we demand that each solution have an interval as its domain and x cannot be 0, each solution must be defined on an interval to the right of 0 or on an interval to the left of 0. The two general solutions we have found are:

For $x > 0$: $y = \ln(\ln x + C)$ $\ln x > -C;\ x > e^{-C}$

and

For $x < 0$: $y = \ln(\ln(-x) + C)$ $\ln(-x) > -C;\ x < -e^{-C}$

The particular solution to our problem must have $x = 1$ in its domain and satisfy $y(1) = 0$ so it is the special case of the first of these general solutions in which $C = 1$:

$$y = \ln(\ln x + 1)\qquad x > 1/e$$

From now on, instead of writing out all these cases (there may be infinitely many, as in exercises 9 and 11), we will adopt the universal convention and combine the solutions into one formula. Thus, in this case, we simply write $y = \ln(\ln|x| + C)$ for the general solution and $y = \ln(\ln|x| + 1)$ for the particular solution.

EXAMPLE Solve the differential equation $2yy' = x^3 - 1$, with initial condition $y(2) = 1$.

Solution We have $\displaystyle\int 2y\,dy = \int (x^3 - 1)\,dx$. Thus, $y^2 = \dfrac{x^4}{4} - x + C$

and so the general solution is $y = \pm\sqrt{\dfrac{x^4}{4} - x + C}$.

Since $y(2) = 1 > 0$, we can't have $y = -\sqrt{\dfrac{x^4}{4} - x + C}$. Therefore,

we have $y = \sqrt{\dfrac{x^4}{4} - x + C}$. Substituting $x = 2$ and $y = 1$ gives $1 = \sqrt{2 + C}$ so that $C = -1$. The particular solution is $y = \sqrt{\dfrac{x^4}{4} - x - 1}$.

EXAMPLE Suppose an experimenter discovers that the rate of change of the amount of a substance present at time t in a solution is directly proportional to the amount of the substance present at time t. If $y = y(t)$ is the amount of substance present at time t, then (a) write a differential equation to find y as a function of t and (b) solve the differential equation for y.

Solution (a) The equation is $y' = ky$, where k is some nonzero constant.

(b) If $y \neq 0$, then separating the variables gives us $\dfrac{y'}{y} = k$. Thus,

$\displaystyle\int \frac{dy}{y} = \int k\,dt$ and so $\ln|y| = kt + C$. Thus, $|y| = e^C e^{kt} = Ae^{kt}$, where

$A = e^C > 0$. (Notice that since $\ln|y(0)| = C$, we see that $A = e^C = |y(0)|$.) Since $Ae^{kt} > 0$ and the amount y of substance cannot be negative, we conclude that $y = Ae^{kt}$. The function $y = 0$ also satisfies $y' = ky$, and so our general solution is $y = Ae^{kt}$, where $A \geq 0$ and k are constants.

Note. Let us consider the most interesting case when $A > 0$. If also $k > 0$, then y is an increasing function of t and we have **exponential growth**. If $k < 0$, then y is a decreasing function of t and we have **exponential decay**. As we saw in Chapter 5, section 6, certain populations grow exponentially and certain radioactive decay is exponential.

We close this section with an example of a differential equation which involves a second derivative.

EXAMPLE Find a solution to the differential equation $y'' = \cos x$, with initial conditions $y'(0) = 4$ and $y(\pi/2) = 2$.

Solution Since $y'' = \cos x$, we see, taking primitives, that $y' = \sin x + C$. Again, taking primitives, we get the general solution $y = -\cos x + Cx + C_1$. Since $y'(0) = 4$ (that is, $y' = 4$ when $x = 0$), we see that $4 = \sin 0 + C$ so that $C = 4$. Also, since $y(\pi/2) = 2$ (that is, $y = 2$ when $x = \pi/2$), we obtain $2 = -\cos \pi/2 + 4 \cdot \pi/2 + C_1$ so that $C_1 = 2 - 2\pi$. Thus, $y = -\cos x + 4x + (2 - 2\pi)$ is the particular solution.

EXERCISES

In 1–15, (a) solve the differential equation for a general solution and
(b) find the particular solution subject to the given initial condition(s).

1. $y' = -x$; $y(0) = 0$ **3.** $yy' = \dfrac{1}{x}$; $y(1) = 2$

2. $y' = \ln x$; $y(1) = 2$

4. $y' = 3y - 1$; $y(1) = \dfrac{2}{3}$, $y > \dfrac{1}{3}$

5. $y'(1 + y) = x + 2$; $y(0) = -2$ [*Hint:* After taking indefinite integrals, use the quadratic formula.]

6. $y'\sqrt{x} = e^{-y}$; $y(4) = \ln 4$

7. $y'e^y = \cos x$; $y(\pi/3) = 0$

8. $y'e^y = \sin x$; $y(2\pi/3) = 0$

9. $y'e^y = \tan x$; $y(0) = 0$

10. $y'' = \sin x$; $y(0) = 1$, $y'(0) = -1$

11. $y'' = \cot^2 x$; $y(\pi/2) = y'(\pi/2) = 0$

12. $y' - \dfrac{xe^x}{y} = 0$; $y(1) = -2$

13. $y' - \dfrac{xe^x}{y} = 0$; $y(1) = 2$

14. $yy' = x \sin x$; $y(0) = 1$

15. $y'' = e^x + 2$; $y'(0) = 1$, $y(1) = 0$

16. When a hot object is placed in a cooler environment, the rate of its cooling is proportional to the difference between its temperature, y, and the environment's temperature, y_0. We assume that the environment's temperature, y_0, remains constant. If $y = y(t)$ is the temperature of the object after t minutes, then:
(a) Write a differential equation involving y'. (Use $k < 0$ as the constant of proportionality.)
(b) Find the general solution to the equation found in part (a).

17. The rate of growth of a population of bacteria is proportional to the population. If at time $t = 0$ there are 1000 bacteria and at time $t = 4$ there are 10,000 bacteria present, how many bacteria are there when $t = 7$? When will there be 12,000 bacteria present?

18. Suppose that in a town of population A, the rate at which a disease spreads is proportional to the product of the number of people with the disease and the number of people without the disease. Suppose $y = y(t)$ is the number of people with the disease at time t.
(a) Write a differential equation describing this situation.
(b) Solve the equation in part (a) to find a general solution for y.

19. A psychologist determines that, for a certain population of children, at 24 months of age the average child has a vocabulary of 20 three-word sentences. If $v = v(t)$ is the average vocabulary size of a child who is t months old, the psychologist determines that $v' = v \ln \left(\dfrac{t - 18}{2} \right)$ for $24 \leq t \leq 30$. How many three-word sentences should the psychologist expect the average 28-month-old to have in his vocabulary?

20. Let $y(x) = \begin{cases} 1 & \text{if } x > 0 \\ -1 & \text{if } x < 0 \end{cases}$

Explain why $y(x)$ is *not* a solution to the equation $y' = 0$ even though $y'(x) = 0$ for all x in the domain of y.

2 The Differential Equation y' + yP(x) = Q(x)

In this section, we will investigate a special type of differential equation which is nonseparable. Equations of the type

$$y' + yP(x) = Q(x) \tag{1}$$

where P and Q are functions for which we can find primitives, often arise in the solution of practical problems. Therefore, it is worthwhile to study a technique which we may use to solve them.

We use a trick to solve (1). The idea is to multiply both sides of (1) by $e^{\int P(x)\,dx}$ (which is never 0). This gives us

$$e^{\int P(x)\,dx} y' + e^{\int P(x)\,dx} P(x) y = e^{\int P(x)\,dx} Q(x) \tag{2}$$

We have done this multiplication because the left side of (2) is

$$\frac{d}{dx} \left(e^{\int P(x)\,dx} y \right)$$

Thus, (2) becomes

$$\frac{d}{dx} \left(e^{\int P(x)\,dx} y \right) = e^{\int P(x)\,dx} Q(x) \tag{3}$$

We integrate both sides with respect to x and obtain

$$e^{\int P(x)\,dx} y = \int e^{\int P(x)\,dx} Q(x)\,dx + C \tag{4}$$

Now divide both sides of (4) by $e^{\int P(x)\,dx}$ to obtain

$$y = e^{-\int P(x)\,dx} \left[\int e^{\int P(x)\,dx} Q(x)\,dx + C \right] \tag{5}$$

which is the desired solution.

Note. In theory, any function whose derivative is $P(x)$ would serve for $\int P(x)\,dx$. However, we always use the simplest such antiderivative to make our task easier. For example, if $P(x) = 1$, we use $\int 1\,dx = x$ instead of $\int 1\,dx = x + C$. Also, if $P(x) = \dfrac{1}{x}$, we do not use $\int \dfrac{1}{x}\,dx = \ln |x|$ since our solution must be defined on an interval. Since $\dfrac{1}{x}$ is not defined at 0, x must take only positive or only negative values. Unless x is restricted to be negative, we will take $\int \dfrac{1}{x}\,dx = \ln x$. If x is restricted to negative values, then we must take $\int \dfrac{1}{x}\,dx = \ln (-x)$.

EXAMPLE   Solve the differential equation $y' - 4y = e^x$, with initial condition $y(0) = 2$.

Solution   Here $P(x) = -4$ and $Q(x) = e^x$. We multiply through by $e^{\int -4\,dx} = e^{-4x}$ and obtain

$$e^{-4x}y' - e^{-4x} \cdot 4y = e^{-3x}$$

which is the same as $\dfrac{d}{dx}(e^{-4x}y) = e^{-3x}$. We now integrate both sides with respect to x to obtain

$$e^{-4x}y = -\frac{1}{3}e^{-3x} + C$$

Thus,

$$y = -\frac{1}{3}e^x + Ce^{4x}$$

is the general solution.

Since $y(0) = 2$, we have

$$2 = -\frac{1}{3} + C$$

so that $C = \dfrac{7}{3}$. Thus, $y = -\dfrac{1}{3}e^x + \dfrac{7}{3}e^{4x}$ is the particular solution.

EXAMPLE W dollars a year are being withdrawn continuously from a savings account which earns interest at an annual interest rate R compounded continuously. If $y(t)$ is the balance in the account at time t years, then:

(a) Write a differential equation that is satisfied by y.

(b) Solve the equation found in part (a).

(c) Analyze the growth of the balance in terms of the initial balance $y(0)$.

Solution (a) Since, at any time t, the balance is being reduced at a rate (per year) of W dollars and the balance is being increased, by interest, at a rate of Ry dollars (per year), we see that the balance is changing at a rate of $-W + Ry$ dollars per year. Therefore $y' = -W + Ry$.

(b) We have $y' - Ry = -W$. Here $P(t) = -R$ and $Q(t) = -W$. Multiply through by $e^{\int P(t)dt} = e^{\int -R\,dt} = e^{-Rt}$ and obtain $e^{-Rt}y' - e^{-Rt}Ry = -e^{-Rt}W$, which is

$$\frac{d}{dt}(e^{-Rt}y) = -e^{-Rt}W$$

Integration with respect to t yields

$$e^{-Rt}y = \frac{W}{R}e^{-Rt} + C$$

so that $y = \dfrac{W}{R} + Ce^{Rt}$.

(c) We have $y(0) = \dfrac{W}{R} + C$ so that $C = y(0) - \dfrac{W}{R}$. Thus,

$$y = \frac{W}{R} + \left(y(0) - \frac{W}{R}\right)e^{Rt}$$

Now, if $y(0) < \dfrac{W}{R}$, then as t increases, y decreases. If $y(0) = \dfrac{W}{R}$, then y is constantly $\dfrac{W}{R}$. Finally, if $y(0) > \dfrac{W}{R}$, then as t increases, y increases.

E X E R C I S E S

In 1–6, find the general solution to the differential equation.

1. $y' + y = 2$

2. $xy' + 2y = x$

3. $y' - 2y = x + 3$

4. $y' + y = e^x$

5. $y' - y = \dfrac{1}{1 + e^x}$

6. $y' - \dfrac{2y}{x - 1} = (x - 1)^{3/2}$

In 7–12, find the particular solution to the differential equation.

   7. $y' + y = x$; $y(0) = 1$
   8. $y' + 2y = e^x$; $y(0) = 0$
   9. $xy' - 2y = 1$; $y(1) = 2$
  10. $y' - y = e^{2x}$; $y(1) = 1$
  11. $y' - 2y = 2 - 2x$; $y(0) = -2$
  12. $xy' + y = e^x(1 + x)$; $y(1) = 2e$

13. A 1000-gallon mixing vat is full of a 20% (by volume) mixture of alcohol in water. The mixture is then drained at a rate of 10 gallons per minute and simultaneously replaced by pure alcohol. (Assume that the mixture is always homogeneous.) Let $y(t)$ be the amount (by volume) of pure alcohol in the tank after t minutes of simultaneous draining and filling.
    (a) Find $y(t)$.
    (b) How long will it take till the tank contains 40% alcohol by volume?

14. A polluted lake of volume V (in liters) is simultaneously fed by a river of pure water and drained by another river. Both rivers are moving water at the rate of R liters per hour. (Assume that the pollution in the lake is always uniform.) At time $t = 0$, the lake contains 4 grams per liter of pollutant.
    (a) In terms of V and R, find the function $y(t)$ which gives the number of grams of pollutant in the lake at time t.
    (b) In terms of V and R, how long will it take to cut the initial pollution level in half?

15. If an object is dropped through air, its velocity $v(t)$ at time t is affected by gravity and also air resistance. Suppose that $v'(t) = -9.8 - Cv(t)$ for some $C > 0$ (a constant depending on the air resistance). Also assume that the initial velocity is 0, that is, $v(0) = 0$. Find $v(t)$.

16. Suppose that $x = x(t)$ varies with respect to time according to the formula $Ax' + Bx = C$, where A, B, and C are positive constants. Assume that $x(0) = 0$.
    (a) Express x as a function of t.
    (b) Evaluate $\lim_{t \to \infty} x(t)$
    (c) At what time is x half the limiting value found in part (b)?

3   The Differential Equation $y'' + p_1y' + p_2y = 0$

Differential equations of the form

$$y'' + p_1y' + p_2y = 0 \tag{1}$$

where p_1 and p_2 are constants, often arise in physical applications. Although we will not prove it here, the following theorem gives the general solutions to (1).

$\Rightarrow$ **Theorem**   The general solutions to (1) are as follows:

(i) If $p_1^2 > 4p_2$, then

$$y = C_1e^{r_1x} + C_2e^{r_2x}$$

is the general solution to (1), where C_1 and C_2 are arbitrary constants and

$$r_1 = \frac{-p_1 + \sqrt{p_1^2 - 4p_2}}{2} \quad \text{and} \quad r_2 = \frac{-p_1 - \sqrt{p_1^2 - 4p_2}}{2}$$

(ii) If $p_1^2 = 4p_2$, then

$$y = C_1e^{r_0x} + C_2xe^{r_0x}$$

is the general solution to (1), where C_1 and C_2 are arbitrary constants and $r_0 = \frac{-p_1}{2}$.

(iii) If $p_1^2 < 4p_2$, then

$$y = C_1e^{ax}\cos bx + C_2e^{ax}\sin bx$$

is the general solution to (1), where C_1 and C_2 are arbitrary constants and

$$a = \frac{-p_1}{2} \quad \text{and} \quad b = \frac{\sqrt{4p_2 - p_1^2}}{2}$$

Note. The constants r_1 and r_2 in part (i) above need not be memorized. You need only remember that they are the solutions to the equation $x^2 + p_1x + p_2 = 0$, which bears an obvious relation to the original equation (1).

EXAMPLE   Find the general solution to each of the differential equations:

(a) $y'' + 2y' - 3y = 0$
(b) $y'' + 2y' + y = 0$
(c) $y'' + y' + 2y = 0$

Solution   (a) Here $p_1 = 2$ and $p_2 = -3$. Since $p_1^2 = 4 > -12 = 4p_2$, case (i) applies. We have

$$r_1 = \frac{-2 + \sqrt{4 + 12}}{2} = 1$$

and

$$r_2 = \frac{-2 - \sqrt{4 + 12}}{2} = -3$$

Thus, the general solution is

$$y = C_1 e^x + C_2 e^{-3x}$$

(b) Here $p_1 = 2$ and $p_2 = 1$. Since $p_1^2 = 4 = 4p_2$, case (ii) applies. We have $r_0 = \frac{-2}{2} = -1$. Thus, the general solution is

$$y = C_1 e^{-x} + C_2 x e^{-x}$$

(c) Here $p_1 = 1$ and $p_2 = 2$. Since $p_1^2 = 1 < 8 = 4p_2$, case (iii) applies. Here $a = -\frac{1}{2}$ and $b = \frac{\sqrt{8-1}}{2} = \frac{\sqrt{7}}{2}$.

Thus, the general solution is

$$y = C_1 e^{-\frac{x}{2}} \cos \frac{\sqrt{7}}{2} x + C_2 e^{-\frac{x}{2}} \sin \frac{\sqrt{7}}{2} x$$

Let us now analyze the motion of a spring. Suppose a weight of mass m attached to a spring is sliding in a straight line along a horizontal surface (see Fig. 11-1). Suppose the spring constant is k^2,

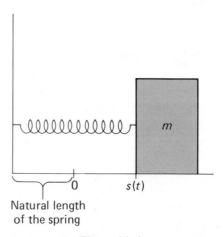

Figure 11-1

$k > 0$; that is, the spring exerts a force of $-k^2s$ when the spring is stretched a distance s ($s > 0$) or compressed a distance s ($s < 0$). This is called **Hooke's Law**. Here, as usual, $s = s(t)$ is a function of time. Suppose the frictional force is proportional to the velocity, s', of the weight. That is, the frictional force may be written as $-2fs'$, $f \geq 0$. (We use the negative sign because the frictional force is in the opposite direction to the motion. Also, we write $2f$, instead of f, for the magnitude of the frictional force to make the notation simple in what follows.) The force $-2fs'$ is called a **damping force** because it damps, or retards, the motion.

Now, since we take force to be the product of the mass and the acceleration, s'', we see that

$$ms'' = -2fs' - k^2s$$

That is,

$$s'' + \frac{2fs'}{m} + \frac{k^2}{m}s = 0 \tag{2}$$

Since (2) is of the form (1) with $p_1 = \dfrac{2f}{m}$ and $p_2 = \dfrac{k^2}{m}$, we may proceed to solve (2) and thereby analyze the motion of the weight. There are three cases:

(i) If $p_1^2 > 4p_2$, that is, $f^2 > k^2m$, we see that the general solution is

$$s = s(t) = C_1 \exp\left(\frac{-f + \sqrt{f^2 - k^2m}}{m}\,t\right)$$
$$+ C_2 \exp\left(\frac{-f - \sqrt{f^2 - k^2m}}{m}\,t\right) \tag{3}$$

Notice that, since $\sqrt{f^2 - k^2m} < f$, each quantity inside the parentheses in (3) approaches $-\infty$ as $t \to \infty$. Thus, no matter what the values C_1 and C_2 are, $s \to 0$ as $t \to \infty$. Also, it can be shown that the right side of (3) changes sign at most once (see exercise 11). This case is called the **overdamped** case.

(ii) If $p_1^2 = 4p_2$, that is, $f^2 = k^2m$, we see that the general solution is

$$s = s(t) = C_1 \exp(-ft/m) + C_2 t \exp(-ft/m) \tag{4}$$

Here again, as $t \to \infty$, $s \to 0$ and the right side of (4) changes sign at most once (see exercise 11). This case is called the **critical damping** case.

(iii) If $p_1^2 < 4p_2$, that is, $f^2 < k^2m$, we see that the general solution is

$$s = s(t) = C_1 \exp(-ft/m) \cos\left(\frac{\sqrt{k^2m - f^2}}{m}t\right)$$

$$+ C_2 \exp(-ft/m) \sin\left(\frac{\sqrt{k^2m - f^2}}{m}t\right) \qquad (5)$$

If we write $C = \sqrt{C_1^2 + C_2^2}$, define θ_0 by $\sin\theta_0 = \dfrac{C_1}{C}$ and $\cos\theta_0 = \dfrac{C_2}{C}$, and let $\omega = \dfrac{\sqrt{k^2m - f^2}}{m}$, then we can write (5) as

$$s = s(t) = C \exp(-ft/m)\left[\frac{C_1}{C}\cos\omega t + \frac{C_2}{C}\sin\omega t\right]$$

which is the same as (using the formula for $\sin(\alpha + \beta)$)

$$s = s(t) = C \exp(-ft/m) \sin(\omega t + \theta_0) \qquad (5')$$

Notice that $C \exp(-ft/m)$ is always positive and approaches 0 as $t \to \infty$. Since $0 < |\sin(\omega t + \theta_0)| \leq 1$ for all t, we see that $s \to 0$ as $t \to \infty$. Also, it is clear that as $t \to \infty$, s oscillates infinitely often about the point 0 (the **equilibrium point**), because as $t \to \infty$, $\sin(\omega t + \theta_0)$ alternates infinitely often from positive to negative. This case is called the **underdamped** case. It is very different from the overdamped and critically damped cases because, as we have seen, in those two cases there is no oscillation, since s changes sign at most once.

If $f = 0$ in the previous problem (there are no frictional forces), then equation (2) becomes

$$s'' + \frac{k^2}{m}s = 0 \qquad (6)$$

This is a special case of case (iii) and (5') becomes

$$s = s(t) = C \sin\left(\frac{kt}{\sqrt{m}} + \theta_0\right) \qquad (7)$$

This case is an example of **simple harmonic motion**, whose general equation is

$$s = s(t) = C \sin(\beta t + \gamma) \qquad C \neq 0, \beta \neq 0 \qquad (8)$$

The value $2\pi/\beta$ is called the **period** of the motion, because for any t, $s(t) = s(t + 2\pi/\beta)$; $\beta/2\pi$ is called the **frequency** because it is the number of complete cycles in one unit of time. Also, $|C|$ is called the **amplitude** because s oscillates between the values $-|C|$ and $|C|$ (see

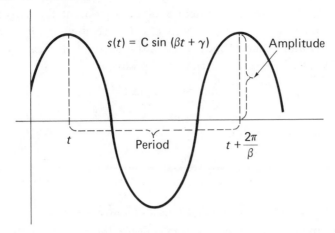

Figure 11-2

Fig. 11-2). The reader should compare this with the discussion in Chapter 5, section 2, pages 222–223.

EXAMPLE   Suppose a pendulum of length l and mass m is swinging. The gravitational force mg, where g is the gravitational constant, on the pendulum may be resolved into a force $-mg \sin \theta$ acting against the pendulum opposite to the direction of motion and a force acting along the pendulum (see Fig. 11-3). If $s(t)$ is the distance along its arc which the pendulum is displaced, then analyze $s(t)$ for small values of θ, provided we neglect friction.

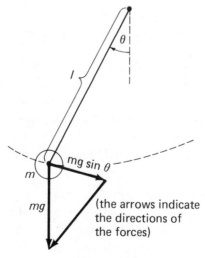

Figure 11-3

Solution The indicated angle θ of displacement is measured in radians, and so we have $s = l\theta$, and $s'' = l\theta''$. (Notice that θ, as well as s, is a function of time.) Since force is the product of mass and acceleration, s'', and there is no friction, we have

$$ms'' = -mg \sin \theta \tag{9}$$

because the force acting along the path of motion is $-mg \sin \theta$. Equation (9) may be rewritten as

$$\theta'' + \frac{g}{l} \sin \theta = 0 \tag{10}$$

Now, since we are assuming θ is small, and since $\lim_{\theta \to 0} \frac{\sin \theta}{\theta} = 1$, we may approximate $\sin \theta$ by θ. If this is done, then (10) becomes

$$\theta'' + \frac{g}{l}\theta = 0 \tag{11}$$

which is equivalent to

$$s'' + \frac{g}{l}s = 0 \tag{12}$$

Thus, we have simple harmonic motion. We leave it to the reader to show that the frequency is $\dfrac{1}{2\pi\sqrt{l/g}}$.

E X E R C I S E S

In 1–3, find the general solution to the differential equation.

  1. $y'' + 4y' + 3y = 0$ **2.** $y'' - 6y' + 9y = 0$ **3.** $y'' + y' + y = 0$

In 4–6, find the particular solution to the differential equation. (You will have to solve two equations in the unknowns C_1 and C_2.)

  4. $y'' - 3y' + 2y = 0; \ y(0) = 1, \ y(1) = 0$
  5. $y'' - 2y' + y = 0; \ y(0) = -1, \ y(1) = 1$
  6. $y'' - 2y' + 5y = 0; \ y(0) = 2, \ y(\pi/4) = 1$

  7. Find an equation of motion for an object in simple harmonic motion if the period is $\pi/2$, $s(0) = 0$, and $v(0) = s'(0) = 1$. [*Hint:* Begin with the equation $s(t) = C \sin (\beta t + \gamma)$. Since every function of the form $C \sin (\beta t + \gamma)$ can be written in the form $D \sin (\beta t + \alpha)$ with $0 \le \alpha < 2\pi$ and $D \ge 0$, you may assume that $0 \le \gamma < 2\pi$ and $C \ge 0$. First solve for β. Then find $s'(t)$ and solve for C and then γ.]

8. Find an equation of motion for an object in simple harmonic motion if the frequency is $4/\pi$, $s(0) = 1$, and $v(0) = s'(0) = -1$.

9. If an object is in simple harmonic motion, then find the position, $s(t)$, at which its speed ($|v(t)| = |s'(t)|$) is maximal.

10. A frictionless pendulum moving in simple harmonic motion passes through its equilibrium (bottom) point ($s = 0$) at $t = 0$ and at 2-second intervals after that. If $v(0) = s'(0) = 4$, find an equation for $s(t)$.

11. Show that the right side of equation (3) and the right side of equation (4) on page 513 each change sign at most once by showing that in each case $s'(t) = 0$ can have at most one solution.

12. A spring is hanging vertically with length l_1. An object of mass m is then attached to the spring and the spring stretches a length l_2. A man then pulls the weight down a distance l_3 further and releases the object (see Fig. 11-4). Use Hooke's Law, $F = -k^2(s + l_2)$, which states that the force of the spring is proportional to the distance it is stretched (or compressed) and that the force is in the opposite direction to the stretching (or compressing), and Newton's Law, which states that the force on the mass is ms'', to show that the object is in simple harmonic motion. Remember to consider the gravitational force mg on the object.

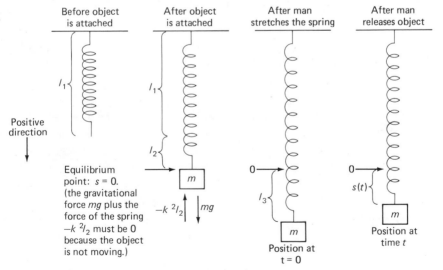

Figure 11–4

4   The Differential Equation y″ + P₁y′ + P₂y = P(x)

Differential equations of the form

$$y'' + P_1 y' + P_2 y = P(x) \tag{1}$$

where P_1 and P_2 are constants, can often be solved by the method of **undetermined coefficients.** This method will work when $P(x)$ is a sum of terms whose factors are of the form x^m (m a positive integer), $\sin ax$, $\cos ax$, e^{ax}, or a constant a.

Here is an outline (without proof) of how the method of undetermined coefficients works:

(1) Associate sets with factors, as follows:

x^m	$\{x^m, x^{m-1}, \ldots, x, 1\}$
$\sin ax$	$\{\sin ax, \cos ax\}$
$\cos ax$	$\{\sin ax, \cos ax\}$
e^{ax}	$\{e^{ax}\}$
constant a	$\{1\}$

(2) Each term of $P(x)$ is associated with the "product" set generated by the sets associated with each of its factors. For example, if $x^2 \cos 3x$ is a term of $P(x)$, then, since x^2 is associated with $\{x^2, x, 1\}$ and $\cos 3x$ is associated with $\{\sin 3x, \cos 3x\}$, $x^2 \cos 3x$ will then be associated with $\{x^2 \sin 3x, x \sin 3x, \sin 3x, x^2 \cos 3x, x \cos 3x, \cos 3x\}$.

(3) If any set constructed in step 2 contains another such set, discard the smaller set.

(4) Find the general solution y^* of the equation $y'' + P_1 y' + P_2 y = 0$. We saw how to do this in the last section.

(5) If any associated set found in step 2 has a member which is a constant multiple of a term of y^*, replace each member of that associated set by the product of itself and the lowest integral power of x such that no member of the new associated set will be a term of y^*.

(6) Express a function y_1 as a linear combination of all the members of those associated sets found in steps 2 and 5. For example, if after step 5 our associated sets are $\{x^3, x^2, x, 1\}$ and $\{e^{2x}\}$, then we write $y_1 = Ax^3 + Bx^2 + Cx + D + Ee^{2x}$, where A, B, C, D, and E represent constants.

(7) Substitute y_1 into the left-hand side of equation (1) and formally set it equal to $P(x)$.

(8) Solve for the constants from step 6 (A, B, C, D, and E) to find y_1.

(9) The general solution of (1) is given by $y = y_1 + y^*$.

EXAMPLE   Solve $y'' + 4y' + 4y = e^x$.

Solution

(1) e^x is associated with $\{e^x\}$

(2) The only set is $\{e^x\}$

(3) There is nothing to do.

(4) $y'' + 4y' + 4y = 0$ must now be solved. Since $P_1 = 4$ and $P_2 = 4$, we have $P_1^2 = 4P_2$ and so

$$y^* = C_1 e^{\frac{-P_1 x}{2}} + C_2 x e^{\frac{-P_1 x}{2}} = C_1 e^{-2x} + C_2 x e^{-2x}$$

(5) There is nothing to do.

(6) Write $y_1 = Ae^x$

(7) The left-hand side of the original equation becomes

$$y_1'' + 4y_1' + 4y_1 = Ae^x + 4Ae^x + 4Ae^x = 9Ae^x$$

Set $y_1'' + 4y_1' + 4y_1 = 9Ae^x$ formally equal to e^x to obtain $9Ae^x = e^x$.

(8) Thus, $A = \dfrac{1}{9}$ and $y_1 = \dfrac{1}{9}e^x$.

(9) Our solution is $y = y_1 + y^* = \dfrac{1}{9}e^x + C_1 e^{-2x} + C_2 x e^{-2x}$.

EXAMPLE   Solve $-y'' + y' = \cos 2x + xe^{3x}$

Solution   First rewrite the equation: $y'' - y' = -\cos 2x - xe^{3x}$.

(1) $\cos 2x$ is associated with $\{\sin 2x, \cos 2x\}$.

x is associated with $\{x, 1\}$.

e^{3x} is associated with $\{e^{3x}\}$.

-1 is associated with $\{1\}$.

(2) The set associated with $-\cos 2x$ is $\{\sin 2x, \cos 2x\}$. The set associated with $-xe^{2x}$ is $\{xe^{3x}, e^{3x}\}$.

(3) Neither set in step 2 is a subset of the other.

(4) The equation $y'' - y' = 0$ must now be solved. Since $P_1 = -1$ and $P_2 = 0$, we see that $P_1^2 > 4P_2$. Thus, the function y^* is given by $y^* = C_1 e^{r_1 x} + C_2 e^{r_2 x}$, where C_1 and C_2 are arbitrary constants and

$$r_1 = \frac{-P_1 + \sqrt{P_1^2 - 4P_2}}{2} = 1 \quad \text{and} \quad r_2 = \frac{-P_1 - \sqrt{P_1^2 - 4P_2}}{2} = 0$$

Thus, $y^* = C_1 e^x + C_2$.

(5) There is nothing to be done.

(6) Write $y_1 = A \sin 2x + B \cos 2x + Cxe^{3x} + De^{3x}$.

(7) The left-hand side of the rewritten original equation becomes

$$y_1'' - y_1' = -4A \sin 2x - 4B \cos 2x + 9Cxe^{3x} + (6C + 9D)e^{3x}$$
$$- (2A \cos 2x - 2B \sin 2x + 3Cxe^{3x} + (C + 3D)e^{3x})$$

Thus,

$$y_1'' - y_1' = (-4A + 2B) \sin 2x + (-4B - 2A) \cos 2x$$
$$+ 6Cxe^{3x} + (5C + 6D)e^{3x}$$

Set $y_1'' - y_1'$ formally equal to $-\cos 2x - xe^{3x}$ to obtain

$$-4A + 2B = 0$$
$$-4B - 2A = -1$$
$$6C = -1$$
$$5C + 6D = 0$$

(8) Solve the system from step 7 to obtain

$$A = \frac{1}{10}, \qquad B = \frac{1}{5}, \qquad C = -\frac{1}{6}, \qquad D = \frac{5}{36}$$

Thus, $y_1 = \frac{1}{10} \sin 2x + \frac{1}{5} \cos 2x - \frac{1}{6} xe^{3x} + \frac{5}{36} e^{3x}$.

(9) Our solution is

$$y = y_1 + y^* = \frac{1}{10} \sin 2x + \frac{1}{5} \cos 2x - \frac{1}{6} xe^{3x} + \frac{5}{36} e^{3x} + C_1 e^x + C_2$$

E X E R C I S E S

In 1–6, find the general solution of the differential equation.

1. $y'' + y' = e^x$
2. $y'' - y' = \sin x$
3. $y'' - y' - 2y = \cos x$
4. $y'' - 3y' + 2y = 1 + x^2$
5. $y'' + 4y = \sin^2 x$
6. $y'' - 2y' + y = x + e^x$ [You will need to use step 5.]

7. Find the particular solution to the equation of exercise 1 if $y'(0) = 0$ and $y(0) = 1$.

8. Find the particular solution to the equation of exercise 2 if $y'(0) = y(0) = 0$.

Chapter 12

Vectors in the Plane

1 Arrows and Vectors

In physics and engineering many quantities occur which possess both a **magnitude** and a **direction.** Some examples are displacement, velocity, acceleration, force, and momentum. Such a quantity can be represented geometrically by a directed line segment $\overrightarrow{PQ}$ from a point P to a point Q (see Fig. 12-1). Such a directed line segment is called an **arrow.** The direction of the arrow and its length indicate the direction and the magnitude of the quantity that the arrow represents. The particular location of the arrow is unimportant for representing a quantity that has only direction and magnitude. Thus, two arrows $\overrightarrow{PQ}$ and $\overrightarrow{RS}$ are said to be equal, written $\overrightarrow{PQ} = \overrightarrow{RS}$, if they are in the same direction (along parallel lines) and have the same length (see Fig. 12-2). The collection of all arrows that are equal to a given arrow is called a (**geometrical**) **vector** and each arrow in that collection is called a **representative** of that vector. The point P is called the **initial point** and the point Q is called the **terminal point** of the arrow $\overrightarrow{PQ}$. In some books arrows are called vectors.

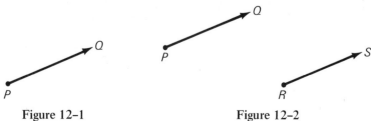

Figure 12–1   Figure 12–2

If $P = (x_1, y_1)$ and $Q = (x_2, y_2)$ are points in the plane, then it is clear that there is exactly one point T in the plane which determines the arrow $\overrightarrow{OT}$ having initial point at the origin O such that $\overrightarrow{PQ} = \overrightarrow{OT}$. In fact, $T = (x_2 - x_1, y_2 - y_1)$ (see Fig. 12-3). The arrow $\overrightarrow{OT}$ is called the **principal representative** of the vector determined by $\overrightarrow{PQ}$. Thus, there is a one-to-one correspondence between the set of all points T in the plane and the set of all (geometrical) vectors in the plane: T corresponds to the vector having $\overrightarrow{OT}$ as principal representative.

We are now ready to give an analytical definition of the term "plane vector."

▷ *Definition* By a **plane vector** we mean an ordered pair $\mathbf{A} = \langle a_1, a_2 \rangle$ of real numbers. The number a_1 is called the **first component** of the vector $\mathbf{A}$ while a_2 is called the **second component** of $\mathbf{A}$. The **length** (or **magnitude**) of $\mathbf{A}$ is the number

$$|\mathbf{A}| = [a_1^2 + a_2^2]^{1/2}$$

An arrow $\overrightarrow{PQ}$, where $P = (x_1, y_1)$ and $Q = (x_2, y_2)$, is said to be a **representation** of $\mathbf{A}$ if $x_2 - x_1 = a_1$ and $y_2 - y_1 = a_2$. In particular, $\overrightarrow{OT}$ is the **principal representation** if $O = (0,0)$ is the origin and $T = (a_1, a_2)$. The **direction** of $\mathbf{A}$ is the direction of any one of its representations (provided that $|\mathbf{A}| \neq 0$). The **zero vector** $\mathbf{O} = \langle 0,0 \rangle$ has no direction. The direction of a nonzero vector $\mathbf{A}$ is determined by the angles θ_1 and θ_2 that its principal representation $\overrightarrow{OT}$ makes with the positive x-axis and the positive y-axis, respectively, where $0 \leqq \theta_1 \leqq \pi$ and $0 \leqq \theta_2 \leqq \pi$ (see Fig. 12-4). These are called the **direction angles** of $\mathbf{A}$.

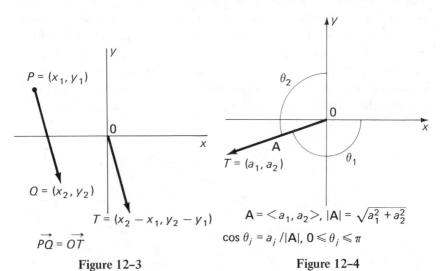

$P = (x_1, y_1)$

$Q = (x_2, y_2)$

$T = (x_2 - x_1, y_2 - y_1)$

$\overrightarrow{PQ} = \overrightarrow{OT}$

Figure 12–3

$T = (a_1, a_2)$

$\mathbf{A} = \langle a_1, a_2 \rangle, \quad |\mathbf{A}| = \sqrt{a_1^2 + a_2^2}$

$\cos \theta_j = a_j / |\mathbf{A}|, \quad 0 \leqslant \theta_j \leqslant \pi$

Figure 12–4

Notice that

$$\cos^2 \theta_1 + \cos^2 \theta_2 = 1$$

We shall write $\mathbf{A} = \overrightarrow{PQ}$ if $\overrightarrow{PQ}$ is a representation of $\mathbf{A}$. Notice that we have used wedge-shaped brackets to denote plane vectors so as not to confuse them with points in the plane. Of course, this distinction is rather minor since the point (a_1,a_2) is the terminal point of the principal representation of $\langle a_1,a_2 \rangle$. However, we shall continue to make this distinction for the sake of the beginner.

EXAMPLE If $\mathbf{A} = \langle 2,-2\sqrt{3} \rangle$, $P = (2,-2\sqrt{3})$, and $R = (-2,3\sqrt{3})$, find points Q and S such that $\overrightarrow{PQ}$ and $\overrightarrow{RS}$ are both representations of $\mathbf{A}$. Also find $|\mathbf{A}|$ and the direction angles of $\mathbf{A}$. Illustrate with a figure.

Solution Writing $Q = (x,y)$ and $S = (u,v)$, we need $x - 2 = 2$, $y + 2\sqrt{3} = -2\sqrt{3}$, $u + 2 = 2$, and $v - 3\sqrt{3} = -2\sqrt{3}$. Thus $x = 4$, $y = -4\sqrt{3}$, $u = 0$, and $v = \sqrt{3}$. Therefore $Q = (4,-4\sqrt{3})$ and $S = (0,\sqrt{3})$. We have $|\mathbf{A}| = [2^2 + (-2\sqrt{3})^2]^{1/2} = 4$, $\cos \theta_1 = 2/4 = 1/2$, and $\cos \theta_2 = -2\sqrt{3}/4 = -\sqrt{3}/2$. Since $0 \leqq \theta_j \leqq \pi$, we conclude that $\theta_1 = \pi/3$ and $\theta_2 = 5\pi/6$. See Fig. 12-5 for an illustration.

EXAMPLE If $P = (-1,2)$, $Q = (1,3)$, and $R = (-2,-1)$, find the point S such that $\overrightarrow{RS} = \overrightarrow{PQ}$. Also, find T so that $\overrightarrow{OT}$ is the principal representation of the vector $\mathbf{A} = \overrightarrow{PQ}$. Illustrate with a figure.

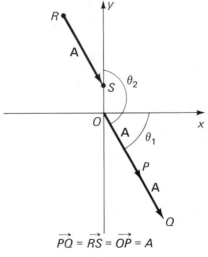

$$\overrightarrow{PQ} = \overrightarrow{RS} = \overrightarrow{OP} = A$$

Figure 12-5

Solution   Writing $S = (x,y)$, we want $x - (-2) = 1 - (-1) = 2$ and $y - (-1) = 3 - 2 = 1$ and so we must have $x = 0$ and $y = 0$. Thus $S = (0,0) = O$. Also, $\mathbf{A} = \langle 1-(-1),3-2 \rangle = \langle 2,1 \rangle$ so that $T = (2,1)$. See Fig. 12-6 for an illustration.

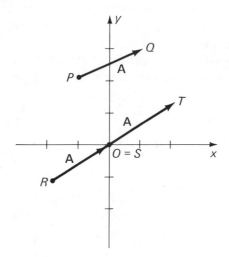

Figure 12-6

EXERCISES

In 1-8, find the point Q so that $\mathbf{A} = \overrightarrow{PQ}$, where $\mathbf{A}$ and P are given. Illustrate with a figure.

1. $\mathbf{A} = \langle -1,0 \rangle$, $P = (3,1)$
2. $\mathbf{A} = \langle 2,-2 \rangle$, $P = (0,1)$
3. $\mathbf{A} = \langle 4,-2 \rangle$, $P = (-2,1)$
4. $\mathbf{A} = \langle 0,1 \rangle$, $P = (-1,-1)$

5. $\mathbf{A} = \langle 1,-1 \rangle$, $P = (1,-1)$
6. $\mathbf{A} = \langle 0,-3 \rangle$, $P = (0,0)$
7. $\mathbf{A} = \langle 0,0 \rangle$, $P = (2,3)$
8. $\mathbf{A} = \langle -1,-1 \rangle$, $P = (1,1)$

In 9-12, find S so that $\overrightarrow{PQ} = \overrightarrow{RS}$.

9. $P = (0,0)$, $Q = (0,4)$, $R = (-2,2)$
10. $P = (-2,5)$, $Q = (7,-2)$, $R = (4,1)$
11. $P = (e,1)$, $Q = (1,e)$, $R = (2,-2)$
12. $P = (2,-3)$, $Q = (\pi,\sqrt{2})$, $R = (-1,1)$

In 13-16, find all values of c so that the given vector $\mathbf{A}$ has the given length.

13. $\mathbf{A} = \langle c,-c \rangle$, $|\mathbf{A}| = 4$
14. $\mathbf{A} = \langle c-1,2 \rangle$, $|\mathbf{A}| = 2$
15. $\mathbf{A} = \langle c+2,c \rangle$; $|\mathbf{A}| = 2$
16. $\mathbf{A} = \langle c+1,c-1 \rangle$, $|\mathbf{A}| = 1$

In 17–22, find the direction angles of the given vector.

17. $\langle 0,-1 \rangle$ **19.** $\langle -\pi,-\pi \rangle$ **21.** $\langle -\sqrt{3},1 \rangle$

18. $\langle -2,-2 \rangle$ **20.** $\langle \pi,-\pi\sqrt{3} \rangle$ **22.** $\langle \pi/\sqrt{3},\pi/3 \rangle$

2 Operations on Vectors

The term **scalar** is used to mean the same thing as the term number. If $\mathbf{A} = \langle a_1,a_2 \rangle$ and $\mathbf{B} = \langle b_1,b_2 \rangle$ are vectors and c is a scalar, we define the **sum** and **difference** of $\mathbf{A}$ and $\mathbf{B}$ to be the respective vectors

$$\mathbf{A} + \mathbf{B} = \langle a_1 + b_1, a_2 + b_2 \rangle$$

and

$$\mathbf{A} - \mathbf{B} = \langle a_1 - b_1, a_2 - b_2 \rangle$$

and we define the **scalar multiple** c times $\mathbf{A}$ to be the vector

$$c\mathbf{A} = \langle ca_1, ca_2 \rangle$$

We define the negative of $\mathbf{A}$ to be $-\mathbf{A} = \langle -a_1,-a_2 \rangle$. We also define the **dot product** (or **inner product**, or **scalar product**) of $\mathbf{A}$ and $\mathbf{B}$ to be the scalar

$$\mathbf{A} \cdot \mathbf{B} = a_1 b_1 + a_2 b_2$$

EXAMPLE   If $\mathbf{A} = \langle 2,-3 \rangle$, $\mathbf{B} = \langle -5,4 \rangle$, and $c = -5$, find $\mathbf{A} + \mathbf{B}$, $\mathbf{A} - \mathbf{B}$, $c\mathbf{A}$, and $\mathbf{A} \cdot \mathbf{B}$.

Solution   We have

$$\mathbf{A} + \mathbf{B} = \langle 2+(-5),-3+4 \rangle = \langle -3,1 \rangle$$
$$\mathbf{A} - \mathbf{B} = \langle 2-(-5),-3-4 \rangle = \langle 7,-7 \rangle$$
$$c\mathbf{A} = \langle (-5) \cdot 2, (-5)(-3) \rangle = \langle -10,15 \rangle$$
$$\mathbf{A} \cdot \mathbf{B} = 2 \cdot (-5) + (-3) \cdot 4 = -22$$

It is easy to see that the principal representation of $\mathbf{A} + \mathbf{B}$ is the diagonal from the origin O of the parallelogram having the principal representations of $\mathbf{A}$ and $\mathbf{B}$ as two of its sides, while the other diagonal (directed from the terminal end of $\mathbf{B}$ to the terminal end of $\mathbf{A}$) is a representation of $\mathbf{A} - \mathbf{B}$ (see Fig. 12-7).

The principal representation of $c\mathbf{A}$ is along the same line through the origin as that of $\mathbf{A}$, it is $|c|$ times as long as that of $\mathbf{A}$, and it is in

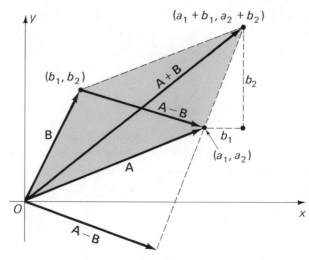

Figure 12-7

the same direction as that of $\mathbf{A}$ if $c > 0$ while it is in the opposite direction if $c < 0$. In fact, $|c\mathbf{A}| = |c| \cdot |\mathbf{A}|$, as one checks analytically:

$$(ca_1)^2 + (ca_2)^2 = c^2(a_1{}^2 + a_2{}^2)$$
$$|c\mathbf{A}| = \sqrt{(ca_1)^2 + (ca_2)^2} = \sqrt{c^2} \cdot \sqrt{a_1{}^2 + a_2{}^2} = |c| \cdot |\mathbf{A}|$$

Fig. 12-8 shows some arrows representing scalar multiples of a vector $\mathbf{A}$.

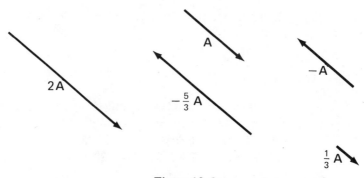

Figure 12-8

The geometrical significance of the dot product is that it involves the angle between the (representations of the) two factors. Fig. 12-9 shows (the principal representations of) two nonzero vectors $\mathbf{A} = \langle a_1, a_2 \rangle$ and $\mathbf{B} = \langle b_1, b_2 \rangle$ which make angles α and β, respectively, with the positive x-axis. Let $\theta = \alpha - \beta$ be the angle between $\mathbf{A}$ and $\mathbf{B}$.

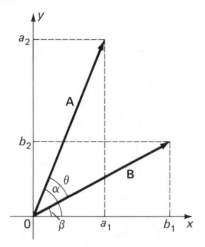

Figure 12-9

Then

$$\begin{aligned}
\cos \theta &= \cos \alpha \cos \beta + \sin \alpha \sin \beta \\
&= (a_1/|\mathbf{A}|)(b_1/|\mathbf{B}|) + (a_2/|\mathbf{A}|)(b_2/|\mathbf{B}|) \\
&= (a_1 b_1 + a_2 b_2)/(|\mathbf{A}| \cdot |\mathbf{B}|) \\
&= (\mathbf{A} \cdot \mathbf{B})/(|\mathbf{A}| \cdot |\mathbf{B}|)
\end{aligned}$$

and so

$$\boxed{\begin{array}{c}
\mathbf{A} \cdot \mathbf{B} = |\mathbf{A}| \cdot |\mathbf{B}| \cos \theta \\
\text{where } \theta = \text{angle between } \mathbf{A} \text{ and } \mathbf{B}
\end{array}} \qquad (1)$$

Since $\cos(-\theta) = \cos(2\pi - \theta) = \cos \theta$, the above formula is independent of which angle between $\mathbf{A}$ and $\mathbf{B}$ is taken and of the direction in which it is measured.

There are many algebraic identities and inequalities relative to the operations on vectors that we have just defined. We summarize the most important ones next. Notice that these results are unsurprising and easy to remember.

Theorem 1 Let $\mathbf{A}$, $\mathbf{B}$, and $\mathbf{C}$ be plane vectors and let c and d be scalars. Then

    (i) $\mathbf{A} + (\mathbf{B} + \mathbf{C}) = (\mathbf{A} + \mathbf{B}) + \mathbf{C}$
    (ii) $\mathbf{A} + \mathbf{B} = \mathbf{B} + \mathbf{A}$
    (iii) $\mathbf{A} + 0 = \mathbf{A}$
    (iv) $-\mathbf{A} = (-1)\mathbf{A}$ and $\mathbf{A} = 1\mathbf{A}$

(v) $-\mathbf{A} + \mathbf{A} = 0$

(vi) $(c + d)\mathbf{A} = c\mathbf{A} + d\mathbf{A}$

(vii) $c(\mathbf{A} + \mathbf{B}) = c\mathbf{A} + c\mathbf{B}$

(viii) $(cd)\mathbf{A} = c(d\mathbf{A})$

(ix) $c(\mathbf{A} \cdot \mathbf{B}) = (c\mathbf{A}) \cdot \mathbf{B} = \mathbf{A} \cdot (c\mathbf{B})$

(x) $\mathbf{A} \cdot \mathbf{B} = \mathbf{B} \cdot \mathbf{A}$

(xi) $\mathbf{A} \cdot (\mathbf{B} + \mathbf{C}) = (\mathbf{A} \cdot \mathbf{B}) + (\mathbf{A} \cdot \mathbf{C})$

(xii) $\mathbf{A} \cdot \mathbf{A} = |\mathbf{A}|^2$

(xiii) $|\mathbf{A} \cdot \mathbf{B}| \leqq |\mathbf{A}| \cdot |\mathbf{B}|$

(xiv) $|\mathbf{A} \pm \mathbf{B}| \leqq |\mathbf{A}| + |\mathbf{B}|$

(xv) $\Big| |\mathbf{A}| - |\mathbf{B}| \Big| \leqq |\mathbf{A} \pm \mathbf{B}|$

Proof Most of these are proved easily by simply applying the definitions. We prove a few and leave the rest as exercises. Writing $\mathbf{A} = \langle a_1, a_2 \rangle$, $\mathbf{B} = \langle b_1, b_2 \rangle$, and $\mathbf{C} = \langle c_1, c_2 \rangle$, we have

$$\mathbf{B} + \mathbf{C} = \langle b_1 + c_1, b_2 + c_2 \rangle$$

and so

$$\mathbf{A} \cdot (\mathbf{B} + \mathbf{C}) = a_1(b_1 + c_1) + a_2(b_2 + c_2) = (a_1 b_1 + a_1 c_1) + (a_2 b_2 + a_2 c_2)$$
$$= (a_1 b_1 + a_2 b_2) + (a_1 c_1 + a_2 c_2) = (\mathbf{A} \cdot \mathbf{B}) + (\mathbf{A} \cdot \mathbf{C})$$

which proves (xi). Next notice that

$$|\mathbf{A}|^2 |\mathbf{B}|^2 = (a_1^2 + a_2^2)(b_1^2 + b_2^2)$$
$$= a_1^2 b_1^2 + a_2^2 b_2^2 + (a_1^2 b_2^2 + a_2^2 b_1^2)$$
$$\geqq a_1^2 b_1^2 + a_2^2 b_2^2 + 2a_1 b_1 a_2 b_2$$
$$= (a_1 b_1 + a_2 b_2)^2 = |\mathbf{A} \cdot \mathbf{B}|^2$$

where the inequality follows from the fact that $a_1^2 b_2^2 + a_2^2 b_1^2 - 2a_1 b_1 a_2 b_2 = (a_1 b_2 - a_2 b_1)^2 \geqq 0$. Upon taking nonnegative square roots, we obtain (xiii). To prove (xiv), we use (xii), (xi), (ix), (iv), (x), and (xiii) to write

$$|\mathbf{A} \pm \mathbf{B}|^2 = (\mathbf{A} \pm \mathbf{B}) \cdot (\mathbf{A} \pm \mathbf{B})$$
$$= (\mathbf{A} \cdot \mathbf{A}) \pm (\mathbf{A} \cdot \mathbf{B}) \pm (\mathbf{B} \cdot \mathbf{A}) + (\mathbf{B} \cdot \mathbf{B})$$
$$= |\mathbf{A}|^2 \pm 2(\mathbf{A} \cdot \mathbf{B}) + |\mathbf{B}|^2$$
$$\leqq |\mathbf{A}|^2 + 2|\mathbf{A}| \cdot |\mathbf{B}| + |\mathbf{B}|^2$$
$$= (|\mathbf{A}| + |\mathbf{B}|)^2$$

and then take nonnegative square roots. ∎

Inequality (xiv) is called the **triangle inequality** because it says geometrically that the length of any side of a triangle cannot exceed the sum of the lengths of the other two sides (see Fig. 12-7).

EXAMPLE Prove that the **parallelogram law**,

$$|\mathbf{A} + \mathbf{B}|^2 + |\mathbf{A} - \mathbf{B}|^2 = 2|\mathbf{A}|^2 + 2|\mathbf{B}|^2$$

is valid for any two plane vectors **A** and **B**. What does this equality tell us about the lengths of the diagonals and sides of a parallelogram?

Solution We use Theorem 1 to write

$$
\begin{aligned}
|\mathbf{A} + \mathbf{B}|^2 &= (\mathbf{A} + \mathbf{B}) \cdot (\mathbf{A} + \mathbf{B}) \\
&= (\mathbf{A} \cdot \mathbf{A}) + (\mathbf{A} \cdot \mathbf{B}) + (\mathbf{B} \cdot \mathbf{A}) + (\mathbf{B} \cdot \mathbf{B})
\end{aligned}
$$

and

$$
\begin{aligned}
|\mathbf{A} - \mathbf{B}|^2 &= (\mathbf{A} - \mathbf{B}) \cdot (\mathbf{A} - \mathbf{B}) \\
&= (\mathbf{A} \cdot \mathbf{A}) - (\mathbf{A} \cdot \mathbf{B}) - (\mathbf{B} \cdot \mathbf{A}) + (\mathbf{B} \cdot \mathbf{B})
\end{aligned}
$$

Now add these equations to obtain

$$
\begin{aligned}
|\mathbf{A} + \mathbf{B}|^2 + |\mathbf{A} - \mathbf{B}|^2 &= 2(\mathbf{A} \cdot \mathbf{A}) + 2(\mathbf{B} \cdot \mathbf{B}) \\
&= 2|\mathbf{A}|^2 + 2|\mathbf{B}|^2
\end{aligned}
$$

With an eye on Fig. 12-7, we see that this says that the sum of the squares of the diagonals of a parallelogram is equal to the sum of the squares of all four of its sides.

Formula (1) can be used to find the area of a triangle whose three vertices are given. Suppose that $P = (x_1, y_1)$, $Q = (x_2, y_2)$, and $R = (x_3, y_3)$ are the vertices. Form the vectors $\mathbf{A} = \overrightarrow{PQ}$ and $\mathbf{B} = \overrightarrow{PR}$ and let θ denote the angle between them, with $0 \leq \theta \leq \pi$ (see Fig. 12-10). Taking $b = |\mathbf{B}|$ as base, the height is $h = |\mathbf{A}| \sin \theta = |\mathbf{A}| \sqrt{1 - \cos^2 \theta}$ and so we have

$$
\begin{aligned}
\text{Area} &= \frac{1}{2}bh = \frac{1}{2}|\mathbf{A}| \cdot |\mathbf{B}| \sqrt{1 - \cos^2 \theta} \\
&= \frac{1}{2}\sqrt{(|\mathbf{A}| \cdot |\mathbf{B}|)^2 - (\mathbf{A} \cdot \mathbf{B})^2}
\end{aligned}
$$

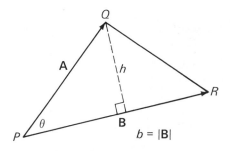

Figure 12-10

EXAMPLE   Find the area of the triangle having vertices $P = (2,-1)$, $Q = (-2,1)$, and $R = (3,4)$.

Solution   Writing $\mathbf{A} = \overrightarrow{PQ} = \langle -4,2 \rangle$ and $\mathbf{B} = \overrightarrow{PR} = \langle 1,5 \rangle$, we have $|\mathbf{A}|^2 = (-4)^2 + 2^2 = 20$, $|\mathbf{B}|^2 = 1^2 + 5^2 = 26$, and $\mathbf{A} \cdot \mathbf{B} = (-4) \cdot 1 + 2 \cdot 5 = 6$ and so

$$\text{Area} = \frac{1}{2}\sqrt{(20)(26) - 6^2} = \frac{1}{2}\sqrt{484} = 11$$

E X E R C I S E S

In 1–12, let $\mathbf{A} = \langle 3,1 \rangle$ and $\mathbf{B} = \langle -2,5 \rangle$.

1. Find $\mathbf{A} + \mathbf{B}$
2. Find $\mathbf{A} \cdot \mathbf{B}$
3. Find the angle between $\mathbf{A}$ and $\mathbf{B}$
4. Find $|\mathbf{A} - 2\mathbf{B}|$
5. Find $|\mathbf{A}| - 2|\mathbf{B}|$
6. Find $(2\mathbf{A}) \cdot (-\mathbf{B})$
7. Find $\mathbf{A} \cdot (2\mathbf{A} - \mathbf{B})$
8. Verify that $\left| |\mathbf{A}| - |\mathbf{B}| \right| \leq |\mathbf{A} - \mathbf{B}|$
9. Verify that $|\mathbf{A} \cdot \mathbf{B}| \leq |\mathbf{A}| \cdot |\mathbf{B}|$
10. Find c and d so that $c\mathbf{A} + d\mathbf{B} = \langle 8,-3 \rangle$
11. Find c and d so that $c\mathbf{A} + d\mathbf{B} = \langle 7,8 \rangle$
12. Find $\mathbf{C}$ so that $|\mathbf{C}| = 1$ and $\mathbf{A} \cdot \mathbf{C} = 0$

13. Find the area of the triangle having vertices $(2,1)$, $(3,4)$, and $(1,3)$.
14. Find the area of the triangle having vertices $(1,2)$, $(2,3)$, and $(3,1)$.
15. Find the area of the parallelogram having consecutive vertices $(-1,-2)$, $(-2,1)$, and $(3,-1)$. What is the fourth vertex?
16. Find the fourth vertex and the area of the parallelogram having consecutive vertices $(7,3)$, $(1,4)$, and $(2,4)$.
17. Prove Theorem 1(i).
18. Prove Theorem 1(vi).
19. Prove Theorem 1(vii).
20. Prove Theorem 1(viii).
21. Prove Theorem 1(xv). [*Hint:* $|\mathbf{A}| = |\mathbf{B} + (\mathbf{A} - \mathbf{B})| \leq |\mathbf{B}| + |\mathbf{A} - \mathbf{B}|$.]
22. Give a geometrical proof of the associative law, $\mathbf{A} + (\mathbf{B} + \mathbf{C}) = (\mathbf{A} + \mathbf{B}) + \mathbf{C}$.
23. Find c so that the angle between $\mathbf{A} = \langle 2,1 \rangle$ and $\mathbf{B} = \langle 1,c \rangle$ is $45°$.
24. Find c so that the angle between $\mathbf{A} = \langle 2,1 \rangle$ and $\mathbf{B} = \langle 1,c \rangle$ is $30°$.

25. Prove the **Law of Cosines:** If θ is the angle between vectors **A** and **B,** then

$$|\mathbf{A} - \mathbf{B}|^2 = |\mathbf{A}|^2 + |\mathbf{B}|^2 - 2|\mathbf{A}| \cdot |\mathbf{B}| \cos \theta$$

26. Prove the **Pythagorean Theorem:** If vectors **A** and **B** are perpendicular, then

$$|\mathbf{A} - \mathbf{B}|^2 = |\mathbf{A}|^2 + |\mathbf{B}|^2$$

3 Components and Orthogonality

Let $\overrightarrow{OP}$ and $\overrightarrow{OQ}$ be the principal representations of the (nonzero) plane vectors **A** and **B,** respectively, and let θ be the angle between **A** and **B** (see Fig. 12-11). Let R be the foot of the perpendicular dropped from P to the line through O and Q. Then vector $\mathbf{C} = \overrightarrow{OR}$ is called the **vector projection** of **A** onto **B.** It is clear that **C** is a scalar multiple of **B:** $\mathbf{C} = s\mathbf{B}$. Also, s has the same sign as $\cos \theta$ and $|\mathbf{C}| = \left||\mathbf{A}| \cos \theta\right|$. Thus, formula (1) of section 2 yields

$$s|\mathbf{B}| = |\mathbf{A}| \cos \theta = (\mathbf{A} \cdot \mathbf{B})/|\mathbf{B}|$$

and so the vector projection of **A** onto **B** is given by

$$\text{proj}_{\mathbf{B}}\mathbf{A} = \mathbf{C} = \left(\frac{\mathbf{A} \cdot \mathbf{B}}{|\mathbf{B}|^2}\right)\mathbf{B} = (\mathbf{A} \cdot \mathbf{U})\mathbf{U}$$

where $\mathbf{U} = (1/|\mathbf{B}|)\mathbf{B}$. This vector **U** is in the same direction as **B** and satisfies $|\mathbf{U}| = (1/|\mathbf{B}|)|\mathbf{B}| = 1$. Any vector of length 1 is called a **unit vector.** The number

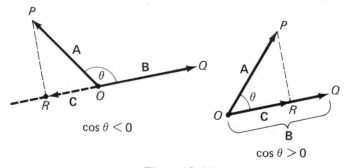

$$\cos \theta < 0$$

$$\cos \theta > 0$$

Figure 12-11

$$\boxed{\text{comp}_B A = (A \cdot B)/|B| = A \cdot U}$$

is called the **component of A in the direction B** (or the **scalar projection** of A onto B). It gives the directed distance along B to the terminal end of C.

EXAMPLE   Find the vector and scalar projections of $A = \langle -2,1 \rangle$ onto $B = \langle 2,3 \rangle$.

Solution   We have

$$A \cdot B = (-2)(2) + 1 \cdot 3 = -1$$

and

$$|B|^2 = 2^2 + 3^2 = 13$$

so that

$$\text{comp}_B A = -1/\sqrt{13}$$
$$\text{proj}_B A = (-1/13)B = \langle -2/13, -3/13 \rangle$$

Two vectors are said to be **parallel** if their representations lie along parallel lines, that is, one is a scalar multiple of the other. If the two vectors are nonzero and θ is the angle between them, then they are parallel if and only if $\theta = 0$ or $\theta = \pi$. Thus A is parallel to B if and only if $|A \cdot B| = |A| \cdot |B|$. Notice that every vector is parallel to the zero vector.

The principal representations of two nonzero vectors form a right angle if and only if the cosine of the angle between them is 0. In view of formula (1) of section 2, we say that two vectors A and B are **orthogonal** (or **perpendicular**) if $A \cdot B = 0$. Notice that the zero vector is orthogonal to every vector.

EXAMPLE   Find c so that $\langle c - 1, c + 2 \rangle$ is orthogonal to $\langle 2c, -1 \rangle$.

Solution   We need

$$0 = 2c(c - 1) - (c + 2) = 2c^2 - 3c - 2$$
$$= (2c + 1)(c - 2)$$

So there are two solutions: $c = -1/2$ and $c = 2$.

If $A = \langle x_0, y_0 \rangle$ is a given nonzero vector, then there are two unit vectors U and V that are orthogonal to A (see Fig. 12-12), namely,

$$\mathbf{U} = \langle -y_0/a, x_0/a \rangle \quad \text{and} \quad \mathbf{V} = -\mathbf{U} = \langle y_0/a, -x_0/a \rangle$$

where $a = \sqrt{x_0^2 + y_0^2} = |\mathbf{A}|$. In fact,

$$\mathbf{A} \cdot \mathbf{U} = x_0(-y_0/a) + y_0(x_0/a)$$
$$= (-x_0 y_0 + x_0 y_0)/a = 0$$

and $\mathbf{A} \cdot \mathbf{V} = -(\mathbf{A} \cdot \mathbf{U}) = 0$. Also,

$$|\mathbf{V}| = |\mathbf{U}| = [(-y_0/a)^2 + (x_0/a)^2]^{1/2} = [(y_0^2 + x_0^2)/a^2]^{1/2} = 1$$

EXAMPLE Find two unit vectors that are orthogonal to $\mathbf{A} = \langle -7,1 \rangle$.

Solution We have $a = |\mathbf{A}| = \sqrt{50} = 5\sqrt{2}$ and so we take $\mathbf{U} = \langle -1/(5\sqrt{2}), -7/(5\sqrt{2}) \rangle = (-\sqrt{2}/10)\,\langle 1,7 \rangle$ and $\mathbf{V} = -\mathbf{U} = (\sqrt{2}/10)\,\langle 1,7 \rangle$.

The above ideas can be used to find the (perpendicular) distance between a given point and a given line. The technique is adequately explained by an example.

EXAMPLE Find the distance d between the point $P = (4,2)$ and the line $3x - 2y = 1$.

Solution Choose any two distinct points Q and R on the given line, say, $Q = (1,1)$ and $R = (3,4)$. Let $\mathbf{A} = \overrightarrow{QP} = \langle 3,1 \rangle$, $\mathbf{B} = \overrightarrow{QR} = \langle 2,3 \rangle$, and let $\mathbf{C}$ be any nonzero vector orthogonal to $\mathbf{B}$. For instance, $\mathbf{C} = \langle 3,-2 \rangle$ (see Fig. 12-13). Then

$$d = |\operatorname{comp}_{\mathbf{C}}\mathbf{A}| = |\mathbf{A} \cdot \mathbf{C}|/|\mathbf{C}| = 7/\sqrt{13} = (7/13)\,\sqrt{13}$$

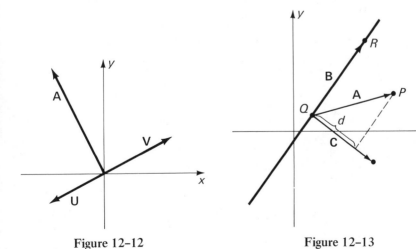

Figure 12–12   Figure 12–13

Suppose that $\mathbf{U} = \langle u_1, u_2 \rangle$ and $\mathbf{V} = \langle v_1, v_2 \rangle$ are orthogonal unit vectors. Given $\mathbf{A} = \langle a_1, a_2 \rangle$, we wish to find scalars x and y such that $x\mathbf{U} + y\mathbf{V} = \mathbf{A}$. Looking at the first and second components of both sides, our problem is to solve the system

$$\begin{cases} u_1 x + v_1 y = a_1 \\ u_2 x + v_2 y = a_2 \end{cases}$$

If we multiply the first equation by u_1 and the second by u_2 and then add the resulting equations, we obtain

$$\begin{aligned} x &= |\mathbf{U}|^2 x + (\mathbf{U} \cdot \mathbf{V})y \\ &= (u_1^2 + u_2^2)x + (u_1 v_1 + u_2 v_2)y \\ &= u_1 a_1 + u_2 a_2 = \mathbf{A} \cdot \mathbf{U} \end{aligned}$$

Similarly $y = \mathbf{A} \cdot \mathbf{V}$. Thus our problem has the unique solution

$$\boxed{\mathbf{A} = (\mathbf{A} \cdot \mathbf{U})\mathbf{U} + (\mathbf{A} \cdot \mathbf{V})\mathbf{V}}$$

expressing $\mathbf{A}$ as a linear combination of $\mathbf{U}$ and $\mathbf{V}$.

A special case of the above is the pair $\mathbf{i} = \langle 1,0 \rangle$ and $\mathbf{j} = \langle 0,1 \rangle$ of orthogonal unit vectors. If $\mathbf{A} = \langle a_1, a_2 \rangle$, then $\mathbf{A} \cdot \mathbf{i} = a_1$ and $\mathbf{A} \cdot \mathbf{j} = a_2$. Thus the above representation of $\mathbf{A}$ becomes the obvious equality

$$\boxed{\mathbf{A} = a_1 \mathbf{i} + a_2 \mathbf{j}}$$

In many books vectors are always expressed in this way. (The vector $\mathbf{i}$ should not be confused with $\sqrt{-1}$.)

EXAMPLE   Find orthogonal unit vectors $\mathbf{U}$ and $\mathbf{V}$ in the directions of $\mathbf{B} = \langle -3,4 \rangle$ and $\mathbf{C} = \langle 4,3 \rangle$, respectively, and then express $\mathbf{A} = \langle 5,1 \rangle$ as a linear combination of $\mathbf{U}$ and $\mathbf{V}$.

Solution   Since $\mathbf{B} \cdot \mathbf{C} = 0$, this is possible. Simply take

$$\mathbf{U} = (1/|\mathbf{B}|)\mathbf{B} = (1/5)\,\langle -3,4 \rangle = \langle -3/5, 4/5 \rangle$$

and

$$\mathbf{V} = \mathbf{C}/|\mathbf{C}| = (1/5)\,\langle 4,3 \rangle = \langle 4/5, 3/5 \rangle$$

Since

$$\mathbf{A} \cdot \mathbf{U} = \langle 5,1 \rangle \cdot \langle -3/5, 4/5 \rangle = -11/5$$

and

$$\mathbf{A} \cdot \mathbf{V} = \langle 5,1 \rangle \cdot \langle 4/5, 3/5 \rangle = 23/5$$

we have $\mathbf{A} = (-11/5)\mathbf{U} + (23/5)\mathbf{V}$.

E X E R C I S E S

In 1–6, find the component of **A** in the direction of **B** and find the vector projection of **A** onto **B**.

1. $\mathbf{A} = \langle -7,1 \rangle$, $\mathbf{B} = \langle 3,4 \rangle$ **4.** $\mathbf{A} = \langle 2,0 \rangle$, $\mathbf{B} = \langle -1,1 \rangle$
2. $\mathbf{A} = \langle 7,-1 \rangle$, $\mathbf{B} = \langle 3,4 \rangle$ **5.** $\mathbf{A} = \langle 0,5 \rangle$, $\mathbf{B} = \langle 1,1 \rangle$
3. $\mathbf{A} = \langle 10,5 \rangle$, $\mathbf{B} = \langle 12,5 \rangle$ **6.** $\mathbf{A} = \langle 1,0 \rangle$, $\mathbf{B} = \langle 2,3 \rangle$

In 7–10, find the distance between the given point and the given line.

7. $(2,0)$, $2x + 3y = 6$ **9.** $(0,0)$, $4x + 5y + 8 = 0$
8. $(-4,-2)$, $2x + y = 1$ **10.** $(2,3)$, $4x + y + 1 = 0$

In 11–16, find a unit vector whose first component is positive that is orthogonal to the given vector.

11. $\langle 0,0 \rangle$ **13.** $6\mathbf{i} + \mathbf{j}$ **15.** $-12\mathbf{i} + 5\mathbf{j}$
12. $\langle -1,1 \rangle$ **14.** $-4\mathbf{i} - 3\mathbf{j}$ **16.** $-15\mathbf{i} + 8\mathbf{j}$

In 17–20, find orthogonal unit vectors **U** and **V** in the directions of **B** and **C**, respectively, and then express **A** as a linear combination of **U** and **V**.

17. $\mathbf{A} = \langle 20,17 \rangle$, $\mathbf{B} = \langle 15,8 \rangle$, $\mathbf{C} = \langle -8,15 \rangle$
18. $\mathbf{A} = \langle -2,5 \rangle$, $\mathbf{B} = \langle -3,-1 \rangle$, $\mathbf{C} = \langle -1,3 \rangle$
19. $\mathbf{A} = \langle 1,1 \rangle$, $\mathbf{B} = \langle 2,4 \rangle$, $\mathbf{C} = \langle -3,2 \rangle$
20. $\mathbf{A} = \langle 5,3 \rangle$, $\mathbf{B} = \langle -12,5 \rangle$, $\mathbf{C} = \langle 5,12 \rangle$

In 21–24, find the scalar c so that **A** and **B** are (a) parallel and (b) orthogonal.

21. $\mathbf{A} = \langle 6,c \rangle$, $\mathbf{B} = \langle 2c,12 \rangle$ **23.** $\mathbf{A} = \langle 2c - 1,c \rangle$, $\mathbf{B} = \langle 6,-6 \rangle$
22. $\mathbf{A} = \langle c,-2 \rangle$, $\mathbf{B} = \langle 1,-c \rangle$ **24.** $\mathbf{A} = \langle 2c - 1,-2 \rangle$, $\mathbf{B} = \langle c - 2,6 \rangle$

25. Prove the **Pythagorean Theorem:** The vectors **A** and **B** are orthogonal if and only if $|\mathbf{A} - \mathbf{B}|^2 = |\mathbf{A}|^2 + |\mathbf{B}|^2$.

4 Vector-valued Functions and Parametric Equations

Let f and g be real-valued functions of a real variable t. Each number t at which both f and g are defined determines a vector

$$\mathbf{R}(t) = \langle f(t),g(t) \rangle$$

The function **R** thereby defined is called a **vector-valued function.** The vector $\mathbf{R}(t)$ determines a **position** in the plane, namely, the terminal point $(x,y) = (f(t),g(t))$ of the principal representation of $\mathbf{R}(t)$. The set of all such positions of $\mathbf{R}(t)$, as t varies through those values for which both f and g are defined, is called the **path** (or **trace**) of $\mathbf{R}$. Such a path can be described also by the set of **parametric equations**

$$\begin{cases} x = f(t) \\ y = g(t) \end{cases}$$

as discussed previously in this book. In graphing, the **parameter** t does not appear as an axis in the plane. It is a third variable which is used only to determine the paired values of x and y. In physical applications the parameter t is often used to denote time while $\mathbf{R}(t)$ determines the position of a particle in the plane at time t. We are frequently interested only in those values of the parameter in some interval on which both f and g are continuous. Thus, the **path** (or **curve**, or **arc**)

$$\mathbf{R}(t) \qquad a \leqq t \leqq b$$

or

$$\begin{cases} x = f(t) \\ y = g(t) \end{cases} \qquad a \leqq t \leqq b$$

has as a graph the set of all points $(f(t),g(t))$ for $a \leqq t \leqq b$. The point $(f(a),g(a))$ is the **initial point** and the point $(f(b),g(b))$ is the **terminal point** of this path. In order to sketch (the graph of) a path it is often useful to eliminate the parameter first.

EXAMPLE Sketch the paths, marking the initial and terminal points of each: (a) $\mathbf{R}(t) = \langle t^3, t^2 \rangle$, $-1 \leqq t \leqq 2$, and (b) $\mathbf{R}(t) = \langle 2 \cos t, 4 \sin t \rangle$, $-\pi/2 \leqq t \leqq 3\pi/4$.

Solution (a) Writing $x = t^3$ and $y = t^2$, we see that $x^2 = t^6 = y^3$ and that x varies from $x = -1$ to $x = 8$ as t varies from -1 to 2. The required path is the graph of $y^3 = x^2$ (or, equivalently, $y = x^{2/3}$) for $-1 \leqq x \leqq 8$ (see Fig. 12-14). The initial point is $(-1,1)$ and the terminal point is $(8,4)$.

(b) Taking advantage of the identity $\cos^2 t + \sin^2 t = 1$, we see that our path has the equation

$$\frac{x^2}{4} + \frac{y^2}{16} = 1$$

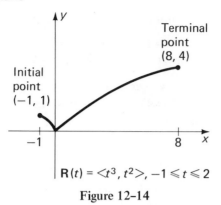

Figure 12-14

Moreover, t is the angle that the principal representation of $\mathbf{R}(t)$ makes with the positive x-axis. Thus, the required path is that portion of the above ellipse corresponding to those angles from $-\pi/2$ to $3\pi/4$ (see Fig. 12-15).

Occasionally the formulas $x = r \cos \theta$ and $y = r \sin \theta$ for transforming from polar coordinates to rectangular coordinates may be useful in determining the shape of a graph that is given by a vector equation or by parametric equations.

EXAMPLE   Draw a graph of the vector equation

$$\mathbf{R}(t) = \langle 2 \cos^2 t - \cos t, \sin 2t - \sin t \rangle$$

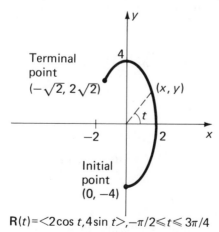

Figure 12-15

Solution   The corresponding parametric equations are

$$\begin{cases} x = (2 \cos t - 1) \cos t \\ y = \sin 2t - \sin t = (2 \cos t - 1) \sin t \end{cases}$$

and so if we write $\theta = t$, we see that the desired graph is the graph of the polar equation $r = 2 \cos \theta - 1$, which is shown in Fig. 12-16. This graph is called a **limaçon**.

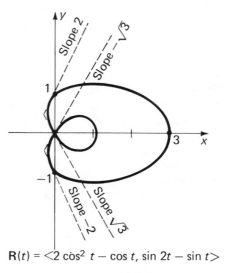

$R(t) = \langle 2 \cos^2 t - \cos t, \sin 2t - \sin t \rangle$

Figure 12–16

The slope of the tangent line to a curve given by parametric equations can be found by use of the Chain Rule. In fact,

$$\frac{dy}{dt} = \frac{dy}{dx} \cdot \frac{dx}{dt}$$

so that

$$\frac{dy}{dx} = \frac{dy}{dt} \bigg/ \frac{dx}{dt} \qquad \text{if } \frac{dx}{dt} \neq 0$$

The tangent line is vertical if $dx/dt = 0$ while $dy/dt \neq 0$.

EXAMPLE   Find the slopes of the tangent lines to the curve in the preceding example (Fig. 12-16) at those points where the curve crosses the y-axis.

Solution The curve is traced exactly once as t increases from 0 to 2π. We are interested in those values of t in $[0,2\pi]$ for which $0 = x = (2 \cos t - 1) \cos t$. These values of t are $\pi/3$, $5\pi/3$, $\pi/2$, and $3\pi/2$. We have

$$\frac{dy}{dx} = \frac{2 \cos 2t - \cos t}{-4 \cos t \sin t + \sin t}$$

and so the slopes are

$$\left.\frac{dy}{dx}\right|_{t=\pi/3} = \frac{2(-1/2) - 1/2}{-4(1/2)(\sqrt{3}/2) + \sqrt{3}/2} = \sqrt{3}$$

$$\left.\frac{dy}{dx}\right|_{t=5\pi/3} = \frac{2(-1/2) - 1/2}{-4(1/2)(-\sqrt{3}/2) - \sqrt{3}/2} = -\sqrt{3}$$

$$\left.\frac{dy}{dx}\right|_{t=\pi/2} = \frac{2(-1) - 0}{-4 \cdot 0 \cdot 1 + 1} = -2$$

$$\left.\frac{dy}{dt}\right|_{t=3\pi/2} = \frac{2(-1) - 0}{-4 \cdot 0 \cdot (-1) - 1} = 2$$

EXAMPLE Let $x = te^t$ and $y = t \ln t$ for $t > 0$. Find the first and second derivatives y' and y'' of y with respect to x as functions of the parameter t.

Solution Since $dy/dt = 1 + \ln t$ and $dx/dt = (t + 1)e^t$, we have

$$y' = \frac{dy}{dt} \Big/ \frac{dx}{dt} = \frac{1 + \ln t}{(t + 1)e^t}$$

Next, we find that

$$\frac{d(y')}{dt} = \frac{(1 + t)e^t(1/t) - (1 + \ln t)[(t + 2)e^t]}{(t + 1)^2 e^{2t}}$$

$$= \frac{1 - t - t^2 - (t^2 + 2t) \ln t}{t(1 + t)^2 e^t}$$

so that

$$y'' = \frac{d(y')}{dx} = \frac{d(y')}{dt} \Big/ \frac{dx}{dt}$$

$$= \frac{1 - t - t^2 - (t^2 + 2t) \ln t}{t(1 + t)^3 e^{2t}}$$

EXERCISES

In 1–14, sketch the given paths in the xy-plane and find an equation in x and y that has this path as its graph.

1. $\mathbf{R}(t) = \langle t + 2, 3t - 1 \rangle$ 5. $\mathbf{R}(t) = \langle t^{-1}, t^{-2} \rangle$
2. $\mathbf{R}(t) = \langle 2t + 3, 3t - 2 \rangle$ 6. $\mathbf{R}(t) = \langle (t + 1)^2, (t + 1)^{-2} \rangle$
3. $\mathbf{R}(t) = \langle t - 1, t^2 + 1 \rangle$ 7. $\mathbf{R}(t) = \langle t + t^{-1}, t - t^{-1} \rangle$
4. $\mathbf{R}(t) = \langle t^2, t + 1 \rangle$ 8. $\mathbf{R}(t) = \langle 2e^t, e^{-t} \rangle$

9. $\mathbf{R}(t) = \langle \sin t, \sin t \rangle$ $\left(0 \leqq t \leqq \dfrac{\pi}{2} \right)$

10. $\mathbf{R}(t) = \langle a \cos t, a \sin t \rangle$ $(a > 0)$
11. $\mathbf{R}(t) = \langle \cos^3 t, \sin^3 t \rangle$
12. $\mathbf{R}(t) = \langle \cos^2 t, \sin^2 t \rangle$
13. $\mathbf{R}(t) = \langle \cos^3 t, \cos^2 t \sin t \rangle$
14. $\mathbf{R}(t) = \langle 2 \cos t, 3 \sin t \rangle$

In 15–20, find the first and second derivatives y' and y'' of y with respect to x as functions of t.

15. $x = t^3$, $y = t^2$ 18. $x = t^{-1}$, $y = \sin t$
16. $x = 2t^2$, $y = t + 1$ 19. $x = e^t + e^{-t}$, $y = e^t - e^{-t}$
17. $x = t^2$, $y = 2t^3 - t^2$ 20. $x = t^2 + 1$, $y = \text{Tan}^{-1} t$

21. Show that the curve having parametric equations

$$x = t - \frac{e^t - e^{-t}}{e^t + e^{-t}} \qquad y = \frac{2}{e^t + e^{-t}}$$

has the property that, for each of its tangent lines, the distance between the point of tangency and the point where the tangent line meets the x-axis is 1.

5 Motion in the Plane

In this section we suppose that a particle is moving in the plane in such a way that its position at time t is given by a vector function $\mathbf{R}(t) = \langle f(t), g(t) \rangle$, where f and g are twice differentiable functions of the parameter t. That is, at time t the particle is located at the point $(x, y) = (f(t), g(t))$. As done earlier in this book, we shall denote derivatives with respect to time t by dots. Thus

$$\dot{x} = \frac{dx}{dt} = f'(t) \qquad \dot{y} = \frac{dy}{dt} = g'(t)$$

$$\ddot{x} = \frac{d^2x}{dt^2} = f''(t) \qquad \ddot{y} = \frac{d^2y}{dt^2} = g''(t)$$

We define the **velocity** of the particle at time t to be the vector

$$\mathbf{V}(t) = \dot{\mathbf{R}}(t) = \langle \dot{x}(t), \dot{y}(t) \rangle = \langle f'(t), g'(t) \rangle$$

and the **acceleration** of the particle at time t to be the vector

$$\mathbf{A}(t) = \dot{\mathbf{V}}(t) = \ddot{\mathbf{R}}(t) = \langle \ddot{x}(t), \ddot{y}(t) \rangle = \langle f''(t), g''(t) \rangle$$

Thus, $\mathbf{V}(t)$ is the rate of change of position with respect to time, while $\mathbf{A}(t)$ is the rate of change of velocity with respect to t. The magnitude (or length) of the velocity $\mathbf{V}(t)$ is called the **speed** of the particle at time t and we denote it by

$$v(t) = |\mathbf{V}(t)| = \sqrt{[\dot{x}(t)]^2 + [\dot{y}(t)]^2}$$

The slope of (any representation of) the velocity vector is $\dot{y}/\dot{x} = dy/dx$ if $\dot{x} \neq 0$, while it is vertical if $\dot{x} = 0$ and $\dot{y} \neq 0$. Thus the direction of $\mathbf{V}(t)$ is parallel to the tangent line to the path of motion at the position $\mathbf{R}(t)$. In Fig. 12-17 the path of motion and the representations of the velocity vectors $\mathbf{V}(t_j)$ having initial points at the positions $\mathbf{R}(t_j)$ for three times t_1, t_2, and t_3 are shown. Notice that the velocity vector indicates the general direction of motion along the path. For example, in Fig. 12-17, $\dot{x}(t_3) < 0$ and $\dot{y}(t_3) > 0$ so that the x-coordinate of the particle is decreasing and the y-coordinate is increasing as the particle passes the position $\mathbf{R}(t_3)$.

EXAMPLE The position of a particle is given by $\mathbf{R}(t) = \langle t^2 + 1, 2t - 1 \rangle$ at time t. Find $\mathbf{V}(t)$, $\mathbf{A}(t)$, and $v(t)$. Sketch the path of the particle, showing the representations of $\mathbf{V}(2)$ and $\mathbf{A}(2)$ having initial points at the position $\mathbf{R}(2)$.

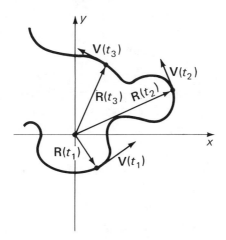

Figure 12–17

Solution   Writing $x = t^2 + 1$ and $y = 2t - 1$, we see that $t = (y + 1)/2$
and so $x = \dfrac{(y + 1)^2}{4} + 1$ and hence the path is the parabola having
equation

$$x - 1 = \frac{1}{4}(y + 1)^2$$

which is shown in Fig. 12-18. We have $\mathbf{V}(t) = \langle 2t, 2 \rangle$, $\mathbf{A}(t) = \langle 2, 0 \rangle$, and
$v(t) = \sqrt{4t^2 + 4} = 2\sqrt{t^2 + 1}$. In particular, $\mathbf{V}(2) = \langle 4, 2 \rangle$, $\mathbf{A}(2) = \langle 2, 0 \rangle$,
and $\mathbf{R}(2) = \langle 5, 3 \rangle$.

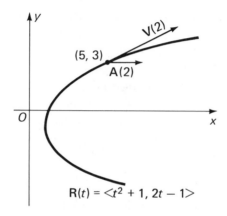

Figure 12–18

EXAMPLE   The position of a particle is given by $\mathbf{R}(t) = \langle \sin t, \cos 2t \rangle$ at time t. Find the earliest time $t_0 > 0$ at which the particle attains its maximum speed. Sketch the path of the particle showing $\mathbf{V}(t_0)$ and $\mathbf{A}(t_0)$. What happens to the particle when $t = \pi/2$?

Solution   We have $x = \sin t$ and $y = \cos 2t = 1 - 2\sin^2 t = 1 - 2x^2$.
Thus, the path is on the parabola $y = 1 - 2x^2$, but notice that $-1 \leq x = \sin t \leq 1$ and $-1 \leq y \leq 1$. The path is shown in Fig. 12-19. We have
$\mathbf{V}(t) = \langle \cos t, -2 \sin 2t \rangle$, $\mathbf{A}(t) = \langle -\sin t, -4 \cos 2t \rangle$, and

$$\begin{aligned}
[v(t)]^2 &= \cos^2 t + 4 \sin^2 2t \\
&= \cos^2 t + 4(2 \sin t \cos t)^2 \\
&= \cos^2 t + 16(\cos^2 t)(1 - \cos^2 t) \\
&= 17 \cos^2 t - 16 \cos^4 t
\end{aligned}$$

Since the function $f(u) = 17u - 16u^2$ attains its (absolute) maximum
value when $u = 17/32$, we see that v^2 (and therefore also v) is largest

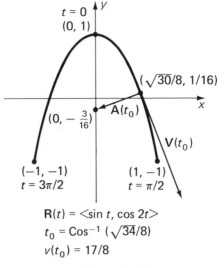

$$R(t) = \langle \sin t, \cos 2t \rangle$$
$$t_0 = \text{Cos}^{-1}\,(\sqrt{34}/8)$$
$$v(t_0) = 17/8$$

Figure 12–19

when $\cos^2 t = 17/32$. Thus $0 < t_0 < \pi/2$ and $\cos t_0 = \sqrt{34}/8$. We have

$$\sin^2 t_0 = 15/32$$
$$\cos 2t_0 = 1 - 2\sin^2 t_0 = 1/16$$
$$\sin 2t_0 = \sqrt{1 - \cos^2 2t_0} = \sqrt{255}/16$$

so that $R(t_0) = \langle \sqrt{30}/8, 1/16 \rangle$, $V(t_0) = \langle \sqrt{34}/8, -\sqrt{255}/8 \rangle$, and $A(t_0) = \langle -\sqrt{30}/8, -1/4 \rangle$ (see Fig. 12-19). When $t = \pi/2$ (or any odd multiple of $\pi/2$), the particle stops moving instantaneously and reverses its direction along the path.

EXAMPLE   Find the position vector $R(t)$ if the acceleration vector is $A(t) = \langle -\cos t, -2t(1 + t^2)^{-2} \rangle$ and $V(0) = \langle 0,1 \rangle$ and $R(0) = \langle 1,0 \rangle$.

Solution   Our problem is to find the functions x and y, where

$$\ddot{x}(t) = -\cos t \qquad\qquad \dot{x}(0) = 0,\ x(0) = 1$$
$$\ddot{y}(t) = -2t(1 + t^2)^{-2} \qquad \dot{y}(0) = 1,\ y(0) = 0$$

Integration with respect to t yields

$$\dot{x}(t) = -\sin t + C_1$$
$$x(t) = \cos t + C_1 t + C_2$$
$$\dot{y}(t) = (1 + t^2)^{-1} + C_3$$

and

$$y(t) = \text{Tan}^{-1} t + C_3 t + C_4$$

We substitute $t = 0$ to obtain $C_1 = \dot{x}(0) = 0$, $C_2 + 1 = x(0) = 1$, $1 + C_3 = \dot{y}(0) = 1$, and $C_4 = y(0) = 0$ so that $x(t) = \cos t$ and $y(t) = \text{Tan}^{-1} t$. Therefore, $\mathbf{R}(t) = \langle x(t), y(t) \rangle = \langle \cos t, \text{Tan}^{-1} t \rangle$.

EXERCISES

In 1–10, sketch the path of the particle having the given position vector $\mathbf{R}(t)$ and show the representations of the vectors $\mathbf{V}(t_0)$ and $\mathbf{A}(t_0)$ having initial points at $\mathbf{R}(t_0)$ for the given time t_0.

1. $\mathbf{R}(t) = \langle t^3, t^2 \rangle$, $t_0 = 1$
2. $\mathbf{R}(t) = \langle 3 \cos t, \sin t \rangle$, $t_0 = \pi/4$
3. $\mathbf{R}(t) = \langle t - 1, 2t^2 + 3 \rangle$, $t_0 = 1$
4. $\mathbf{R}(t) = \langle -2/t, t/4 \rangle$, $t_0 = 4$
5. $\mathbf{R}(t) = \langle \ln \sec t, t \rangle$, $t_0 = \pi/4$
6. $\mathbf{R}(t) = \langle \tan t, \sin t \rangle$, $t_0 = \pi/6$
7. $\mathbf{R}(t) = \langle e^{3t}, e^{2t} \rangle$, $t_0 = 0$
8. $\mathbf{R}(t) = \langle e^{2t}, e^{-t} \rangle$, $t_0 = \ln 2$
9. $\mathbf{R}(t) = \langle 1 - \sin t, 1 - \cos t \rangle$, $t_0 = \pi/3$
10. $\mathbf{R}(t) = \langle t^2 + 3t, 3t^2 - 1 \rangle$, $t_0 = \dfrac{1}{2}$

In 11–16, find the earliest time $t_0 \geq 0$ at which the particle having position vector $\mathbf{R}(t)$ attains a maximum speed. Also find $v(t_0)$, $\mathbf{V}(t_0)$, and $\mathbf{A}(t_0)$.

11. $\mathbf{R}(t) = \langle 2 \cos t, 3 \sin t \rangle$
12. $\mathbf{R}(t) = \langle 3 \sin t, 4 \cos t \rangle$
13. $\mathbf{R}(t) = \langle 2 \cos 2t, \sin t \rangle$
14. $\mathbf{R}(t) = \langle 2 \cos t, \sin 2t \rangle$
15. $\mathbf{R}(t) = \langle (t^2 + 1)^{-1}, t \rangle$
16. $\mathbf{R}(t) = \langle t, t^2(2 \ln t - 1) \rangle$

In 17–20, find $\mathbf{R}(t)$.

17. $\mathbf{V}(t) = \langle t^2 + 1, t^{-2} \rangle$, $\mathbf{R}(1) = \langle 2, 0 \rangle$
18. $\mathbf{V}(t) = \langle e^t, 1/(1 + t) \rangle$, $\mathbf{R}(0) = \langle 3, 1 \rangle$
19. $\mathbf{A}(t) = \langle 6t, t^{-2} \rangle$, $\mathbf{R}(1) = \langle 0, 0 \rangle$, $\mathbf{V}(1) = \langle 4, -1 \rangle$
20. $\mathbf{A}(t) = \langle \sec^2 t, 12t^2 \rangle$, $\mathbf{R}(0) = \langle 0, 2 \rangle$, $\mathbf{V}(0) = \langle 0, -1 \rangle$

Appendix A
Some Difficult Theorems

THE MORE DIFFICULT THEOREMS that were used but not proved in the main text are proved in this appendix. The reader will find little here in the way of discussion, motivation, or examples. We simply set down the needed definitions, theorems, and proofs. The index should be consulted for definitions not given here.

Limit Theorem Let $a < b$ be extended real numbers and let f_1 and f_2 be real-valued functions that are defined on $]a,b[$ and satisfy

$$\lim_{x \to a^+} f_1(x) = L_1 \qquad \text{and} \qquad \lim_{x \to a^+} f_2(x) = L_2$$

where L_1 and L_2 are real numbers (not ∞ or $-\infty$). Suppose also that n is a given positive integer. Then we have

(i) $\lim_{x \to a^+} [f_1(x) + f_2(x)] = L_1 + L_2$

(ii) $\lim_{x \to a^+} [f_1(x) - f_2(x)] = L_1 - L_2$

(iii) $\lim_{x \to a^+} [f_1(x) f_2(x)] = L_1 L_2$

(iv) $\lim_{x \to a^+} [f_1(x)/f_2(x)] = L_1/L_2 \qquad$ if $L_2 \neq 0$

(v) $\lim_{x \to a^+} [f_1(x)]^n = L_1^n$

(vi) $\lim_{x \to a^+} [f_1(x)]^{1/n} = L_1^{1/n}$

provided, in the case that n is even, that

$$f_1(x) \geq 0 \qquad \text{for } x \text{ in }]a,b[$$

This theorem remains true if $x \to a^+$ is replaced by $x \to b^-$ throughout its statement.

Proof Let $\epsilon > 0$ be given. Choose any number η that satisfies $0 < \eta < 1$, $2\eta < \epsilon$, and $(|L_1| + |L_2| + 1)\eta < \epsilon$. In case $L_2 \neq 0$, we also require that $2\eta < |L_2|^2 \epsilon$ and $2\eta < |L_2|$. The hypotheses assure us that for $j = 1$ and $j = 2$ there exists a number c_j in $]a,b[$ such that $|f_j(x) - L_j| < \eta$ whenever $a < x < c_j$. Let c be the smaller of the two numbers c_1 and c_2. Now let x be any number for which $a < x < c$. Since $a < x < c_1$ and $a < x < c_2$, we have

$$|[f_1(x) + f_2(x)] - [L_1 + L_2]| = |[f_1(x) - L_1] + [f_2(x) - L_2]|$$
$$\leq |f_1(x) - L_1| + |f_2(x) - L_2| < \eta + \eta < \epsilon$$

$$|[f_1(x) - f_2(x)] - [L_1 - L_2]| = |[f_1(x) - L_1] + [L_2 - f_2(x)]|$$
$$\leq |f_1(x) - L_1| + |L_2 - f_2(x)| < \eta + \eta < \epsilon$$

$$|f_2(x)| = |[f_2(x) - L_2] + L_2|$$
$$\leq |f_2(x) - L_2| + |L_2| < \eta + |L_2|$$
$$< 1 + |L_2|$$

and

$$|[f_1(x)f_2(x)] - L_1 L_2| = |[f_1(x) - L_1]f_2(x) + L_1[f_2(x) - L_2]|$$
$$\leq |f_1(x) - L_1| \cdot |f_2(x)| + |L_1| \cdot |f_2(x) - L_2|$$
$$< \eta \cdot (1 + |L_2|) + |L_1| \cdot \eta$$
$$= (|L_1| + |L_2| + 1)\eta < \epsilon$$

This proves (i), (ii), and (iii).

Supposing that $L_2 \neq 0$ and $a < x < c$, we have

$$|f_2(x)| \geq |L_2| - |f_2(x) - L_2|$$
$$> |L_2| - \eta > |L_2|/2$$

and so

$$\left| \frac{1}{f_2(x)} - \frac{1}{L_2} \right| = \left| \frac{L_2 - f_2(x)}{f_2(x)L_2} \right|$$
$$= \frac{|L_2 - f_2(x)|}{|f_2(x)| \cdot |L_2|} < \frac{\eta}{|L_2|^2/2} < \epsilon$$

which proves that

$$\lim_{x \to a^+} \frac{1}{f_2(x)} = \frac{1}{L_2}$$

This result combined with (iii) shows that if $L_2 \neq 0$, then

$$\lim_{x \to a^+} [f_1(x)/f_2(x)] = \left(\lim_{x \to a^+} f_1(x)\right)\left(\lim_{x \to a^+} \frac{1}{f_2(x)}\right)$$

$$= L_1 \cdot \frac{1}{L_2} = L_1/L_2$$

Thus (iv) obtains.

Notice that (v) is obvious if $n = 1$. Suppose that $k \geqq 1$ is some integer such that (v) holds when $n = k$.

By the use of (iii) it follows that

$$\lim_{x \to a^+} [f_1(x)]^{k+1} = \lim_{x \to a^+} [f_1(x)][f_1(x)]^k$$

$$= L_1 L_1{}^k = L_1{}^{k+1}$$

so that (v) also holds when $n = k + 1$.

Since we have shown that the set T of all n for which (v) obtains contains 1 and also contains $k + 1$ whenever it contains k, we see that T contains every positive integer. Thus (v) is established.

Suppose either than n is even and $L_1 > 0$ or that n is odd. Let α and β be any given real numbers for which $\alpha < L_1{}^{1/n} < \beta$ (and $\alpha \geqq 0$ if n is even). Then $\alpha^n < L_1 < \beta^n$ and so there is some c in $]a,b[$ such that $\alpha^n < f_1(x) < \beta^n$ whenever $a < x < c$. Then $\alpha < [f_1(x)]^{1/n} < \beta$ for $a < x < c$. This proves (vi) in these cases.

Finally, suppose that n is even and $L_1 = 0$. Given any $\epsilon > 0$, we can choose c in $]a,b[$ such that $0 \leqq f_1(x) < \epsilon^n$ if $a < x < c$. Then $a < x < c$ implies

$$-\epsilon < 0 \leqq [f_1(x)]^{1/n} = [f_1(x)]^{1/n} - L_1{}^{1/n} < \epsilon$$

This completes the proof of the theorem as stated. For $x \to b^-$, the proof is almost the same and so we omit it. ∎

Notice that if f_1 and f_2 are both defined in some deleted neighborhood of a real number a and if $\lim_{x \to a} f_j(x) = L_j$, where L_j is a real number ($j = 1$ and $j = 2$), then all of the conclusions of the above theorem hold good with $x \to a$ in place of $x \to a^+$. This is because limits exist and are equal to the one-sided limits if and only if the two one-sided limits both exist and are equal.

Our next three theorems concern fundamental properties that are shared by all continuous real-valued functions on closed intervals. These three theorems are important. They were each used in the main text and they are also needed to prove other useful theorems. Any proofs of these three must rely in the end on some kind of "completeness" property of the real number system [the real line has no holes (missing points) in it].

We choose to base the proofs on the Supremum Principle, which we state after some needed definitions.

▷ **Definition**   Let S be a set of real numbers. To say that b is an **upper bound** for S means that b is a real number and $x \leqq b$ for every x in S. A real number u is called a **supremum** for S if u is an upper bound for S, but no number smaller than u is an upper bound for S; that is,

(i) $x \leqq u$ for all x in S, and

(ii) for each $a < u$ there is some x in S with $a < x$.

Clearly, there can exist at most one such u. If such a u does exist, we denote it by $u = \sup S$. The supremum of S (if it exists) is also called the **least upper bound** of S because, as (ii) shows, it is less than every other upper bound.

▷ **Supremum Principle**   If S is a set of real numbers having at least one member and at least one upper bound, then the real number $\sup S$ exists.

We accept this principle here without proof. It can be proved as a theorem about the real number system once that system has been defined more precisely than it has been or will be in this book.

EXAMPLES   (a) The supremum of a set may or may not be in that set. If $A = [0,2[$ and $B = [0,2]$, then $\sup A = \sup B = 2$; note that 2 is in B, but 2 is not in A.

(b) Let S denote the set of all *rational* numbers x such that $x^2 < 2$. Then $\sup S = \sqrt{2}$, which is not in S.

▷ **Definition**   Let f be a real-valued function defined on some interval I of real numbers. We say that f is **continuous on** I if for each $\epsilon > 0$ and each c in I there exists some $\delta > 0$ (which may depend on both ϵ and c) such that

$$|f(x) - f(c)| < \epsilon$$

whenever x is in I and $|x - c| < \delta$. We say that f is **uniformly continuous on** I if for each $\epsilon > 0$ there exists some $\delta > 0$ (which depends only on ϵ) such that

$$|f(x) - f(t)| < \epsilon$$

whenever x and t are in I and $|x - t| < \delta$.

It is clear that uniform continuity on I implies continuity on I. The following theorem, which is used in Chapter 6 to prove the Existence Theorem for Integrals, shows that the converse is also true if I is closed.

▷ **Uniform Continuity Theorem** Let $a < b$ be real numbers and let f be a real-valued function that is continuous on the closed interval $[a,b]$. Then f is uniformly continuous on $[a,b]$.

Proof Assume that f *fails* to be uniformly continuous on $[a,b]$. Then there is some number $\epsilon > 0$ for which there is *no* corresponding δ as in the above definition. Thus, for each positive integer n, numbers x_n and t_n exist in $[a,b]$ such that

$$\left| x_n - t_n \right| < \frac{1}{n} \quad \text{and} \quad \left| f(x_n) - f(t_n) \right| \geq \epsilon \tag{1}$$

For each integer $k > 0$, let S_k denote the set of all x_n for which $n \geq k$. Plainly x_k is in S_k and b is an upper bound for S_k and so the number $c_k = \sup S_k$ exists in $[a,b]$. Since c_k is an upper bound for S_{k+1}, we have

$$c_{k+1} \leq c_k \quad \text{for all } k > 0 \tag{2}$$

Now let T denote the set of all t in $[a,b]$ such that $t \leq c_k$ for all $k > 0$. Then a is in T and b is an upper bound for T so that the number $c = \sup T$ exists in $[a,b]$. Since f is continuous on $[a,b]$, there is some $\delta > 0$ such that

$$\left| f(x) - f(c) \right| < \frac{\epsilon}{4} \tag{3}$$

if x is in $[a,b]$ and $|x - c| < \delta$. Now $c + \delta/2$ is not in T (because c is an upper bound for T) and so there is some k_0 with $c_{k_0} < c + \delta/2$. Choose $k_1 > k_0$ such that $k_1 > 2/\delta$. By the use of (2) and the fact that c_{k_1} is an upper bound for T, we see that

$$c \leq c_{k_1} \leq c_{k_0} < c + \delta/2 \tag{4}$$

Now $c_{k_1} - \delta/2$ is not an upper bound for S_{k_1} and so there is some $n_0 \geq k_1$ with $c_{k_1} - \delta/2 < x_{n_0} \leq c_{k_1}$. Now (4) yields

$$c - \delta/2 < x_{n_0} < c + \delta/2$$

so that $|x_{n_0} - c| < \delta/2$. Also, (1) yields

$$\left| t_{n_0} - x_{n_0} \right| < 1/n_0 \leq 1/k_1 < \delta/2$$

and so

$$|t_{n_0} - c| \leq |t_{n_0} - x_{n_0}| + |x_{n_0} - c| < \delta/2 + \delta/2 = \delta$$

We next invoke (1) and (3) to obtain

$$\epsilon \leq |f(x_{n_0}) - f(t_{n_0})| \leq |f(x_{n_0}) - f(c)| + |f(c) - f(t_{n_0})| < \epsilon/4 + \epsilon/4 = \epsilon/2$$

Thus $\epsilon < \epsilon/2$. This contradiction proves that our assumption that f is not uniformly continuous on $[a,b]$ is false. The proof is complete. ∎

We now use this theorem to prove that any continuous function on a closed interval is bounded.

▷ **Lemma** Let f be a real-valued function that is defined and continuous on some closed interval $[a,b]$. Then there exists some real number M such that $|f(x)| < M$ for every x in $[a,b]$.

Proof Since f is uniformly continuous on $[a,b]$, we can take $\epsilon = 1$ in the definition of uniform continuity to obtain $\delta > 0$ such that $|f(x) - f(t)| < 1$ whenever x and t are in $[a,b]$ and $|x-t| < \delta$. Choose an integer $N > (b-a)/\delta$, write $h = (b-a)/N$, and define $x_n = a + nh$ ($n = 0, 1, 2, \ldots, N$). We have $a = x_0 < x_1 < \ldots < x_N = b$ and $x_n - x_{n-1} = h < \delta$. Let L be the largest of the $N+1$ numbers $|f(x_n)|$ ($n = 0, 1, \ldots, N$). Let $M = L + 1$. Given any x in $[a,b]$, choose n such that $x_{n-1} \leq x \leq x_n$. Then $|x - x_n| \leq x_n - x_{n-1} < \delta$ so that

$$|f(x)| \leq |f(x) - f(x_n)| + |f(x_n)| < 1 + L = M$$

This proves the lemma. ∎

▷ **Extreme Value Theorem** Let $a < b$ be real numbers and let f be a real-valued function that is defined and continuous on $[a,b]$. Then (i) there is at least one number v in $[a,b]$ such that $f(x) \leq f(v)$ for all x in $[a,b]$, and (ii) there is at least one number u in $[a,b]$ such that $f(u) \leq f(x)$ for all x in $[a,b]$.

Proof Choose M as in the preceding lemma and let S denote the set of all y such that $y = f(x)$ for some x in $[a,b]$. Then $f(a)$ is in S and M is an upper bound for S and so the real number $y_0 = \sup S$ exists. Then $f(x) \leq y_0$ for all x in $[a,b]$. If y_0 is in S, we can choose some v in $[a,b]$ such that $f(v) = y_0$ as required in (i). Assume that y_0 is not in S. Then $y_0 > f(x)$ for x in $[a,b]$ and so the function g defined by

$$g(x) = \frac{1}{y_0 - f(x)} \qquad (a \leq x \leq b)$$

is continuous on $[a,b]$. The preceding lemma, applied to g, provides a positive real number B such that $g(x) < B$ for all x in $[a,b]$. The number $y_0 - 1/B$ is not an upper bound for S and so there is some y_1 in S (and a corresponding x_1 in $[a,b]$ with $f(x_1) = y_1$) such that $f(x_1) > y_0 - 1/B$. It follows that

$$\frac{1}{B} > y_0 - f(x_1) > 0$$

$$B < \frac{1}{y_0 - f(x_1)} = g(x_1) < B$$

This contradiction proves that y_0 must be in S so that (i) is true.

To prove (ii), apply (i) to the function $-f$ to obtain u in $[a,b]$ such that $-f(x) = (-f)(x) \leq (-f)(u) = -f(u)$ [whence $f(x) \geq f(u)$] for all x in $[a,b]$. ∎

▷ ***Intermediate Value Theorem*** Let $a < b$ be real numbers and let f be a real-valued function that is defined and continuous on $[a,b]$. Suppose that u and v are in $[a,b]$ and that y_0 is a number for which $f(u) < y_0 < f(v)$. Then there is at least one number x_0 between u and v such that $f(x_0) = y_0$.

Proof First suppose that $u < v$. Let S be the set of all x in $[u,v]$ such that $f(x) < y_0$. Then u is in S and v is an upper bound for S and so the number $x_0 = \sup S$ exists in $[u,v]$. Assume that $f(x_0) \neq y_0$. Choose any $\epsilon > 0$ such that $\epsilon < f(v) - y_0$ and $\epsilon < |f(x_0) - y_0|/2$. Since f is continuous at x_0, there is some $\delta > 0$ such that $|f(x) - f(x_0)| < \epsilon$ whenever x is in $[a,b]$ and $|x - x_0| < \delta$. Since $x_0 - \delta$ is not an upper bound for S, there is some x_1 in S such that $x_0 - \delta < x_1 \leq x_0$. It follows that

$$f(x_0) - \epsilon < f(x_1) < y_0 < f(v) - \epsilon \tag{5}$$

Now $f(x_0) < f(v)$ so that $x_0 < v$. Choose any x_2 such that $x_0 < x_2 < x_0 + \delta$ and $x_2 < v$. Then x_2 is not in S and so

$$y_0 \leq f(x_2) < f(x_0) + \epsilon \tag{6}$$

By combining (5) and (6) we get $-\epsilon < y_0 - f(x_0) < \epsilon$ and so

$$2\epsilon < |f(x_0) - y_0| < \epsilon$$

This contradiction proves the absurdity of our assumption that $f(x_0) \neq y_0$. Thus $f(x_0) = y_0$. The proof for the case that $v < u$ is very similar (start with the set S of all x in $[v,u]$ such that $f(x) > y_0$) and so we leave its details to the reader. ∎

Next we prove some theorems concerning derivatives that were used in the main text.

Recall from Chapter 3 that a function f defined on an open interval I is said to be **differentiable at a point** c in I if

$$\lim_{h \to 0} \frac{f(c + h) - f(c)}{h} = f'(c)$$

exists and is *finite*. Alternatively, we can substitute $x = c + h$ and write

$$f'(c) = \lim_{x \to c} \frac{f(x) - f(c)}{x - c}$$

We say that f is **differentiable on** I if f is differentiable at each c in I.

▷ **Rolle's Theorem**   Let $a < b$ be real numbers and let f be a real-valued function defined on $[a,b]$. Suppose that
(i) f is continuous on $[a,b]$
(ii) f is differentiable on $]a,b[$
(iii) $f(a) = f(b)$
Then there exists at least one number c such that $a < c < b$ and $f'(c) = 0$.

Proof   Case 1. Suppose that f is constant on $[a,b]$: $f(x) = f(a)$ for all x in $[a,b]$. Then $f'(x) = 0$ for all x in $]a,b[$ and so any c in $]a,b[$ satisfies our conclusion, say, $c = (a + b)/2$.

Case 2. Suppose there is some x_0 in $[a,b]$ such that $f(x_0) > f(a)$. By (i) and the Extreme Value Theorem, there exists some c in $[a,b]$ such that $f(x) \leq f(c)$ for every x in $[a,b]$. From (iii) we see that $f(c) \geq f(x_0) > f(a) = f(b)$ so that $a < c < b$. Since $f(x) - f(c) \leq 0$ for all x in $[a,b]$, the difference quotient at c satisfies

$$\frac{f(x) - f(c)}{x - c} \geq 0 \qquad \text{if } a \leq x < c$$
$$\frac{f(x) - f(c)}{x - c} \leq 0 \qquad \text{if } c < x \leq b$$

From (ii) we see that this difference quotient has a (two-sided) limit $f'(c)$ as $x \to c$. Thus

$$f'(c) = \lim_{x \to c^-} \frac{f(x) - f(c)}{x - c} \geq 0$$

and

$$f'(c) = \lim_{x \to c^+} \frac{f(x) - f(c)}{x - c} \leq 0$$

We conclude that $f'(c) = 0$.

Case 3. Suppose that $f(x) \leq f(a)$ for all x in $[a,b]$. Apply either Case 1 or Case 2 to the function $-f$ [which satisfies (i)–(iii)] to obtain c in $]a,b[$ such that $-f'(c) = (-f)'(c) = 0$. Then $f'(c) = 0$. ■

▷ **Generalized Mean Value Theorem** Let $a < b$ be real numbers and let f and g be real-valued functions defined on $[a,b]$. Suppose that

    (i) f and g are continuous on $[a,b]$

    (ii) f and g are differentiable on $]a,b[$

    (iii) $g'(x) \neq 0$ for all x in $]a,b[$

Then there exists some c such that $a < c < b$ and

$$\frac{f(b) - f(a)}{g(b) - g(a)} = \frac{f'(c)}{g'(c)}$$

Proof Define a function ϕ on $[a,b]$ by

$$\phi(x) = [f(b) - f(a)]g(x) - [g(b) - g(a)]f(x)$$

Then ϕ satisfies the three hypotheses of Rolle's Theorem:

$$\phi(a) = f(b)g(a) - g(b)f(a) = \phi(b)$$

Thus, there exists some c in $]a,b[$ such that $\phi'(c) = 0$. This implies that

$$[f(b) - f(a)]g'(c) = [g(b) - g(a)]f'(c)$$

We divide both sides of this equation by the nonzero number $[g(b) - g(a)]g'(c)$ to obtain the desired conclusion. We may do this because we must have $g(b) - g(a) \neq 0$, for otherwise we could apply Rolle's Theorem to g to obtain some d in $]a,b[$ with $g'(d) = 0$, contrary to (iii). Also, (iii) assures us that $g'(c) \neq 0$. ■

▷ **Mean Value Theorem** Let $a < b$ be real numbers and let f be a real-valued function that is defined on $[a,b]$. Suppose that

    (i) f is continuous on $[a,b]$

    (ii) f is differentiable on $]a,b[$

Then there exists some c such that $a < c < b$ and $f(b) - f(a) = f'(c)(b - a)$.

Proof Defining g on $[a,b]$ by $g(x) = x$, we see that f and g satisfy the hypotheses of the preceding theorem and so that theorem provides the required c. ■

▷ ***L'Hôpital's Rule***   Let $a < b$ be extended real numbers [possibly $a = -\infty$ or $b = \infty$] and let f and g be real-valued functions that are defined on the open interval $]a,b[$. Suppose that

(i) f and g are differentiable on $]a,b[$

(ii) $g'(x) \neq 0$ for all x in $]a,b[$

Suppose also that either

(iii) $\lim\limits_{x \to a^+} f(x) = \lim\limits_{x \to a^+} g(x) = 0$

or

(iii') $\lim\limits_{x \to a^+} g(x) = \infty$ or $-\infty$

and that

(iv) $\lim\limits_{x \to a^+} \dfrac{f'(x)}{g'(x)} = L$

where L is some extended real number (possibly $L = -\infty$ or $L = \infty$). Then

(v) $\lim\limits_{x \to a^+} \dfrac{f(x)}{g(x)} = L$

The same is true if $x \to a^+$ is replaced by $x \to b^-$ throughout.

Proof   It follows from (i) that f and g are continuous on each closed subinterval of $]a,b[$ and so the preceding six theorems all apply on any such subinterval. In view of (ii), it follows from Rolle's Theorem that g never takes the same value at two distinct points of $]a,b[$. Thus we deduce from the Intermediate Value Theorem that

$$g \text{ is strictly monotonic (increasing or decreasing) on }]a,b[\qquad (7)$$

Thus, there is at most one x in $]a,b[$ such that $g(x) = 0$ and so we can choose c_1 in $]a,b[$ such that

$$g(x) \neq 0 \qquad \text{if } a < x < c_1 \qquad (8)$$

Suppose first that $L > -\infty$. Let $\alpha < L$ be given and choose α' with $\alpha < \alpha' < L$. In view of (iv), there exists a number c_2 with $a < c_2 < c_1$ such that

$$\frac{f'(x)}{g'(x)} > \alpha' \qquad \text{if } a < x < c_2 \qquad (9)$$

For any choice of s and t with $a < s < t < c_2$, the Generalized Mean Value Theorem provides u in $]s,t[$ such that

$$\frac{f(t) - f(s)}{g(t) - g(s)} = \frac{f'(u)}{g'(u)}$$

This fact and (9) show that

$$\frac{f(t) - f(s)}{g(t) - g(s)} > \alpha' \qquad \text{if } a < s < t < c_2 \tag{10}$$

If (iii) holds, we can use (8) and let $s \to a^+$ in (10) to obtain

$$\frac{f(t)}{g(t)} \geq \alpha' > \alpha \qquad \text{if } a < t < c_2 \tag{11}$$

Suppose that (iii') holds. If $g(x) \to \infty$, it follows from (7) and (8) that $g(s) - g(t) > 0$ and $g(s) > 0$ for $a < s < t < c_1$, while if $g(x) \to -\infty$, it follows similarly that $g(s) - g(t) < 0$ and $g(s) < 0$ for $a < s < t < c_1$. In either case we can multiply inequality (10) by the *positive* number $[g(s) - g(t)]/g(s)$ and then rearrange terms to get

$$\frac{f(s)}{g(s)} \geq \frac{f(t)}{g(s)} + \left[1 - \frac{g(t)}{g(s)}\right]\alpha' \tag{12}$$

if $a < s < t < c_2$. Fixing any such t and letting $s \to a^+$, we see that the right side of (12) has limit α'. Therefore, there exists some c_3 with $a < c_3 < c_2$ such that

$$\frac{f(s)}{g(s)} > \alpha \qquad \text{if } a < s < c_3 \tag{13}$$

Under either hypothesis (iii) or (iii') we have proved, in the case that $L > -\infty$, that to each $\alpha < L$ corresponds a number c in $]a,b[$ such that

$$\frac{f(x)}{g(x)} > \alpha \qquad \text{if } a < x < c \tag{14}$$

If $L = \infty$, this completes the proof.

Suppose next that $L < \infty$. Starting with any given $\beta > L$, we argue in a way similar to the preceding paragraph to prove that there corresponds a number c' in $]a,b[$ such that

$$\frac{f(x)}{g(x)} < \beta \qquad \text{if } a < x < c' \tag{15}$$

If $L = -\infty$, this completes the proof.

In case L is finite and α and β are given numbers with $\alpha < L < \beta$, we let c and c' be as in (14) and (15) and then let c'' be the smaller of c and c' to obtain

$$\alpha < \frac{f(x)}{g(x)} < \beta \qquad \text{if } a < x < c''$$

This proves (v) for finite L.

The proof of the theorem for $x \to b^-$ is almost the same as for $x \to a^+$ and so we leave it to the reader as an exercise. ∎

We next give a proof that composites of continuous functions are continuous.

▷ **Theorem** Let f be a real-valued function defined on some interval J and let g be a function defined on an interval I such that $g(x)$ is in J whenever x is in I. Suppose that a is in I, that g is continuous at a, and that f is continuous at $g(a)$. Then the composite function $f \circ g$ defined on I by $f \circ g(x) = f[g(x)]$ is continuous at a. [Here, continuity should be interpreted as the appropriate one-sided continuity if a is an endpoint of I or $g(a)$ is an endpoint of J.]

Proof Here, neighborhoods are to be regarded as the appropriate one-sided neighborhoods if a is an endpoint of I or $g(a)$ is an endpoint of J. Let W be any neighborhood of $f \circ g(a)$. Since f is continuous at $g(a)$, there is some neighborhood V of $g(a)$ such that

$$f(y) \text{ is in } W \text{ whenever } y \text{ is in } V \qquad (16)$$

Since g is continuous at a, there is some neighborhood U of a such that

$$g(x) \text{ is in } V \text{ whenever } x \text{ is in } U \qquad (17)$$

We combine (17) and (16) and write $y = g(x)$ to conclude that if x is in U, then $g(x)$ is in V and so $f \circ g(x) = f[g(x)]$ is in W. That is, for the given W we have found U such that $f \circ g(x)$ is in W whenever x is in U. This completes the proof. ∎

▷ **The Chain Rule** Let f, J, g, and I be just as in the preceding theorem. Suppose that a is in I, that g is differentiable at a, and that f is differentiable at $g(a)$. Then the composite function $f \circ g$ is differentiable at a and

$$(f \circ g)'(a) = f'(g(a)) \cdot g'(a)$$

[Here the derivatives are to be interpreted as the appropriate one-sided derivatives if a is an endpoint of I or $g(a)$ is an endpoint of J.]

Proof Write $b = g(a)$. Define functions α and β on I and J, respectively, by

$$\alpha(x) = \frac{g(x) - g(a)}{x - a} - g'(a)$$

if x is in I with $x \neq a$, $\alpha(a) = 0$,

$$\beta(y) = \frac{f(y) - f(b)}{y - b} - f'(b)$$

if y is in J with $y \neq b$, and $\beta(b) = 0$. It follows from the very definition of derivative that

$$\lim_{x \to a} \alpha(x) = 0 = \lim_{y \to b} \beta(y) \qquad (18)$$

Writing $y = g(x)$, we see that if x is in I, then

$$
\begin{aligned}
f \circ g(x) - f \circ g(a) &= f(y) - f(b) = (y - b)\{f'(b) + \beta(y)\} \\
&= [g(x) - g(a)]\{f'(g(a)) + \beta(g(x))\} \\
&= (x - a)[g'(a) + \alpha(x)]\{f'(g(a)) + \beta(g(x))\}
\end{aligned}
$$

Since $\lim_{x \to a} g(x) = b$, it follows from (18), the preceding theorem, and Limit Theorem (iii) that

$$\lim_{x \to a} \frac{f \circ g(x) - f \circ g(a)}{x - a} = [g'(a)]\{f'(g(a))\}$$

This completes the proof. ■

We conclude this appendix with a theorem on differentiation of inverse functions.

Inverse Function Theorem Let I be an open interval and let g be a real-valued function that is defined and differentiable on I with $g'(x) \neq 0$ for each x in I. Then there exists an open interval J and a differentiable function $f = g^{-1}$ from J onto I such that
  (i) if x is in I, then $g(x)$ is in J and $f(g(x)) = x$; and
  (ii) if y is in J, then $f(y)$ is in I, $g(f(y)) = y$, and $f'(y) = \dfrac{1}{g'(f(y))}$.

Proof First, we claim that g must be strictly monotonic on I. Assuming this to be false, we can find $x_1 < x_2 < x_3$ in I and then some y_0 with either $g(x_1) < y_0 < g(x_2)$ and $g(x_2) > y_0 > g(x_3)$ or else $g(x_1) > y_0 > g(x_2)$ and $g(x_2) < y_0 < g(x_3)$. In either case, the continuity of g and the Intermediate Value Theorem (IVT) provide us with numbers u and v such that $x_1 < u < x_2 < v < x_3$ and $g(u) = y_0 = g(v)$. Now Rolle's Theorem provides a number c in $]u, v[$ with $g'(c) = 0$. Since c is in I, this contradicts our hypothesis that g' is never 0 on I. Thus g is strictly monotonic on I. To fix ideas, we shall suppose that g is decreasing. The proof is very similar if g is increasing.

Let $g(I)$ denote the set of all numbers $g(x)$ for x in I. If $g(I)$ is bounded above, let $b = \sup g(I)$ and let $b = \infty$ otherwise. If $g(I)$ is bounded below, let a be the supremum of all lower bounds and otherwise let $a = -\infty$. Given x_0 in I, we use the fact that I is open to obtain $x_1 < x_0 < x_2$ in I. Since g is decreasing, we have $a \leqq g(x_2) < g(x_0) < g(x_1) \leqq b$. This proves that $g(I) \subset \,]a, b[$. Given y_0 in $]a, b[$, we see that y_0 is *not* an upper bound for $g(I)$ so there is some x' in I with $g(x') > y_0$. Also, y_0 is not a lower bound for $g(I)$ so there is some x'' in I with $g(x'') < y_0$. Another application of IVT produces an x_0 between x' and x'' (and so x_0 is in I) such that $g(x_0) = y_0$. This proves that $]a, b[\subset g(I)$. Writing $J = \,]a, b[$, we have proven that $g(I) = J$. For y_0 in J, the strict monotonicity of g assures us that there is only one x_0 in I with $g(x_0) = y_0$. Write $x_0 = f(y_0)$. This defines f on J and we have $g(f(y_0)) = g(x_0) = y_0$ for each y_0 in J. Moreover, if we start with any x_0 in I, then $g(x_0)$ is in J so, writing $y_0 = g(x_0)$, we have $g(f(g(x_0))) = g(f(y_0)) = y_0 = g(x_0)$ and therefore $f(g(x_0)) = x_0$. It remains only to prove our assertions about f'.

Let y_0 in J be given. Write $x_0 = f(y_0)$. Then $g'(x_0) < 0$. Consider any neighborhood $]\alpha, \beta[$ of $\dfrac{1}{g'}(x_0)$ with $\alpha < \dfrac{1}{g'(x_0)} < \beta < 0$. Since $\dfrac{1}{\alpha} > g'(x_0) > \dfrac{1}{\beta}$, there is a neighborhood $]x_1, x_2[$ of x_0 with x_1 and x_2 in I such that

$$\frac{1}{\alpha} > \frac{g(x) - g(x_0)}{x - x_0} > \frac{1}{\beta}$$

whenever $x_1 < x < x_2$ and $x \neq x_0$. Thus

$$\alpha < \frac{x - x_0}{g(x) - g(x_0)} < \beta \qquad (*)$$

for all such x. Let $y_1 = g(x_1)$ and $y_2 = g(x_2)$. Then $y_2 < y_0 < y_1$ in J. For any y in $]y_2, y_1[$ with $y \neq y_0$, we have $x_1 < f(y) < x_2$ and $f(y) \neq x_0 = f(y_0)$ so we may take $x = f(y)$ in (*) to obtain

$$\alpha < \frac{f(y) - f(y_0)}{y - y_0} < \beta$$

This proves that

$$\lim_{y \to y_0} \frac{f(y) - f(y_0)}{y - y_0} = \frac{1}{g'(x_0)} = \frac{1}{g'(f(y_0))}$$

and so f is differentiable at y_0 and $f'(y_0) = 1/g'(f(y_0))$. ∎

Appendix B

The Exponential Function

IN THIS APPENDIX we give a precise definition of the exponential function e^x and we study properties of it and its inverse, the natural logarithm. We also use these functions to study arbitrary powers a^b. First, we need a simple inequality.

Bernoulli's Inequality If t is a real number with $t > -1$ and $t \neq 0$ and if n is an integer with $n > 1$, then

$$(1 + t)^n > 1 + nt \tag{1}$$

Proof Let $t > -1$, $t \neq 0$, be given and let N be the set of all $n > 1$ for which (1) is true. Since

$$(1 + t)^2 = 1 + 2t + t^2 > 1 + 2t$$

we see that 2 is in N. Now let k be any member of N:

$$(1 + t)^k > 1 + kt \tag{2}$$

To show that $k + 1$ is also in N, we multiply both sides of (2) by the *positive* number $1 + t$ to obtain

$$\begin{aligned}
(1 + t)^{k+1} &> (1 + t)(1 + kt) \\
&= 1 + t + kt + kt^2 \\
&> 1 + (k + 1)t
\end{aligned}$$

Since 2 is in N and $k + 1$ is in N whenever k is in N, the proof is complete. ■

Definition For each integer $n \geq 1$, define the functions a_n and b_n by

$$a_n(x) = \left(1 + \frac{x}{n}\right)^n \qquad b_n(x) = \left(1 - \frac{x}{n}\right)^{-n}$$

▷ **Theorem 1** For real numbers $x \neq 0$ and positive integers n and m, we have the following:

    (i) If $n > -x$, then $a_n(x) < a_{n+1}(x)$.
    (ii) If $n > x$, then $b_{n+1}(x) < b_n(x)$.
    (iii) If $n > |x|$ and $m > |x|$, then $a_n(x) < b_m(x)$.
    (iv) If $n > |x|$, then $0 < b_n(x) - a_n(x) < x^2 b_n(x)/n$.

Proof (i) Suppose $n > -x$. Since

$$a_2(x) = \left(1 + \frac{x}{2}\right)^2 = 1 + x + \frac{x^2}{4} > 1 + x = a_1(x)$$

we see that (i) holds if $n = 1$. Now suppose $n \geq 2$. Since $n + x > 0$ and $x < (n + 1)(n + x)$, it follows from Bernoulli's Inequality and a little algebra that

$$\begin{aligned}
\frac{a_{n+1}(x)}{a_n(x)} &= \left(\frac{n + 1 + x}{n + 1}\right)\left[\frac{n + 1 + x}{n + 1} \cdot \frac{n}{n + x}\right]^n \\
&= \left(\frac{n + 1 + x}{n + 1}\right)\left[1 - \frac{x}{(n + 1)(n + x)}\right]^n \\
&> \left(\frac{n + 1 + x}{n + 1}\right)\left(1 - \frac{nx}{(n + 1)(n + x)}\right) \\
&= \frac{[(n + 1) + x][n(n + 1) + x]}{(n + 1)^2(n + x)} \\
&= \frac{n(n + 1)^2 + (nx + x)(n + 1) + x^2}{(n + 1)^2(n + x)} \\
&= 1 + \frac{x^2}{(n + 1)^2(n + x)} > 1
\end{aligned}$$

and so (i) obtains.

    (ii) For $n > x = -(-x)$, it follows from (i) that

$$b_n(x) = \frac{1}{a_n(-x)} > \frac{1}{a_{n+1}(-x)} = b_{n+1}(x)$$

and so (ii) obtains.

    (iii) Suppose that $n > |x|$ and $m > |x|$. Since $x^2/n^2 < 1$, we have

$$\frac{a_n(x)}{b_n(x)} = \left(1 + \frac{x}{n}\right)^n\left(1 - \frac{x}{n}\right)^n = \left(1 - \frac{x^2}{n^2}\right)^n < 1$$

and so $a_n(x) < b_n(x)$. If $m \leq n$, then (ii) yields $a_n(x) < b_n(x) \leq b_m(x)$. If $m \geq n$, then (i) yields $a_n(x) \leq a_m(x) < b_m(x)$. Thus (iii) obtains.

(iv) For $n > |x|$, we have $x^2/n^2 < 1$ and so Bernoulli's Inequality shows that

$$0 < b_n(x) - a_n(x) = b_n(x)\left[1 - \frac{a_n(x)}{b_n(x)}\right]$$

$$= b_n(x)\left[1 - \left(1 - \frac{x^2}{n^2}\right)^n\right]$$

$$< b_n(x)\left[1 - \left(1 - \frac{x^2}{n}\right)\right] = \frac{x^2 b_n(x)}{n}$$

This proves (iv) and completes our proof of Theorem 1. ∎

Note. For $x = 0$, we have $a_n(0) = b_n(0) = 1$ for all $n \geq 1$ so that all of the inequalities in Theorem 1 become equalities in this case.

Definition Let x be any given real number. Let N be the smallest integer such that $N > |x|$ and let S_x denote the set of all numbers $a_n(x)$ for $n \geq N$. According to Theorem 1, part (iii), the set S_x has the number $b_N(x)$ as an upper bound. By the Supremum Principle (see Appendix A), the real number

$$E(x) = \sup S_x$$

exists. This defines a function E at each real number x. We call E the **exponential function.**

Theorem 2 For each real number x we have

$$E(x) = \lim_{n \to \infty} a_n(x) = \lim_{n \to \infty} b_n(x)$$

Proof Let a real number x and a positive number ϵ be given. Define N and S_x as in the above definition. Since $E(x) - \epsilon$ is not an upper bound for S_x, there exists some $n_0 \geq N$ such that $a_{n_0}(x) > E(x) - \epsilon$. It follows from Theorem 1, part (i), that if $n \geq n_0$, then

$$E(x) - \epsilon < a_{n_0}(x) \leq a_n(x) \leq E(x)$$

This proves that $\lim_{n \to \infty} a_n(x) = E(x)$. From Theorem 1, part (iii), we see that if $m \geq N$, then $b_m(x)$ is an upper bound for S_x and so $E(x) \leq b_m(x)$. Now choose $n_1 > n_0$ such that $x^2 b_N(x)/n_1 < \epsilon$ and then use (ii) and (iv) of Theorem 1 to infer that if $n \geq n_1$, then

$$E(x) \leq b_n(x) \leq a_n(x) + x^2 b_n(x)/n$$
$$\leq E(x) + x^2 b_N(x)/n_1 < E(x) + \epsilon$$

This proves that $\lim_{n \to \infty} b_n(x) = E(x)$. ∎

▷ **Theorem 3**   The function E has the following properties.

(i) $E(x) > 0$ for all x

(ii) $E(0) = 1$

(iii) $E(x + y) = E(x)E(y)$ for all x and y

(iv) $E(-x) = 1/E(x)$ for all x

(v) E is differentiable and $E'(x) = E(x)$ for all x

(vi) $\lim\limits_{x \to \infty} E(x)/x^n = \infty$ for each integer $n \geq 0$

(vii) $\lim\limits_{x \to -\infty} E(x) = 0$

(viii) For each $y > 0$, there exists exactly one real number x such that $E(x) = y$.

Proof   (i) For all $n > -x$, we have $0 < a_n(x) \leq E(x)$.

(ii) Since $a_n(0) = 1$ for all n, we have $E(0) = \lim\limits_{n \to \infty} a_n(0) = 1$.

(iii) Let x and y be given real numbers. For $n > -(x + y)$ let $t_n = xy/(n + x + y)$ and observe that

$$\frac{a_n(x)a_n(y)}{a_n(x + y)} = \left[\frac{(n + x)(n + y)}{n(n + x + y)}\right]^n$$

$$= \left[1 + \frac{t_n}{n}\right]^n = a_n(t_n) \tag{3}$$

For all n so large that $-1 < t_n < 1$, it follows from Theorem 1 that

$$1 + t_n = a_1(t_n) \leq a_n(t_n) \leq b_1(t_n) = \frac{1}{1 - t_n}$$

Since $\lim\limits_{n \to \infty} t_n = 0$, we obtain $\lim\limits_{n \to \infty} a_n(t_n) = 1$. This fact and (3) yield

$$\frac{E(x)E(y)}{E(x + y)} = \lim\limits_{n \to \infty} \frac{a_n(x)a_n(y)}{a_n(x + y)} = 1$$

and so (iii) obtains.

(iv) $E(x)E(-x) = E[x + (-x)] = E(0) = 1$.

(v) For $-1 < h < 1$ and $h \neq 0$, it follows from Theorem 1 that

$$1 + h = a_1(h) < E(h) < b_1(h) = 1 + \frac{h}{1 - h}$$

so that

$$1 < \frac{E(h) - 1}{h} < \frac{1}{1 - h} \qquad \text{if } 0 < h < 1$$

and

$$\frac{1}{1-h} < \frac{E(h)-1}{h} < 1 \qquad \text{if} -1 < h < 0.$$

Therefore

$$E'(x) = \lim_{h \to 0} \frac{E(x+h)-E(x)}{h}$$

$$= \lim_{h \to 0} \frac{E(x)E(h)-E(x)}{h}$$

$$= E(x) \cdot \lim_{h \to 0} \frac{E(h)-1}{h} = E(x)$$

(vi) Given $n > 0$, we have $E(x) > a_{n+1}(x) > \left(\dfrac{x}{n+1}\right)^{n+1}$ and so $E(x)/x^n > x/(n+1)^{n+1}$ for all $x > 0$. Also, $E(x) > 1 + x = a_1(x)$ for all $x > 0$.

(vii) Using (vi) with $n = 0$, we have

$$\lim_{x \to -\infty} E(x) = \lim_{x \to \infty} \frac{1}{E(x)} = 0$$

(viii) Let $y > 0$ be given. From (vii) and (vi) (with $n = 0$), we infer that there exist numbers $a < b$ such that $E(a) < y < E(b)$. From (v), it follows that E is continuous on $[a,b]$ and so the Intermediate Value Theorem (see Appendix A) provides an x in $[a,b]$ such that $E(x) = y$. Since $E'(t) = E(t) > 0$ for all t, E is strictly increasing so that at most one such x can exist. ∎

▷ **Definition** For each real number $y > 0$, let $L(y)$ denote that unique real number x such that $E(x) = y$ [see Theorem 3, part viii]. Thus $E[L(y)] = y$ and $L[E(x)] = x$. This defines the real-valued function L on $]0,\infty[$. It is called the **natural logarithm function.**

▷ **Theorem 4** The function L has the following properties.
    (i) $L(1) = 0$.
    (ii) If $u > 0$ and $v > 0$, then $L(uv) = L(u) + L(v)$ and $L(u/v) = L(u) - L(v)$.
    (iii) L is strictly increasing on $]0,\infty[$.
    (iv) L is differentiable on $]0,\infty[$ and $L'(y) = 1/y$ for all $y > 0$.
    (v) $\lim_{y \to \infty} L(y) = \infty$
    (vi) $\lim_{y \to 0^+} L(y) = -\infty$

Proof (i) Since $E(0) = 1$, $L(1) = 0$.

(ii) Let $u > 0$ and $v > 0$ be given. Then

$$E[L(u) + L(v)] = E[L(u)] \cdot E[L)v)] = uv$$

and

$$E[L(u) - L(v)] = E[L(u)]E[-L(v)] = E[L(u)]/E[L(v)] = u/v$$

and so (ii) follows from the definition of L.

(iii) Given $0 < y_1 < y_2$, we have $L(y_1) < L(y_2)$, since otherwise it would follow from the fact that E is strictly increasing that

$$y_2 = E[L(y_2)] \leqq E[L(y_1)] = y_1$$

(iv) Let $y_0 > 0$ be given. Then $\lim_{y \to y_0} L(y) = L(y_0)$ because if $\alpha < L(y_0) < \beta$, then $E(\alpha) < y_0 < E(\beta)$ and it follows from (iii) that for $E(\alpha) < y < E(\beta)$ we have

$$\alpha = L[E(\alpha)] < L(y) < L[E(\beta)] = \beta$$

Therefore

$$\lim_{y \to y_0} \frac{L(y) - L(y_0)}{y - y_0} = \lim_{y \to y_0} \frac{L(y) - L(y_0)}{E[L(y)] - E[L(y_0)]}$$
$$= \frac{1}{E'[L(y_0)]} = \frac{1}{E[L(y_0)]} = \frac{1}{y_0}$$

(v) Given any real number β, we see that $y > E(\beta)$ implies

$$L(y) > L[E(\beta)] = \beta$$

(vi) Given any real number α, we see that $0 < y < E(\alpha)$ implies

$$L(y) < L[E(\alpha)] = \alpha \quad \blacksquare$$

▷ **Theorem 5** Let $a > 0$ be a real number and let m and n be integers with $n > 0$. Then $E\left[\dfrac{m}{n}L(a)\right] = a^{m/n} = \sqrt[n]{a^m}$.

Proof By repeated application of Theorem 3, part (iii), we have

$$\left\{E\left[\frac{m}{n}L(a)\right]\right\}^n = E\left[\overbrace{\frac{m}{n}L(a) + \frac{m}{n}L(a) + \ldots + \frac{m}{n}L(a)}^{n \text{ summands}}\right]$$
$$= E[mL(a)] \tag{4}$$

If $m = 0$, then $E[mL(a)] = E(0) = 1 = a^0 = a^m$. If $m > 0$, then

$$\overbrace{E[mL(a)] = E[L(a) + L(a) + \ldots + L(a)]}^{m \text{ summands}}$$
$$= \{E[L(a)]\}^m = a^m$$

If $m < 0$, then $E[mL(a)] = \dfrac{1}{E[-mL(a)]} = \dfrac{1}{a^{-m}} = a^m$

Thus (4) yields

$$\left\{E\left[\frac{m}{n}L(a)\right]\right\}^n = a^m$$

This proves that $E\left[\dfrac{m}{n}L(a)\right]$ is that unique positive number whose nth power is a^m; namely, $\sqrt[n]{a^m}$. ∎

Theorem 5 shows that the following definition of powers of positive numbers agrees with our old definitions in the case that the exponent is rational.

Definition   Let a and b be real numbers with $a > 0$. Define $a^b = E[bL(a)]$.

Notice that Theorem 3, part (i), shows that $a^b > 0$.

Theorem 6 (Laws of Exponents)   Let a, b, and c be real numbers. Then
  (i) $a > 0$ implies $a^b a^c = a^{b+c}$
  (ii) $a > 0$ and $b > 0$ imply $a^c b^c = (ab)^c$
  (iii) $a > 0$ implies $(a^b)^c = a^{bc}$

Proof   (i) $a^b a^c = E[bL(a)]E[cL(a)] = E[(b + c)L(a)] = a^{b+c}$
  (ii) $a^c b^c = E[cL(a)]E[cL(b)] = E\{c[L(a) + L(b)]\}$
        $= E[cL(ab)] = (ab)^c$
  (iii) $(a^b)^c = E[cL(a^b)] = E[cL\{E[bL(a)]\}]$
        $= E\{c[bL(a)]\} = E[bcL(a)] = a^{bc}$ ∎

Definition   We define the number e by $e = E(1)$.

Remarks. Since $a_n(1) = \left(1 + \dfrac{1}{n}\right)^n$ and

$$b_{n+1}(1) = \left(1 - \frac{1}{n+1}\right)^{-(n+1)} = \left(1 + \frac{1}{n}\right)^{n+1}$$

we see from Theorems 1 and 2 that $\left(1 + \dfrac{1}{n}\right)^n$ $(n = 1, 2, \ldots)$ is an increasing sequence and that $\left(1 + \dfrac{1}{n}\right)^{n+1}$ $(n = 1, 2, \ldots)$ is a decreasing sequence with

$$\lim_{n \to \infty} \left(1 + \frac{1}{n}\right)^n = e = \lim_{n \to \infty} \left(1 + \frac{1}{n}\right)^{n+1}$$

Also notice that $L(e) = L[E(1)] = 1$.

▷ **Theorem 7**   For every real number x we have

$$E(x) = e^x$$

Proof $e^x = E[xL(e)] = E(x)$ ∎

Notation. Now that E and L have been defined precisely and their most important properties have been proved, we revert, without fear of admitting preconceived notions, to the more familiar notations $L(y) = \ln y$ for $y > 0$ and $E(x) = e^x = \exp x$ for all x.

Appendix C

Integrals and Tables

Forms Containing $a + bu$

1. $\displaystyle\int (a + bu)^n \, du = \frac{(a + bu)^{n+1}}{b(n + 1)}, \; n \neq -1$

2. $\displaystyle\int \frac{du}{a + bu} = \frac{1}{b} \ln |a + bu|$

3. $\displaystyle\int \frac{u \, du}{a + bu} = \frac{1}{b^2} [(a + bu) - a \ln |a + bu|]$

4. $\displaystyle\int \frac{u^2 \, du}{a + bu} = \frac{1}{b^3} [\tfrac{1}{2}(a + bu)^2 - 2a(a + bu) + a^2 \ln |a + bu|]$

5. $\displaystyle\int \frac{du}{u(a + bu)} = -\frac{1}{a} \ln \frac{|a + bu|}{|u|}$

6. $\displaystyle\int \frac{du}{u^2(a + bu)} = -\frac{1}{au} + \frac{b}{a^2} \ln \frac{|a + bu|}{|u|}$

7. $\displaystyle\int \frac{u \, du}{(a + bu)^2} = \frac{1}{b^2} \left[\frac{a}{a + bu} + \ln |a + bu| \right]$

8. $\displaystyle\int \frac{u^2 \, du}{(a + bu)^2} = \frac{1}{b^3} \left[(a + bu) - \frac{a^2}{a + bu} - 2a \ln |a + by| \right]$

9. $\displaystyle\int \frac{du}{u(a + bu)^2} = \frac{1}{a(a + bu)} - \frac{1}{a^2} \ln \frac{|a + bu|}{|u|}$

10. $\displaystyle\int \frac{du}{u^2(a + bu)^2} = -\frac{a + 2bu}{a^2 u(a + bu)} + \frac{2b}{a^3} \ln \frac{|a + bu|}{|u|}$

Forms Containing $\sqrt{a + bu}$

11. $\displaystyle\int u\sqrt{a + bu} \, du = -\frac{2(2a - 3bu)(a + bu)^{3/2}}{15b^2}$

12. $\int u^n \sqrt{a + bu}\, du = \dfrac{2u^n(a + bu)^{3/2}}{b(2n + 3)} - \dfrac{2an}{b(2n + 3)} \int u^{n-1}\sqrt{a + bu}\, du$

13. $\int \dfrac{u\, du}{\sqrt{a + bu}} = -\dfrac{2(2a - bu)\sqrt{a + bu}}{3b^2}$

14. $\int \dfrac{u^n\, du}{\sqrt{a + bu}} = \dfrac{2u^n\sqrt{a + bu}}{b(2n + 1)} - \dfrac{2an}{b(2n + 1)} \int \dfrac{u^{n-1}du}{\sqrt{a + bu}}$

15. $\int \dfrac{du}{u\sqrt{a + bu}} = \dfrac{1}{\sqrt{a}} \ln \left| \dfrac{\sqrt{a + bu} - \sqrt{a}}{\sqrt{a + bu} + \sqrt{a}} \right|$, if $a > 0$

$\quad\int \dfrac{du}{u\sqrt{a + bu}} = \dfrac{2}{\sqrt{-a}} \operatorname{Tan}^{-1} \sqrt{\dfrac{a + bu}{-a}}$, if $a < 0$

16. $\int \dfrac{du}{u^n\sqrt{a + bu}} = -\dfrac{\sqrt{a + bu}}{a(n - 1)u^{n-1}} - \dfrac{b(2n - 3)}{2a(n - 1)} \int \dfrac{du}{u^{n-1}\sqrt{a + bu}}$

17. $\int \dfrac{\sqrt{a + bu}}{u}\, du = 2\sqrt{a + bu} + a \int \dfrac{du}{u\sqrt{a + bu}}$

18. $\int \dfrac{\sqrt{a + bu}}{u^n}\, du = -\dfrac{(a + bu)^{3/2}}{a(n - 1)u^{n-1}} - \dfrac{b(2n - 5)}{2a(n - 1)} \int \dfrac{\sqrt{a + bu}}{u^{n-1}}\, du$

Forms Containing $\sqrt{u^2 \pm a^2}$

19. $\int \dfrac{du}{u^2 + a^2} = \dfrac{1}{a} \operatorname{Tan}^{-1} \dfrac{u}{a}$

20. $\int \dfrac{du}{u^2 - a^2} = \dfrac{1}{2a} \ln \left| \dfrac{u - a}{u + a} \right|$

21. $\int \dfrac{du}{\sqrt{u^2 \pm a^2}} = \ln | u + \sqrt{u^2 \pm a^2} |$

22. $\int \dfrac{u^2\, du}{\sqrt{u^2 \pm a^2}} = \tfrac{1}{2}u\sqrt{u^2 \pm a^2} \mp \tfrac{1}{2}a^2 \ln | u + \sqrt{u^2 \pm a^2} |$

23. $\int \dfrac{du}{u\sqrt{u^2 + a^2}} = -\dfrac{1}{a} \ln \dfrac{(a + \sqrt{u^2 + a^2})}{| u |}$

24. $\int \dfrac{du}{u\sqrt{u^2 - a^2}} = \dfrac{1}{a} \operatorname{Sec}^{-1} \dfrac{u}{a}$

25. $\int \dfrac{du}{u^2\sqrt{u^2 \pm a^2}} = \mp \dfrac{\sqrt{u^2 \pm a^2}}{a^2 u}$

26. $\int \sqrt{u^2 \pm a^2}\, du = \tfrac{1}{2}u\sqrt{u^2 \pm a^2} \pm \tfrac{1}{2}a^2 \ln | u + \sqrt{u^2 \pm a^2} |$

27. $\int u^2\sqrt{u^2 \pm a^2}\, du = \tfrac{1}{4}u(u^2 \pm a^2)^{3/2} \mp \tfrac{1}{8}a^2 u\sqrt{u^2 \pm a^2}$
$\qquad\qquad\qquad\qquad\qquad\qquad - \tfrac{1}{8}a^4 \ln | u + \sqrt{u^2 \pm a^2} |$

28. $\int \dfrac{\sqrt{u^2 + a^2}}{u}\, du = \sqrt{u^2 + a^2} - a \ln \dfrac{(a + \sqrt{u^2 + a^2})}{| u |}$

29. $\int \dfrac{\sqrt{u^2 - a^2}}{u}\, du = \sqrt{u^2 - a^2} - a \operatorname{Sec}^{-1} \dfrac{u}{a}$

30. $\int \dfrac{\sqrt{u^2 \pm a^2}}{u^2}\, du = -\dfrac{\sqrt{u^2 \pm a^2}}{u} + \ln |u + \sqrt{u^2 \pm a^2}|$

31. $\int (u^2 \pm a^2)^{3/2}\, du = \tfrac{1}{4}u(u^2 \pm a^2)^{3/2} \pm \tfrac{3}{8}a^2 u\sqrt{u^2 \pm a^2}$
$$+ \tfrac{3}{8}a^4 \ln |u + \sqrt{u^2 \pm a^2}|$$

32. $\int \dfrac{(u^2 + a^2)^{3/2}}{u}\, du = \tfrac{1}{3}(u^2 + a^2)^{3/2}$
$$+ a^2\sqrt{u^2 + a^2} - a^3 \ln \dfrac{(a + \sqrt{u^2 + a^2})}{|u|}$$

33. $\int \dfrac{(u^2 - a^2)^{3/2}}{u}\, du = \tfrac{1}{3}(u^2 - a^2)^{3/2} - a^2\sqrt{u^2 - a^2} + a^3 \operatorname{Sec}^{-1} \dfrac{u}{a}$

34. $\int \dfrac{du}{(u^2 \pm a^2)^{3/2}} = \pm \dfrac{u}{a^2\sqrt{u^2 \pm a^2}}$

35. $\int \dfrac{u^2\, du}{(u^2 \pm a^2)^{3/2}} = -\dfrac{u}{\sqrt{u^2 \pm a^2}} + \ln |u + \sqrt{u^2 \pm a^2}|$

36. $\int \dfrac{du}{u(u^2 + a^2)^{3/2}} = \dfrac{1}{a^2\sqrt{u^2 + a^2}} - \dfrac{1}{a^3} \ln \dfrac{(a + \sqrt{u^2 + a^2})}{|u|}$

37. $\int \dfrac{du}{u(u^2 - a^2)^{3/2}} = -\dfrac{1}{a^2\sqrt{u^2 - a^2}} - \dfrac{1}{a^3} \operatorname{Sec}^{-1} \dfrac{u}{a}$

Forms Containing $\sqrt{a^2 - u^2}$

38. $\int \dfrac{du}{a^2 - u^2} = \dfrac{1}{2a} \ln \left| \dfrac{a + u}{a - u} \right|$

39. $\int \dfrac{du}{\sqrt{a^2 - u^2}} = \operatorname{Sin}^{-1} \dfrac{u}{a}$

40. $\int \dfrac{u^2\, du}{\sqrt{a^2 - u^2}} = -\tfrac{1}{2}u\sqrt{a^2 - u^2} + \tfrac{1}{2}a^2 \operatorname{Sin}^{-1} \dfrac{u}{a}$

41. $\int \dfrac{du}{u\sqrt{a^2 - u^2}} = -\dfrac{1}{a} \ln \dfrac{|a + \sqrt{a^2 - u^2}|}{|u|}$

42. $\int \dfrac{du}{u^2\sqrt{a^2 - u^2}} = -\dfrac{\sqrt{a^2 - u^2}}{a^2 u}$

43. $\int \sqrt{a^2 - u^2}\, du = \tfrac{1}{2}u\sqrt{a^2 - u^2} + \tfrac{1}{2}a^2 \operatorname{Sin}^{-1} \dfrac{u}{a}$

44. $\int u^2\sqrt{a^2 - u^2}\, du = -\tfrac{1}{4}u(a^2 - u^2)^{3/2} + \tfrac{1}{8}a^2 u\sqrt{a^2 - u^2} + \tfrac{1}{8}a^4 \operatorname{Sin}^{-1} \dfrac{u}{a}$

45. $\int \dfrac{\sqrt{a^2 - u^2}}{u}\, du = \sqrt{a^2 - u^2} - a \ln \dfrac{|a + \sqrt{a^2 - u^2}|}{|u|}$

46. $\int \dfrac{\sqrt{a^2 - u^2}}{u^2}\, du = -\dfrac{\sqrt{a^2 - u^2}}{u} - \operatorname{Sin}^{-1} \dfrac{u}{a}$

47. $\int \dfrac{du}{(a^2 - u^2)^{3/2}} = \dfrac{u}{a^2\sqrt{a^2 - u^2}}$

48. $\displaystyle\int \frac{u^2 \, du}{(a^2 - u^2)^{3/2}} = \frac{u}{\sqrt{a^2 - u^2}} - \mathrm{Sin}^{-1} \frac{u}{a}$

49. $\displaystyle\int \frac{du}{u(a^2 - u^2)^{3/2}} = \frac{1}{a^2 \sqrt{a^2 - u^2}} - \frac{1}{a^3} \ln \frac{|a + \sqrt{a^2 - u^2}|}{|u|}$

50. $\displaystyle\int \frac{du}{u^2(a^2 - u^2)^{3/2}} = -\frac{\sqrt{a^2 - u^2}}{a^4 u} + \frac{u}{a^4 \sqrt{a^2 - u^2}}$

51. $\displaystyle\int (a^2 - u^2)^{3/2} \, du = \tfrac{1}{4}u(a^2 - u^2)^{3/2} + \tfrac{3}{8}a^2 u \sqrt{a^2 - u^2} + \tfrac{3}{8}a^4 \, \mathrm{Sin}^{-1} \frac{u}{a}$

52. $\displaystyle\int \frac{(a^2 - u^2)^{3/2}}{u} \, du = \tfrac{1}{3}(a^2 - u^2)^{3/2} + a^2 \sqrt{a^2 - u^2} - a^3 \ln \frac{|a + \sqrt{a^2 - u^2}|}{|u|}$

Trigonometric Forms

53. $\displaystyle\int \sin u \, du = -\cos u$

54. $\displaystyle\int \sin^2 u \, du = \tfrac{1}{2}u - \tfrac{1}{2} \sin u \cos u$

55. $\displaystyle\int \sin^3 u \, du = -\cos u + \tfrac{1}{3} \cos^3 u$

56. $\displaystyle\int \sin^n u \, du = -\frac{1}{n} \sin^{n-1} u \cos u + \frac{n-1}{n} \int \sin^{n-2} u \, du$

57. $\displaystyle\int \cos u \, du = \sin u$

58. $\displaystyle\int \cos^2 u \, du = \tfrac{1}{2}u + \tfrac{1}{2} \sin u \cos u$

59. $\displaystyle\int \cos^3 u \, du = \sin u - \tfrac{1}{3} \sin^3 u$

60. $\displaystyle\int \cos^n u \, du = \frac{1}{n} \cos^{n-1} u \sin u + \frac{n-1}{n} \int \cos^{n-2} u \, du$

61. $\displaystyle\int \tan u \, du = \ln |\sec u|$

62. $\displaystyle\int \tan^n u \, du - \frac{\tan^{n-1} u}{n-1} - \int \tan^{n-2} u \, du$

63. $\displaystyle\int \cot u \, du = \ln |\sin u|$

64. $\displaystyle\int \cot^n u \, du = -\frac{\cot^{n-1} u}{n-1} - \int \cot^{n-2} u \, du$

65. $\displaystyle\int \sec u \, du = \ln |\sec u + \tan u|$

66. $\int \sec^2 u\ du = \tan u$

67. $\int \sec^n u\ du = \dfrac{\sec^{n-2} u \tan u}{n-1} + \dfrac{n-2}{n-1} \int \sec^{n-2} u\ du$

68. $\int \csc u\ du = \ln |\csc u - \cot u|$

69. $\int \csc^2 u\ du = -\cot u$

70. $\int \csc^n u\ du = -\dfrac{\csc^{n-2} u \cot u}{n-1} + \dfrac{n-2}{n-1} \int \csc^{n-2} u\ du$

71. $\int \sec u \tan u\ du = \sec u$

72. $\int \csc u \cot u\ du = -\csc u$

73. $\int \sin au \sin bu\ du = \dfrac{\sin(a-b)u}{2(a-b)} - \dfrac{\sin(a+b)u}{2(a+b)}$

74. $\int \sin au \cos bu\ du = -\dfrac{\cos(a-b)u}{2(a-b)} - \dfrac{\cos(a+b)u}{2(a+b)}$

75. $\int \cos au \cos bu\ du = \dfrac{\sin(a-b)u}{2(a-b)} + \dfrac{\sin(a+b)u}{2(a+b)}$

76. $\int \sin^m u \cos^n u\ du = \dfrac{\sin^{m+1} u \cos^{n-1} u}{m+n} + \dfrac{n-1}{m+n} \int \sin^m u \cos^{n-2} u\ du$

77. $\int \sin^m u \cos^n u\ du = -\dfrac{\sin^{m-1} u \cos^{n+1} u}{m+n}$

$$+ \dfrac{m-1}{m+n} \int \sin^{m-2} u \cos^n u\ du$$

Miscellaneous Forms

78. $\int e^u\ du = e^u$

79. $\int a^u\ du = \dfrac{a^u}{\ln a}$

80. $\int u e^{au}\ du = e^{au}(au - 1)/a^2$

81. $\int u^2 e^{au}\ du = e^{au}(a^2 u^2 - 2au + 2)/a^3$

82. $\int u^n \ln u\ du = u^{n+1}\left[\dfrac{\ln u}{n+1} - \dfrac{1}{(n+1)^2}\right]$

83. $\int u \sin u\ du = \sin u - u \cos u$

84. $\int u^2 \sin u\ du = 2u \sin u - (u^2 - 2) \cos u$

85. $\displaystyle\int u \cos u \, du = \cos u + u \sin u$

86. $\displaystyle\int u^2 \cos u \, du = (u^2 - 2) \sin u + 2u \cos u$

87. $\displaystyle\int e^{au} \sin bu \, du = \frac{e^{au}(a \sin bu - b \cos bu)}{a^2 + b^2}$

88. $\displaystyle\int e^{au} \cos bu \, du = \frac{e^{au}(a \cos bu + b \sin bu)}{a^2 + b^2}$

89. $\displaystyle\int \text{Sin}^{-1} u \, du = u \, \text{Sin}^{-1} u + \sqrt{1 - u^2}$

90. $\displaystyle\int \text{Tan}^{-1} u \, du = u \, \text{Tan}^{-1} u - \tfrac{1}{2} \ln (1 + u^2)$

91. $\displaystyle\int \sinh u \, du = \cosh u$ **94.** $\displaystyle\int \coth u \, du = \ln |\sinh u|$

92. $\displaystyle\int \cosh u \, du = \sinh u$ **95.** $\displaystyle\int \text{sech } u \, du = 2 \, \text{Tan}^{-1} e^u$

93. $\displaystyle\int \tanh u \, du = \ln \cosh u$ **96.** $\displaystyle\int \text{csch } u \, du = \ln |\tanh \tfrac{1}{2}u|$

Wallis Formulas

97. $\displaystyle\int_0^{\frac{1}{2}\pi} \sin^n x \, dx = \int_0^{\frac{1}{2}\pi} \cos^n x \, dx$

$$= \begin{cases} \dfrac{1}{2} \cdot \dfrac{3}{4} \cdot \dfrac{5}{6} \cdots \dfrac{n-1}{n} \cdot \dfrac{\pi}{2}, & \text{if } n \text{ is an even integer} \geqq 2 \\[2ex] \dfrac{2}{3} \cdot \dfrac{4}{5} \cdot \dfrac{6}{7} \cdots \dfrac{n-1}{n}, & \text{if } n \text{ is an odd integer} \geqq 3 \end{cases}$$

98. $\displaystyle\int_0^{\frac{1}{2}\pi} \sin^m x \cos^n x \, dx$

$$= \begin{cases} \dfrac{2 \cdot 4 \cdot 6 \cdots (n-1)}{(m+1)(m+3)(m+5) \cdots (m+n)}, & \text{if } n \text{ is an odd integer} \geq 3 \\[2ex] \dfrac{2 \cdot 4 \cdot 6 \cdots (m-1)}{(n+1)(n+3)(n+5) \cdots (n+m)}, & \text{if } m \text{ is an odd integer} \geq 3 \\[2ex] \dfrac{1 \cdot 3 \cdots (m-1) \cdot 1 \cdot 3 \cdots (n-1)}{2 \cdot 4 \cdot 6 \cdots (m+n)} \cdot \dfrac{\pi}{2}, & \text{if } m \text{ and } n \text{ are both} \\ & \text{even integers} \geq 2 \end{cases}$$

The Greek Alphabet

α alpha	ζ zeta	λ,Λ lambda	π,Π pi	ϕ,Φ phi
β beta	η eta	μ mu	ρ rho	χ chi
γ,Γ gamma	θ,Θ theta	ν nu	σ,Σ sigma	ψ,Ψ psi
δ,Δ delta	ι iota	ξ,Ξ xi	τ tau	ω,Ω omega
ϵ epsilon	κ kappa	o omicron	υ,Υ upsilon	

I *Powers, Roots, Reciprocals*

n	n^2	$\sqrt{n}$	$\sqrt{10n}$	n^3	$\sqrt[3]{n}$	$\sqrt[3]{10n}$	$\sqrt[3]{100n}$	$1/n$
1.0	1.00	1.00000	3.16228	1.000	1.00000	2.15443	4.64159	1.00000
1.1	1.21	1.04881	3.31662	1.331	1.03228	2.22398	4.79142	.90909
1.2	1.44	1.09545	3.46410	1.728	1.06266	2.28943	4.93242	.83333
1.3	1.69	1.14018	3.60555	2.197	1.09139	2.35133	5.06580	.76923
1.4	1.96	1.18322	3.74166	2.744	1.11869	2.41014	5.19249	.71429
1.5	2.25	1.22474	3.87298	3.375	1.14471	2.46621	5.31329	.66667
1.6	2.56	1.26491	4.00000	4.096	1.16961	2.51984	5.42884	.62500
1.7	2.89	1.30384	4.12311	4.913	1.19348	2.57128	5.53966	.58824
1.8	3.24	1.34164	4.24264	5.832	1.21644	2.62074	5.64622	.55556
1.9	3.61	1.37840	4.35890	6.859	1.23856	2.66840	5.74890	.52632
2.0	4.00	1.41421	4.47214	8.000	1.25992	2.71442	5.84804	.50000
2.1	4.41	1.44914	4.58258	9.261	1.28058	2.75892	5.94392	.47619
2.2	4.84	1.48324	4.69042	10.648	1.30059	2.80204	6.03681	.45455
2.3	5.29	1.51658	4.79583	12.167	1.32001	2.84387	6.12693	.43478
2.4	5.76	1.54919	4.89898	13.824	1.33887	2.88450	6.21447	.41667
2.5	6.25	1.58114	5.00000	15.625	1.35721	2.92402	6.29961	.40000
2.6	6.76	1.61245	5.09902	17.576	1.37507	2.96250	6.38250	.38462
2.7	7.29	1.64317	5.19615	19.683	1.39248	3.00000	6.46330	.37037
2.8	7.84	1.67332	5.29150	21.952	1.40946	3.03659	6.54213	.35714
2.9	8.41	1.70294	5.38516	24.389	1.42604	3.07232	6.61911	.34483
3.0	9.00	1.73205	5.47723	27.000	1.44225	3.10723	6.69433	.33333
3.1	9.61	1.76068	5.56776	29.791	1.45810	3.14138	6.76790	.32258
3.2	10.24	1.78885	5.65685	32.768	1.47361	3.17480	6.83990	.31250
3.3	10.89	1.81659	5.74456	35.937	1.48881	3.20753	6.91042	.30303
3.4	11.56	1.84391	5.83095	39.304	1.50369	3.23961	6.97953	.29412
3.5	12.25	1.87083	5.91608	42.875	1.51829	3.27107	7.04730	.28571
3.6	12.96	1.89737	6.00000	46.656	1.53262	3.30193	7.11379	.27778
3.7	13.69	1.92354	6.08276	50.653	1.54668	3.33222	7.17905	.27027
3.8	14.44	1.94936	6.16441	54.872	1.56049	3.36198	7.24316	.26316
3.9	15.21	1.97484	6.24500	59.319	1.57406	3.39121	7.30614	.25641
4.0	16.00	2.00000	6.32456	64.000	1.58740	3.41995	7.36806	.25000
4.1	16.81	2.02485	6.40312	68.921	1.60052	3.44822	7.42896	.24390
4.2	17.64	2.04939	6.48074	74.088	1.61343	3.47603	7.48887	.23810
4.3	18.49	2.07364	6.55744	79.507	1.62613	3.50340	7.54784	.23256
4.4	19.36	2.09762	6.63325	85.184	1.63864	3.53035	7.60590	.22727
4.5	20.25	2.12132	6.70820	91.125	1.65096	3.55689	7.66309	.22222
4.6	21.16	2.14476	6.78233	97.336	1.66310	3.58305	7.71944	.21739
4.7	22.09	2.16795	6.85565	103.823	1.67507	3.60883	7.77498	.21277
4.8	23.04	2.19089	6.92820	110.592	1.68687	3.63424	7.82974	.20833
4.9	24.01	2.21359	7.00000	117.649	1.69850	3.65931	7.88374	.20408
5.0	25.00	2.23607	7.07107	125.000	1.70998	3.68403	7.93701	.20000
5.1	26.01	2.25832	7.14143	132.651	1.72130	3.70843	7.98957	.19608
5.2	27.04	2.28035	7.21110	140.608	1.73248	3.73251	8.04145	.19231
5.3	28.09	2.30217	7.28011	148.877	1.74351	3.75629	8.09267	.18868
5.4	29.16	2.32379	7.34847	157.464	1.75441	3.77976	8.14325	.18519

Powers, Roots, Reciprocals (continued)

n	n^2	$\sqrt{n}$	$\sqrt{10n}$	n^3	$\sqrt[3]{n}$	$\sqrt[3]{10n}$	$\sqrt[3]{100n}$	$1/n$
5.5	30.25	2.34521	7.41620	166.375	1.76517	3.80295	8.19321	.18182
5.6	31.36	2.36643	7.48331	175.616	1.77581	3.82586	8.24257	.17857
5.7	32.49	2.38747	7.54983	185.193	1.78632	3.84850	8.29134	.17544
5.8	33.64	2.40832	7.61577	195.112	1.79670	3.87088	8.33955	.17241
5.9	34.81	2.42899	7.68115	205.379	1.80697	3.89300	8.38721	.16949
6.0	36.00	2.44949	7.74597	216.000	1.81712	3.91487	8.43433	.16667
6.1	37.21	2.46982	7.81025	226.981	1.82716	3.93650	8.48093	.16393
6.2	38.44	2.48998	7.87401	238.328	1.83709	3.95789	8.52702	.16129
6.3	39.69	2.50998	7.93725	250.047	1.84691	3.97906	8.57262	.15873
6.4	40.96	2.52982	8.00000	262.144	1.85664	4.00000	8.61774	.15625
6.5	42.25	2.54951	8.06226	274.625	1.86626	4.02073	8.66239	.15385
6.6	43.56	2.56905	8.12404	287.496	1.87578	4.04124	8.70659	.15152
6.7	44.89	2.58844	8.18535	300.763	1.88520	4.06155	8.75034	.14925
6.8	46.24	2.60768	8.24621	314.432	1.89454	4.08166	8.79366	.14706
6.9	47.61	2.62679	8.30662	328.509	1.90378	4.10157	8.83656	.14493
7.0	49.00	2.64575	8.36660	343.000	1.91293	4.12129	8.87904	.14286
7.1	50.41	2.66458	8.42615	357.911	1.92200	4.14082	8.92112	.14085
7.2	51.84	2.68328	8.48528	373.248	1.93098	4.16017	8.96281	.13889
7.3	53.29	2.70185	8.54400	389.017	1.93988	4.17934	9.00411	.13699
7.4	54.76	2.72029	8.60233	405.224	1.94870	4.19834	9.04504	.13514
7.5	56.25	2.73861	8.66025	421.875	1.95743	4.21716	9.08560	.13333
7.6	57.76	2.75681	8.71780	438.976	1.96610	4.23582	9.12581	.13158
7.7	59.29	2.77489	8.77496	456.533	1.97468	4.25432	9.16566	.12987
7.8	60.84	2.79285	8.83176	474.552	1.98319	4.27266	9.20516	.12821
7.9	62.41	2.81069	8.88819	493.039	1.99163	4.29084	9.24434	.12658
8.0	64.00	2.82843	8.94427	512.000	2.00000	4.30887	9.28318	.12500
8.1	65.61	2.84605	9.00000	531.441	2.00830	4.32675	9.32170	.12346
8.2	67.24	2.86356	9.05539	551.368	2.01653	4.34448	9.35990	.12195
8.3	68.89	2.88097	9.11043	571.787	2.02469	4.36207	9.39780	.12048
8.4	70.56	2.89828	9.16515	592.704	2.03279	4.37952	9.43539	.11905
8.5	72.25	2.91548	9.21954	614.125	2.04083	4.39683	9.47268	.11765
8.6	73.96	2.93258	9.27362	636.056	2.04880	4.41400	9.50969	.11628
8.7	75.69	2.94958	9.32738	658.503	2.05671	4.43105	9.54640	.11494
8.8	77.44	2.96648	9.38083	681.472	2.06456	4.44796	9.58284	.11364
8.9	79.21	2.98329	9.43398	704.969	2.07235	4.46475	9.61900	.11236
9.0	81.00	3.00000	9.48683	729.000	2.08008	4.48140	9.65489	.11111
9.1	82.81	3.01662	9.53939	753.571	2.08776	4.49794	9.69052	.10989
9.2	84.64	3.03315	9.59166	778.688	2.09538	4.51436	9.72589	.10870
9.3	86.49	3.04959	9.64365	804.357	2.10294	4.53065	9.76100	.10753
9.4	88.36	3.06594	9.69536	830.584	2.11045	4.54684	9.79586	.10638
9.5	90.25	3.08221	9.74679	857.375	2.11791	4.56290	9.83048	.10526
9.6	92.16	3.09839	9.79796	884.736	2.12532	4.57886	9.86485	.10417
9.7	94.09	3.11448	9.84886	912.673	2.13267	4.59470	9.89898	.10309
9.8	96.04	3.13050	9.89949	941.192	2.13997	4.61044	9.93288	.10204
9.9	98.01	3.14643	9.94987	970.299	2.14723	4.62607	9.96655	.10101

II *Natural Logarithms*

Use ln 10 = 2.30259 to find logarithms of numbers greater than 10 or less than 1

Examples: ln (.347) = ln (3.47 × 10⁻¹)

$$= \ln (3.47) - \ln 10 \approx 1.2442 - 2.3026 = -1.0584$$
$$\ln 143 = \ln 1.43 + 2 \ln 10 \approx 0.3577 + 4.6052 = 4.9629$$

N	0	1	2	3	4	5	6	7	8	9
1.0	0.0000	0100	0198	0296	0392	0488	0583	0677	0770	0862
1.1	0953	1044	1133	1222	1310	1398	1484	1570	1655	1740
1.2	1823	1906	1989	2070	2151	2231	2311	2390	2469	2546
1.3	2624	2700	2776	2852	2927	3001	3075	3148	3221	3293
1.4	3365	3436	3507	3577	3646	3716	3784	3853	3920	3988
1.5	0.4055	4121	4187	4253	4318	4383	4447	4511	4574	4637
1.6	4700	4762	4824	4886	4947	5008	5068	5128	5188	5247
1.7	5306	5365	5423	5481	5539	5596	5653	5710	5766	5822
1.8	5878	5933	5988	6043	6098	6152	6206	6259	6313	6366
1.9	6419	6471	6523	6575	6627	6678	6729	6780	6831	6881
2.0	0.6932	6981	7031	7080	7130	7178	7227	7276	7324	7372
2.1	7419	7467	7514	7561	7608	7655	7701	7747	7793	7839
2.2	7885	7930	7975	8020	8065	8109	8154	8198	8242	8286
2.3	8329	8373	8416	8459	8502	8544	8587	8629	8671	8713
2.4	8755	8796	8838	8879	8920	8961	9002	9042	9083	9123
2.5	0.9163	9203	9243	9282	9322	9361	9400	9439	9478	9517
2.6	9555	9594	9632	9670	9708	9746	9783	9821	9858	9895
2.7	9933	9970	*0006	*0043	*0080	*0116	*0152	*0189	*0225	*0260
2.8	1.0296	0332	0367	0403	0438	0473	0508	0543	0578	0613
2.9	0647	0682	0716	0750	0784	0818	0852	0886	0919	0953
3.0	1.0986	1019	1053	1086	1119	1151	1184	1217	1249	1282
3.1	1314	1346	1378	1410	1442	1474	1506	1537	1569	1600
3.2	1632	1663	1694	1725	1756	1787	1817	1848	1878	1909
3.3	1939	1970	2000	2030	2060	2090	2119	2149	2179	2208
3.4	2238	2267	2296	2326	2355	2384	2413	2442	2470	2499
3.5	1.2528	2556	2585	2613	2641	2670	2698	2726	2754	2782
3.6	2809	2837	2865	2892	2920	2947	2975	3002	3029	3056
3.7	3083	3110	3137	3164	3191	3218	3244	3271	3297	3324
3.8	3350	3376	3403	3429	3455	3481	3507	3533	3558	3584
3.9	3610	3635	3661	3686	3712	3737	3762	3788	3813	3838
4.0	1.3863	3883	3913	3938	3962	3987	4012	4036	4061	4085
4.1	4110	4134	4159	4183	4207	4231	4255	4279	4303	4327
4.2	4351	4375	4398	4422	4446	4469	4493	4516	4540	4563
4.3	4586	4609	4633	4656	4679	4702	4725	4748	4771	4793
4.4	4816	4839	4861	4884	4907	4929	4952	4974	4996	5019
4.5	1.5041	5063	5085	5107	5129	5151	5173	5195	5217	5239
4.6	5261	5282	5304	5326	5347	5369	5390	5412	5433	5454
4.7	5476	5497	5518	5539	5560	5581	5603	5624	5644	5665
4.8	5686	5707	5728	5749	5769	5790	5810	5831	5852	5872
4.9	5892	5913	5933	5953	5974	5994	6014	6034	6054	6074
5.0	1.6094	6114	6134	6154	6174	6194	6214	6233	6253	6273
5.1	6292	6312	6332	6351	6371	6390	6409	6429	6448	6467
5.2	6487	6506	6525	6544	6563	6582	6601	6620	6639	6658
5.3	6677	6696	6715	6734	6752	6771	6790	6808	6827	6846
5.4	6864	6883	6901	6919	6938	6956	6975	6993	7011	7029

Natural Logarithms (continued)

N	0	1	2	3	4	5	6	7	8	9
5.5	1.7048	7066	7084	7102	7120	7138	7156	7174	7192	7210
5.6	7228	7246	7263	7281	7299	7317	7334	7352	7370	7387
5.7	7405	7422	7440	7457	7475	7492	7509	7527	7544	7561
5.8	7579	7596	7613	7630	7647	7664	7682	7699	7716	7733
5.9	7750	7767	7783	7800	7817	7834	7851	7868	7884	7901
6.0	1.7918	7934	7951	7968	7984	8001	8017	8034	8050	8067
6.1	8083	8099	8116	8132	8148	8165	8181	8197	8213	8229
6.2	8246	8262	8278	8294	8310	8326	8342	8358	8374	8390
6.3	8406	8421	8437	8453	8469	8485	8500	8516	8532	8547
6.4	8563	8579	8594	8610	8625	8641	8656	8672	8687	8703
6.5	1.8718	8733	8749	8764	8779	8795	8810	8825	8840	8856
6.6	8871	8886	8901	8916	8931	8946	8961	8976	8991	9006
6.7	9021	9036	9051	9066	9081	9095	9110	9125	9140	9155
6.8	9169	9184	9199	9213	9228	9243	9257	9272	9286	9301
6.9	9315	9330	9344	9359	9373	9387	9402	9416	9431	9445
7.0	1.9459	9473	9488	9502	9516	9530	9545	9559	9573	9587
7.1	9601	9615	9629	9643	9657	9671	9685	9699	9713	9727
7.2	9741	9755	9769	9782	9796	9810	9824	9838	9851	9865
7.3	9879	9892	9906	9920	9933	9947	9961	9974	9988	*0001
7.4	2.0015	0028	0042	0055	0069	0082	0096	0109	0122	0136
7.5	2.0149	0162	0176	0189	0202	0216	0229	0242	0255	0268
7.6	0282	0295	0308	0321	0334	0347	0360	0373	0386	0399
7.7	0412	0425	0438	0451	0464	0477	0490	0503	0516	0528
7.8	0541	0554	0567	0580	0592	0605	0618	0631	0643	0656
7.9	0669	0681	0694	0707	0719	0732	0744	0757	0769	0782
8.0	2.0794	0807	0819	0832	0844	0857	0869	0882	0894	0906
8.1	0919	0931	0943	0956	0968	0980	0992	1005	1017	1029
8.2	1041	1054	1066	1078	1090	1102	1114	1126	1138	1151
8.3	1163	1175	1187	1199	1211	1223	1235	1247	1259	1270
8.4	1282	1294	1306	1318	1330	1342	1354	1365	1377	1389
8.5	2.1401	1412	1424	1436	1448	1459	1471	1483	1494	1506
8.6	1518	1529	1541	1552	1564	1576	1587	1599	1610	1622
8.7	1633	1645	1656	1668	1679	1691	1702	1713	1725	1736
8.8	1748	1759	1770	1782	1793	1804	1816	1827	1838	1849
8.9	1861	1872	1883	1894	1905	1917	1928	1939	1950	1961
9.0	2.1972	1983	1994	2006	2017	2028	2039	2050	2061	2072
9.1	2083	2094	2105	2116	2127	2138	2149	2159	2170	2181
9.2	2192	2203	2214	2225	2235	2246	2257	2268	2279	2289
9.3	2300	2311	2322	2332	2343	2354	2365	2375	2386	2397
9.4	2407	2418	2428	2439	2450	2460	2471	2481	2492	2502
9.5	2.2513	2523	2534	2544	2555	2565	2576	2586	2597	2607
9.6	2618	2628	2638	2649	2659	2670	2680	2690	2701	2711
9.7	2721	2732	2742	2752	2762	2773	2783	2793	2803	2814
9.8	2824	2834	2844	2854	2865	2875	2885	2895	2905	2915
9.9	2925	2935	2946	2956	2966	2976	2986	2996	3006	3016

III *Exponential and Hyperbolic Functions*

x	e^x	e^{-x}	sinh x	cosh x	tanh x
0	1.0000	1.0000	.00000	1.0000	.00000
0.1	1.1052	.90484	.10017	1.0050	.09967
0.2	1.2214	.81873	.20134	1.0201	.19738
0.3	1.3499	.74082	.30452	1.0453	.29131
0.4	1.4918	.67032	.41075	1.0811	.37995
0.5	1.6487	.60653	.52110	1.1276	.46212
0.6	1.8221	.54881	.63665	1.1855	.53705
0.7	2.0138	.49659	.75858	1.2552	.60437
0.8	2.2255	.44933	.88811	1.3374	.66404
0.9	2.4596	.40657	1.0265	1.4331	.71630
1.0	2.7183	.36788	1.1752	1.5431	.76159
1.1	3.0042	.33287	1.3356	1.6685	.80050
1.2	3.3201	.30119	1.5095	1.8107	.83365
1.3	3.6693	.27253	1.6984	1.9709	.86172
1.4	4.0552	.24660	1.9043	2.1509	.88535
1.5	4.4817	.22313	2.1293	2.3524	.90515
1.6	4.9530	.20190	2.3756	2.5775	.92167
1.7	5.4739	.18268	2.6456	2.8283	.93541
1.8	6.0496	.16530	2.9422	3.1075	.94681
1.9	6.6859	.14957	3.2682	3.4177	.95624
2.0	7.3891	.13534	3.6269	3.7622	.96403
2.1	8.1662	.12246	4.0219	4.1443	.97045
2.2	9.0250	.11080	4.4571	4.5679	.97574
2.3	9.9742	.10026	4.9370	5.0372	.98010
2.4	11.023	.09072	5.4662	5.5569	.98367
2.5	12.182	.08208	6.0502	6.1323	.98661
2.6	13.464	.07427	6.6947	6.7690	.98903
2.7	14.880	.06721	7.4063	7.4735	.99101
2.8	16.445	.06081	8.1919	8.2527	.99263
2.9	18.174	.05502	9.0596	9.1146	.99396
3.0	20.086	.04979	10.018	10.068	.99505
3.1	22.198	.04505	11.076	11.122	.99595
3.2	24.533	.04076	12.246	12.287	.99668
3.3	27.113	.03688	13.538	13.575	.99728
3.4	29.964	.03337	14.965	14.999	.99777
3.5	33.115	.03020	16.543	16.573	.99818
3.6	36.598	.02732	18.285	18.313	.99851
3.7	40.447	.02472	20.211	20.236	.99878
3.8	44.701	.02237	22.339	22.362	.99900
3.9	49.402	.02024	24.691	24.711	.99918
4.0	54.598	.01832	27.290	27.308	.99933
4.1	60.340	.01657	30.162	30.178	.99945
4.2	66.686	.01500	33.336	33.351	.99955
4.3	73.700	.01357	36.843	36.857	.99963
4.4	81.451	.01228	40.719	40.732	.99970
4.5	90.017	.01111	45.003	45.014	.99975
4.6	99.484	.01005	49.737	49.747	.99980
4.7	109.95	.00910	54.969	54.978	.99983
4.8	121.51	.00823	60.751	60.759	.99986
4.9	134.29	.00745	67.141	67.149	.99989
5.0	148.41	.00674	74.203	74.210	.99991

IV Trigonometric Functions

Deg.	Rad.	Sin	Cos	Tan	Cot		
0	0.0000	0.0000	1.0000	0.0000		1.5708	90
1	0.0175	0.0175	0.9998	0.0175	57.290	1.5533	89
2	0.0349	0.0349	0.9994	0.0349	28.636	1.5359	88
3	0.0524	0.0523	0.9986	0.0524	19.081	1.5184	87
4	0.0698	0.0698	0.9976	0.0699	14.301	1.5010	86
5	0.0873	0.0872	0.9962	0.0875	11.430	1.4835	85
6	0.1047	0.1045	0.9945	0.1051	9.5144	1.4661	84
7	0.1222	0.1219	0.9925	0.1228	8.1443	1.4486	83
8	0.1396	0.1392	0.9903	0.1405	7.1154	1.4312	82
9	0.1571	0.1564	0.9877	0.1584	6.3138	1.4137	81
10	0.1745	0.1736	0.9848	0.1763	5.6713	1.3963	80
11	0.1920	0.1908	0.9816	0.1944	5.1446	1.3788	79
12	0.2094	0.2079	0.9781	0.2126	4.7046	1.3614	78
13	0.2269	0.2250	0.9744	0.2309	4.3315	1.3439	77
14	0.2443	0.2419	0.9703	0.2493	4.0108	1.3265	76
15	0.2618	0.2588	0.9659	0.2679	3.7321	1.3090	75
16	0.2793	0.2756	0.9613	0.2867	3.4874	1.2915	74
17	0.2967	0.2924	0.9563	0.3057	3.2709	1.2741	73
18	0.3142	0.3090	0.9511	0.3249	3.0777	1.2566	72
19	0.3316	0.3256	0.9455	0.3443	2.9042	1.2392	71
20	0.3491	0.3420	0.9397	0.3640	2.7475	1.2217	70
21	0.3665	0.3584	0.9336	0.3839	2.6051	1.2043	69
22	0.3840	0.3746	0.9272	0.4040	2.4751	1.1868	68
23	0.4014	0.3907	0.9205	0.4245	2.3559	1.1694	67
24	0.4189	0.4067	0.9135	0.4452	2.2460	1.1519	66
25	0.4363	0.4226	0.9063	0.4663	2.1445	1.1345	65
26	0.4538	0.4384	0.8988	0.4877	2.0503	1.1170	64
27	0.4712	0.4540	0.8910	0.5095	1.9626	1.0996	63
28	0.4887	0.4695	0.8829	0.5317	1.8807	1.0821	62
29	0.5061	0.4848	0.8746	0.5543	1.1434	1.0647	61
30	0.5236	0.5000	0.8660	0.5774	1.7321	1.0472	60
31	0.5411	0.5150	0.8572	0.6009	1.6643	1.0297	59
32	0.5585	0.5299	0.8480	0.6249	1.6003	1.0123	58
33	0.5760	0.5446	0.8387	0.6494	1.5399	0.9948	57
34	0.5934	0.5592	0.8290	0.6745	1.4826	0.9774	56
35	0.6109	0.5736	0.8192	0.7002	1.4281	0.9599	55
36	0.6283	0.5878	0.8090	0.7265	1.3764	0.9425	54
37	0.6458	0.6018	0.7986	0.7536	1.3270	0.9250	53
38	0.6632	0.6157	0.7880	0.7813	1.2799	0.9076	52
39	0.6807	0.6293	0.7771	0.8098	1.2349	0.8901	51
40	0.6981	0.6428	0.7660	0.8391	1.1918	0.8727	50
41	0.7156	0.6561	0.7547	0.8693	1.1504	0.8552	49
42	0.7330	0.6691	0.7431	0.9004	1.1106	0.8378	48
43	0.7505	0.6820	0.7314	0.9325	1.0724	0.8203	47
44	0.7679	0.6947	0.7193	0.9657	1.0355	0.8029	46
45	0.7854	0.7071	0.7071	1.0000	1.0000	0.7854	45
		Cos	Sin	Cot	Tan	Rad.	Deg.

V   *Common Logarithms*

N	0	1	2	3	4	5	6	7	8	9
10	0000	0043	0086	0128	0170	0212	0253	0294	0334	0374
11	0414	0453	0492	0531	0569	0607	0645	0682	0719	0755
12	0792	0828	0864	0899	0934	0969	1004	1038	1072	1106
13	1139	1173	1206	1239	1271	1303	1335	1367	1399	1430
14	1461	1492	1523	1553	1584	1614	1644	1673	1703	1732
15	1761	1790	1818	1847	1875	1903	1931	1959	1987	2014
16	2041	2068	2095	2122	2148	2175	2201	2227	2253	2279
17	2304	2330	2355	2380	2405	2430	2455	2480	2504	2529
18	2553	2577	2601	2625	2648	2672	2695	2718	2742	2765
19	2788	2810	2833	2856	2878	2900	2923	2945	2967	2989
20	3010	3032	3054	3075	3096	3118	3139	3160	3181	3201
21	3222	3243	3263	3284	3304	3324	3345	3365	3385	3404
22	3424	3444	3464	3483	3502	3522	3541	3560	3579	3598
23	3617	3636	3655	3674	3692	3711	3729	3747	3766	3784
24	3802	3820	3838	3856	3874	3892	3909	3927	3945	3962
25	3979	3997	4014	4031	4048	4065	4082	4099	4116	4133
26	4150	4166	4183	4200	4216	4232	4249	4265	4281	4298
27	4314	4330	4346	4362	4378	4393	4409	4425	4440	4456
28	4472	4487	4502	4518	4533	4548	4564	4579	4594	4609
29	4624	4639	4654	4669	4683	4698	4713	4728	4742	4757
30	4771	4786	4800	4814	4829	4843	4857	4871	4886	4900
31	4914	4928	4942	4955	4969	4983	4997	5011	5024	5038
32	5051	5065	5079	5092	5105	5119	5132	5145	5159	5172
33	5185	5198	5211	5224	5237	5250	5263	5276	5289	5302
34	5315	5328	5340	5353	5366	5378	5391	5403	5416	5428
35	5441	5453	5465	5478	5490	5502	5514	5527	5539	5551
36	5563	5575	5587	5599	5611	5623	5635	5647	5658	5670
37	5682	5694	5705	5717	5729	5740	5752	5763	5775	5786
38	5798	5809	5821	5832	5843	5855	5866	5877	5888	5899
39	5911	5922	5933	5944	5955	5966	5977	5988	5999	6010
40	6021	6031	6042	6053	6064	6075	6085	6096	6107	6117
41	6128	6138	6149	6160	6170	6180	6191	6201	6212	6222
42	6232	6243	6253	6263	6274	6284	6294	6304	6314	6325
43	6335	6345	6355	6365	6375	6385	6395	6405	6415	6425
44	6435	6444	6454	6464	6474	6484	6493	6503	6513	6522
45	6532	6542	6551	6561	6571	6580	6590	6599	6609	6618
46	6628	6637	6646	6656	6665	6675	6684	6693	6702	6712
47	6721	6730	6739	6749	6758	6767	6776	6785	6694	6803
48	6812	6821	6830	6839	6848	6857	6866	6875	6884	6893
49	6902	6911	6920	6928	6937	6946	6955	6964	6972	6981
50	6990	6998	7007	7016	7024	7033	7042	7050	7059	7067
51	7076	7084	7093	7101	7110	7118	7126	7135	7143	7152
52	7160	7168	7177	7185	7193	7202	7210	7218	7226	7235
53	7243	7251	7259	7267	7275	7284	7292	7300	7308	7316
54	7324	7332	7340	7348	7356	7364	7372	7380	7388	7396

Common Logarithms (continued)

N	0	1	2	3	4	5	6	7	8	9
55	7404	7412	7419	7427	7435	7443	7451	7459	7466	7474
56	7482	7490	7497	7505	7513	7520	7528	7536	7543	7551
57	7559	7566	7574	7582	7589	7597	7604	7612	7619	7627
58	7634	7642	7649	7657	7664	7672	7679	7686	7694	7701
59	7709	7716	7723	7731	7738	7745	7752	7760	7767	7774
60	7782	7789	7796	7803	7810	7818	7825	7832	7839	7846
61	7853	7860	7868	7875	7882	7889	7896	7903	7910	7917
62	7924	7931	7938	7945	7952	7959	7966	7973	7980	7987
63	7993	8000	8007	8014	8021	8028	8035	8041	8048	8055
64	8062	8069	8075	8082	8089	8096	8102	8109	8116	8122
65	8129	8136	8142	8149	8156	8162	8169	8176	8182	8189
66	8195	8202	8209	8215	8222	8228	8235	8241	8248	8254
67	8261	8267	8274	8280	8287	8293	8299	8306	8312	8319
68	8325	8331	8338	8344	8351	8357	8363	8370	8376	8382
69	8388	8395	8401	8407	8414	8420	8426	8432	8439	8445
70	8451	8457	8463	8470	8476	8482	8488	8494	8500	8506
71	8513	8519	8525	8531	8537	8543	8549	8555	8561	8567
72	8573	8579	8585	8591	8597	8603	8609	8615	8621	8627
73	8633	8639	8645	8651	8657	8663	8669	8675	8681	8686
74	8692	8698	8704	8710	8716	8722	8727	8733	8739	8745
75	8751	8756	8762	8768	8774	8779	8785	8791	8797	8802
76	8808	8814	8820	8825	8831	8837	8842	8848	8854	8859
77	8865	8871	8876	8882	8887	8893	8899	8904	8910	8915
78	8921	8927	8932	8938	8943	8949	8954	8960	8965	8971
79	8976	8982	8987	8993	8998	9004	9009	9015	9020	9025
80	9031	9036	9042	9047	9053	9058	9063	9069	9074	9079
81	9085	9090	9096	9101	9106	9112	9117	9122	9128	9133
82	9138	9143	9149	9154	9159	9165	9170	9175	9180	9186
83	9191	9196	9201	9206	9212	9217	9222	9227	9232	9238
84	9243	9248	9253	9258	9263	9269	9274	9279	9284	9289
85	9294	9299	9304	9309	9315	9320	9325	9330	9335	9340
86	9345	9350	9355	9360	9365	9370	9375	9380	9385	9390
87	9395	9400	9405	9410	9415	9420	9425	9430	9435	9440
88	9445	9450	9455	9460	9465	9469	9474	9479	9484	9489
89	9494	9499	9504	9509	9513	9518	9523	9528	9533	9538
90	9542	9547	9552	9557	9562	9566	9571	9576	9581	9586
91	9590	9595	9600	9605	9609	9614	9619	9624	9628	9633
92	9638	9643	9647	9652	9657	9661	9666	9671	9675	9680
93	9685	9689	9694	9699	9703	9708	9713	9717	9722	9727
94	9731	9736	9741	9745	9750	9754	9759	9763	9768	9773
95	9777	9782	9786	9791	9795	9800	9805	9809	9814	9818
96	9823	9827	9832	9836	9841	9845	9850	9854	9859	9863
97	9868	9872	9877	9881	9886	9890	9894	9899	9903	9908
98	9912	9917	9921	9926	9930	9934	9939	9943	9948	9952
99	9956	9961	9965	9969	9974	9978	9983	9987	9991	9996

Answers

Odd-numbered Exercises

REVIEW

1 Polynomials . . . *(page 2)*

1. (a) $4x^2 + 6x + 2$
   (b) $-2x^2 + 4x - 6$
3. (a) $x^2 + 2$ (b) $2x - 1$
5. (a) $z^3 + (\pi + 1)z^2 + z$
   (b) $z^3 + (\pi - 1)z^2 - z + 2$

(Page 3)

1. $2x^4 - x^3 + 6x^2 - x + 6$
3. $\frac{1}{2}x^5 + \frac{9}{2}x^2 - x + 2$
5. $3ax^4 + 4ax^3 + 3bx + 4b$
7. $x^3 + 3x^2 + 3x + 1$
9. $13x^2 - 2x + 2$
11. The degree of the product is the sum of the degrees of the factors.

(Page 4)

1. $(x - y)(x + y)$
3. $(c - d)(c^4 + c^3d + c^2d^2 + cd^3 + d^4)$
5. 63
7. $\dfrac{63}{32}$

2 The Quadratic Formula *(page 6)*

1. (a) real, unequal (b) $1, 2$
3. (a) real, unequal (b) $\dfrac{-1 \pm \sqrt{3}}{-2}$
5. (a) real, unequal (b) $-2 \pm \sqrt{2}$
7. $\dfrac{1 \pm \sqrt{5}}{2}$
9. No real solutions

3 The Binomial Theorem *(page 9)*

1. 5 5. 56
3. 9 7. 1
9. $x^5 + 5x^4y + 10x^3y^2 + 10x^2y^3 + 5xy^4 + y^5$
11. $x^4 - 4x^3y + 6x^2y^2 - 4xy^3 + y^4$
13. $-x^3 + 6x^2y - 12xy^2 + 8y^3$
15. $\dfrac{1}{16}x^4 + \dfrac{1}{2}x^3y + \dfrac{3}{2}x^2y^2 + 2xy^3 + y^4$

4 Rational Exponents
(page 11)

1. 3	**17.** 1/3
3. 2	**19.** $y^{11/6}$
5. 4	**21.** $2^{1/2}$
7. 1/8	**23.** x^2
9. −1/27	**25.** $5^{1/4}$
11. .04	**27.** $x^{-17/6}$
13. .008	**29.** $2x^{1/2}$
15. 4	**31.** $zx^{-8/3}$

5 Inequalities and Intervals
(page 13)

1. True	**7.** True
3. False	**9.** True
5. False	**11.** True

13. $1 < 2 < 3$ or $3 > 2 > 1$
15. $0 \le 0 < 4$ or $4 > 0 \ge 0$
17. $-1 < 0 < \pi$ or $\pi > 0 > -1$
19. $2 \le 2 \le 2$ or $2 \ge 2 \ge 2$
21. $1 < 2 < 3 < 4$ or $4 > 3 > 2 > 1$
23. $1/2 < 2 \le 2 < 3$
　　 or $3 > 2 \ge 2 > 1/2$

(Page 15)

1. False	**7.** True	**13.**]2,6[
3. True	**9.** True	**15.** [1/2,3/2[
5. True	**11.** True	

(Page 17)

1. $x < 3$	**7.** $x \ge -25$
3. $x < 4$	**9.** $x > 36/5$
5. $x \ge 6$	**11.** $x > -10$

CHAPTER 1

1 The Cartesian Plane . . .
(page 21)

1.

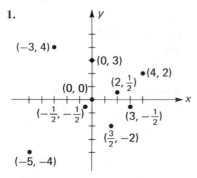

3. The y-coordinate is 0.

(Page 23)

1. (5,5)	**9.** (−2.35,.4)
3. (3/4,7/4)	**11.** $x = 7$, $y = -10$
5. (−2,−3)	**13.** $x_1 = -x_2$, $y_1 = -y_2$
7. (7/12,1/4)	

(Page 27)

1. 5　　**3.** $\frac{1}{2}\sqrt{17}$　　**5.** $\sqrt{25.04}$

7. $AB = \sqrt{41}$, $BC = \sqrt{41}$, $AC = \sqrt{82}$, so $AB^2 + BC^2 = AC^2$. Also, $AB = BC$.

9. $AB = BC = CD = AD = \sqrt{8}$, so the four sides have equal length. Also, $AC = 4$ so $AB^2 + BC^2 = AC^2$. Thus, angle ABC is a right angle.

11. (a) $\sqrt{(x-0)^2 + (y-0)^2} = 5$
　　(b) $\sqrt{(x-h)^2 + (y-k)^2} = 5$
　　(c) $\sqrt{(x-h)^2 + (y-k)^2} = r$
　　(d) $\sqrt{(x-h)^2 + (y-k)^2} = r$

2 Straight Lines
(pages 41–42)

1. 2	**5.** −10
3. 0	**7.** −14/9

9. (a) 3　(b) 1　(c) −1/3
11. (a) 1　(b) −1　(c) 1
13. (a) −3/2　(b) −1/2　(c) −1/3
15. (a) 0　(b) −2　(c) None
17. (a) 4/3　(b) −2　(c) 3/2
19. (a) 2　(b) 10　(c) −5
21. $y = 2x + 5$
23. $y = 2x - 1$
25. (−22/7,3/7)

27. $x = 1$, $y = -1$ 31. Neither

29. Perpendicular   33. Neither

35. The slope of $\overline{AB}$ is 5/4; the slope of $\overline{BC}$ is $-1/3$; the slope of $\overline{CD}$ is 5/4; the slope of $\overline{AD}$ is $-1/3$. Or, the midpoint of AC is $\left(-\frac{11}{2}, 1\right)$, the midpoint of BD is $\left(-\frac{11}{2}, 1\right)$.

37. To show it is a straight line, use the general form $Ax + By + C = 0$.
$\frac{x}{a} + \frac{y}{b} = 1$ becomes $\left(\frac{1}{a}\right)x + \left(\frac{1}{b}\right)y - 1 = 0$.
Set $y = 0$ and get $x = a$.
Set $x = 0$ and get $y = b$.

3   The Parabola *(page 51)*

1. (a) $x = 0$ (b) $(0,0)$ (c) $(0,1)$
   (d) $y = -1$

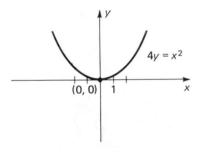

$4y = x^2$

$(0, 0)$ 1

3. (a) $x = 0$ (b) $(0,0)$ (c) $(0,1/16)$
   (d) $y = -1/16$

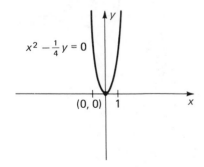

$x^2 - \frac{1}{4}y = 0$

$(0, 0)$ 1

5. (a) $y = -2$ (b) $(0,-2)$
   (c) $(1/4,-2)$ (d) $x = -\frac{1}{4}$

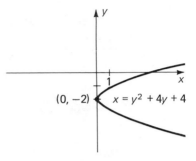

$(0, -2)$ $x = y^2 + 4y + 4$

7. (a) $x = -1/2$ (b) $(-1/2, 1\frac{1}{2})$
   (c) $(-1/2,11/8)$ (d) $y = 13/8$

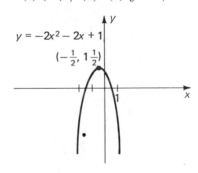

$y = -2x^2 - 2x + 1$

$\left(-\frac{1}{2}, 1\frac{1}{2}\right)$

11. $12y = x^2$

13. $8y = (x + 1)^2$

4   The Circle *(pages 53-54)*

1.

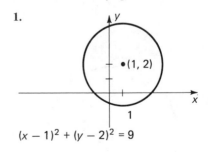

$\bullet(1, 2)$

1

$(x - 1)^2 + (y - 2)^2 = 9$

3.

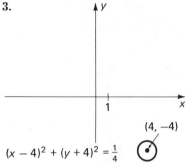

$(x - 4)^2 + (y + 4)^2 = \frac{1}{4}$

5.

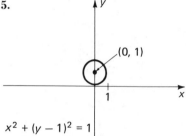

$x^2 + (y - 1)^2 = 1$

7.

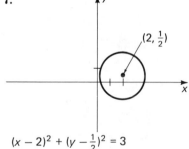

$(x - 2)^2 + (y - \frac{1}{2})^2 = 3$

9. (a) $C = (0,0)$; $r = 5$

(b)

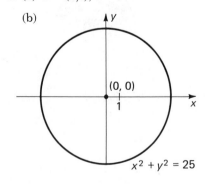

$x^2 + y^2 = 25$

11. (a) $C = (-2,-3)$; $r = 4$

(b)

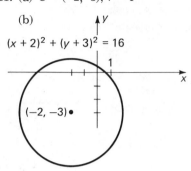

$(x + 2)^2 + (y + 3)^2 = 16$

13. (a) $C = (1,-1/2)$; $r = 1$

(b)

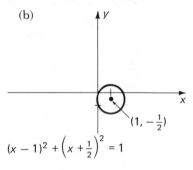

$(x - 1)^2 + \left(x + \frac{1}{2}\right)^2 = 1$

15. (a) $C = (1,1)$; $r = \sqrt{3}$

(b)

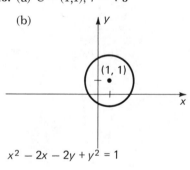

$x^2 - 2x - 2y + y^2 = 1$

17. (a) $C = (-1/6, 1/4)$; $r = \dfrac{\sqrt{301}}{12}$

(b)

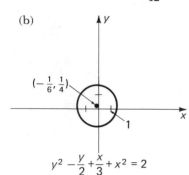

$$y^2 - \frac{y}{2} + \frac{x}{3} + x^2 = 2$$

19. The equations are
$$6a + 2b + c = -10$$
$$-2b + c = -1$$
$$2a + c = -1$$
Thus, $a = -9/2$, $b = 9/2$, $c = 8$. The equation is $x^2 - 9x + y^2 + 9y + 8 = 0$.

21. (a) $(-2,8)$ (b) $(-6,4)$

5 The Ellipse *(pages 58–59)*

1. (a)

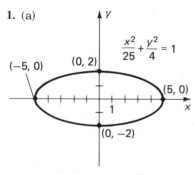

(b) 10 and 4   (c) $(\sqrt{21},0)$ and $(-\sqrt{21},0)$

3. (a)

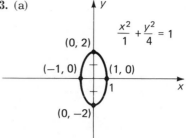

(b) 4 and 2   (c) $(0,\sqrt{3})$ and $(0,-\sqrt{3})$

5. (a)

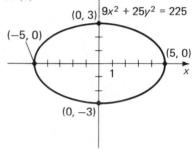

(b) 10 and 6   (c) $(4,0)$ and $(-4,0)$

7. (a)

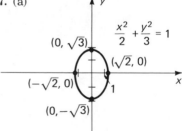

(b) $2\sqrt{3}$ and $2\sqrt{2}$ (c) $(0,1)$ and $(0,-1)$

9. (a)

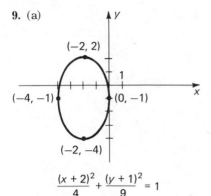

$$\frac{(x + 2)^2}{4} + \frac{(y + 1)^2}{9} = 1$$

(b) 6 and 4   (c) $(-2, -1 + \sqrt{5})$
and $(-2, -1 - \sqrt{5})$

11. The equation is equivalent to
$\frac{(x - 1)^2}{9} + \frac{(y + 2)^2}{4} = 1$. The major
axis has length 6 and the minor
axis has length 4. The foci are
$(1 + \sqrt{5}, -2)$ and $(1 - \sqrt{5}, -2)$.

13. Show that $\sqrt{x^2 + (y + c)^2} +$
$\sqrt{x^2 + (y - c)^2} = 2b$ is equivalent
to $\frac{x^2}{a^2} + \frac{y^2}{b^2} = 1$ by moving one radical in the first equation to the
other side of the equation and
squaring both sides.

15. $64x^2 + 96y^2 - 24xy - 52x -$
$84y - 341 = 0$

6   The Hyperbola
(pages 65–66)

1. (a) $y = 2x$ and $y = -2x$

(b)

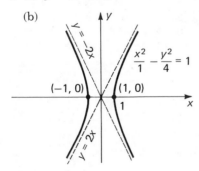

3. (a) $y = \frac{3}{5}x$ and $y = -\frac{3}{5}x$

(b)

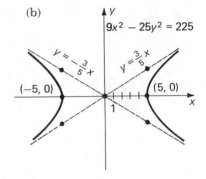

5. (a) $x = 0$ and $y = 0$

(b)

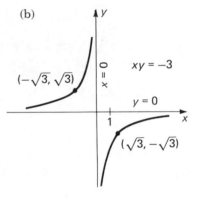

7. (a) $y = \frac{1}{2}x - 3$ and $y = -\frac{1}{2}x + 1$

(b) $\frac{(y + 1)^2}{1} - \frac{(x - 4)^2}{4} = 1$

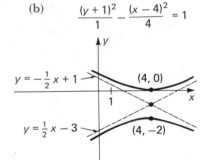

9. (a) $x = -2$ and $y = 3$

(b)

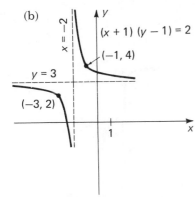

$(x + 1)(y - 1) = 2$

$(-1, 4)$

$y = 3$

$(-3, 2)$

11. (a) $y = \sqrt{2}x$ and $y = -\sqrt{2}x$

(b)

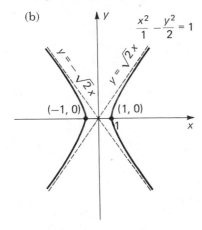

$$\frac{x^2}{1} - \frac{y^2}{2} = 1$$

$(-1, 0)$ $(1, 0)$

13. Square both sides of the equation
$|\sqrt{x^2 + y^2} - \sqrt{x^2 + (y - 2)^2}| = 1$
to obtain $x^2 + y^2 -$
$2\sqrt{(x^2 + y^2)(x^2 + (y - 2)^2)} + x^2 +$
$(y - 2)^2 = 1$. Isolate the radical,
square, and simplify to obtain
$4x^2 - 12y^2 + 24y - 9 = 0$.

7 Functions (page 68)

1. dom $f = R$; rg $f = R$
3. dom $f = \{x \mid x \neq 0\}$;
   rg $f = \{x \mid x \neq 0\}$
5. dom $g = \{x \mid x \neq -2\}$;
   rg $g = \{x \mid x \neq 0\}$
7. dom $f = \{x \mid x \geq 1\}$;
   rg $f = \{x \mid x \geq 0\}$

9. dom $h = \left\{x \mid x \neq -\frac{1}{2}\right\}$;
   rg $h = \{x \mid x \neq 0\}$
11. dom $g = R$; rg $g = \{x \mid x \geq 1\}$
13. dom $f = R$; rg $f = R$
15. dom $f = \{x \mid -1 \leq x \leq 1\}$;
    rg $f = \{x \mid 0 \leq x \leq 1\}$
17. (a) -1 (b) 1 (c) -7 (d) 0
    (e) $4x - 1$ (f) $\frac{3}{y} - 1$
    (g) $2x^2 - 1$ (h) $2x^2 + 1$
19. $x = \pm 1$
21. No. dom $f = R$ but dom $g = \{x \mid x \neq 1\}$.
23. (a) $(x + h)^2 = x^2 + 2hx + h^2$
    (b) $2hx + h^2$ (c) $2x + h$

(Page 72)

1. (a) $f \circ g(x) = x^2 - 2x + 1$
   (b) $g \circ f(x) = x^2 - 1$
3. (a) $f \circ g(x) = x^6$
   (b) $g \circ f(x) = x^6$
5. (a) $f \circ g(x) = |2x|$
   (b) $g \circ f(x) = 2|x| = |2x|$
7. (a) $f \circ g(x) = 2x^4 + 4x^3 + x^2 - x + 3$
   (b) $g \circ f(x) = 4x^4 - 4x^3 + 15x^2 - 7x + 12$
9. $f \circ g \circ h(x) = 18x^2 - 12x + 2$
11. $g^{-1}(x) = \sqrt[3]{x}$
13. $f^{-1}(x) = -x, x \geq 0$
15. $g^{-1}(x) = -\sqrt{\dfrac{x + 3}{2}}, x \geq -3$
17. For any $x \in R, f \circ g(x) = f(g(x)) = g(x)$. Also, $g \circ f(x) = g(f(x)) = g(x)$.

8 Graphing Functions
(page 74)

1.

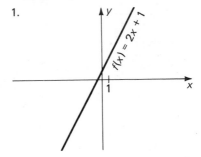

$f(x) = 2x + 1$

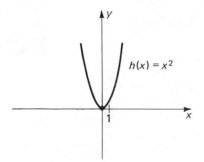

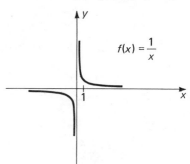

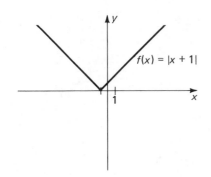

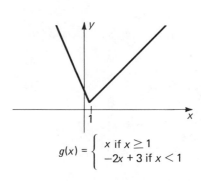

$$g(x) = \begin{cases} x \text{ if } x \geq 1 \\ -2x + 3 \text{ if } x < 1 \end{cases}$$

(Pages 75–76)

1. Yes   5. Yes   9. Yes
3. No   7. Yes   11. No
13. A function is 1–1 if and only if
    each horizontal line meets its
    graph in at most one point.
15. Even   21. Even
17. Odd   23. Neither
19. Even

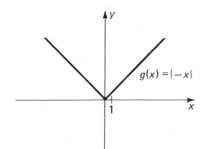

9 The Arithmetic of Functions *(page 78)*

1. $(f + g)(x) = 4x - 1$; $(f - g)(x) = -2x + 1$; $(f \cdot g)(x) = 3x^2 - x$;
   $\left(\dfrac{f}{g}\right)(x) = \dfrac{x}{3x - 1}$, $x \neq \dfrac{1}{3}$

3. $(f + g)(x) = x^2 + x$; $(f - g)(x) = x^2 - x$; $(f \cdot g)(x) = x^3$;
   $\left(\dfrac{f}{g}\right)(x) = \dfrac{x^2}{x}$, $x \neq 0$ or $\left(\dfrac{f}{g}\right)(x) = x$, $x \neq 0$

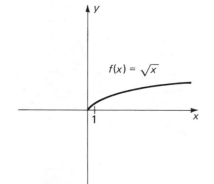

5. $(f + g)(x) = x^2 - x + 1;$
$(f - g)(x) = -x^2 + 5x - 3;$
$(f \cdot g)(x) = 2x^3 - 7x^2 + 7x - 2;$
$\left(\dfrac{f}{g}\right)(x) = \dfrac{2x - 1}{x^2 - 3x + 2}, \; x \neq 1, 2$

7. (a) $(f + g)(3) = 6$
(b) $(f - g)(2) = 4$
(c) $(f \cdot g)(1) = -1$
(d) $\left(\dfrac{f}{g}\right)(-4) = 1$

9. It is not defined.

CHAPTER 2

1 Neighborhoods . . .
(pages 80–81)

1. $]0,4[$ **3.** $]5,10[$ **5.** (b) **7.** (c)

2 The Limit of a Function
(page 82)

1. $f(x)$ gets closer and closer to 2.
3. $f(x)$ gets closer and closer to 8.
5. $g(x)$ gets closer and closer to −4.
7. $h(x)$ gets closer and closer to 2.
9. $f(x)$ gets closer and closer to 6.
In fact, it is constantly 6.
11. $f(x)$ gets closer and closer to 0.

(Pages 86–89)

1. 3   **9.** −1   **17.** 2
3. 1   **11.** 3   **19.** 4
5. 1   **13.** 2   **21.** 4
7. 6   **15.** −1   **23.** $\dfrac{1}{6}$

25. (a) 1 (b) −2 (c) a
27. a^n
29. (a) 2 (b) −3 (c) $\sqrt[3]{b}$
31. (a) 2 (b) 4 (c) 6 (d) $2x_0$
33. (a) $\dfrac{1}{2}$ (b) $\dfrac{1}{2}\sqrt{2}$ (c) $\dfrac{1}{2}\sqrt{3}$
(d) $\dfrac{1}{2}\sqrt{x_0}$

35. $2x$

37. $-\dfrac{1}{x^2}$

39. $\dfrac{1}{2}\dfrac{1}{\sqrt{x - 1}}$

41. Given $\epsilon > 0$, let $\delta = \epsilon$. Then if
$|x - 1| < \delta$ then $|x - 1| < \epsilon$.
So $|(x + 2) - 3| = |x - 1| < \epsilon$.

43. Given $\epsilon > 0$, let $\delta = \epsilon/3$. Then if
$|x - (-2)| < \delta$ then $|x + 2| < \epsilon/3$.
So $|(3x - 2) - (-8)| = |3x + 6| =$
$3|x + 2| < 3 \cdot \epsilon/3 = \epsilon.$

45. Given $\epsilon > 0$, let δ be positive and
less than $\epsilon/3$ and also less than
1. Then if $|x - 1| < \delta$, then
$|x - 1| < \epsilon/3$ and $|x + 1| =$
$|x - 1 + 2| \leq |x - 1| + 2 < 3.$
So $|(x^2 + 1) - 2| = |x^2 - 1| =$
$|x - 1| \cdot |x + 1| < \epsilon/3 \cdot 3 = \epsilon.$

47. Given $\epsilon > 0$, let δ be positive and
less than $\epsilon/5$ and also less than
1. Then if $|x - (-2)| < \delta$, then
$|x + 2| < \epsilon/5$ and $|x - 2| =$
$|x + 2 - 4| \leq |x + 2| + 4 < 5.$ So
$|(x^2 + 2) - 6| = |x^2 - 4| =$
$|x - 2| \cdot |x + 2| < 5 \cdot \epsilon/5 = \epsilon.$

3 Limits at Infinity
(pages 91–92)

1. 0   **7.** 0   **13.** 1
3. $\dfrac{2}{3}$ **9.** 0   **15.** 0
5. $-\dfrac{1}{2}$ **11.** 0

4 The Limit Theorems
(page 97)

1. (a) 3 (b) 3 (c) −2 (d) −1
(e) 32 (f) $\sqrt[4]{2}$
3. $\lim\limits_{x \to a} (f(x) - l) = \lim\limits_{x \to a} f(x) -$
$\lim\limits_{x \to a} l = l - l = 0$
5. No. Example: $\lim\limits_{x \to 2} x^2 = 4$ and
$\lim\limits_{x \to 3} x^2 = 9; \lim\limits_{x \to 5} x^2 = 25 \neq 4 + 9$

7. $\lim\limits_{x \to 2} ((x^2 + 2x + 3)(x^3 + 3x - 13)) =$

$$\lim\limits_{x \to 2} (x^2 + 2x + 3) \cdot$$

$$\lim\limits_{x \to 2} (x^3 + 3x - 13) = 11 \cdot 1 = 11$$

9. $\lim\limits_{x \to -\infty} \left(\dfrac{1}{x} + \dfrac{1}{x+1} \right) = \lim\limits_{x \to -\infty} \dfrac{1}{x} +$

$$\lim\limits_{x \to -\infty} \dfrac{1}{x+1} = 0 + 0 = 0$$

11. $\lim\limits_{x \to -2} \dfrac{\sqrt[3]{x^2 + 4} - \sqrt{-x + 7}}{x^2 + 3x + 1} =$

$$\lim\limits_{x \to -2} \dfrac{\sqrt[3]{x^2 + 4}}{x^2 + 3x + 1} -$$

$$\lim\limits_{x \to -2} \dfrac{\sqrt{-x + 7}}{x^2 + 3x + 1}$$

$$= \dfrac{\sqrt[3]{8}}{-1} - \dfrac{\sqrt{9}}{-1} = \dfrac{2}{-1} - \dfrac{3}{-1} = 1$$

5 One-sided Limits
(pages 101–102)

1. 0   **3.** 0   **5.** (Answers will vary.)
7. $\lim\limits_{x \to 1^+} f(x) = 1, \ \lim\limits_{x \to 1^-} f(x) = 1,$

$$\lim\limits_{x \to 1} f(x) = 1$$

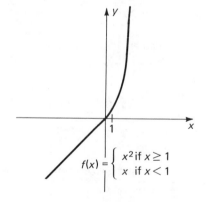

$$f(x) = \begin{cases} x^2 \text{ if } x \ge 1 \\ x \text{ if } x < 1 \end{cases}$$

9. $\lim\limits_{t \to 2^+} h(t) = 5, \ \lim\limits_{t \to 2^-} h(t) = 5,$

$$\lim\limits_{t \to 2} h(t) = 5$$

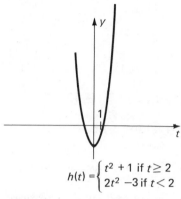

$$h(t) = \begin{cases} t^2 + 1 \text{ if } t \ge 2 \\ 2t^2 - 3 \text{ if } t < 2 \end{cases}$$

11. $\lim\limits_{x \to 0^+} f(x) = -3, \ \lim\limits_{x \to 0^-} f(x) = -3,$

$$\lim\limits_{x \to 0} f(x) = -3$$

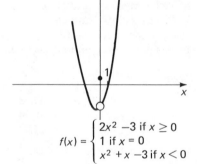

$$f(x) = \begin{cases} 2x^2 - 3 \text{ if } x \ge 0 \\ 1 \text{ if } x = 0 \\ x^2 + x - 3 \text{ if } x < 0 \end{cases}$$

13. As x gets closer and closer to a, then since x is either smaller or larger than a, we see that (in either case) $f(x)$ gets closer and closer to l.

15. (a)

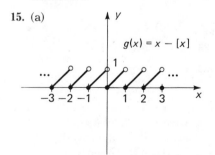

$$g(x) = x - [x]$$

(b) $\lim_{x \to 1^+} g(x) = 0$, $\lim_{x \to 1^-} g(x) = 1$

(c) $\lim_{x \to 1\frac{1}{2}^+} g(x) = \frac{1}{2}$, $\lim_{x \to 1\frac{1}{2}^-} g(x) = \frac{1}{2}$

(d) $\lim_{x \to a} g(x)$ exists if and only if a is not an integer.

6 Infinite Limits
(pages 105–106)

1. ∞ 7. ∞ 13. $-\infty$
3. 0   9. ∞ 15. 53/14
5. 0   11. ∞
17. (a) ∞ (b) ∞ (c). Yes. The limit is ∞, which is the common value of both one-sided limits.
19. a

7 Continuous Functions
(pages 112–113)

1. $\{x \mid x \neq 2\}$ 5. All points
3. $\{x \mid x \neq 0\}$ 7. $\{x \mid x \neq \pm 1\}$

9. $\{x \mid x \neq 1, 2\}$ 13. $\{x \mid x \neq 0\}$
11. $\{t \mid t \geq 0\}$ 15. All points
17. 4
19. No. $\lim_{x \to 0} 1/x = \infty$
21. If $f + g$ were continuous at a, then $\lim_{x \to a} (f(x) + g(x)) = f(a) + g(a)$. Since $\lim_{x \to a} f(x) = f(a)$, then $\lim_{x \to a} g(x) = \lim_{x \to a} (f(x) + g(x)) - \lim_{x \to a} f(x) = f(a) + g(a) - f(a) = g(a)$. Thus, g would be continuous at a, which is a contradiction.
23. (a) $\lim_{x \to 3^+} f(x) = 2 = f(3)$
    (b) $\lim_{x \to 3^-} f(x) = 1 \neq f(3)$
25. (a) $\{x \mid x$ is not an integer$\}$
    (b) all points
    (c) $\{x \mid x$ is not an integer$\}$
27. $x = \sqrt[3]{200}$
29. $x = 3$

CHAPTER 3

1 The Definition of the Derivative *(page 122)*

1. (a) 4   (b) 4
3. (a) 9   (b) $4t + 1$
5. (a) 12   (b) $3t^2$
7. (a) -5 (b) $2x - 1$
9. (a) 13   (b) $3x^2 + 1$

2 Differentiation of Positive Integral Powers *(page 123)*

1. (a) 0 (b) 12 (c) 12 (d) 4/3
   (e) 6 (f) $3a^2$
3. 1

3 The Linearity of the Derivative . . . *(page 126)*

1. (a) 3 (b) 16 (c) 14 (d) 6
   (e) 1/2 (f) -11 (g) -1
   (h) -15 (i) 169 (j) 10/512

3. Since $g(x) = (f + g)(x) - f(x)$, then $g'(x) = (f + g)'(x) - f'(x)$.

4 Derivatives . . .
(pages 130–131)

1. (a) $f'(x) = 3x^2 - 2$, $f'(1) = 1$
3. $4x^3 + 2x$
5. $6x^2 + 22x + 11$
7. (a) $\dfrac{-2}{x^3}$, $x \neq 0$ (b) $\dfrac{-3}{x^4}$, $x \neq 0$
   (c) $\dfrac{-4}{x^5}$, $x \neq 0$ (d) $\dfrac{-100}{x^{101}}$, $x \neq 0$
9. -1
11. $\dfrac{11}{(-2x + 1)^2}$
13. $\dfrac{10t^2 + 8t + 7}{(5t + 2)^2}$
15. (a) 2 (b) 0
17. (a) 2 (b) $\dfrac{1}{2}$

19. (a) $f_2(x) = x \cdot x$ so
$$f_2'(x) = x \cdot 1 + 1 \cdot x = 2x$$
(b) $f_3(x) = x^2 \cdot x$ so
$$f_3'(x) = 2x \cdot x + 1 \cdot x^2 = 3x^2$$
(c) For $n = 1$, $f_n'(x) = 1 \cdot x^0 = 1$
since $f_1(x) = x$.
Parts (a) and (b) show that it is true for $n = 2$ and 3. To complete the proof we show that if it is true for $n - 1$, then it is also true for n. Now, if it is true for $n - 1$, we have $f_{n-1}'(x) = (n-1)x^{n-2}$. Now $f_n(x) = f_{n-1}(x) \cdot x$ so $f_n'(x) = f_{n-1}'(x) \cdot x + 1 \cdot f_{n-1}(x) = (n-1)x^{n-2} \cdot x + x^{n-1} = nx^{n-1}$.

21. $g(x) = (f(x))^2 f(x)$ so $g'(x) = (f(x))^2 f'(x) + 2f(x)f'(x)f(x) = 3(f(x))^2 f'(x)$

23. (a) $(f \cdot g \cdot h)(x) = f(x)(g \cdot h)(x) = f(x)(g \cdot h)'(x) + (g \cdot h)(x)f'(x) = f(x)(g(x)h'(x) + h(x)g'(x)) + g(x)h(x)f'(x) = f(x)g(x)h'(x) + f(x)h(x)g'(x) + g(x)h(x)f'(x) = f'(x)g(x)h(x) + g'(x)f(x)h(x) + h'(x)f(x)g(x)$

(b) The derivative of a product of n functions is the sum of the n functions obtained by taking the derivative of each factor and multiplying it by the product of the remaining $n - 1$ factors.

5 The "Little d" Notation . . .
(pages 132 – 133)

1. If $f_1, f_2, \ldots, f_n$ are all differentiable at x and $a_1, a_2, \ldots, a_n$ are any constants, then the function $f = a_1 f_1 + a_2 f_2 + \ldots + a_n f_n$ is differentiable at x and
$$\frac{d}{dx} f(x) = \frac{d}{dx}(a_1 f_1 + a_2 f_2 + \ldots + a_n(f_n)(x))$$
$$= a_1 \frac{d}{dx} f_1(x) + a_2 \frac{d}{dx} f_2(x) + \ldots + a_n \frac{d}{dx} f_n(x)$$

3. If f and g are differentiable at x, then $f \cdot g$ is differentiable at x and
$$\frac{d}{dx}(f \cdot g)(x) = f(x)\frac{d}{dx}g(x) + g(x)\frac{d}{dx}f(x)$$

5. (a) $1 - \dfrac{1}{x^2}$ (b) $\dfrac{-3}{x^4}$

(c) $\dfrac{-x^2 - 2x + 3}{(x-1)^4}$ or $\dfrac{-x-3}{(x-1)^3}$

(d) $\dfrac{2}{x^3} - \dfrac{2x+3}{x^4}$ or $\dfrac{-3}{x^4}$

7. (a) 1 (b) 2 (c) 3 (d) $\dfrac{1}{2}$

(e) $\sqrt{2}$

9. (a) $\pi/2$ (b) π (c) $3\pi/2$
(d) $\pi/4$ (e) $\pi\sqrt{2}/2$

11. $x = \dfrac{-1}{2}, -2$

(Pages 138 – 139)

1. $4(x+1)^3$

3. $23(x+2)^{22}$

5. $-2\left(\dfrac{x+2}{x^2+2}\right)^{-3}\left(\dfrac{-x^2-4x+2}{(x^2+2)^2}\right)$

7. $7(1 + (t+1)^3)^6(3(t+1)^2)$

9. $-3(1 + (x-1)^2)^{-4}(2(x-1))(2)$

11. $3(x^{-1} - 2x^{-2})^2(-x^{-2} + 4x^{-3})$

13. $4\left(\dfrac{t^2-1}{t^2+1} + \dfrac{t^3}{2}\right)^3 \cdot$
$$\left(\dfrac{(t^2+1)(2t) - (t^2-1)(2t)}{(t^2+1)^2} + \dfrac{3t^2}{2}\right)$$

15. $(x^2+1)^2(3(x^2+2)^2(2x)) + (x^2+2)^3(2(x^2+1)(2x))$

17. $2(x^2+1)(2x)$

19. $\dfrac{-2}{(x+2)^2} + 3\left(\dfrac{2}{x+2}\right)^2\left(\dfrac{-2}{(x+2)^2}\right)$

21. $2\left(\dfrac{x^2+1}{x^3+1}\right) \cdot$
$$\left(\dfrac{(x^3+1)(2x) - (x^2+1)(3x^2)}{(x^3+1)^2}\right)$$

23. $\dfrac{-2}{(3x-1)^3}(3)$

25. $\dfrac{-2}{(x^2+1)^3}(2x)$

27. $\dfrac{+((2x+1)^2-1)^2 - 2(2x+1)^2((2x+1)^2-1)+2}{(((2x+1)^2-1)^2+2)^2} - (2)(2x+1)(2)$

29. $(x+1)(-(x+2)^{-2}) + (x+2)^{-1}$

31. $\left(2-\dfrac{2}{t}\right)^3\left(-2\left(1+\dfrac{1}{t}\right)^{-3}\left(-\dfrac{1}{t^2}\right)\right) + \left(1+\dfrac{1}{t}\right)^{-2}\left(3\left(2-\dfrac{2}{t}\right)^2\left(\dfrac{2}{t^2}\right)\right)$

6 The Derivatives of Inverse Functions . . .
(pages 144–145)

1. $2/3(x+1)^{-1/3}$

3. $5/3(2/x)^{2/3}(-2/x^2)$

5. $t(t^2+1)^{-1/2}$

7. $5/4(t+1)^{2/3}(t-1)^{1/4} + $
$\quad\quad 2/3(t-1)^{5/4}(t+1)^{-1/3}$

9. $-1/2x^{-3/2} + 1/2(x+1)^{-3/2}$

11. $(x^2-1)^{1/2}(-x^{-2}) + (x^2-1)^{-1/2}$

13. $(t^2+1)^{1/4}(-1/5(t^2+2)^{-6/5}(2t)) + $
$\quad\quad 1/4(t^2+1)^{-3/4}(2t)(t^2+2)^{-1/5}$

15. $-2/7((x^2+x)^{1/2}+x^{1/2})^{-9/7} \cdot$
$\quad\quad (1/2(x^2+x)^{-1/2})(2x+1)$
$\quad\quad\quad + 1/2x^{-1/2}$

17. $1/2\left(\dfrac{x^{1/2}+4}{(x+4)^{1/2}}\right)^{-1/2}((x^{1/2}+4) \cdot$
$\quad\quad (-1/2(x+4)^{-3/2}$
$\quad\quad\quad + 1/2x^{-1/2}(x+4)^{-1/2})$

19. $(x^2+1)^{1/2}(x-2)^{5/3}(-1/4(x+1)^{-5/4}$
$\quad + ((x^2+1)^{1/2}(5/3(x-2)^{2/3})(x+1)^{-1/4}$
$\quad + 1/2(x^2+1)^{-1/2}(2x)(x-2)^{5/3}) \cdot$
$\quad\quad\quad (x+1)^{-1/4}$

21. $\dfrac{d}{dx}\sqrt{g(x)} = 1/2(g(x))^{-1/2} \cdot g'(x)$

23. $\dfrac{x^2}{2}+c$ **27.** $\dfrac{2}{3}x^{3/2}+c$

25. $\dfrac{x^3}{3}+\dfrac{x^2}{2}+c$ **29.** $\dfrac{2}{5}x^{5/2}+c$

31. $-2(x+1)^{-1/2}+c$

33. $\dfrac{5}{18}x^{9/5}+c$

35. $\dfrac{4}{3}x^{3/2}+\dfrac{9}{4}x^{4/3}+c$

37. $y=\dfrac{8}{3}x-\dfrac{2}{3}$

39. $y=-4x+2$

41. $\dfrac{3}{19}$

7 Higher-order Derivatives
(page 146)

1. (a) 1 (b) 0 (c) 0

3. (a) $3x^2$ (b) $6x$ (c) 6

5. (a) $-\dfrac{1}{x^2}$ (b) $\dfrac{2}{x^3}$ (c) $\dfrac{-6}{x^4}$

7. (a) $3(x-3)^2$ (b) $6(x-3)$
$\quad$ (c) 6

9. (a) $\dfrac{1}{(x+2)^2}$ (b) $\dfrac{-2}{(x+2)^3}$
$\quad$ (c) $\dfrac{6}{(x+2)^4}$

11. (a) $-1/3(x-1)^{-4/3}$;
$\quad$ (b) $4/9(x-1)^{-7/3}$;
$\quad$ (c) $-28/27(x-1)^{-10/3}$

13. $1/3x^{3/2}(-2/3(x+1)^{-5/3}) +$
$\quad 1/3(3/2x^{1/2})(x+1)^{-2/3} +$
$\quad 3/2x^{1/2}(1/3(x+1)^{-2/3}) +$
$\quad 3/2(1/2x^{-1/2}(x+1)^{1/3})$

15. $\dfrac{x^3}{6}+C_1x+C_2$ for any constants
$\quad C_1$ and C_2

17. $f'(x)=2a_2x+a_1, f''(x)=2a_2,$
$\quad f'''(x)=0$

19. Each time we take a derivative,
we reduce the exponent by 1
and multiply by the exponent.
Thus, after n differentiations,
the exponent becomes 0 and we
have multiplied by n, $n-1$,
$n-2, \ldots, 1$. Thus, $f^{(n)}(x)=n!$

8 Implicit Differentiation . . .
(pages 149–150)

1. $\dfrac{-x}{y}$ **3.** $\dfrac{-2x}{3y}$ **5.** $\dfrac{y^{1/2}}{x^{1/2}}$

7. $\dfrac{1-2xy-y^2}{x^2+2yx}$

9. $\dfrac{2x + yx^{-2} - y^{-1}}{(x^{-1} - xy^{-2})}$

11. $\dfrac{-y^2 - x^2}{y^3}$

13. $3y(-(4y - 3x)^{-2}(12y(4y - 3x)^{-1} - 3)) + 9y(4y - 3x)^{-2}$

15. $-x^2y^{-3} + y^{-1}$

17. $dy = 2x\,dx$

19. $dy = \dfrac{-2}{(x - 1)^2}dx$

21. $dy = ((x - 1)^{2/3}(1/2(x + 3)^{-1/2}) + (x + 3)^{1/2}(2/3(x - 1)^{-1/3}))dx$

CHAPTER 4

1 Monotonicity . . .
(pages 168–169)

1. $c = 5/2$ 3. $c = \sqrt{1/3}$ 5. $c = 9/4$
7. You can't solve $2/3c^{-1/3} = 0$.
   $f(x) = x^{2/3}$ is not differentiable
   at 0.
9. (a) 0, 2/3   (b) $]-\infty,0]$, $[2/3,\infty[$
   (c) $[0,2/3]$ (d) $f(0) = 0$
   (e) $f(2/3) = -4/27$

(f)
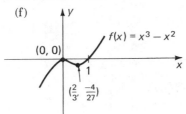

11. (a) 2   (b) $]-\infty,2]$ (c) $[2,\infty[$
    (d) $f(2) = 48$ (e) None

(f)
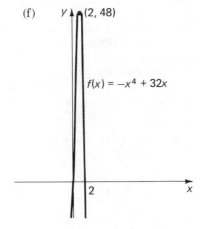

13. (a) $-1, -1/3$
    (b) $]-\infty,-1]$, $[-1/3,\infty[$
    (c) $[-1,-1/3]$ (d) $f(-1) = -3$
    (e) $f(-1/3) = \dfrac{-85}{27}$

(f)
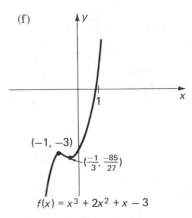

15. (a) 0   (b) $[0,\infty[$ (c) Nowhere
    (d) None   (e) None

(f)
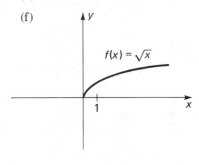

17. (a) 0,1/4 (b) [1/4,∞[
(c) [0,1/4] (d) None
(e) $f(1/4) = -1/4$

(f)

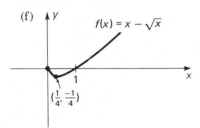

$f(x) = x - \sqrt{x}$

$(\frac{1}{4}, \frac{-1}{4})$

19. (a) None (b) Nowhere
(c)]−∞,1[,]1,∞[(d) None
(e) None

(f)

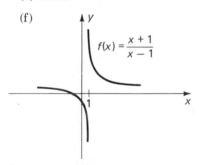

$f(x) = \dfrac{x+1}{x-1}$

21. (a) −1, 0, 1 (b) [−1,0], [1,∞[
(c)]−∞,−1], [0,1] (d) $f(0) = 1$
(e) $f(-1) = 0, f(1) = 0$

(f)

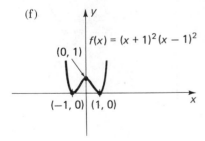

$f(x) = (x+1)^2(x-1)^2$

(0, 1)

(−1, 0) (1, 0)

23. (a) 1/4 (b) [1/4,∞[(c)]0,1/4]
(d) None (e) $f(1/4) = 5/2$

(f)

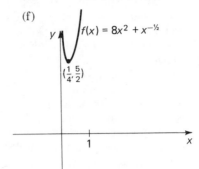

$f(x) = 8x^2 + x^{-\frac{1}{2}}$

$(\frac{1}{4}, \frac{5}{2})$

25. (a) 0,2 (b) [2,∞[(c)]−∞,2]
(d) None (e) $f(2) = -6\sqrt[3]{2}$

(f)

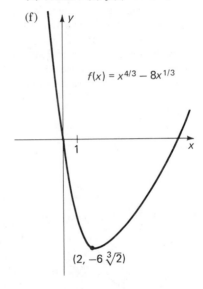

$f(x) = x^{4/3} - 8x^{1/3}$

$(2, -6\sqrt[3]{2})$

27. (a) abs. min. = 0, abs. max. = 4
(b) abs. min. = 0, abs. max. = 16
(c) abs. min. = 0, no abs. max.

29. (a) abs. min. = −8, abs. max. = 20
(b) abs. min. = 40/27,
abs. max. = 4
(c) abs. min. = −8, abs. max. = 20

31. (a) no abs. min., no abs. max.
(b) abs. min. = 4, abs. max. = 16/3

2 Concavity . . . *(page 174)*

1. Concave upward on $[-1/3,\infty[$;
   concave downward on $]-\infty,1/3]$;
   points of inflection $(-1/3,20/27)$
3. Concave upward everywhere
5. Concave upward on $]0,\infty[$;
   concave downward on $]-\infty,0[$;
   no point of inflection
7. Concave upward on $[0,\infty[$;
   concave downward on $]-\infty,0]$;
   point of inflection $(0,0)$
9. Concave upward on $]-1,0]$ and
   $]1,\infty[$; concave downward on
   $]-\infty,-1[$ and $[0,1[$
11. Assume that $f''(x_0) = 0$ and
    $f'''(x_0) \neq 0$. Then, applying SDT
    to f', we see that f' has a local
    extremum at x_0. Thus, there is
    some neighborhood of x_0 in
    which either f' is increasing to
    the left of x_0 and decreasing to
    the right or vice versa. In either
    case f has a point of inflection
    at x_0.

(Pages 187–188)

1.

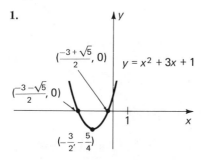

3.

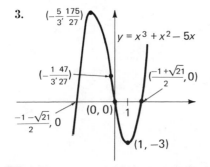

5. $y = (x - 1)(x + 1)(x + 2)$

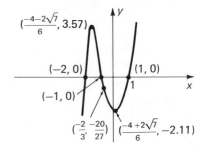

7.

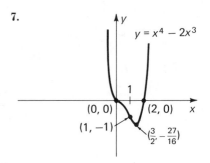

9.

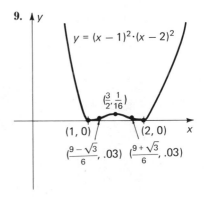

11.

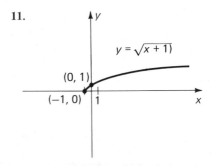

13.

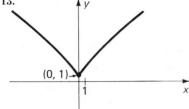

(0, 1)
1

15.

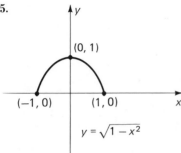

(0, 1)
(−1, 0)   (1, 0)
$y = \sqrt{1 - x^2}$

17.

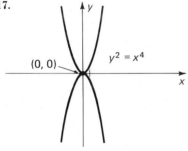

(0, 0) $y^2 = x^4$

19.

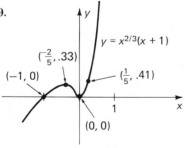

$y = x^{2/3}(x + 1)$
$(-\frac{2}{5}, .33)$
(−1, 0) $(\frac{1}{5}, .41)$
1
(0, 0)

21.

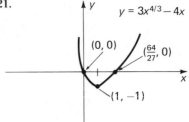

$y = 3x^{4/3} - 4x$
(0, 0) $(\frac{64}{27}, 0)$
(1, −1)

23.

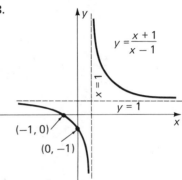

$y = \dfrac{x + 1}{x - 1}$
x = 1
y = 1
(−1, 0)
(0, −1)

25.

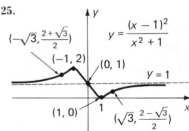

$y = \dfrac{(x - 1)^2}{x^2 + 1}$
$(-\sqrt{3}, \frac{2 + \sqrt{3}}{2})$
(−1, 2)   (0, 1)
y = 1
(1, 0)   1
$(\sqrt{3}, \frac{2 - \sqrt{3}}{2})$

27.

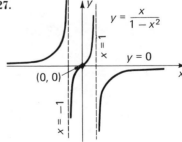

$y = \dfrac{x}{1 - x^2}$
x = 1
y = 0
(0, 0)
x = −1

29.

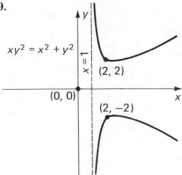

$xy^2 = x^2 + y^2$

$(2, 2)$

$(0, 0)$

$(2, -2)$

31.

$y^2 = x(4 - x)^2$

$\left(\frac{4}{3}, \frac{16}{3\sqrt{3}}\right)$

$(0, 0)$ $(4, 0)$

$\left(\frac{4}{3}, -\frac{16}{3\sqrt{3}}\right)$

3 Distance . . .
(pages 191–192)

1. $\dot{s}(t) = 2t + 4$; $\dot{v}(t) = 2$

3. $\dot{s}(t) = \frac{1}{2}(t + 3)^{-1/2}$;

$\dot{v}(t) = -\frac{1}{4}(t + 3)^{-3/2}$

5. (a) 7.22 sec   (b) 90.77 m/sec
   (c) After 4.67 sec, the rock is
       200 meters from the ground.
       $v(4.67) = 65.73$ m/sec

7. (a) 75 sec   (b) 90,000 ft
   (c) 150 sec   (d) −2400 ft/sec

9. The particle always moves to
   the right with constant
   acceleration 6.

11. The particle is always moving
   the right and always
   decelerating.

4 Miscellaneous Problems . . .
(pages 195–199)

1. 30 and 30

3. A square with side 10 feet

5. If x represents one dimension,
   then $\frac{P - 2x}{2}$ represents the other
   dimension. Maximize $x\left(\frac{P - 2x}{2}\right)$
   to obtain $x = P/4$ and
   $\frac{P - 2x}{2} = P/4$.

7. 20

9. 4 by 4 inches

11. $r = \frac{12}{4 + \pi}$, $h = \frac{12}{4 + \pi}$

13. $r = \sqrt{50/3\pi}$ inches,
   $h = \left(\frac{100}{2\pi\sqrt{50/3\pi}} - \sqrt{50/3\pi}\right)$ inches

15. 3.75 weeks

17. 450

19. $r = \sqrt[4]{\frac{s^2}{3\pi^2}}$, $h = \frac{s\sqrt{6}}{3\pi r}$

21. $10\sqrt{10}$ by $10\sqrt{10}$ feet

23. $r = 20/3$ inches, $h = 10$ inches

25. Maximize $P = R\left(\frac{E}{R + r}\right)^2$, where
   E and r are constants. We obtain
   $P' = \frac{E^2(R + r)^2 - 2RE^2(R + r)}{(R + r)^4}$.
   Now, set $P' = 0$ and obtain $R = r$.

5 Some Applications . . .
(pages 202–204)

1. (a) 83   (b) 84

3. (a) 0   (b) 0

5. (a) 299   (b) 304

7. (a) 0   (b) 0

9. (a) $P'(x) = -x + 50$
   (b) $P'(30) = \$20$ (c) \$19.50
   (d) 50

11. (a) $p = 500 - x$
   (b) $R(x) = x(500 - x)$
   (c) $x = 250$, $p = 250$
   (d) $P(x) = -x^2 + 450x - 2000$
   (e) $x = 225$, $p = 275$

13. Since $P(x) = R(x) - C(x)$, $P'(x) =$ $R'(x) - C'(x)$. If $P(x)$ is maximal, then $P'(x) = 0$ and so $R'(x) = C'(x)$.

15. (a) $C(x) = 20{,}000 + 20x + 8000/x$
    (b) $x = 20$, 100 bottles per order
    (c) Since, if there are x orders per year, $C(x) = DE + Ax + DB/2x$, the optimal number, x, of orders is $\sqrt{DB/2A}$. The optimal reorder number is $D/\sqrt{DB/2A}$.

6 Related Rates . . .
(pages 209–210)

1. $1/40\pi$ in./sec

3. $-\dfrac{5}{6}$ ft/sec

5. 96 in./sec

7. .4 ft/sec

9. $-10\sqrt{3}$ mph

11. $\dfrac{1409 + 9/\sqrt{3} + 12\sqrt{3}}{2\sqrt{709 + 18\sqrt{3}}}$

13. (a) $\dfrac{dy}{dx} = \dfrac{-1}{t^2(4t-1)}$,

   $\dfrac{d^2y}{dx^2} = \dfrac{2(6t-1)}{t^3(4t-1)^3}$

   (b) $\dfrac{dy}{dx} = 4t^{3/2}$, $\dfrac{d^2y}{dx^2} = 12t$

(c) $\dfrac{dy}{dx} = -\dfrac{2}{3}t(t^2-1)^{-3/2}(t+1)^{-1/2}$

$\dfrac{d^2y}{dx^2} =$

$$\dfrac{\dfrac{-2}{3}(t^2-1)^{-3/2}(t+1)^{-1/2} - \dfrac{2}{3}t\left(-\dfrac{3}{2}(t^2-1)^{-5/2}(2t)(t+1)^{-1/2} - \dfrac{1}{2}(t+1)^{-3/2}(t^2-1)^{-3/2}\right)}{\dfrac{3}{2}(t+1)^{1/2}}$$

(d) $\dfrac{dy}{dx} = \dfrac{3t^2}{1 + \dfrac{1}{2}t^{-1/2}}$

$\dfrac{d^2y}{dx^2} = \dfrac{6t\left(1 + \dfrac{1}{2}t^{-1/2}\right)^{-1} - 3t^2\left(1 + \dfrac{1}{2}t^{-1/2}\right)^{-2}\left(-\dfrac{1}{4}t^{-3/2}\right)}{1 + \dfrac{1}{2}t^{-1/2}}$

CHAPTER 5

2 Trigonometric Identities
(pages 224–225)

1. (a) $-\cos \dfrac{2\pi}{7}$ (b) $-\sin \dfrac{2\pi}{7}$

3. (a) $\cos \dfrac{2\pi}{5}$ (b) $\sin \dfrac{2\pi}{5}$

5. (a) $\cos (45 - 14\pi)$
   (b) $\sin (45 - 14\pi)$

7. $\sin x$

9. $\sin x$

11. $\dfrac{\sqrt{2}}{2}(\cos x - \sin x)$

13. (a) $\dfrac{\sqrt{2} - \sqrt{6}}{4}$ (b) $\dfrac{-\sqrt{2} - \sqrt{6}}{4}$

15. (a) $\dfrac{\sqrt{2} - \sqrt{6}}{4}$ (b) $\dfrac{-\sqrt{2} - \sqrt{6}}{4}$

17. (a) $\dfrac{1}{2}\sqrt{2 + \sqrt{2}}$ (b) $-\dfrac{1}{2}\sqrt{2 - \sqrt{2}}$

21. $f(t) = \cos\left[2\pi\left(t - \dfrac{3}{4}\right)\right]$

23. $f(t) = 2\cos\left[\pi\left(t - \dfrac{1}{6}\right)\right]$

25. $f(t) = \cos\left[\pi(t - 1)\right]$

3 The Derivatives . . .
(pages 232–235)

1. $y = 1 + \sin 2x$, $y' = 2\cos 2x$
3. $y = \sqrt{2}\cos x$, $y' = -\sqrt{2}\sin x$

5. $y = \dfrac{1}{2}\sin 4x$, $y' = 2\cos 4x$

7. $y = 2\cot 2x$, $y' = -4\csc^2 2x$

9. $y = 2\tan x$, $y' = 2\sec^2 x$

11. $y' = 2x \cos (x^2 + 1)$

13. $y' = 4x \sin (x^2) \cos (x^2)$

15. $y' = \sec^2 x - 1 = \tan^2 x$

17. $y' = -4\tan^3 x \sec^2 x$

19. $y' = -(\sin y + y \cos x)/$
    $(\sin x + x \cos y)$

21. $y' = 1/(2\sin y \cos y) = \csc 2y$

23. $y' = 1$

25. $dy = \cos 2x \, dx$

27. $dy = \left(\dfrac{1}{2\sqrt{x}} - \sec x \tan x - \right.$
    $\left. \csc x \cot x \right)dx$

29. $\max = \sqrt{a^2 + b^2}$,
    $\min = -\sqrt{a^2 + b^2}$

31. $A = 3a^2\sqrt{3}/4$, $\theta = \dfrac{\pi}{3}$

33. $-\pi h/3$ meters/hour

35. $15\pi/4$ miles/minute

37. 1 41. 2

39. a/b 43. 1/2

4 Inverse Trigonometric Functions *(page 244)*

1. $\pi/3$ 5. $-\pi/3$ 9. $1/\sqrt{10}$
3. $-\pi/4$ 7. 4/5 11. $-\pi/4$

13. $-\dfrac{\sin x}{|\sin x|}$

15. $-\dfrac{4\cos^{-1} 2x}{\sqrt{1 - 4x^2}}$

17. 0

19. $\dfrac{x^2}{(1 - x^2)^{3/2}}$

21. $y' = \dfrac{1 + x/|x|}{\sqrt{1 - x^2}}$

23. $y' = -x/y$

25. $y' = \dfrac{\pi}{2\sqrt{1 - x^2}\,(\mathrm{Cos}^{-1} x)^2}$

5 Exponentials and Logarithms *(pages 249–250)*

1. $x = 8$ 7. $x = 2$
3. $x = 0.01$ 9. $x = 2$
5. $x = \sqrt{3}$

11. $x = (\log 18)/(\log 0.75)$

13. $x = (\log 5)/(\log 3)$

15. $x = 2^{(\log 3)/(\log 6)}$
    $= 3^{(\log 2)/(\log 6)} \approx 1.5296$

17. $x = 2$

19. $x = \sqrt{10^y - 1}$ and $x = -\sqrt{10^y - 1}$

21. $x = \dfrac{1}{2} \cdot 3^{\tan y}$

23. $x = 2$ and $x = -2$

25. $x = 1/13$

27. $x = -5$

6 Derivatives of Exponential and Logarithmic Functions . . .
(pages 259–261)

1. $y' = \dfrac{4}{x+1}$　　3. $y' = \dfrac{1}{x^2 + x}$

5. $y' = \tan^{-1} x$

7. $y' = \dfrac{2x - 1}{(x^2 - x)\ln a}$

9. $y' = 2x$

11. $y' = \dfrac{1}{x^2 - 1}$

13. $y' = \dfrac{1 - \ln x}{x^2}$

15. $y' = (\cos x)\exp(\sin x)$

17. $y' = \dfrac{-2e^x}{e^{2x} - 1}$

19. $y' = 3x^2$

21. $y' = (\sin x)^x(x\cot x + \ln(\sin x))$

23. $y' = x^{(x^2 + 1)}[1 + 2\ln x]$

25. $y' = \dfrac{(x + 1)^6(3x^2 + 6x + 17)}{(x^2 + 2x + 3)^3}$

27. $y' =$
$$(1 + x)^{1/x}\left[\dfrac{x - (1 + x)\ln(1 + x)}{x^2(1 + x)}\right]$$

29. $y' = 2xe^{x^2}$

31. $y' = \dfrac{2^x(y\ln 2) - y^2\cos(xy)}{1 + xy\cos(xy)}$

33. $dy = e^x\left(\dfrac{1}{x} + \ln x\right)dx$

35. $dy = (\sec x \tan x - 3^x \ln 3)dx$

37. $(1, 1/e)$ max.

39. $(1, -1)$ max.

41. $(1/e, -1/e)$ min.

43. $(1/e, 1/e^{1/e})$ min.

45. $y = x + 1$

47. (a) $5412.16; $412.16
　　(b) $5862.90; $862.90
　　(c) $6107.02; $1107.02;
　　　　$244.28/yr; $298.37/yr.

49. (a) 60,000
　　(b) 1,310,140,000
　　(c) 7087827.1 bacteria/min
　　(d) 2.43879 × 10¹⁷ bacteria/min
　　(e) −3048.5 bacteria/min
　　(f) The population first decreases, then increases.

51. (a) 74%　　　　(c) −.08
　　(b) 5.1 years　(d) −.03
　　(e) As time goes on, the proportion is decreasing at a slower rate.

53. (a) 50,000　　(d) 25,000
　　(b) 138,630　(e) 6250
　　(c) 13.65 years
　　(f) As time goes on, the population is growing at a slower rate.

7 The Indeterminate Forms $\dfrac{0}{0}$ and $\dfrac{\infty}{\infty}$ *(page 267)*

1. 10　　　　13. 0

3. $\ln(a/b)$　　15. Does not exist

5. $-1/2$　　17. 2

7. $-1/6$　　19. 0

9. ∞　　　21. 0

11. -2

8 Limits of Other Indeterminate Forms *(page 270)*

1. 1　　　　13. 2

3. ∞　　　15. $\dfrac{1}{3}$

5. 0　　　　17. 1

7. 1　　　　19. 1

9. 0　　　　21. $e^{1/6}$

11. 1

9 Graphing Equations . . . *(page 274)*

1.

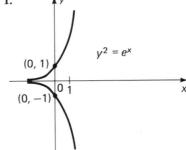

3.

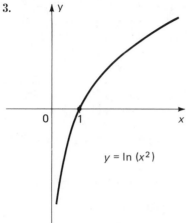

$y = \ln(x^2)$

9.

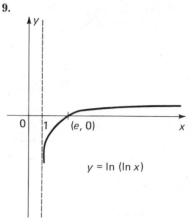

$(e, 0)$

$y = \ln(\ln x)$

5.

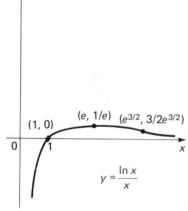

$(1, 0)$ $(e, 1/e)$ $(e^{3/2}, 3/2e^{3/2})$

$y = \dfrac{\ln x}{x}$

11.

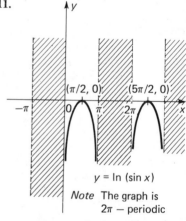

$(\pi/2, 0)$ $(5\pi/2, 0)$

$y = \ln(\sin x)$

Note The graph is
2π — periodic

7.

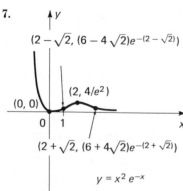

$(2 - \sqrt{2},\ (6 - 4\sqrt{2})e^{-(2-\sqrt{2})})$

$(2, 4/e^2)$

$(0, 0)$

$(2 + \sqrt{2},\ (6 + 4\sqrt{2})e^{-(2+\sqrt{2})})$

$y = x^2 e^{-x}$

13.

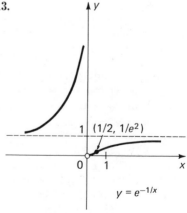

$(1/2, 1/e^2)$

$y = e^{-1/x}$

15.

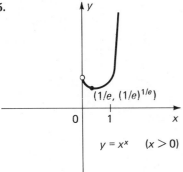

$(1/e, (1/e)^{1/e})$

$y = x^x \quad (x > 0)$

17.

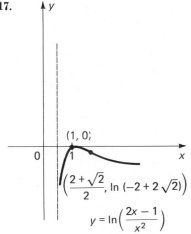

$(1, 0)$

$\left(\dfrac{2 + \sqrt{2}}{2}, \ln(-2 + 2\sqrt{2})\right)$

$y = \ln\left(\dfrac{2x - 1}{x^2}\right)$

19.

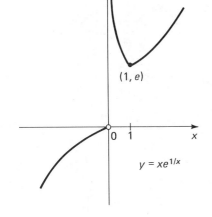

$(1, e)$

$y = xe^{1/x}$

21.

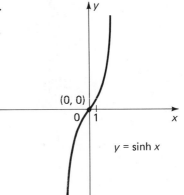

$(0, 0)$

$y = \sinh x$

23.

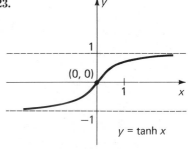

$(0, 0)$

$y = \tanh x$

10 Polar Coordinates
(page 280)

1. $r = a \sec \theta$
3. $r = (1/a) \sin \theta \sec^2 \theta$
5. $r^2 = a \sec \theta \csc \theta$
7. $r^2 = a \cos 2\theta$
9. $x^2 + y^2 = a^2$
11. $y = x \tan(x^2 + y^2)$
13. $(x^2 + y^2)^2 = a^2(x^2 - y^2)$
15. $(x^2 + y^2)^2 = x^2$
17.

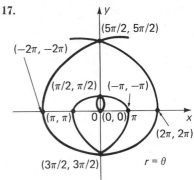

$(5\pi/2, 5\pi/2)$
$(-2\pi, -2\pi)$
$(\pi/2, \pi/2) \quad (-\pi, -\pi)$
$(\pi, \pi) \quad 0 (0, 0) \; \pi$
$(2\pi, 2\pi)$
$(3\pi/2, 3\pi/2) \quad r = \theta$

19.

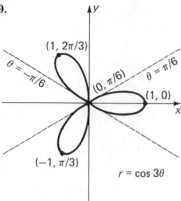

$(1, 2\pi/3)$

$\theta = -\pi/6$

$\theta = \pi/6$

$(0, \pi/6)$

$(1, 0)$

$(-1, \pi/3)$

$r = \cos 3\theta$

25.

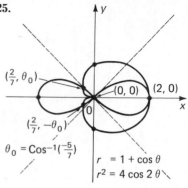

$\left(\frac{2}{7}, \theta_0\right)$

$(0, 0)$ $(2, 0)$

$\left(\frac{2}{7}, -\theta_0\right)$

$\theta_0 = \text{Cos}^{-1}\left(\frac{-5}{7}\right)$

$r = 1 + \cos \theta$

$r^2 = 4 \cos 2\theta$

21.

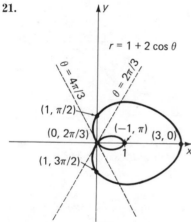

$r = 1 + 2 \cos \theta$

$\theta = 4\pi/3$

$\theta = 2\pi/3$

$(1, \pi/2)$

$(0, 2\pi/3)$ $(-1, \pi)$ $(3, 0)$

$(1, 3\pi/2)$

27.

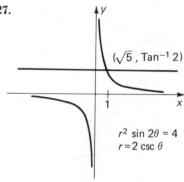

$(\sqrt{5}, \text{Tan}^{-1} 2)$

$r^2 \sin 2\theta = 4$

$r = 2 \csc \theta$

29.

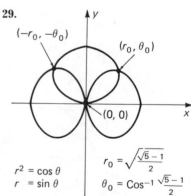

$(-r_0, -\theta_0)$

(r_0, θ_0)

$(0, 0)$

$r^2 = \cos \theta$

$r = \sin \theta$

$r_0 = \sqrt{\dfrac{\sqrt{5}-1}{2}}$

$\theta_0 = \text{Cos}^{-1} \sqrt{\dfrac{\sqrt{5}-1}{2}}$

23.

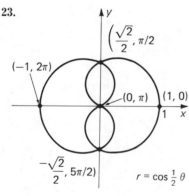

$\left(\dfrac{\sqrt{2}}{2}, \pi/2\right)$

$(-1, 2\pi)$

$(0, \pi)$ $(1, 0)$

$-\dfrac{\sqrt{2}}{2}, 5\pi/2)$

$r = \cos \frac{1}{2} \theta$

CHAPTER 6

1 An Area Problem
(pages 285–286)

1. $A = 15/2$

3. $A = \dfrac{255}{64}$

5. $A = 4$

7. $A = \dfrac{2}{3}$

9. $A = 2 - \dfrac{2}{n}$

11. $A = \dfrac{1}{2}$

13. $A = 1$

15. $A = 1$

17. $A = 1$

19. $A = \infty$

2 The Summation Symbol
(page 287)

1. (a) $\dfrac{29}{20}$ (b) 25 (c) $\dfrac{127}{64}$

   (d) 350 (e) $\dfrac{63}{8}$ (f) $2^{100} - 2^{10}$

3. (a) $\displaystyle\sum_{j=1}^{n} j^3$ (b) $\displaystyle\sum_{k=1}^{n} \dfrac{1}{k}$

5 The Fundamental Theorem . . . *(page 308)*

1. $\displaystyle\int_0^2 2x = x^2 \Big|_0^2 = 4$

3. $\displaystyle\int_1^4 (-2x^{-3})\, dx = x^{-2} \Big|_1^4 = -\dfrac{15}{16}$

5. $\displaystyle\int_2^8 \dfrac{dx}{x} = \ln x \Big|_2^8 = \ln 4$

7. $\displaystyle\int_{-3}^3 18x^{17}\, dx = x^{18} \Big|_{-3}^3 = 0$

9. $\displaystyle\int_1^2 e^x\, dx = e^x \Big|_1^2 = e^2 - e$

11. $\displaystyle\int_{-1}^2 (3x^2 + 1)\, dx = (x^3 + x) \Big|_{-1}^2 = 12$

13. $\displaystyle\int_1^{\sqrt{3}} \dfrac{dx}{x^2 + 1} = \mathrm{Tan}^{-1} x \Big|_1^{\sqrt{3}} = \dfrac{\pi}{12}$

15. $\displaystyle\int_0^{\pi/4} \sec x \tan x\, dx =$

   $\sec x \Big|_0^{\pi/4} = \sqrt{2} - 1$

17. $\displaystyle\int_1^2 2^x\, dx = \dfrac{2^x}{\ln 2} \Big|_1^2 = \dfrac{2}{\ln 2}$

19. $\displaystyle\int_0^1 (x^2 - 3xy^2)\, dy =$

   $(x^2 y - xy^3) \Big|_{y=0}^{y=1} = x^2 - x$

7 Application to Area Problems *(pages 318–319)*

1. $A = \int_0^1 (x - x^2)\, dx = \dfrac{1}{6}$

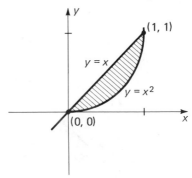

3. $A = \int_{-2}^4 (4 + y - \dfrac{1}{2} y^2)\, dy = 18$

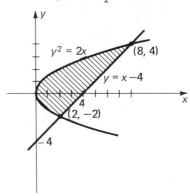

5.

$$A = \int_0^2 [(x-1)^3 - x^2 + x + 1] \, dx = \frac{4}{3}$$

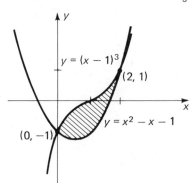

7.

$$A = \int_1^1 \left(\frac{3}{2} + \frac{3}{2}x \right) dx + \int_1^3 \left(\frac{9}{2} - \frac{3}{2}x \right) dx = 6$$

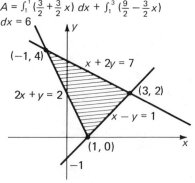

9.

$$A = \int_{-1}^1 (y^{2/3} + 2y + 1) \, dy + \int_1^8 (y^{2/3} + 4 - y) \, dy = \frac{183}{10}$$

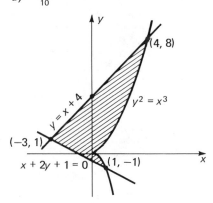

11. $A = \int_{-2}^2 (y^2 + 4y + 4) \, dy + \int_2^6 (12 + 4y - y^2) \, dv = 64$

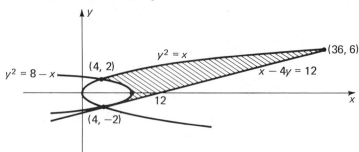

13.

$$A = \int_{\pi/4}^{5\pi/4} (\sin x - \cos x)\, dx = 2\sqrt{2}$$

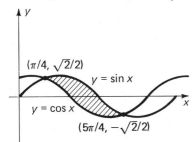

15.

$$A = 2 \int_0^1 2x^{3/2}\,(1 - x^2)\, dx = \tfrac{32}{45}$$

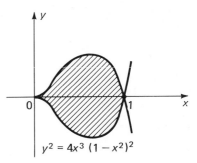

CHAPTER 7

2 Integration by Direct Substitution
(pages 339–340)

1. $-\dfrac{1}{2}\cos x^2,\ u = x^2$

3. $\sin e^x,\ u = e^x$

5. $-\dfrac{1}{2}e^{-2x} - e^{-x},\ u = e^x$

7. $\dfrac{1}{2}(\ln x)^2,\ u = \ln x$

9. $-2\cos\sqrt{x},\ u = \sqrt{x}$

11. $-\dfrac{1}{3}(2x + 8)\sqrt{2 - x},\ u = \sqrt{2 - x}$

13. $\left[\dfrac{2}{7}(x + 4)^3 - \dfrac{16}{5}(x + 4)^2 + \dfrac{32}{3}(x + 4)\right]\sqrt{x + 4},\ u = \sqrt{x + 4}$

15. $2\,\mathrm{Tan}^{-1}\sqrt{x},\ u = \sqrt{x}$

17. $2\sqrt{x} - 4\sqrt[4]{x} + 4\ln(1 + \sqrt[4]{x}),$ $u = \sqrt[4]{x}$

19. $2\sqrt{e^x + 1},\ u = e^x + 1$

21. $\dfrac{1}{2}\,\mathrm{Tan}^{-1}x^2,\ u = x^2$

23. $\dfrac{1}{3}\,\mathrm{Sin}^{-1}x^3,\ u = x^3$

25. $\dfrac{1}{3}\,\mathrm{Sec}^3 x,\ u = \sec x$

27. $\dfrac{1}{\sqrt{3}}\,\mathrm{Tan}^{-1}(\sqrt{3}\sin x),$ $u = \sqrt{3}\sin x$

29. $\dfrac{1}{4}e^{x^4}$

31. $-2\ln\left|\cos\dfrac{x}{2}\right| = \ln\left(\sec^2\dfrac{x}{2}\right),$ $u = \cos\dfrac{x}{2}$

33. $\dfrac{1}{4}\sec^4 x,\ u = \sec x$

35. $\cos x - \dfrac{2}{3}\cos^3 x,\ u = \cos x$

37. $\pi/12,\ u = x/3$

39. $e - 1,\ u = \sin x$

41. $(12\sqrt{3} - 16)/5,\ u = \sqrt{x + 3}$

43. $-1 - 4\ln(4/3),\ u = \sqrt{x}$

45. $11 - 6\ln(3/2),\ u = x^{1/6}$

47. $\pi/12,\ 4u = x^2$

49. $1/(2e)$

3 Some Trigonometric Integrals *(page 343)*

1. $\dfrac{1}{2}x - \dfrac{1}{4}\sin 2x$

3. $\sin x - \dfrac{1}{3}\sin^3 x$

5. $\dfrac{3}{8}x - \dfrac{1}{4}\sin 2x + \dfrac{1}{32}\sin 4x$

7. $\dfrac{1}{8}x - \dfrac{1}{32}\sin 4x$

9. $\dfrac{3}{4}(\sin x)^{4/3} - \dfrac{3}{10}(\sin x)^{10/3}$

11. $\frac{1}{4} \sin 2x - \frac{1}{16} \sin 4x - \frac{1}{4}x$

13. $-\frac{2}{5} \cos^5 x$

15. $\frac{1}{3} \sin^3 x - \frac{1}{5} \sin^5 x$

4 Integration by Parts
(pages 347–348)

1. $-x \cos x + \sin x$

3. $(x^2 - 2x + 2)e^x$

5. $2^x(x \ln 2 - 1)/(\ln 2)^2$

7. $x \operatorname{Sin}^{-1} x + \sqrt{1 - x^2}$

9. $\frac{1}{4} \sec^3 x \tan x + \frac{3}{8} \sec x \tan x +$
$\qquad \frac{3}{8} \ln |\sec x + \tan x|$

11. $-\frac{1}{10} \cos 5x - \frac{1}{2} \cos x$

13. $\frac{1}{2}(x^2 + 1) \operatorname{Tan}^{-1} x - \frac{1}{2}x$

15. $\left(\frac{1}{3}x^3 + x\right) \ln x - \frac{1}{9}x^3 - x$

17. $2\sqrt{x} \operatorname{Tan}^{-1} \sqrt{x} - \ln |1 + x|$

19. $x \operatorname{Sec}^{-1} x - \ln |x + \sqrt{x^2 - 1}|$
if $x \geqq 1$,
$x \operatorname{Sec}^{-1} x + \ln |x + \sqrt{x^2 - 1}|$
if $x \leqq -1$

21. $e^{ax}(a \sin bx - b \cos bx)/(a^2 + b^2)$
if $a^2 + b^2 \neq 0$

23. $2\sqrt{1 + x} \operatorname{Sin}^{-1} x + 4\sqrt{1 - x}$

25. $\frac{2}{3}x^{3/2}\left(\ln x - \frac{2}{3}\right)$

27. $x \ln (x^2 + 1) - 2x + 2 \operatorname{Tan}^{-1} x$

29. $e^{x^2}(x^2 - 1)/2$

31. $\frac{\pi^2}{32}$

33. $2(\sqrt{2} + 1)/15$

35. $\pi/4$

37. $1/2$

39. $1 - 5/(2e)$

5 Reduction Formulas
(pages 350–351)

1. $\sqrt{x + 2}\left(\frac{2}{9}x^4 - \frac{32}{63}x^3 + \frac{128}{105}x^2\right.$
$\qquad\qquad \left. - \frac{1024}{315}x + \frac{4096}{315}\right)$

3. $\frac{(x - 1)\sqrt{2x - 1}}{2x^2} + \operatorname{Tan}^{-1}\sqrt{2x - 1}$

5. $\frac{1}{3} \tan^3 x - \tan x + x$

7. $\frac{1}{4} \sec^3 x \tan x + \frac{3}{8} \sec x \tan x +$
$\qquad \frac{3}{8} \ln |\sec x + \tan x|$

9. $\frac{1}{8} \sin^5 x \cos^3 x + \frac{1}{16} \sin^5 x \cos x -$
$\qquad \frac{1}{64} \sin^3 x \cos x - \frac{3}{128} \sin x \cos x$
$\qquad\qquad + \frac{3}{128}x$

7 Trigonometric Substitutions *(page 359)*

1. $x/(4\sqrt{4 + x^2})$

3. $x/(4\sqrt{4 - x^2})$

5. $\frac{9}{2} \operatorname{Sin}^{-1}\frac{x}{3} + \frac{1}{2}x \sqrt{9 - x^2}$

7. $\sec^{-1} x$ if $x > 1$, $-\sec^{-1} x$ if
$\qquad x < -1$

9. $-\sqrt{16 - x^2}/(16x)$

11. $-\dfrac{(4 - t^2)^{3/2}}{12t^3}$

13. $-\sqrt{9 + 4x^2}/(9x)$

15. $\operatorname{Sin}^{-1}(x - 1)$

17. $4 \operatorname{Sin}^{-1}\frac{1}{2}\sqrt{x} + \sqrt{4x - x^2}$

19. $\frac{1}{2} \operatorname{Sin}^{-1}(2e^t/3)$

21. $\dfrac{4\sqrt{3}}{9} \operatorname{Tan}^{-1}\left(\dfrac{2x + 1}{\sqrt{3}}\right) +$
$\qquad \dfrac{2x + 1}{3(x^2 + x + 1)}$

23. $\dfrac{2\sqrt{3}}{9} \operatorname{Tan}^{-1}\left(\dfrac{2x + 1}{\sqrt{3}}\right) +$
$\qquad\qquad \dfrac{x - 1}{3(x^2 + x + 1)}$

25. π

27. $2 \operatorname{Sin}^{-1}(2/3)$

29. $\dfrac{1}{\sqrt{10}} \ln\left[\dfrac{\sqrt{46} - \sqrt{10}}{6(\sqrt{11} - \sqrt{10})}\right]$

8 Integration of Rational Functions *(page 366)*

1. $\dfrac{1}{4} \ln \left| \dfrac{x}{x+4} \right|$

3. $x + \ln \dfrac{|x-1|}{(x+1)^2}$

5. $3 \ln |1-x| - \dfrac{1}{x}$

7. $\dfrac{1}{3} \ln |x+1| - \dfrac{1}{6} \ln (x^2 - x + 1) +$

$\dfrac{1}{\sqrt{3}} \, \text{Tan}^{-1} \dfrac{2x-1}{\sqrt{3}}$

9. $\ln \dfrac{|x|}{\sqrt{x^2+1}}$

11. $\dfrac{1}{9} \ln \dfrac{|x|}{\sqrt{x^2+3}} + \dfrac{1}{6(x^2+3)}$

13. $\dfrac{1}{2}x^2 + \dfrac{1}{4} \ln (2x^2 - 3x + 2) +$

$\dfrac{\sqrt{7}}{2} \, \text{Tan}^{-1} \dfrac{4x-3}{\sqrt{7}}$

15. $\dfrac{-x}{2x^2 - x + 1}$

17. $\dfrac{1}{x} + 2 \ln |x| + \dfrac{1}{2} \ln (x^2 - x + 1) +$

$\sqrt{3} \, \text{Tan}^{-1} \dfrac{2x-1}{\sqrt{3}}$

19. $\dfrac{1}{3} \ln 2 + \dfrac{\pi\sqrt{3}}{9}$

21. $\dfrac{e-1}{e} + \dfrac{\pi}{4} - \text{Tan}^{-1} e$

23. $\pi/\sqrt{3}$

9 The Half-angle Substitution *(page 368)*

1. $\dfrac{1}{4}\theta - \dfrac{5}{6} \, \text{Tan}^{-1} \left(\dfrac{1}{3} \tan \dfrac{1}{2}\theta \right)$

3. $\ln \left| 1 + \tan \dfrac{1}{2}\theta \right|$

5. $\dfrac{1}{2} \ln \left| \tan \dfrac{1}{2}\theta \right| - \dfrac{1}{4} \tan^2 \dfrac{1}{2}\theta$

7. $\dfrac{1}{2}x + \dfrac{1}{4} \ln \dfrac{1 + \tan^2 x}{|\tan^2 x + 2 \tan x - 1|}$

9. $\dfrac{1}{2} - \dfrac{1}{4} \ln 3$

11. $\dfrac{\pi}{4}$

10 Some Miscellaneous Techniques *(pages 371–372)*

1. $\dfrac{2}{3}(x + 75) \sqrt{x} - 5x -$

$250 \ln |5 + \sqrt{x}|$

3. $\dfrac{313}{3} + 4 \ln 2$

5. $\dfrac{1}{\sqrt{41}} \ln \left| \dfrac{4 \cos \theta + 5 \sin \theta - \sqrt{41}}{4 \sin \theta - 5 \cos \theta} \right|$

7. $(\ln x)^2/2$

9. $(x^2 - 2) \sin x + 2x \cos x$

11. $\dfrac{446}{15} - 64 \, \text{Tan}^{-1} \left(\dfrac{1}{2} \right)$

13. $-2 \cos \sqrt{x}$

15. $\ln |x| - \ln |3x + 1 + \sqrt{x^2 + 6x + 1}|$

17. $\dfrac{1}{3} \sin^3 x$ **19.** $\dfrac{1}{2}x - \dfrac{5}{4} \sin \dfrac{2}{5}x$

21. $\pi/4$

23. $x + \ln \left| \dfrac{x-2}{x+2} \right| - 2 \, \text{Tan}^{-1} (x/2)$

25. $\dfrac{1}{2}x^2 - x + \ln \left(\dfrac{|x|}{\sqrt{x^2+1}} \right) + \text{Tan}^{-1} x$

27. $\dfrac{1}{10} \ln \left[\dfrac{(x-1)^2}{x^2+4} \right] - \dfrac{1}{10} \, \text{Tan}^{-1} \dfrac{x}{2}$

29. $\dfrac{1}{5} \ln (5 - \sqrt{25 - x^2}) - \dfrac{1}{5} \ln |x|$

31. $\dfrac{1}{5}(6x^{5/6} - 10x^{1/2} + 15x^{1/3})$

$- 3 \ln (x^{1/3} + x^{1/6} + 1) +$

$2\sqrt{3} \, \text{Tan}^{-1} \dfrac{2x^{1/6} + 1}{\sqrt{3}}$

33. 13

35. $2 + 4 \ln 5 - 8 \ln 4$

37. 0

11 Improper Integrals *(page 376)*

1. 3   **13.** 2

3. 6   **15.** 1

5. $\dfrac{1}{2e}$ **17.** $\pi/2$

7. $\dfrac{1}{2}$ **19.** -1

9. 0   **21.** 1

11. 10   **23.** Does not exist

                   25. π

CHAPTER 8

1 Areas *(pages 380–381)*

1. 1/3   **7.** $2\sqrt{2}$ **11.** $\dfrac{12}{5}$

3. 3/4   **9.** $\dfrac{64}{3}$

5. 3

13. $\dfrac{8}{3} + \dfrac{4}{3}\sqrt{2} + 2\sqrt{3}$

15. $\dfrac{2}{3}(10\sqrt{5} - 17)$

17. 16

19. $\dfrac{\pi}{2} + \dfrac{1}{3}$

21. $5 \ln 5 - \dfrac{4}{3}$

23. $40 \ln (8/5) - 15$

25. $2 \ln (\sqrt{2} + 1) - \dfrac{\pi}{2}$

2 Solids of Revolution
(pages 389–390)

1. $\dfrac{2\pi}{15}$ **11.** $\dfrac{11\pi}{30}$

3. $\dfrac{16\pi}{15}$ **13.** 14π

5. $\dfrac{9\pi\sqrt{3}}{14}$ **15.** $\dfrac{875\pi}{48}$

7. $\pi\left(\ln 2 + \dfrac{\pi}{4} - 1\right)$ **17.** $\dfrac{\pi}{2}(e^2 + 1)$

9. $\dfrac{\pi}{2}(e^2 + 1)$ **19.** $\dfrac{4\pi}{15}$

23. (a) $4\pi ab^2/3$ (b) $4\pi a^2 b/3$ **21.** $2\pi^2 a^2 b$

25. $\dfrac{512\pi}{5}$ **29.** 4π

27. $\dfrac{53\pi}{315}$ **31.** $3888\pi/5$

33. $\pi^2\sqrt{2} - 4\pi$

3 Volumes of Solids . . .
(page 395)

1. $16a^3/3$ **7.** $\dfrac{5\pi a^3}{24}$

3. $\dfrac{\pi a^2 h}{2}$ **9.** $\dfrac{16}{5}$

5. $(\sqrt{2}/12)\, s^3$

4 Arc Length *(pages 400–401)*

1. 4

3. $\dfrac{1}{2}(\sqrt{2} + \ln (1 + \sqrt{2}))$

5. $\dfrac{61}{27}$ **7.** 6   **9.** $\ln (1 + \sqrt{2})$

11. $2\sqrt{3}$

13. $\sqrt{2} + \ln (1 + \sqrt{2})$

15. $2\pi a$

5 Surfaces of Revolution
(pages 404)

1. $2\pi[\sqrt{2} + \ln (1 + \sqrt{2})]$

3. $\dfrac{\pi}{6}[5\sqrt{5} - 1]$

5. $5\pi + 2\pi \ln (8/3)$

7. $4\pi a^2 \sqrt{2}$ **9.** 3π **11.** $4\pi^2 ab$

6 Centroids *(pages 409–410)*

1. $\left(\dfrac{9}{20}, \dfrac{9}{20}\right)$ **7.** $\left(0, \dfrac{6}{5}\right)$

3. $\left(0, \dfrac{12}{5}\right)$ **9.** $\left(\dfrac{e^2 + 1}{4}, \dfrac{e - 2}{2}\right)$

5. $(3, 7)$ **11.** $2\pi^2 abc$

13. $V = \dfrac{9\pi a^3}{2}, S = 6\pi a^2 \sqrt{3}$

15. $V = 16\pi/3$ **25.** $\left(\dfrac{\pi}{2}, 0\right)$

17. $\left(\dfrac{\pi - 2}{4}, 0\right)$ **27.** $\left(\dfrac{48}{5}, -11\right)$

19. $\left(\dfrac{203}{328}, 0\right)$ **29.** $\left(\dfrac{138}{11}, 0\right)$

21. $(0, 1)$

23. $\left(0, \dfrac{3}{28}\right)$

7 Areas in Polar Coordinates *(page 414)*

1. $9\pi/2$ **11.** $(2\pi - 3\sqrt{3})/2$

3. 1   **13.** $(4 - \pi)/2$

5. $9\pi/4$ **15.** $(\pi + 1)/2$

7. $2\pi + 8/3$ **17.** $3 - \sqrt{3} + \pi/3$

9. 6

8 Work (pages 418–419)

1. $4,680\pi$ ft-lb
3. $14,040\pi$ ft-lb
5. $1,842,328.8\pi$ ft-lb
7. $375,000$ ft-lb
9. $1/4$ ft-ton $= 500$ ft-lb
11. 75 lb/in
13. $4,200$ ft-lb
15. $\dfrac{1295\pi}{16}$ ft-lb

9 Fluid Pressure (page 422)

1. $(wab^2)/2$
3. $wa^3\sqrt{2}/12$
5. $wh^2(a + 2b)/6$
7. $wa^2(a + 2c\sqrt{3})/8$
9. $2wa^2(4a + 3\pi c)/12$
11. $299,520\pi$ lb
13. $133,120\pi\sqrt{6}$ lb

10 Moments of Inertia (pages 427–428)

1. (a) $1/5$ (b) $\sqrt{15}/5$
3. (a) $67/60$ (b) $\sqrt{134}/10$
5. (a) $(23,328)/35$ (b) $18\sqrt{70}/35$
7. (a) $8/3$ (b) $2\sqrt{3}/3$
9. (a) $(132)/5$ (b) $\sqrt{55}/5$
11. (a) $(495)/7$ (b) $\sqrt{385}/7$
13. (a) $4/9$ (b) $\sqrt{2}/3$
15. (a) $(299 - 128 \ln 4)/6 \approx 20,265$
    (b) $[(299 - 128 \ln 4)/$
    $(45 - 24 \ln 4)]^{1/2} \approx 3.219$
17. (a) $3\pi a^4$ (b) $a\sqrt{3}$
19. (a) $b^3\sqrt{4a^2 - b^2}$ (b) $b/\sqrt{24}$
21. (a) $\dfrac{a^3b^3}{6(a^2 + b^2)}$ (b) $\dfrac{ab}{\sqrt{6(a^2 + b^2)}}$

11 Some Applications . . . (page 431)

1. (a) $\$205,167$ (b) $\$203,047$
3. $23,760$

CHAPTER 9

1 Newton's Method . . . (page 439)

1. 2.25 5. 1.20 9. $-.3$
3. 1.50 7. 1.60 11. $-.86$
13. For $f(x) = x^2 - 3$ and $a = 2$:
    $x_0 = 1.8$, $x_1 = 1.73$
15. For $f(x) = x^2 - 77$ and $a = 8$:
    $x_0 = 8.8$, $x_1 = 8.78$
17. For $f(x) = x^3 - 9$ and $a = 2$:
    $x_0 = 2.1$, $x_1 = 2.08$
19. For $a = 1$: $x_0 = 1.2$, $x_1 = 1.18$
21. (a) For $a = 1$: $x_0 = .8$, $x_1 = .73$
    (b) For $a = -1$: $x_0 = -1.3$,
    $x_1 = -1.23$

23. (a)

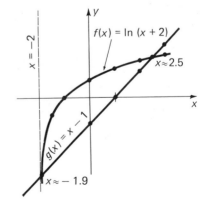

(b) For $a = -1.9$: $x_0 = -1.97$
(c) For $a = 2.5$: $x_0 = 2.51$

2 Taylor's Formula (page 445)

1. 1/64   **5.** .022   **9.** .123
3. .207   **7.** .04   **11.** .279

(Pages 451–452)

1. $P_4(x) = 1 + x + \dfrac{x^2}{2!} + \dfrac{x^3}{3!} + \dfrac{x^4}{4!}$

$R_4(x) = \dfrac{e^c x^5}{5!}$ c between 0 and x

3. (a) $P_4(x) = 0 + x + 0 \cdot x^2 -$

$\dfrac{1}{3!}x^3 + 0 \cdot x^4$

$R_4(x) = \dfrac{\cos c}{5!}x^5$

c between 0 and x

(b) $P_4(x) = \dfrac{\sqrt{3}}{2} - \dfrac{1}{2}(x - 2\pi/3) -$

$\dfrac{\sqrt{3}}{2 \cdot 2!}(x - 2\pi/3)^2$

$+ \dfrac{1}{2 \cdot 3!}(x - 2\pi/3)^3 +$

$\dfrac{\sqrt{3}}{2 \cdot 4!}(x - 2\pi/3)^4$

$R_4(x) = \dfrac{\cos c}{5!}(x - 2\pi/3)^5$

c between $2\pi/3$ and x

5. $P_3(x) = 1 + \dfrac{1}{2}(x - 1) -$

$\dfrac{1}{4 \cdot 2!}(x - 1)^2 + \dfrac{3}{8 \cdot 3!}(x - 1)^3$

$R_3(x) = \dfrac{-15c^{-7/2}}{16 \cdot 4!}(x - 1)^4$

c between 1 and x

7. $P_4(x) = 1 + x^2 + \dfrac{x^4}{2!} + \dfrac{x^6}{3!} + \dfrac{x^8}{4!}$

$R_4(x) = \dfrac{e^c x^{10}}{5!}$ c between 0 and x^2

9. $P_4(x) = -1 + \dfrac{1}{3}(x + 1) +$

$\dfrac{2}{9 \cdot 2!}(x + 1)^2 + \dfrac{10}{27 \cdot 3!}(x + 1)^3 +$

$\dfrac{80}{81 \cdot 4!}(x + 1)^4$

$R_4(x) = \dfrac{880c^{-14/3}}{243 \cdot 5!}(x + 1)^5$

c between −1 and x

11. $P_4(x) = x^3 - \dfrac{1}{3!}x^5$

$R_4(x) = \dfrac{\cos c}{5!}x^7$

c between 0 and x

13. .5299   **21.** 1.7321
15. .095   **23.** 1.260
17. 1.154   **25.** 1.342
19. .6820   **27.** .229

29. $x^4 - x^3 + x^2 + x - 2 = -8(x + 1)$
$+ 10(x + 1)^2 - 5(x + 1)^3 + (x + 1)^4$

31. Expand $\ln(1 + x)$ about 0.
$|\ln(1 + x) - x| =$
$|P_1(x) + R_1(x) - x| = |R_1(x)| <$

$\dfrac{\left(\dfrac{1}{2}\right)^2}{2!} = \dfrac{1}{8}$

33. $f(x) = f(a) + \displaystyle\int_a^x f'(t)\, dt$

$\displaystyle\int_a^x f'(t)\, dt = f'(a)(x - a) +$

$\displaystyle\int_a^x f''(t)(x - t)\, dt$

$\displaystyle\int_a^x f''(t)(x - t)\, dt = \dfrac{f''(a)(x - a)^2}{2!}$

$+ \dfrac{1}{2!}\displaystyle\int_a^x f'''(t)(x - t)^2\, dt$

$\dfrac{1}{2!}\displaystyle\int_a^x f'''(t)(x - t)^2\, dt =$

$\dfrac{f'''(a)(x - a)^3}{3!} + \dfrac{1}{3!}\displaystyle\int_a^x f^{(4)}(x - t)^3 dt$

$\dfrac{1}{(n - 1)!}\displaystyle\int_a^x f^{(n)}(t)(x - t)^{n-1}\, dt =$

$\dfrac{f^{(n)}(a)}{n!}x^n + \dfrac{1}{n!}\displaystyle\int_a^x f^{(n+1)}(t)(x - t)^n\, dt$

Now add these equations and subtract

$\displaystyle\int_a^x f'(t)\, dt + \displaystyle\int_a^x f''(t)(x - t)\, dt +$

$\dfrac{1}{2!}\displaystyle\int_a^x f'''(t)(x - t)^2\, dt + \ldots +$

$$\frac{1}{(n-1)!} \int_a^x f^{(n)}(t)(x-t)^{n-1}\, dt$$

from both sides. The right side becomes

$$P_n(x) + \frac{1}{n!} \int_a^x f(n+1)(t)(x-t)^n\, dt.$$

Since $f(x) = P_n(x) + R_n(x)$, we must have that

$$R_n(x) = \frac{1}{n!} \int_a^x f^{(n+1)}(t)(x-t)^n\, dt.$$

3 The Trapezoidal Rule
(pages 455–456)

1. .34
3. .4062
5. .4606

7. 1.0997
9. 2.3525

11. (a) $\displaystyle \int \sqrt{1-x^2}\, dx = \frac{1}{2}\sin^{-1} x +$
$$\frac{x\sqrt{1-x^2}}{2}$$

Thus, $\displaystyle 2\int_{-1}^1 \sqrt{1-x^2}\, dx =$

$$\left[\sin^{-1} x + x\sqrt{1-x^2}\right]\Big|_{-1}^1 =$$

$$\frac{\pi}{2} + \frac{\pi}{2} = \pi$$

(b) 3.037

4 Simpson's Rule (page 460)

1. 2.0003
3. .6932
5. 1.0117

7. 1.1873
9. .1461

11. (a) Since $x_0 = a$, $x_1 = \dfrac{a+b}{2}$ and
$x_2 = 6$, substitution in Simpson's Rule yields the prismoidal formula.

(b) $\displaystyle \int_0^1 (x^3 - 2x^2 + 3x + 1)\, dx =$

$$\frac{1-0}{6}\left[f(a) + 4f\!\left(\frac{1}{2}\right) + f(1)\right] =$$

$$\frac{1}{6} \cdot \left[1 + 4\!\left(\frac{17}{8}\right) + 3\right] = \frac{25}{12}$$

CHAPTER 10

1 Introduction (page 468)

1. Divergent (nth term test)
3. Divergent (nth term test)
5. Convergent (geometric series)
7. Convergent (compare with $1/2^n$)
9. Convergent (compare with $(2/3)^n$)
11. Convergent (compare with $2/n^2$)
13. Divergent (nth term test)

2 The Integral Test
(page 473)

1. Convergent, $S = 3$
3. Convergent, $S = 1/35$
5. Convergent, $S = 9/2$
7. Convergent, $S = e^3/(4e + 8)$
9. Divergent
11. Divergent
13. Divergent
15. Convergent, $\pi/4 < S < (\pi + 2)/4$

17. Divergent
19. Divergent
21. Convergent, $\dfrac{1}{(p-1)(\ln 2)^{p-1}}$
$$< S < \frac{p-1+2\ln 2}{2(p-1)(\ln 2)^p}$$

23. Convergent, $2 < S < \pi$
$(2x < \sin \pi x < \pi x$ if $0 < x < 1/2)$
25. Convergent, $0 < S < (\pi^2 - 2\pi)/2$
$(2x < \sin \pi x < \pi x$ if $0 < x < 1/2)$

3 Limit Comparison Tests
(page 477)

1. Convergent
3. Convergent
5. Convergent
7. Divergent
9. Convergent

11. Divergent
13. Convergent
15. Convergent
17. Convergent
19. Divergent

4 Alternating Series
(page 482)

1. Convergent
3. Divergent
5. Divergent
7. Convergent
9. Convergent
11. $S \approx .90 (.9007 < S_8 < S < S_7 < .9027)$

5 Absolute Convergence
(pages 486–487)

1. Conditionally convergent (AST, comparison)
3. Absolutely convergent (ratio test)
5. Absolutely convergent (all terms are 0)
7. Absolutely convergent (comparison)
9. Absolutely convergent (ratio test)
11. Conditionally convergent (AST, comparison)
13. Absolutely convergent (p series)
15. Conditionally convergent (AST, limit comparison)
17. Divergent (nth term test)

6 Power Series *(page 493)*

1. $R = 0$, $[0,0]$
3. $R = 1/2$, $]5/2, 7/2[$
5. $R = 1$, $]-1, 1]$
7. $R = 1$, $[-1, 1[$
9. $R = 1$, $[0, 2[$
11. $R = 3$, $]-5, 1[$
13. $R = e$, $]-e, e[$
15. $R = 1$, $]-1, 1[$

7 Taylor Series
(pages 500–501)

1. $(1 + x^3)^{-1} = \sum\limits_{n=0}^{\infty} (-1)^n x^{3n}$, $R = 1$, geometric series.

3. $\cosh x = \sum\limits_{n=0}^{\infty} \dfrac{x^{2n}}{(2n)!}$, $R = \infty$.

5. $\ln (2 + x) = \ln 2 + \ln \left(1 + \dfrac{x}{2}\right) =$
   $\ln 2 + \sum\limits_{n=1}^{\infty} \dfrac{(-1)^{n-1}}{n \cdot 2^n} x^n$, $R = 2$.

7. $e^{-x^2} = \sum\limits_{n=0}^{\infty} \dfrac{(-1)^n x^{2n}}{n!}$, $R = \infty$.

9. $\sin^2 x = \dfrac{1}{2}(1 - \cos 2x) =$
   $\sum\limits_{n=1}^{\infty} \dfrac{(-1)^n 2^{2n-1} x^{2n}}{(2n)!}$, $R = \infty$.

11. $\dfrac{e^x}{1 - x} = \sum\limits_{n=0}^{\infty} c_n x^n$ where
    $c_n = \sum\limits_{k=0}^{n} \dfrac{1}{k!}$, $R = 1$.

13. $x + \dfrac{1}{3}x^3 + \dfrac{2}{15}x^5 + \ldots$

15. $1 + \dfrac{x^2}{2} + \dfrac{5x^4}{24} + \ldots$

17. $-\left(x - \dfrac{\pi}{2}\right) - \dfrac{1}{3}\left(x - \dfrac{\pi}{2}\right)^3 -$
    $\dfrac{2}{15}\left(x - \dfrac{\pi}{2}\right)^5$

19. $\dfrac{1}{2}x^2 + \dfrac{1}{12}x^4 + \dfrac{1}{45}x^6 + \ldots$
21. $1 + 4(x - 1) + 6(x - 1)^2 + 4(x - 1)^3 + (x - 1)^4$
23. $1 + (x + 1) + (x + 1)^2 + (x + 1)^3$
25. $(x + 3)^4 - (x + 3)^2$

27. $\text{Sin}^{-1} x = \sum\limits_{n=0}^{\infty} \dfrac{(2n)!}{2^{2n}(n!)^2(2n + 1)} x^{2n+1}$
    for $-1 < x < 1$ because term-by-term integration is valid.
29. $2/3$

CHAPTER 11

1 Separable Differential Equations *(pages 506–507)*

1. (a) $y = \dfrac{-x^2}{2} + C$

(b) $y = \dfrac{-x^2}{2}$

3. (a) $y = \pm\sqrt{2\ln|x| + C}$
(b) $y = \sqrt{2\ln|x| + 4}$

5. (a) $y = -1 \pm \sqrt{1 + x^2 + 4x + C}$
(b) $y = -1 - \sqrt{1 + x^2 + 4x}$

7. (a) $y = \ln(\sin x + C)$
(b) $y = \ln(\sin x + 1 - \sqrt{3}/2)$

9. (a) $y = \ln(\ln|\sec x| + C)$
(b) $y = \ln(\ln|\sec x| + 1)$

11. (a) $y = -\ln|\sin x| - \dfrac{x^2}{2} + Cx + C_1$

(b) $y = -\ln|\sin x| - \dfrac{x^2}{2} +$
$$\dfrac{\pi}{2}x - \dfrac{\pi^2}{8}$$

13. (a) $y = \pm\sqrt{2(xe^x - e^x + C)}$
(b) $y = \sqrt{2(xe^x - e^x + C)}$

15. (a) $y = e^x + x^2 + Cx + C_1$
(b) $y = e^x + x^2 - e - 1$

17. When $t = 7$, there are $1000\,e^7$
$\dfrac{\ln 10}{4} \approx 56{,}235$ bacteria present.

There will be 12,000 bacteria
present when $t = \dfrac{4\ln 12}{\ln 10} \approx 4.3$.

19. Since $V(t) = (t - 18)\left(\ln\left(\dfrac{t-18}{2}\right)\right)$
$- (t - 18) + C$, and $V(24) = 20$,
$C = 26 - 6\ln 3$.
So, $V(28) = 10\ln 5 + 16 -$
$6\ln 3 \approx 26$.

2 The Differential Equation $y' + yP(x) = Q(x)$ *(pages 509–510)*

1. $y = 2 + Ce^{-x}$

3. $y = \dfrac{-x}{2} - \dfrac{7}{4} + Ce^{2x}$

5. $y = e^x \ln(1 + e^x) + Ce^x$

7. $y = x - 1 + 2e^{-x}$

9. $y = -\dfrac{1}{2} + \dfrac{5}{2}x^2$

11. $y = x - \dfrac{1}{2} - \dfrac{3}{2}e^{2x}$

13. (a) $y = 1000 - 800\,e^{-t/100}$
(b) $-100\ln 3/4$ min ≈ 28.8 min

15. $v(t) = -\sqrt{9.8} + \sqrt{9.8}\,e^{-\sqrt{9.8}\,x}$

3 The Differential Equation $y'' + p_1 y'' = p_2 y = 0$ *(pages 516–517)*

1. $y = C_1 e^{-x} + C_2 e^{-3x}$

3. $y = C_1 e^{-x/2} \cos\left(\dfrac{\sqrt{3}}{2}x\right) +$
$$C_2 e^{-x/2} \sin\left(\dfrac{\sqrt{3}}{2}x\right)$$

5. $y = -e^x + \dfrac{e+1}{e}xe^x$

7. $s(t) = \dfrac{1}{4}\sin 4t$

9. $s(t) = 0$

11. We may assume that C_1 and C_2 are not both 0. Say $C_1 \neq 0$. Observe that $C_2 e^{A_2 t} + C_1 e^{A_1 t} = 0$ if and only if $\dfrac{C_2}{C_1}e^{(A_2 - A_1)t} = -1$.

Since $\dfrac{C_2}{C_1}e^{(A_2 - A_1)t}$ is monotonic $(A_2 \neq A_1)$, $\dfrac{C_2}{C_1}e^{(A_2 - A_1)t} = -1$ can have at most one solution. Thus, the right hand side of $n(3)$ changes sign at most once. Similarly $C_1 e^{At} + C_2 t e^{At} = 0$ if and only if $\dfrac{C_2 t}{C_1} = -1$. This equation has at most one solution and so the right hand side of (4) changes sign at most once.

4 The Differential Equation $y'' + P_1y' + P_2y = P(x)$
(page 520)

1. $y = \dfrac{1}{2}e^x + C_1 \cos x + C_2 \sin x$

3. $y = -\dfrac{1}{10} \sin x - \dfrac{3}{10} \cos x + C_1e^{2x} + C_2e^{-x}$

5. $y = \dfrac{1}{8} - \dfrac{1}{8}x \sin x + C_1 \cos 2x + C_2 \sin x$

7. $y = \dfrac{1}{2}e^x + \dfrac{1}{2} \cos x - \dfrac{1}{2} \sin x$

CHAPTER 12

1 Arrows and Vectors
(pages 524–525)

1. $(2,1)$ 7. $(2,3)$
3. $(2,-1)$ 9. $(-2,6)$
5. $(2,-2)$ 11. $(-10,-6)$
13. $c = 2\sqrt{2}$ or $c = -2\sqrt{2}$
15. $c = -3$ or $c = 1$
17. $\theta_1 = \pi/2,\ \theta_2 = \pi$
19. $\theta_1 = 3\pi/4 = \theta_2$
21. $\theta_1 = 5\pi/6,\ \theta_2 = \pi/3$

2 Operations on Vectors
(page 530)

1. $\langle 1,6 \rangle$
3. $\mathrm{Cos}^{-1} (-1/\sqrt{290})$
5. $\sqrt{10} - 2\sqrt{29}$
7. 21
11. $c = 3,\ d = 1$
13. $5/2$
15. $13,\ (4,-4)$
23. $c = 3$ or $c = -1/3$

3 Components and Orthogonality *(page 535)*

1. $-17/5,\ \langle -51/25,-68/25 \rangle$
3. $\dfrac{145}{13},\ \left\langle \dfrac{1740}{169},\dfrac{725}{169} \right\rangle$
5. $5\sqrt{2}/2,\ \langle 5/2,5/2 \rangle$
7. $2/\sqrt{13}$
9. $8/\sqrt{41}$
11. $\langle 1,0 \rangle$
13. $\langle 1/\sqrt{37},-6/\sqrt{37} \rangle$
15. $\langle 5/13,12/13 \rangle$

17. $\mathbf{U} = \langle 15/17,8/17 \rangle$,
$\mathbf{V} = \langle -8/17,15/17 \rangle$,
$\mathbf{A} = \dfrac{436}{17}\mathbf{U} + \dfrac{95}{17}\mathbf{V}$
19. Impossible since $\mathbf{B} \cdot \mathbf{C} \neq 0$
21. (a) $c = 6$ or -6 (b) $c = 0$
23. (a) $c = 1/3$ (b) $c = 1$

4 Vector-valued Functions . . . *(page 540)*

1. $y = 3x - 7$
3. $y - 1 = (x + 1)^2$
5. $y = x^2,\ x \neq 0$
7. $x^2 - y^2 = 4$
9. $y = x,\ 0 \leq x \leq 1$
11. $x^{2/3} + y^{2/3} = 1$
13. $(x^2 + y^2)^3 = x^4,\ r = \cos^2 \theta$
15. $y' = (2/3)t^{-1},\ y'' = -(2/9)t^{-4}$
17. $y' = 3t - 1(t \neq 0),\ y'' = 3/(2t)$
19. $y' = (e^t + e^{-t})/(e^t - e^{-t})$,
$y'' = -4/(e^t - e^{-t})^3$

5 Motion in the Plane
(page 544)

1.

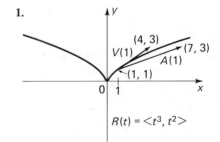

$R(t) = <t^3, t^2>$

3.

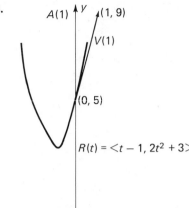

$R(t) = <t - 1, 2t^2 + 3>$

5.

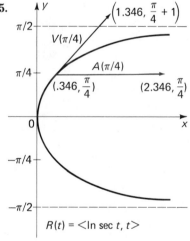

$R(t) = <\ln \sec t, t>$

7.

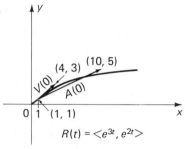

$R(t) = <e^{3t}, e^{2t}>$

9.

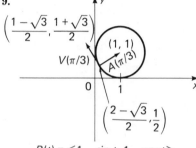

$R(t) = <1 - \sin t, 1 - \cos t>$

11. $t_0 = 0$, $v(t_0) = 3$, $\mathbf{V}(t_0) = \langle 0,3 \rangle$,
$\mathbf{A}(t_0) = \langle -2,0 \rangle$

13. $t_0 = \cos^{-1} \dfrac{\sqrt{130}}{16}$, $v(t_0) = \dfrac{65}{16}$,
$\mathbf{V}(t_0) = \left\langle -\dfrac{\sqrt{4095}}{16}, \dfrac{\sqrt{130}}{16} \right\rangle$,
$\mathbf{A}(t_0) = \left\langle -\dfrac{1}{8}, -\dfrac{\sqrt{126}}{16} \right\rangle$

15. $t_0 = \dfrac{1}{3}\sqrt{3}$, $v(t_0) = \dfrac{1}{8}\sqrt{91}$,
$\mathbf{V}(t_0) = \left\langle -\dfrac{3}{8}\sqrt{3},1 \right\rangle$, $\mathbf{A}(t_0) = \langle 0,0 \rangle$

17. $\mathbf{R}(t) = \langle t^3/3 + t + 2/3, 1 - 1/t \rangle$

19. $\mathbf{R}(t) = \langle t^3 + t - 2, -\ln|t| \rangle$

INDEX

About the Authors

ROBERT E. DRESSLER, Professor of Mathematics, Kansas State University, is the author of *Introductory Algebra for College Students* (with Isidore Dressler and Barnett Rich) and *Intermediate Algebra for College Students* (with Isidore Dressler). He has a B.A. from the University of Rochester and M.S. and Ph.D. degrees from the University of Oregon.

KARL STROMBERG is the author of *An Introduction to Classical Real Analysis* and of *Real and Abstract Analysis* (with Edwin Hewitt). He has B.A. and M.A. degrees from the University of Oregon and a Ph.D. from the University of Washington. He has taught mathematics at the Universities of Oregon, Washington, and Chicago and York University (England), and is now Professor of Mathematics, Kansas State University.